Table of Contents

Welcome to Macmillan/McGraw-Hill Mathematics

Concepts • Skills • Problem Solving

The only true vertically aligned PreK–12 Mathematics Curriculum

Math Connects offers three dimensions of vertical alignment.

❶ Content Design

Vertical content alignment is a process that ensures you and your students experience an articulated, coherent sequence of content from grade level to grade level. This provides you with the assurance that content is introduced, reinforced, and assessed at appropriate times in the series, eliminating gaps and unnecessary duplication. You are able to target your instruction to student needs because you are not teaching content intended to be covered later or that students have previously mastered.

❷ Instructional Design

Our strong vertical alignment in instructional approach from PreKindergarten through Algebra 2 provides a smooth transition for students from elementary to middle school to high school. Our common vocabulary, technology, manipulatives, lesson planning, and Data-Driven Decision Making reduce the confusion students often encounter when transitioning between grade levels without this built-in articulation.

❸ Visual Design

The student pages of *Math Connects* have a consistent visual design from grade to grade. This aids students' transition from elementary school to middle school and from middle school to Algebra 1. Students are more likely to succeed when they are already familiar with how to navigate student pages.

TIER 3 Intensive Intervention

PreK-2   3–5

TIER 1 Daily Intervention

TIER 2 Strategic Intervention

Math Triumphs

Student Study Guide: Book 1

Student Study Guide: Book 2

Student Study Guide: Book 3

Authors and Consultants

CONSULTING AUTHORS

Frances Basich Whitney
Project Director, Mathematics K–12
Santa Cruz County Office of Education
Capitola, California

Kathleen M. Brown
Math Curriculum Staff Developer
Washington Middle School
Long Beach, California

Dixie Dawson
Math Curriculum Leader
Long Beach Unified
Long Beach, California

Philip Gonsalves
Mathematics Coordinator
Alameda County Office of Education
Hayward, California

Robyn Silbey
Math Specialist
Montgomery County Public Schools
Gaithersburg, Maryland

Kathy Vielhaber
Mathematics Consultant
St. Louis, Missouri

CONTRIBUTING AUTHORS

Viken Hovsepian
Professor of Mathematics
Rio Hondo College
Whittier, California

FOLDABLES Study Organizer **Dinah Zike**
Educational Consultant
Dinah-Might Activities, Inc.
San Antonio, Texas

CONSULTANTS

Assessment

Donna M. Kopenski, Ed.D.
Math Coordinator K–5
City Heights Educational Collaborative
San Diego, California

Instructional Planning and Support

Beatrice Luchin
Mathematics Consultant
League City, Texas

ELL Support and Vocabulary

ReLeah Cossett Lent
Author/Educational Consultant
Alford, Florida

Reviewers

Each person below reviewed at least two chapters of the Student Study Guide, providing feedback and suggestions for improving the effectiveness of the mathematics instruction.

Dana M. Addis
Teacher Leader
Dearborn Public Schools
Dearborn, MI

Renee M. Blanchard
Elementary Math Facilitator
Erie School District
Erie, PA

Jeanette Collins Cantrell
5th and 6th Grade Math Teacher
W.R. Castle Memorial Elementary
Wittensville, KY

Helen L. Cheek
K-5 Math Specialist
Durham Public Schools
Durham, NC

Mercy Cosper
1st Grade Teacher
Pershing Park Elementary
Killeen, TX

Bonnie H. Ennis
Math Coordinator
Wicomico County Public Schools
Salisbury, MD

Sheila A. Evans
Instructional Support Teacher - Math
Glenmount Elementary/Middle School
Baltimore, MD

Lisa B. Golub
Curriculum Resource Teacher
Millennia Elementary
Orlando, FL

Donna Hagan
Program Specialist - Special Programs
    Department
Weatherford ISD
Weatherford, TX

Russell Hinson
Teacher
Belleview Elementary
Rock Hill, SC

Tania Shepherd Holbrook
Teacher
Central Elementary School
Paintsville, KY

Stephanie J. Howard
3rd Grade Teacher
Preston Smith Elementary
Lubbock, TX

Rhonda T. Inskeep
Math Support Teacher
Stevens Forest Elementary School
Columbia, MD

Albert Gregory Knights
Teacher/4th Grade/Math Lead Teacher
Cornelius Elementary
Houston, TX

Barbara Langley
Math/Science Coach
Poinciana Elementary School
Kissimmee, FL

David Ennis McBroom
Math/Science Facilitator
John Motley Morehead Elementary
Charlotte, NC

Jan Mercer, MA; NBCT
K-5 Math Lab Facilitator
Meadow Woods Elementary
Orlando, FL

Rosalind R. Mohamed
Instructional Support Teacher - Math
Furley Elementary School
Baltimore, MD

Patricia Penafiel
Teacher
Phyllis Miller Elementary
Miami, FL

Lindsey R. Petlak
2nd Grade Instructor
Prairieview Elementary School
Hainesville, IL

Lana A. Prichard
District Math Resource Teacher K-8
Lawrence Co. School District
Louisa, KY

Stacy L. Riggle
3rd Grade Spanish Magnet Teacher
Phillips Elementary
Pittsburgh, PA

Wendy Scheleur
5th Grade Teacher
Piney Orchard Elementary
Odenton, MD

Stacey L. Shapiro
Teacher
Zilker Elementary
Austin, TX

Kim Wilkerson Smith
4th Grade Teacher
Casey Elementary School
Austin, TX

Wyolonda M. Smith, NBCT
4th Grade Teacher
Pilot Elementary School
Greensboro, NC

Kristen M. Stone
3rd Grade Teacher
Tanglewood Elementary
Lumberton, NC

Jamie M. Williams
Math Specialist
New York Mills Union Free School District
New York Mills, NY

Mathematics Teacher Handbook

5 Keys to Success

❶ Backmapping

According to College Board research, about 80% of students who successfully complete Algebra 1 and Geometry by 10th grade attend and succeed in college. (Changing the Odds: Factors Increasing Access to College, 1990) *Math Connects* was conceived and developed by backmapping with the final result in mind—student success in Algebra 1 and beyond.

❷ Balanced, In-Depth Content

Math Connects was developed to specifically target the skills and topics that give students the most difficulty, such as Problem Solving, in each grade span.

Grades K–2		Grades 3–5	
1.	Problem Solving	1.	Problem Solving
2.	Money	2.	Fractions
3.	Time	3.	Measurement
4.	Measurement	4.	Decimals
5.	Fractions	5.	Time
6.	Computation	6.	Algebra
Grades 6–8		**Grades 9–12**	
1.	Fractions	1.	Problem Solving
2.	Problem Solving	2.	Fractions
3.	Measurement	3.	Algebra
4.	Algebra	4.	Geometry
5.	Computation	5.	Computation
		6.	Probability

– K–12 Math Market Analysis Survey, Open Book Publishing, 2006

❸ Ongoing Assessment

Math Connects includes diagnostic, formative, and summative assessment; data-driven instruction; intervention options; and performance tracking, as well as remediation, acceleration, and enrichment tools throughout the program.

❹ Intervention and Differentiated Instruction

A three-tiered Response To Intervention (RTI) is provided.

TIER ❶ Daily Intervention Reteach masters and Alternative Strategy suggestions address concepts from a different modality or learning style.

TIER ❷ Strategic Intervention Teachers can use the myriad of intervention tips and ancillary materials, such as the Strategic Intervention Guide (1–5) and Study Guide and Intervention (6–8).

TIER ❸ Intensive Intervention For students who are two or more years below grade level, *Math Triumphs* provides step-by-step instruction, vocabulary support, and data-driven decision making to help students succeed.

❺ Professional Development

Math Connects includes many opportunities for teacher professional development. Additional learning opportunities in various formats—video, online, and on-site instruction—are fully aligned and articulated from Kindergarten through Algebra 2.

| 6–8 | Pre-Algebra and Algebra 1 | Geometry and Algebra 2 |

Implementing Intensive Intervention

 TIER 3

Data-Driven Intensive Intervention

Ongoing assessment aids the teacher in student placement, progress monitoring, and exit.

Instructional Design

1 Diagnose and Prescribe
- Course Placement Test
- Online Readiness Quiz
- Chapter Preview
- Chapter Pretest
- Book Pretest

2 Teach and Practice
- Student Study Guide
- Teacher Edition Strategies
- Vocabulary Cards
- Manipulatives

3 Advance and Exit
- Assessment Masters
- Chapter Test
- Book Test

Classroom Implementation

Teacher prepares individual or group intervention plan(s).

Teacher modifies instruction based on results of formative assessments.

Test success indicates that a student can progress to another *Math Triumphs* chapter (if needed) or exit the intervention program.

Alignment to NCTM Focal Points

Foundational Skills for Grades K–2

Preparation for

NCTM Focal Points for Grade 3*

Focal Point 1 Number and Operations and Algebra

Focal Point 2 Number and Operations

Focal Point 3 Geometry

*See front cover folder for key and complete NCTM Focal Points.

Program Organization

Provide Personalized Instruction

Consumable volumes and minimal preparation requirements allow for flexibility and personalized instruction in any setting.

- After school
- Before school
- Tutoring
- Summer school
- Intersession
- Pull-out/Resource room

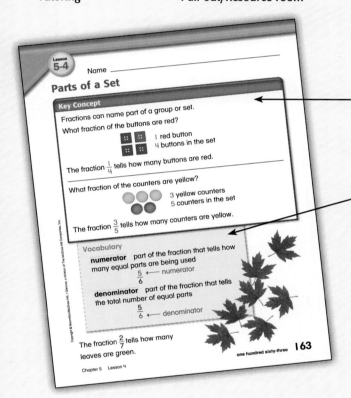

Key Concepts

Key Concepts introduce and break mathematics into conceptual steps. Multiple representations demonstrate the skills being presented.

Vocabulary

Vocabulary helps students identify terms presented in the lesson.

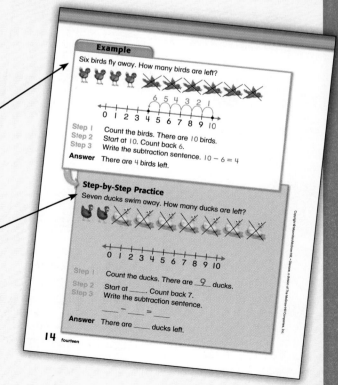

Examples

Fully worked-out **Examples** enable students and parents to see how to solve problems step by step.

Step-by-Step Practice gives students an opportunity to practice skills immediately, guiding them to complete a computational problem through a series of steps.

Balance

McGraw-Hill's *Math Triumphs* is designed to provide students a balanced approach to mathematics learning by offering them the opportunity to:

- investigate concepts and build their conceptual understanding;
- review, learn, and practice basic computational and procedural skills; and
- apply mathematics to problem solving in real-world situations.

Guided Practice

Guided Practice exercises provide computational practice. They can be used as formative assessment to monitor student progress and guide your instruction.

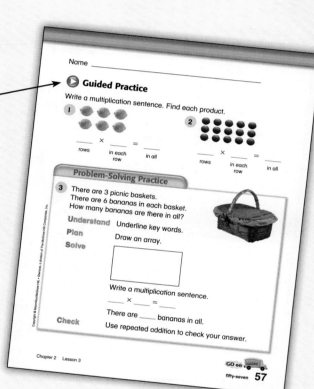

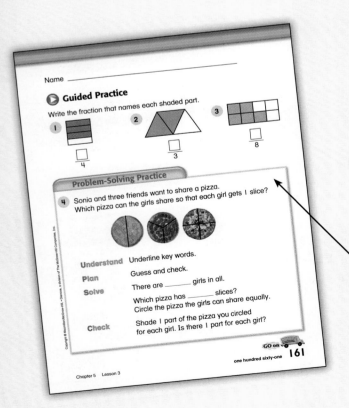

Problem-Solving Practice

Problem-Solving Practice walks the student through a four-step problem-solving strategy (Understand, Plan, Solve, Check) that is relevant to the word problem. Aids help the student break down and visualize what the problem is asking and how to solve it.

Independent Practice

Practice on Your Own provides homework opportunities and independent practice.

Each lesson in the Student Study Guide provides students with **Writing in Math** opportunities to describe, explain, or summarize an answer.

Vocabulary Check exercises relate directly to the core vocabulary introduced in each lesson.

Replay pages appear after every two lessons allowing students to apply their mathematical knowledge in different and engaging ways.

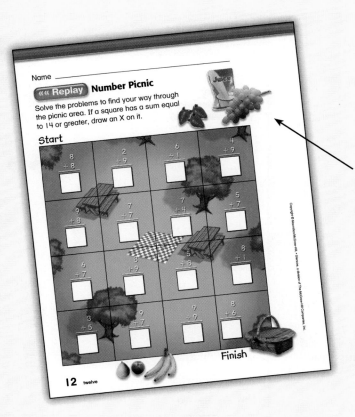

Comprehensive Assessment System

Data-Driven Decision Making

Math Triumphs offers frequent and meaningful assessment of student progress within the curriculum structure and teacher support materials.

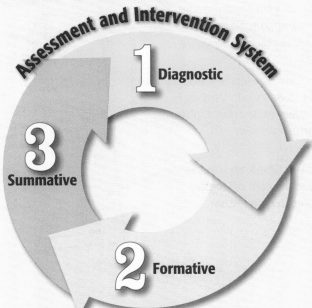

Assessment and Intervention System

1 Diagnostic

2 Formative

3 Summative

1 Diagnostic

Initial Assessment Assess students' knowledge **at the beginning of the year** with the *Diagnostic and Placement Tests*.

Entry–Level Assessment Assess students' prior knowledge **at the beginning of a chapter** with one of the following options.

Student Study Guide
- Get Ready

Teacher Edition
- Vocabulary Preview

Print Resources
- Assessment Masters, Chapter Pretest

Technology Resources

ExamView® Assessment Suite

Math Online Online Readiness Quiz

Advance TRACKER

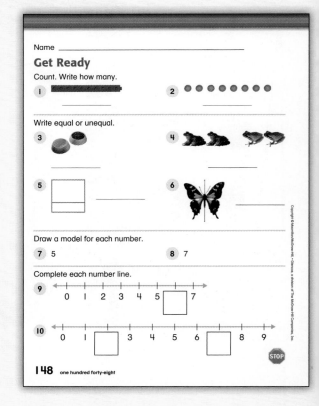

Name _____

Get Ready

Count. Write how many.

1 _____   2 _____

Write equal or unequal.

3 _____   4 _____

5 _____   6 _____

Draw a model for each number.

7 5   8 7

Complete each number line.

9 0 1 2 3 4 5 ☐ 7

10 0 1 ☐ 3 4 5 6 ☐ 8 9

STOP

148 one hundred forty-eight

Formative

Progress Monitoring Determine if students are progressing adequately as you teach each lesson. Use the assessments to differentiate lesson instruction and practice.

Student Study Guide
- Progress Check
- Who is Correct?
- Review

Teacher Edition
- Intervention Strategy
- Are They Getting It?
- See It, Do It, Say It, Write It
- Data-Driven Decision Making

Print Resources
- Assessment Masters
- Chapter Resource Masters
- Foldables®

Technology Resources

Math Online ▸ My Math Zone

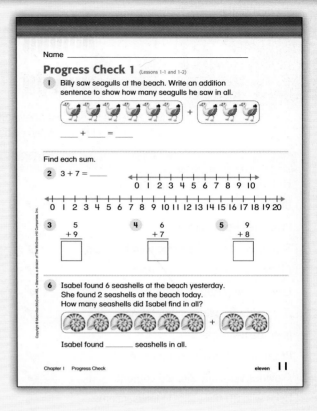

 **Summative**

Summative Evaluation Assess student success in learning the concepts in each chapter.

Student Study Guide
- Chapter Test
- Test Practice

Teacher Edition
- Data-Driven Decision Making

Print Resources
- Assessment Masters
- Chapter Resource Masters
- Foldables®

Technology Resources

Math Online ▸

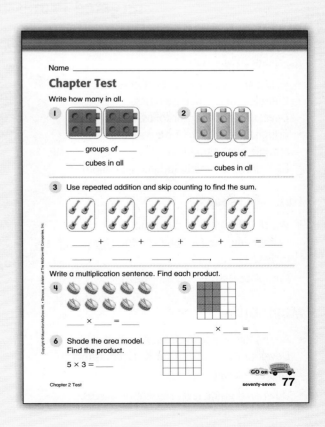

PreK-12 Data-Driven Professional Development

McGraw-Hill Professional Development (MHPD) provides a comprehensive plan for mathematics that is fully aligned and articulated with **Math Connects K–8** and the **Glencoe Mathematics** high school series.

Professional Development Needs	Online Courses	DVD Workshops	Video Library	Teach-Use-Succeed	Ready-Access Math
Has immediate classroom application	✔	✔	✔	✔	✔
Builds content knowledge	✔	✔			✔
Promotes best teaching practices		✔	✔		
Supports new and experienced teachers	✔	✔	✔	✔	✔
Allows customization of courses	✔	✔			✔
Can be self-paced	✔	✔		✔	✔
Adaptable for various timeframes	✔	✔	✔	✔	✔
Is grade-level specific			✔	✔	✔
Promotes a learning community	✔	✔			✔
Provides vertically-aligned content	✔	✔	✔		✔
Helps with RTI (Response to Intervention), Tiers 1–3	✔	✔	✔		✔

Use students' mathematics achievement data to help develop a targeted Professional Development Plan.

Accredited Online Courses
(available for purchase)
- Watch video clips of math classrooms.
- Complete interactive exercises.
- Develop electronic portfolios.
- Complete each 3- to 5-hour online module one segment at a time.
- Earn university credit (additional tuition).

DVD Workshops
- Watch video clips of classroom mathematics lessons and commentaries by leading educators.
- Complete lessons and activities.

MHPD Online
- Access this online Professional Development resource for K–12 educators.
- Link to relevant Web sites.
- Download grade-level student resources.

McGraw-Hill Professional Development Portfolio
- Professional Development Web sites
- McGraw-Hill's Experienced Consultants
- Textbook Implementation Modules
- Accredited Online Courses
- Video Workshops Mentor-led or Self-Study
- Mini Clip Video Library
- Ready Access Math Training Materials

Video Library | Math Online
- Access hundreds of K–12 video clips.
- See clips that illustrate mathematics content and instructional strategies.
- Watch demonstrations or commentaries.

Teach-Use-Succeed Textbook Implementation Modules
- Watch an experienced teacher demonstrate the *Math Connects* K–8 Student Editions, Teacher Editions, and program ancillaries—Online or DVD.

Ready-Access Math, Personalized Professional Development
- Access training materials for nearly 300 lessons.
- Create a customized sequence of professional development sessions.
- Deliver 45–60 minute after-school professional development sessions.

CHAPTER 1 Addition and Subtraction

Preparation for
Focal Points
and Connections
See front cover folder
for key.

Contents

Contents

CHAPTER 3
Introduction to Division

Preparation for Focal Points and Connections
See front cover folder for key.

Contents

CHAPTER 4 — Place Value

Preparation for Focal Points and Connections
See front cover folder for key.

3,702

Contents

CHAPTER 5 Fractions

Preparation for Focal Points and Connections
See front cover folder for key.

Assessment

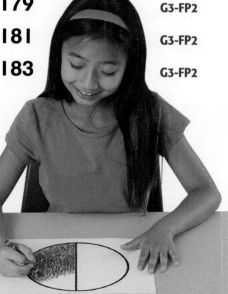

Contents

CHAPTER 6 — Fraction Equivalence

Preparation for **Focal Points and Connections** See front cover folder for key.

CHAPTER 7 Geometry

Preparation for Focal Points and Connections
See front cover folder for key.

Contents

CHAPTER 9

Data Analysis

Preparation for
**Focal Points
and Connections**
See front cover folder
for key.

Chapter Overview

Chapter-at-a-Glance

Lesson	Math Objective	Local/State Standards
1-1 Addition Facts 0 to 10 (pp. 3–6)	Find sums from 0 to 10.	
1-2 Addition Facts through 18 (pp. 7–10)	Find sums through 18.	
Progress Check 1 (p. 11)		
1-3 Subtraction Facts 0 to 10 (pp. 13–16)	Subtract numbers from 0 to 10.	
1-4 Subtraction Facts through 18 (pp. 17–20)	Subtract numbers through 18.	
Progress Check 2 (p. 21)		
1-5 Add Two-Digit Numbers (pp. 23–28)	Add two-digit numbers.	
1-6 Subtract Two-Digit Numbers (pp. 29–34)	Subtract two-digit numbers.	
Progress Check 3 (p. 35)		

Content-at-a-Glance

The diagram below summarizes and unpacks Chapter 1 content.

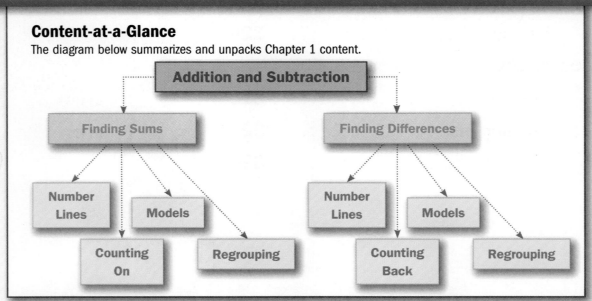

Online Assessment and Reporting
macmillanmh.com

Chapter Assessment Manager

Diagnostic — Diagnose students' readiness.

	Student Study Guide/ Teacher Editions	Assessment Masters	Technology
Course Placement Test		1	● ExamView® Assessment Suite
Book 1 Pretest		6	● ExamView® Assessment Suite
Chapter Pretest		9	● ExamView® Assessment Suite
Get Ready	SSG 2		Math Online > macmillanmh.com StudentWorks™ Plus

Formative — Identify students' misconceptions of content knowledge.

	Student Study Guide/ Teacher Editions	Assessment Masters	Technology
Progress Checks	SSG 11, 21, 35		Math Online > macmillanmh.com StudentWorks™ Plus
Vocabulary Assessments	SSG 6, 10, 16, 20, 28, 34, 37		Math Online > macmillanmh.com
Lesson Assessments			● ExamView® Assessment Suite
Are They Getting It?	TE 5, 9, 15, 19, 27, 33		

Summative — Determine student success in learning the concepts in the lesson, chapter, or book.

	Student Study Guide/ Teacher Editions	Assessment Masters	Technology
Chapter Test	SSG 39	12	● ExamView® Assessment Suite
Test Practice	SSG 41	15	● ExamView® Assessment Suite
Alternative Assessment	TE 39	18	
See It, Do It, Say It, Write It	TE 6, 10, 16, 20, 28, 34		
Book 1 Test		42	● ExamView® Assessment Suite

Back-mapping and Vertical Alignment McGraw-Hill's *Math Triumphs* intervention program was conceived and developed with the final result in mind: student success in grade-level mathematics, including Algebra 1 and beyond. The authors, using the **NCTM Focal Points and Focal Connections** as their guide, developed this brand-new series by back-mapping from grade-level and Algebra 1 concepts, and vertically aligning the topics so that they build upon prior skills and concepts and serve as a foundation for future topics.

Chapter Resource Manager

	Lesson 1-1	Lesson 1-2	Lesson 1-3	Lesson 1-4
Concept	Addition Facts 0 to 10	Addition Facts Through 18	Subtraction Facts 0 to 10	Subtraction Facts through 18
Objective	Find sums from 0 to 10.	Find sums through 18.	Subtract numbers from 0 to 10.	Subtract numbers through 18.
Math Vocabulary	add (addition) addition sentence sum	add (addition) addition sentence sum	difference subtract (subtraction) subtraction sentence	difference subtract (subtraction) subtraction sentence
Lesson Resources	**Materials** • chart paper • egg cartons (1 per pair) • index cards **Manipulatives** • counters **Other Resources** CRM Vocabulary and English Language Development CRM Skills Practice CRM Problem-Solving Practice CRM Homework Practice	**Materials** • index cards • writing paper **Manipulatives** • counters • number cubes **Other Resources** CRM Vocabulary and English Language Development CRM Skills Practice CRM Problem-Solving Practice CRM Homework Practice	**Materials** • poster/chart paper **Manipulatives** • connecting cubes • counters **Other Resources** CRM Vocabulary and English Language Development CRM Skills Practice CRM Problem-Solving Practice CRM Homework Practice	**Materials** • poster/chart paper • index cards **Manipulatives** • money **Other Resources** CRM Vocabulary and English Language Development CRM Skills Practice CRM Problem-Solving Practice CRM Homework Practice
Technology	**Math Online** macmillanmh.com StudentWorks™ Plus ExamView® Assessment Suite	**Math Online** macmillanmh.com StudentWorks™ Plus ExamView® Assessment Suite	**Math Online** macmillanmh.com StudentWorks™ Plus ExamView® Assessment Suite	**Math Online** macmillanmh.com StudentWorks™ Plus ExamView® Assessment Suite

Lesson 1-5	Lesson 1-6	
Add Two-Digit Numbers	Subtract Two-Digit Numbers	**Concept**
Add two-digit numbers.	Subtract two-digit numbers.	**Objective**
ones regroup tens	ones regroup tens	**Math Vocabulary**
Materials	**Materials**	**Lesson Resources**
Manipulatives • number cubes • base-ten blocks • money • spinners	**Manipulatives** • number cubes • base-ten blocks • money	
Other Resources **CRM** Vocabulary and English Language Development **CRM** Skills Practice **CRM** Problem-Solving Practice **CRM** Homework Practice	**Other Resources** **CRM** Vocabulary and English Language Development **CRM** Skills Practice **CRM** Problem-Solving Practice **CRM** Homework Practice	
Math Online macmillanmh.com StudentWorks™ Plus ⊙ ExamView® Assessment Suite	**Math Online** macmillanmh.com StudentWorks™ Plus ⊙ ExamView® Assessment Suite	**Technology**

Chapter Notes

Home Connection

Read the Home Connection letter with students and have them write their names in the space below.

Read and explain the activity under Help at Home. If time allows, complete a portion of the activity so students can introduce the activity to a parent or other caregiver.

Have students:

- draw a picture representing the number of students who ride the bus. Have them draw another picture representing the number of students who walk to school. Help the students add both groups.

- draw a group of objects. Then mark X on some of the objects. Help students find how many objects are left.

Real-World Applications

Collecting Food Talia is collecting cans of food for the local food pantry. On Thursday she collected 15 cans. On Friday she collected 32 cans. How many cans did Talia collect in all? 47 cans

---

Addition and Subtraction

English

Dear Family,
Today our class started **Chapter 1, Addition and Subtraction Facts**. In this chapter, I will learn addition and subtraction facts through 18. I will also learn to add and subtract two-digit numbers.

Love, _____

Spanish

Estimada familia:
Hoy en clase comenzamos **el Capítulo 1, titulado Operaciones de suma y la resta**. En este capítulo aprenderé a sumar y a restar hasta el número 18. También aprenderé a sumar y a restar números de dos dígitos.

Cariños, _____

Copyright © Macmillan/McGraw-Hill, a division of The McGraw-Hill Companies, Inc.

Help at Home

You can help your child succeed with addition and subtraction using common household items. Give your child two groups of items and have him or her find how many items there are in all. Or, give your child a group of items and ask him or her how many are left when a certain number of items are taken away.

Math Online Take the chapter Get Ready quiz at macmillanmh.com.

Ayude en casa

Usted puede ayudar a su hijo(a) a dominar la suma y la resta usando objetos comunes del hogar. De a su hijo(a) dos grupos de objetos y pídale que le diga cuántos hay en total. O bien, déle un grupo de objetos y pregúntele cuántos quedan cuando un cierto número de objetos se retira del grupo.

Chapter 1   one **1**

Key Vocabulary

Find interactive definitions in 13 languages in the **eGlossary** at macmillanmh.com.

English   Español *Introduce the most important vocabulary terms from Chapter 1.*

add (addition)   suma

join sets together to find the total or sum $2 + 5 = 7$ (p. 3)

addition sentence   expressión de suma

a math sentence that has an addition sign in it $4 + 5 = 9$ (p. 3)

sum   suma

the answer to an addition problem
$2 + 4 = 6$ (p. 3)
         ↑
       sum

subtract (subtraction)   restar

take away, take apart, separate, or find the difference between two sets
$5 - 5 = 0$ (p. 13)

subtraction sentence expressión de resta

a math sentence that has a subtraction sign in it $9 - 4 = 5$ (p. 13)

difference   diferencia

the answer to a subtraction problem
$3 - 1 = 2$ ◄— difference (p. 13)

tens   decenas

a place value of a number
The number 23 has 2 tens. (p. 23)

ones   unidades

a place value of a number
The number 23 has 3 ones. (p. 23)

regroup   reagrupar

take apart a number to write it in a new way
1 ten + 2 ones becomes 12 ones. (p. 23)

Name _____

Get Ready

Count. Write the number.

1  ___5___

2 ___9___

Circle the greater number.

3

4

5 Use the number line. Start at 1 and count on 2 more. Circle the number.

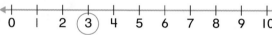

0 1 2 ③ 4 5 6 7 8 9 10

6 Use the number line. Start at 2 and count on 4 more. Circle the number.

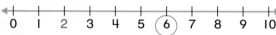

0 1 2 3 4 5 ⑥ 7 8 9 10

7 Juan plays soccer. He drew an X for each goal he scored. How many goals did Juan score?

X   X   X

Juan scored ___3___ goals.

STOP

2 two

Vocabulary Preview

Make a poster to display students' background knowledge.

- List each new vocabulary word in the center of a piece of paper.

- Ask students to tell you what they already know about addition and subtraction facts. Draw lines from the word connecting each student idea to the vocabulary word.

- As students learn more information, add new material, definitions, and examples to the chart.

Background Knowledge

Word

Lesson Notes

Lesson Planner

Objective Find sums from 0 to 10.

Vocabulary add (addition), addition sentence, sum

Materials/Manipulatives chart paper, egg cartons (1 per pair), index cards, counters

Chapter Resource Masters

- [CRM] Vocabulary and English Language Development (p. A5)
- [CRM] Skill Practice (p. A6)
- [CRM] Problem-Solving Practice (p. A7)
- [CRM] Homework Practice (p. A8)

① Introduce

Vocabulary

Nonexamples Write an addition sentence on the board.

- Explain that an addition sentence must have a plus and equal sign.

- Write several addition sentences and non-addition sentences on the board. Point to one. Have students give a thumbs up or a thumbs down to identify if it is or is not an addition sentence.

- Have students give a thumbs up or thumbs down for each example.

② Teach

Key Concept

Foundational Skills and Concepts After students have read through the Key Concept box, guide them through the following questions.

- **How many cats in the first group? In the second group?** 3; 2

- **How many cats in all?** 5

- **What operation is being used?** addition

3 Chapter 1 Addition and Subtraction

Name _____

Addition Facts 0 to 10

Key Concept

Look at the cats.

 $+$

   3     $+$ 2

How many cats are there in all?
$3 + 2 = 5$
There are 5 cats in all.

Vocabulary

add (addition) join sets together to find the total or sum

   2   +   5 $= 7$

addition sentence a math sentence that has an addition sign in it
$4 + 5 = 9$

sum the answer to an addition problem
$2 + 4 = 6 \longleftarrow$ sum

When two groups are added together, they combine to form one larger group.

English Learner Strategy

Sentences Compare sentences with words to addition sentences.

1. Hold up a marker for students to see.

   - **What color is the marker?** Sample answer: blue

2. Write "The marker is blue." Discuss that this is a sentence.

3. Write "$3 + 7 = 10$." Discuss the different parts of the addition sentence with students: an addition sentence has numbers, a plus sign, and an equal sign.

4. Have students work in pairs to create sentence strips with addition sentences for sums 0 to 10.

Example

How many soccer balls are there in all?

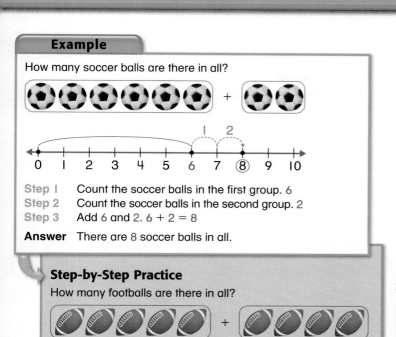

Step 1 Count the soccer balls in the first group. 6
Step 2 Count the soccer balls in the second group. 2
Step 3 Add 6 and 2. 6 + 2 = 8

Answer There are 8 soccer balls in all.

Step-by-Step Practice

How many footballs are there in all?

Step 1 Count the footballs in the first group. **5**
Step 2 Count the footballs in the second group. **4**
Step 3 Add **5** and **4**. **5** + **4** = **9**

Answer There are **9** footballs in all.

4 four

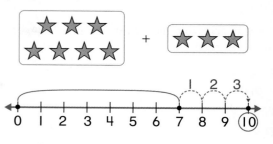

Additional *Example*

How many stars are there in all?

Step 1 Count the stars in the first group. 7

Step 2 Count the stars in the second group. 3

Step 3 Add 7 and 3. 7 + 3 = 10

Answer There are 10 stars in all.

Math Coach Notes

Strategy By using a number line to teach addition, students can see that adding is an extension of counting. Students will realize that counting is not the best method for problems that contain large numbers. Explain the benefit of using the number line as a learning aid.

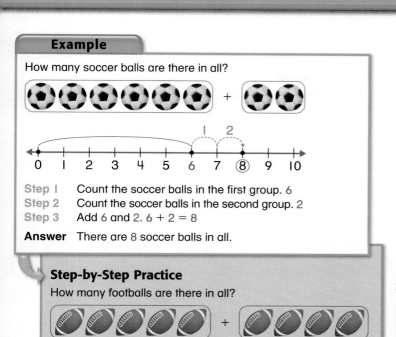

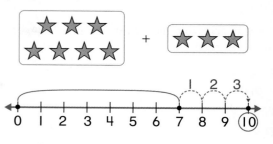

Intervention Strategy Kinesthetic Learners

Materials: counters, egg cartons (1 per pair, cut off 2 cups at the end to create a 10s frame with 5 cups in each row), paper

- Give each pair of students a tens frame and 10 counters.

- Have students copy the chart below.

$$\square + \square = \boxed{10}$$

- Student 1 places "x" number of counters (one counter per cup) in the tens frame and fills in the first box in the chart.

- Student 2 adds the number of counters needed to fill the tens frame and writes the number in the second box in the chart.

- Students read the addition fact out loud and repeat for a different fact.

Guided Practice

Direct students to complete Exercise 1 in Guided Practice.

Exercise 1 Remind students to count the number in each group.

Problem-Solving Practice

Guide students through the four-step problem-solving plan to complete Exercise 2.

- **What are the key words?** 5 blue balloons, 3 more red balloons, how many balloons, in all

- **How could a picture help you solve the problem?** You can count the groups of balloons to find the sum.

Ask students to check their work using the strategy suggested in the Check step. Students can use counters to solve the problem.

Using Manipulatives

Connecting Cubes Allow students to use connecting cubes to model addition sentences with sums 0 to 10.

Have students connect 4 cubes with 3 cubes. Remind students that the addends are 4 and 3.

- **Count the cubes to find the sum. What is the sum?** The sum is 7.

On-Hand Manipulatives Use beans or other common objects as counters to model addition sentences.

Name _____

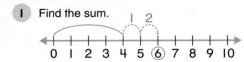 **Guided Practice**

1 Find the sum.

0 1 2 3 4 5 ⑥ 7 8 9 10

 +   __4__ + __2__ = __6__ piñatas
in all

Problem-Solving Practice

2 Carmen has <u>5 blue balloons</u> for her birthday party. Then she blows up <u>3 more red balloons</u>. <u>How many balloons</u> does Carmen have <u>in all</u>?

Understand Underline key words.

Plan Draw a picture.

Solve Draw __5__ circles in the blue box.

Draw __3__ circles in the red box. Count the circles.

○ ○
○ ○ + ○ ○ ○

Carmen has __8__ balloons in all.

Check Use counters.

Copyright © Macmillan/McGraw-Hill, • Glencoe, a division of The McGraw-Hill Companies, Inc.

Are They Getting It?

Check students' understanding of addition facts from 0 to 10 by writing these exercises on the board. Ask students to point out the correct and incorrect answers and explain their reasoning.

1.

   3   +   4   = 6   This is incorrect. The sum is 7.

2.

   5   +   4   = 9   This is correct.

3. $6 + 3 = 9$ This is correct.

4. $2 + 8 = 6$ This is incorrect. The sum is 10.

Write an addition sentence. Find each sum.

3 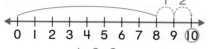 + (button)

$\underline{9} + \underline{1} = \underline{10}$

4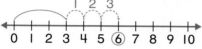

$\underline{3} + \underline{4} = \underline{7}$

Find each sum. Use the number line.

5 $8 + 2 = \underline{10}$

```
    0  1  2  3  4  5  6  7  8  9  ⑩
```

6 $3 + 3 = \underline{6}$

```
    0  1  2  3  4  5  ⑥  7  8  9  10
```

Find each sum.

7 $5 + 2 = \underline{7}$ **8** $1 + 7 = \underline{8}$ **9** $6 + 4 = \underline{10}$

10 **WRITING IN ▶MATH** Julie sees 4 cars. Then she sees 3 more cars. How many cars does Julie see in all? Explain.

Julie sees 7 cars in all. I can draw a picture to find the sum. 4 + 3 = 7

Vocabulary Check Complete.

11 Look at $7 + 1 = 8$. The number 8 is the $\underline{\text{sum}}$.

STOP

6 six

Copyright © Macmillan/McGraw-Hill • Glencoe, a division of The McGraw-Hill Companies, Inc.

Math Challenge

Greater Sums

Give each pair of students 20 index cards. On each card have students write addition facts with sums 0 to 10.

Have one student shuffle the cards and deal each student 10 cards. Each student flips over their top card. The player whose card has the greater sum takes both cards.

Students continue to play until one player has all of the cards.

Practice on Your Own

Direct students to p. 6 in their student books. Have students complete Exercises 3–11 independently. You may need to review the directions of each section before students begin.

④ Assess

See It, Do It, Say It, Write It

Step 1 Model the problem $3 + 5 = $ _____ on the board with stars. Ask students to identify the addends.

Step 2 Students should model the problem with counters or beans.

Step 3 Tell students to write the problem and find the sum. Ask students to read the addition sentence and identify the addends and the sum.

Step 4 Have students write what is meant by addends and sum in an addition sentence.

Looking Ahead: Pre-teach

In the next lesson, students will explore addition facts to 18.

Example

How many bananas in all?

Have students find each sum.

1. $8 + 7 = 15$

2. $9 + 9 = 18$

3. $6 + 6 = 12$

Lesson Notes

Lesson Planner

Objective   Find sums through 18.

Vocabulary   add (addition), addition sentence, sum

Materials/Manipulatives   index cards, counters, writing paper, number cubes

Chapter Resource Masters

- CRM Vocabulary and English Language Development (p. A9)
- CRM Skill Practice (p. A10)
- CRM Problem-Solving Practice (p. A11)
- CRM Homework Practice (p. A12)

---

① Introduce

Vocabulary

Vocabulary Interaction   Write several numbers on the board: 3, 6, 12, 7, 8, 9, 10, 16, 15, 11. Have a student use the numbers to write a true addition sentence on the board: $7 + 8 = 15$; $9 + 7 = 16$. Have another student write a different addition sentence on the board: $3 + 8 = 11$.

- **How are the words add and sum related?**
  You add to find a sum.

Challenge students to identify addition sentences that have the same sum but different addends.

---

② Teach

Key Concept

Foundational Skills and Concepts   After students have read through the Key Concept box, guide them through the following questions.

- **How many cubes in the first group?**   6
- **How many cubes in the second group?**   6
- **What is the sum?**   12

7 Chapter 1 Addition and Subtraction

Name _____

Addition Facts through 18

Key Concept

Look at the cubes.

 +

$$\begin{array}{r} 6 \\ + 6 \\ \hline \end{array}$$ ← This line means equals.

How many cubes are there in all?
$6 + 6 = 12$
There are 12 cubes in all.

Vocabulary

add (addition)   join sets together to find the total or sum

$2 + 5 = 7$

addition sentence   a math sentence that has an addition sign in it
$4 + 5 = 9$

sum   the answer to an addition problem
$2 + 4 = 6$ ← sum

17 is the same as 1 ten and 7 ones.

Remember that 10 ones can be regrouped as 1 ten.

Chapter 1   Lesson 2   **seven**   **7**

English Learner Strategy

Making Sums to 18

1. Write the numbers 1 through 9 on index cards. Say: "Addends are the numbers we add together to get the sum."

2. Have a student pick two index cards. Say: "The numbers on the cards are the addends." Example: 8 and 5.

3. Help students model each addend using counters.

4. Say: "The sum is how many in all." Have students count the total number of counters.

- **What is the sum?**   13

5. Have students write the addition sentence. $8 + 5 = 13$

6. Have students label the addends and the sum.

Repeat the activity with other numbers to reinforce addends and sum.

Example

Find the sum.

$$\begin{array}{r} 8 \\ + 7 \\ \hline \end{array}$$

Step 1   Count the first group. 8 cubes
Step 2   Count the second group. 7 cubes
Step 3   Add 8 and 7.
Step 4   Write the addition sentence. $8 + 7 = 15$

Answer   There are 15 connecting cubes.

Step-by-Step Practice

Find the sum.

Mercedes has 9 baseball cards. She buys 5 more.
How many baseball cards does Mercedes have in all?

 $\underline{9} + \underline{5}$

Step 1   Count the first group. __9__ cards
Step 2   Count the second group. __5__ cards
Step 3   Add __9__ and __5__ .
Step 4   Write the addition sentence.
$\underline{9} + \underline{5} = \underline{14}$

Answer   Mercedes has **14** baseball cards in all.

8 eight

Find the sum.

$$\begin{array}{r} 9 \\ + 6 \\ \hline \end{array}$$

Step 1 Count the first group. 9 cubes

Step 2 Count the second group. 6 cubes

Step 3 Add 9 and 6.

Step 4 Write the addition sentence.
$9 + 6 = 15$

Answer There are 15 connecting cubes.

Math Coach Notes

Strategy   Students can use the same counting on strategy to solve horizontal and vertical addition problems. Remind students that the orientation of the problem does not affect the sum.

It is helpful to point out the addends and sums in vertical addition problems. You should do this in the Guided Practice for Exercises 2–4.

Intervention Strategy   Linguistic Learners

Materials: writing paper, 2 number cubes (one red cube, one blue cube), counters

• Give each pair of students one red number cube and one blue number cube.

• Have students roll the number cubes and write the numbers as addends in an addition sentence.

• **Find the sum of the numbers on the cubes.** Students can use counters, tally marks, etc. to find the sum.   Answers will vary.

• Allow students to continue finding sums. They should write each addition sentence.

3 Practice

Guided Practice

Direct students to complete Exercises 1–4 in Guided Practice.

Exercises 2–4 Remind students to align the ones place in the answer with the ones place in the problem.

Problem-Solving Practice

Guide students through the four-step problem-solving plan to complete Exercise 5.

- **What are the key words?** 6 blue crayons, 5 red crayons, how many, in all

- **How many blue crayons?** 6

- **How many red crayons?** 5

- **How can drawing the crayons help?** You can easily count the total number of crayons.

Ask students to check their work using the strategy suggested in the Check step. Students can use a number line to solve the problem.

Using Manipulatives

Counting Coins Provide each pair of students with 1 dime, 2 nickels, and 10 pennies. Instruct pairs to make as many groups of coins that sum to numbers between 10 and 18. Remind students to make two groups of coins. Reinforce the value of each coin.

$$9 + 5 = 14$$

On-Hand Manipulatives Use beans or other common objects as counters to model numbers.

Name _____

▶ Guided Practice

Find each sum.

1. __9__ + __6__ = __15__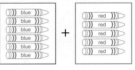

2. 9
   + 9
   ___
   |18|

3. 7
   + 6
   ___
   |13|

4. 4
   + 7
   ___
   |11|

Problem-Solving Practice

5. Catherine has <u>6 blue crayons</u> and <u>5 red crayons</u>. <u>How many</u> crayons does she have <u>in all</u>?

Understand Underline key words.

Plan Draw a picture.

Solve Draw __6__ blue crayons in the blue box.

Draw __5__ red crayons in the red box.

  Count the crayons.

Catherine has __11__ crayons in all.

Check Use a number line.

GO on

Chapter 1 Lesson 2   nine **9**

Copyright © Macmillan/McGraw-Hill • Glencoe, a division of The McGraw-Hill Companies, Inc.

Are They Getting It? ?

Check students' understanding of addition facts through 18 by writing these exercises on the board. Ask students to point out the correct and incorrect answers and explain their reasoning.

1. $9 + 7 = 17$ This is incorrect. The sum is 16.

2. $6 + 6 = 12$ This is correct.

3. $8 + 7 = 13$ This is incorrect. The sum is 15.

4. Luis has 7 pencils. Amber has 4 pencils. Luis and Amber have 11 pencils in all. This is correct.

▶ Practice on Your Own

Find each sum.

6  $\begin{array}{r} 5 \\ + 5 \\ \hline 10 \end{array}$

7  $\begin{array}{r} 4 \\ + 8 \\ \hline 12 \end{array}$

8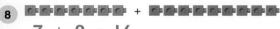

$\underline{7} + \underline{9} = \underline{16}$

Add.

9 $\begin{array}{r} 3 \\ + 9 \\ \hline \boxed{12} \end{array}$ **10** $\begin{array}{r} 8 \\ + 5 \\ \hline \boxed{13} \end{array}$ **11** $\begin{array}{r} 6 \\ + 9 \\ \hline \boxed{15} \end{array}$ **12** $\begin{array}{r} 9 \\ + 4 \\ \hline \boxed{13} \end{array}$

13 **WRITING IN ▶ MATH** Omar has 18 flowers in his garden. How can you show 18 using tens and ones? Explain.

<u>18 is the same as 1 ten and 8 ones.</u>
<u>I can draw a picture to show 1 ten</u>
<u>and 8 ones.</u>

Vocabulary Check Complete.

14 The addition sign (+) is used in an <u>addition</u>
<u>sentence</u>.

STOP

10 ten

Math Challenge

Missing Number

Provide each pair of students with 16 index cards.

- Write the numbers 2 through 9 on index cards in blue. These cards represent addends.
- Write the numbers 10 through 18 on index cards in red. These cards represent sums.
- Have students shuffle each pile of cards and place both piles face down.
- Students flip over the top card in both decks and determine what missing addend is needed to form a true addition sentence.
- Allow students to use counters if they need assistance. Students should write each addition sentence they form.

Practice on Your Own

Direct students to p. 10 in their student books. Have students complete Exercises 6–14 independently. You may need to review the directions of each section before students begin.

④ Assess

See It, Do It, Say It, Write It

Step 1 Write the problem $8 + 5 = $ _____ on the board. Ask students to name the addends in the problem.

Step 2 Have students model the problem with counters.

Step 3 Complete the problem on the board by filling in the sum. Ask students to read the addition sentence out loud: eight plus five equals thirteen.

Step 4 Tell students to write the addition sentence, draw circles around the addends, and draw a box around the sum.

Looking Ahead: Pre-teach

In the next lesson, students will learn subtraction facts 0 to 10.

Example

How many balloons will be left if 4 pop?

$7 - 4 = 3$

Have students find each difference.

1. $8 - 2 = $ 6

2. $4 - 2 = $ 2

3. $6 - 4 = $ 2

Progress Check 1

Formative Assessment

Use the Progress Check to assess students' mastery of the previous lessons. Have students review the lesson indicated for the problems they answered incorrectly.

Common Error *Alert*

Some students will misalign the numbers in the ones and tens place. To help students align the numbers; have them use grid paper.

Some students will have trouble finding the correct sum. Have them use a number line to add. They should circle the first addend and count on by the second addend to find the sum.

Name _____

Progress Check 1 (Lessons 1-1 and 1-2)

1 Billy saw seagulls at the beach. Write an addition sentence to show how many seagulls he saw in all.

__6__ + __3__ = __9__

Find each sum.

2 $3 + 7 =$ __10__

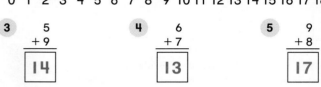

| **3** | 5
 + 9
 14 | **4** | 6
 + 7
 13 | **5** | 9
 + 8
 17 |

6 Isabel found 6 seashells at the beach yesterday. She found 2 seashells at the beach today. How many seashells did Isabel find in all?

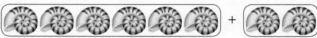

Isabel found __8__ seashells in all.

Data-Driven Decision Making

Students missing Exercises . . .	Have trouble with . . .	Should review and practice . . .
1–2	finding sums 0 to 10.	SSG Lesson 1-1, p. 3 CRM Skills Practice, p. A6
3–5	finding sums through 18.	SSG Lesson 1-2, p. 7 CRM Skills Practice, p. A10
6	problem–solving that involves finding sums 0 to 10.	SSG Lesson 1-1, p. 5 CRM Problem-Solving Practice, p. A7

Name _____

«« Replay Number Picnic

Solve the problems to find your way through the picnic area. If a square has a sum equal to 14 or greater, draw an X on it.

Start

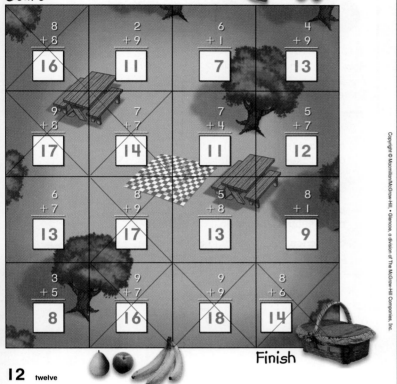

$$8 + 8 = 16$$ $$2 + 9 = 11$$ $$6 + 1 = 7$$ $$4 + 9 = 13$$

$$9 + 8 = 17$$ $$7 + 7 = 14$$ $$7 + 4 = 11$$ $$5 + 7 = 12$$

$$6 + 7 = 13$$ $$8 + 9 = 17$$ $$5 + 8 = 13$$ $$8 + 1 = 9$$

$$3 + 5 = 8$$ $$9 + 7 = 16$$ $$9 + 9 = 18$$ $$8 + 6 = 14$$

Finish

12 twelve

Use the Replay activity to review and reinforce the concepts and skills presented in Lessons 1-1 and 1-2.

Instructions

Have students read the directions at the top of the student page.

Make sure students only draw an X on boxes with a sum equal to 14 or greater. All other boxes should be left unmarked.

Student Technology

Students can use the following technology resources to reinforce chapter content.

- 💿 StudentWorks™ Plus
- **Math Online** ⟩ macmillanmh.com
- eGlossary

Lesson Planner

Math Objective Subtract numbers from 0 to 10.

Vocabulary subtract (subtraction), subtraction sentence, difference

Materials/Manipulatives connecting cubes, colored counters, poster/chart paper

Chapter Resource Masters

- [CRM] Vocabulary and English Language Development (p. A13)
- [CRM] Skill Practice (p. A14)
- [CRM] Problem-Solving Practice (p. A15)
- [CRM] Homework Practice (p. A16)

 **Introduce**

Vocabulary

Compare Vocabulary Help students relate addition and subtraction vocabulary. Write *Math Opposites* on the board. On the left write *subtract, subtraction sentence,* and *difference.* On the right write *add, addition sentence,* and *sum.* Have students work in pairs to discuss the relationships between *add* and *subtract, addition sentence* and *subtraction sentence,* and *sum* and *difference.*

 **Teach**

Key Concept

Foundational Skills and Concepts After students have read through the Key Concept box, guide them through the following questions.

- **How many beach balls are there in all?** 7
- **How many beach balls are crossed out?** 5
- **How many beach balls are left?** 2
- **What is the answer in a subtraction problem called?** difference

13 Chapter 1 Addition and Subtraction

Subtraction Facts 0 to 10

Key Concept

Look at the beach balls.
There were 7. Then 5 were crossed out.

$$7 - 5$$

How many beach balls are left?
$7 - 5 = 2$
There are 2 beach balls left.

Vocabulary

subtract (subtraction) take away, take apart, separate, or find the difference between two sets $5 - 5 = 0$

subtraction sentence a math sentence that has a subtraction sign in it $9 - 4 = 5$

difference the answer to a subtraction problem $3 - 1 = 2$ ⟵ The difference is 2.

 $6 - 2 = 4$

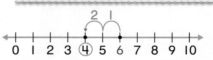

You can also use a number line to subtract.

Chapter 1   Lesson 3   thirteen **13**

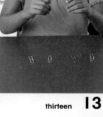

English Learner Strategy

Vocabulary-Math Phrases Be sure students understand what "crossed out" means in the Key Concept box. Then help students learn other words that are often associated with subtraction.

1. Display a chart titled "Subtraction Words."

2. Help students develop a list of words and phrases that are commonly associated with subtraction. In addition to the lesson vocabulary, this list might also include:

crossed out	how many are left
take away	how many more

3. Discuss the meaning of each phrase and model how they relate to subtraction.

Example

Six birds fly away. How many birds are left?

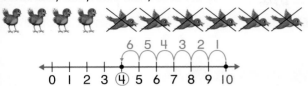

Step 1	Count the birds. There are 10 birds.
Step 2	Start at 10. Count back 6.
Step 3	Write the subtraction sentence. $10 - 6 = 4$
Answer	There are 4 birds left.

Step-by-Step Practice

Seven ducks swim away. How many ducks are left?

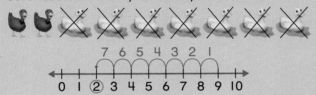

Step 1	Count the ducks. There are __9__ ducks.
Step 2	Start at __9__. Count back 7.
Step 3	Write the subtraction sentence.

$$\underline{9} - \underline{7} = \underline{2}$$

Answer There are __2__ ducks left.

14 fourteen

Additional *Example*

Five flowers are picked. How many flowers are left?

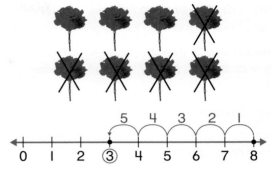

Step 1 Count the flowers. There are 8 flowers.

Step 2 Start at 8. Count back 5.

Step 3 Write the subtraction sentence
$8 - 5 = 3$

Answer There are 3 flowers left.

⚠ Common Error *Alert*

Students might count back from the wrong number.

For example, to find $9 - 5$, tell students to "put 9 in their head," and then count back 5:

9: 8, 7, 6, 5, 4

$9 - 5 = 4$

Some students will start at 9 and end at 5 which is incorrect. Practice with other subtraction facts to ensure students are using the strategy correctly.

Intervention Strategy

Visual/ Kinesthetic Learners

Materials: connecting cubes, recording sheet

1. Draw the recording sheet on the board.

Number of Cubes	minus	Cubes Snapped off	=	Difference
9	–	____	=	____

2. Have students make a train of 9 connecting cubes. Then have them snap off 1 cube.
   How many cubes are left? 8
   Complete the recording sheet.

3. Have students make the train of 9 cubes again. Snap off 2 cubes. Complete the recording sheet. Have students continue modeling subtraction problems.

Guided Practice

Direct students to complete Exercises 1–2 in Guided Practice.

Exercises 1–2 Remind students to use the number line or crossing out strategy to find each difference.

Problem-Solving Practice

Guide students through the four-step problem-solving plan to complete Exercise 3.

- **What are the key words?** 9 birthday presents, opens 5, how many, have left.

- **How do you know where to start on the number line?** Start at 9 because Kelly has 9 presents before she opens any.

- **How many do you count back?** Count back 5.

Ask students to check their work using the strategy suggested in the Check step. Students can draw a picture to solve the problem.

Using Manipulatives

Counters Give students 10 counters. Give them a problem such as: Beth has 8 red counters. She turns 6 over. How many red counters does she have left? 2

On-Hand Manipulatives Use paper clips, erasers, bingo chips or other common objects as counters to model subtraction.

Name _____

▶ Guided Practice

Find each difference.

0 1 2 3 4 5 6 7 8 9 10

1. $\underline{7} - \underline{3} = \underline{4}$

2. $\underline{6} - \underline{5} = \underline{1}$

Problem-Solving Practice

3. Kelly receives 9 birthday presents. She opens 5 of the presents. How many presents does Kelly have left to open?

Understand Underline key words.

Plan Use a number line.

Solve Start at ___9___. Count back ___5___. Circle the number.

5 4 3 2 1

0 1 2 3 ④ 5 6 7 8 9 10

Kelly has ___4___ presents left to open.

Check Draw a picture.

GO on

Are They Getting It? ❓

Check students' understanding of finding differences from 0 to 10 by writing these exercises on the board. Ask students to point out the correct and incorrect answers and explain their reasoning.

1. 😊 😊 😊 😊 😊 😊 ❌ ❌

   $8 - 2 = 6$ This is correct.

2. $9 - 7 = 16$ This is incorrect. The difference is 2.

3. Maria has 7 books. She gives 2 away and says she has 5 left. This is correct.

Practice on Your Own

nd each difference.

4 5 − 2 = __3__

5 6 − 3 = __3__

nd each difference. Use the number line.

6 9 − 9 = __0__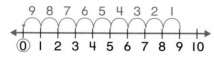

7 8 − 2 = __6__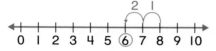

nd each difference.

8 8 − 4 = __4__   9 10 − 2 = __8__   10 4 − 0 = __4__

11 **WRITING IN ▶ MATH**   Mika counts 7 dragonflies. Then 6 dragonflies fly away. How many dragonflies are left? How do you know?

__There is 1 dragonfly left. I can count__
__back on a number line. Start at 7 and__
__count back 6. 7 − 6 = 1__

ocabulary Check   Complete.

12 The answer to a subtraction problem is the __difference__. **STOP**

16 sixteen

Copyright © Macmillan/McGraw-Hill • Glencoe, a division of The McGraw-Hill Companies, Inc.

Math Challenge

How Many?

Have students work in pairs. One student creates a subtraction story.

For example, Tina has 9 pretzels. She gives 3 pretzels to a friend. How many pretzels does Tina have left?

The second student listens to the story and draws a picture to represent the story.

Both students write a subtraction sentence for the story.

Practice on Your Own

Direct students to p. 16 in their student books. Have students complete Exercises 4–12 independently. You may need to review the directions of each section before students begin.

4 Assess

See It, Do It, Say It, Write It

Step 1 Write these two subtraction sentences on the board. 9 − 3 = _____ and 6 − 2 = _____ Ask students to read the problem, but do not give the difference.

Step 2 Have students model the problems using connecting cubes, counters, or other manipulatives.

Step 3 Ask students to suggest a story for each problem such as: "Jamie had 9 pencils. He gave 3 pencils away."

Step 4 Tell students to write each number sentence on their papers and find each difference.

Looking Ahead: Pre-teach

In the next lesson, students will learn how to subtract numbers through 18.

Example

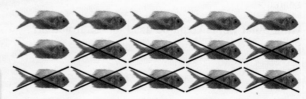

$$15 − 9 = 6$$

Have students find each difference.

1. 17 − 8 = 9

2. 16 − 8 = 8

3. 13 − 9 = 4

Lesson Notes

Lesson Planner

Math Objective Subtract numbers through 18.

Vocabulary subtract (subtraction), subtraction sentence, difference

Materials/Manipulatives poster/chart paper, index cards, money

Chapter Resource Masters

- CRM Vocabulary and English Language Development (p. A17)
- CRM Skill Practice (p. A18)
- CRM Problem-Solving-Practice (p. A19)
- CRM Homework Practice (p. A20)

 **1** Introduce

Vocabulary

Subtraction Action Write several subtraction sentences on the board using numbers through 18. Ask student volunteers to go to the board and solve each problem. Ask students to identify the difference and the symbol that means subtraction in each subtraction sentence.

What other words could be used for "subtraction?"
Sample answers: take away, less than, etc.

 **2** Teach

Key Concept

Foundational Skills and Concepts After students have read through the Key Concept box, guide them through the following questions.

- **How many cubes are there in all?** 11
- **How many cubes are crossed out?** 5
- **How many cubes are left?** 6

Lesson 1-4

Name _____

Subtraction Facts through 18

Key Concept

Look at the cubes.

There were 11. Then 5 were crossed out.

How many cubes are left?

$11 - 5 = 6$

There are 6 cubes left.

$$\begin{array}{r} 11 \\ -\ 5 \\ \hline 6 \end{array}$$ ← This line means equals.

Vocabulary

subtract (subtraction) take away, take apart, separate, or find the difference between two sets
$5 - 5 = 0$

subtraction sentence a math sentence that has a subtraction sign in it
$9 - 4 = 5$

difference the answer to a subtraction problem
$3 - 1 = 2$ ← difference

$10 - 6 = 4$
$4 + 6 = 10$

Subtraction and addition are opposites. Check subtraction with addition.

Chapter 1   Lesson 4   **seventeen** 1

English Learner Strategy

Act It Out

1. Have several students line up shoulder to shoulder.

2. Have students count off by 1s to determine how many students are in line.

3. Tell all students wearing sneakers (or use a favorite color, sport, food, etc.) to sit down.

4. Count the students who are left standing to find the difference. Write the subtraction sentence on the board.

5. Repeat the activity to reinforce the concept of subtraction. Other suggestions for having students sit could include: boys or girls, hair color, eye color, age, clothes, glasses, and so on.

Example

Find the difference.

Step 1   Count the sand dollars. There are 16 sand dollars.

Step 2   How many sand dollars are crossed out? 4

Step 3   Write a subtraction sentence. 16 − 4 = 12

Answer   The difference is 12.

Step-by-Step Practice

Find the difference.

Step 1   Count the starfish. There are __15__ starfish.

Step 2   How many starfish are crossed out? __7__

Step 3   Write a subtraction sentence.

    __15__ − __7__ = __8__

Answer   The difference is __8__.

18   eighteen

Additional *Example*

Find the difference.

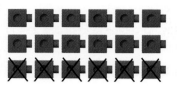

Step 1   Count the cubes.
There are 18 cubes.

Step 2   How many cubes are crossed out? 6

Step 3   Write a subtraction sentence.
18 − 6 = 12

Answer   The difference is 12.

 Common Error *Alert*

Students might confuse where to place the larger number in a subtraction problem. Remind students that the larger number always comes first in a subtraction sentence. If the problem is written vertically the larger number is on top, and if the problem is written horizontally, the larger number is on the left.

It is important for students to write the subtraction sentences correctly so when they begin to regroup, other errors do not occur.

Intervention Strategy

Auditory, Linguistic, Kinesthetic Learners

Materials: poster/chart paper

1. Place students in groups of 2 or 3.

2. Have each group come up with a rhyme, poem, song, or rap that explains how to do a subtraction problem. The lyrics should have accompanying dance moves or hand gestures.

3. Ask each group to perform their song for the class.

4. Have the class vote on their favorite and write those lyrics on chart or poster paper. Perform the lyrics and motions at the start of class throughout the chapter.

Math Coach Notes

Study Skill   Write vertical and horizontal subtraction sentences on the board. Identify each part in both sentences. Emphasize that the bar and the equals sign have the same meaning.

Guided Practice

Direct students to complete Exercises 1–4 in Guided Practice.

Exercises 2–4 Be sure students align the ones place in both the problem and difference.

Problem-Solving Practice

Guide students through the four-step problem-solving plan to complete Exercise 5.

- **What are the key words?** 15 foul shots, 9 foul shots, how many more

- **Where should you start on the number line?** 15

- **How many should you count back?** 9

Ask students to check their work using the strategy suggested in the Check step. Students can use addition to check their answer.

Using Manipulatives

Number Lines Use number lines to model subtraction.

Paper Money and Coins Have students pretend to buy items from a store. The items should be priced as a whole number up to $18. Students can "pay" and make change using subtraction.

$8 $12

On-Hand Manipulatives Use strips of paper (marked in equal spaces) in place of connecting cubes. Have students cut off the number that is being subtracted. Ask students how many are left.

Name _____

▶ **Guided Practice**

Find each difference.

1 $\underline{16} - \underline{8} = \underline{8}$

2 $\begin{array}{r} 18 \\ -\ 9 \\ \hline \end{array}$ **9**

3 $\begin{array}{r} 11 \\ -\ 6 \\ \hline \end{array}$ **5**

4 $\begin{array}{r} 12 \\ -\ 5 \\ \hline \end{array}$ **7**

Problem-Solving Practice

5 Allen needs to make <u>15 foul shots</u>. He has made <u>9 foul shots</u>. <u>How many more</u> shots does Allen need?

Understand Underline key words.

Plan Use a number line to subtract.

Solve Start at $\underline{15}$. Count back $\underline{9}$. Circle the answer.

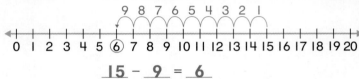

$\underline{15} - \underline{9} = \underline{6}$

He needs to make $\underline{6}$ more.

Check Use addition to check your answer.

GO on

Are They Getting It? ?

Check students' understanding of subtraction facts through 18 by writing these exercises on the board. Ask students to point out the correct and incorrect answers and explain their reasoning.

1. $12 - 6 = 5$ This is incorrect. The difference is 6.

2. $14 - 7 = 7$ This is correct.

3. $15 - 6 = 8$ This is incorrect. The difference is 9.

4. Tegland made 15 goals. Mavis made 8. Mavis says Tegland made 7 more goals than her. This is correct.

▶ Practice on Your Own

Find each difference.

6  $13 - 6 = \underline{7}$

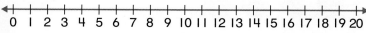

7 $12 - 7 = \underline{5}$ **8** $17 - 8 = \underline{9}$ **9** $14 - 6 = \underline{8}$

10
$$\begin{array}{r} 16 \\ -\ 9 \\ \hline \boxed{7} \end{array}$$

11
$$\begin{array}{r} 13 \\ -\ 8 \\ \hline \boxed{5} \end{array}$$

12
$$\begin{array}{r} 12 \\ -\ 8 \\ \hline \boxed{4} \end{array}$$

---

13 **WRITING IN ▶MATH**   Ian drew 13 stars. He colored 8 stars yellow. How many stars are not yellow? Explain.

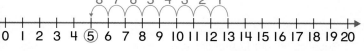

<u>Five stars are not yellow. I can use a</u>
<u>number line to subtract. Start at 13.</u>
<u>Count back 8. 13 − 8 = 5</u>

Vocabulary Check   Complete.

14 When you take away or find the difference between two

sets, you ___<u>subtract</u>___ .   🛑 STOP

20 twenty

Math Challenge

Subtraction

Have students work in pairs or small groups. Number two sets of index cards 0 to 18. Shuffle the two sets and stack them in a deck face down.

Each player in turn:

• draws two cards from the pile and subtracts the lesser number from the greater number. The difference is the score for that draw.

• adds the difference to his or her total score.

Play continues until all cards are used. The player with the highest total score wins.

Practice on Your Own

Direct students to p. 20 in their student books. Have students complete Exercises 6–14 independently. You may need to review the directions of each section before students begin.

④ Assess 🕐

See It, Do It, Say It, Write It

Step 1 Draw a number line from 0 to 20 on the board. Write the subtraction problem: $18 - 9 = $ _____.

Step 2 Have students help you place the numbers on the line by saying them out loud as you write them.

Step 3 When you count back to subtract, you start with the first number in the subtraction sentence. Have one volunteer circle the starting number. 18

Step 4 Have students count back 9 from 18 as you draw the jumps. Have students write the subtraction sentence: $18 - 9 = 9$.

Looking Ahead: Pre-teach

In the next lesson, students will learn how to add two-digit numbers with and without regrouping.

Example

$21 + 22 = \underline{43}$

Have students find each sum.

1. $23 + 21 = 44$

2. $43 + 48 = 91$

3. $18 + 11 = 29$

Formative Assessment

Use the Progress Check to assess students' mastery of the previous lessons. Have students review the lesson indicated for the problems they answered incorrectly.

Common Error *Alert*

Students will often use a number line incorrectly. Make sure students circle the number they are starting with. They should then count back to find the difference.

Exercises 4–6 Make sure students know how to align the numbers in the ones place in both the problem and the solution.

Exercises 7–8 Have students describe the strategy they used to solve each word problem.

Name _____

Progress Check 2 (Lessons 1-3 and 1-4)

Find each difference.

1.    __8__ – __5__ = __3__

```
0  1  2  3  4  5  6  7  8  9  10  11  12  13  14  15  16  17  18  19  20
```

2. $9 - 6 =$ __3__   3. $10 - 2 =$ __8__

4. $\begin{array}{r} 15 \\ -6 \\ \hline \boxed{9} \end{array}$ 5. $\begin{array}{r} 14 \\ -3 \\ \hline \boxed{11} \end{array}$ 6. $\begin{array}{r} 11 \\ -8 \\ \hline \boxed{3} \end{array}$

7. Rebecca bought 17 oranges to make orange juice. She has squeezed 9 oranges so far. How many oranges are left?

   __17__ – __9__ = __8__ oranges are left.

8. Mr. Nguyen bought juice boxes for 18 students. Only 7 students wanted juice. How many students did not want juice?

   __11__ students did not want juice.

Data-Driven Decision Making

Students missing Exercises . . .	Have trouble with . . .	Should review and practice . . .
1–3	subtracting numbers from 0 to 10.	SSG Lesson 1-3, p. 13 CRM Skills Practice, p. A14
4–6	subtracting numbers through 18.	SSG Lesson 1-4, p. 17 CRM Skills Practice, p. A22
7–8	problem-solving that involves subtracting numbers through 18.	SSG Lesson 1-4, p. 19 CRM Problem-Solving Practice, p. A23

Name _____

«« Replay   Play Tic-Tac-Toe!

Find each difference.
Mark an X in the box if the difference is less than 7.
Mark an O in the box if the difference is greater than 7.
Shade the boxes that make Tic-Tac-Toe!

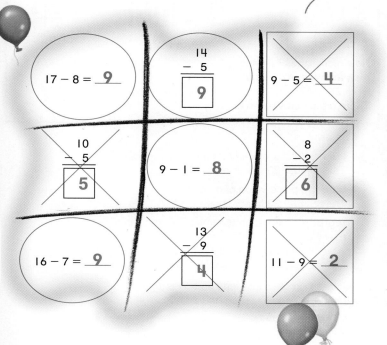

Use the Replay activity to review and reinforce the concepts and skills presented in Lessons 1-3 and 1-4.

Instructions

Have students read the directions at the top of the student page.

Student Technology

Students can use the following technology resources to reinforce chapter content.

- StudentWorks™ Plus
- Math Online   macmillanmh.com
- eGlossary

22 twenty-two

Lesson Notes

Lesson Planner

Math Objective   Add two-digit numbers

Vocabulary   tens, ones, regroup

Materials/Manipulatives   number cubes, base-ten blocks, spinners, money

Chapter Resource Masters

- CRM Vocabulary and English Language Development (p. A21)
- CRM Skill Practice (p. A22)
- CRM Problem-Solving Practice (p. A23)
- CRM Homework Practice (p. A24)

1 Introduce

Vocabulary

Examples   Draw a two-column chart on the board. Label the left column "tens" and the right column "ones." Have students give examples of two-digit numbers. Write the tens digit in the tens column and the ones digit in the ones column.

Have students copy the chart and write their own two-digit numbers, placing each digit in the correct column.

2 Teach

Key Concept

Foundational Skills and Concepts   After students have read through the Key Concept box, guide them through the following questions.

- **How many crayons in the first group? In the second group?** 41; 26
- **How many crayons in all?** 67
- **How many tens and ones in 67?** 6 tens and 7 ones

Name _____

Add Two-Digit Numbers

Key Concept

Look at the crayons. How many crayons are there in all?

 +

	tens	ones
	4	1
+	2	6
	6	7

41   26

How many **ones**? 7 ones
How many **tens**? 6 tens
41 + 26 = 67
There are 67 crayons in all.

Vocabulary

tens   a place value of a number
The number 23 has 2 tens.

ones   a place value of a number
The number 23 has 3 ones.

regroup   take apart a number to write it in a new way
1 ten + 2 ones becomes 12 ones.

You can regroup ones into tens and ones.
For example, 17 ones = 1 ten and 7 ones.

Chapter 1   Lesson 5   twenty-three **23**

English Learner Strategy

Model Ones, Tens, and Regrouping

1. Give each pair of students 2 number cubes. Have base-ten blocks available for students to use. Ask students to make a two-column chart on their paper. Students should label the left column "tens" and the right column "ones."

2. Have the students roll the number cubes and put them side by side to form a two-digit number.

3. Students should write the two-digit number in their chart and then use base-ten blocks to model the number.

4. Repeat the activity until students understand the concept of tens and ones.

Example 1

Find 43 + 24.

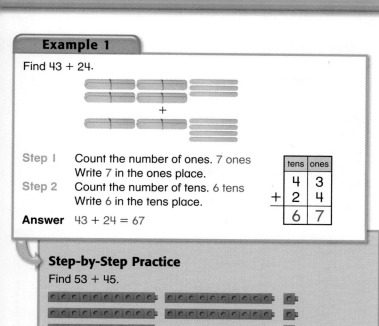

Step 1   Count the number of ones. 7 ones
Write 7 in the ones place.

Step 2   Count the number of tens. 6 tens
Write 6 in the tens place.

Answer   43 + 24 = 67

tens	ones
4	3
+ 2	4
6	7

Step-by-Step Practice

Find 53 + 45.

Step 1   Count the number of ones. __8__ ones

Write __8__ in the ones place.

Step 2   Count the number of tens. __9__ tens

Write __9__ in the tens place.

Answer __53__ + __45__ = __98__

tens	ones
5	3
+ 4	5
9	8

24   twenty-four

Find 36 + 22.

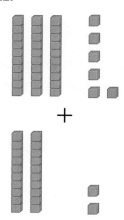

Step 1   Count the number of ones. 8 ones
Write 8 in the ones place.

Step 2   Count the number of tens. 5 tens
Write 5 in the tens place.

Answer   36 + 22 = 58

tens	ones
3	6
+ 2	2
5	8

Intervention Strategy

Linguistic/Naturalist/Interpersonal Learners

Write Problems   Have students work in pairs to create addition word problems. Encourage students to use their environment for inspiration. Ask students to write or draw their addition story problems, including solutions and an explanation. Allow time for students to share their problems with the class. Challenge students to use appropriate math vocabulary in their problems.

Common Error *Alert*

Some students will regroup when it is not needed. Have students check that the sum of the ones is 10 or greater before they write 1 in the regrouping box.

tens	ones
1	
3	6
+ 2	2
6	8

Additional *Example 2*

Find 33 + 58.

Step 1 Add the ones column.

$3 + 8 = 11$

Step 2 Regroup 11 as 1 ten and 1 one.

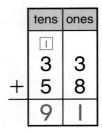

tens	ones
☐	
3	3
+ 5	8
9	1

Step 3 Write 1 in the ones place.
Write 1 above the tens column.

Step 4 Add the tens column.

$1 + 3 + 5 = 9$

Write this sum in the tens place.

Answer $33 + 58 = 91$

Math Coach Notes

Study Skills While studying addition facts, remind students that each addition fact is part of a fact family.

Practicing addition and subtraction facts will reinforce this relationship.

Make fact triangles to help students see the relationship between addition and subtraction.

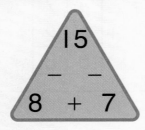

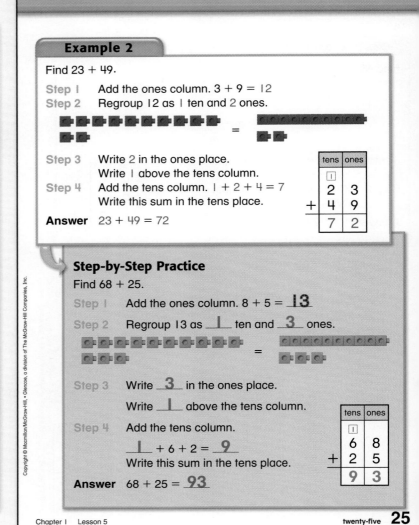

Example 2

Find 23 + 49.

Step 1 Add the ones column. $3 + 9 = 12$

Step 2 Regroup 12 as 1 ten and 2 ones.

Step 3 Write 2 in the ones place.
Write 1 above the tens column.

Step 4 Add the tens column. $1 + 2 + 4 = 7$
Write this sum in the tens place.

tens	ones
☐	
2	3
+ 4	9
7	2

Answer $23 + 49 = 72$

Step-by-Step Practice

Find 68 + 25.

Step 1 Add the ones column. $8 + 5 = $ __13__

Step 2 Regroup 13 as __1__ ten and __3__ ones.

Step 3 Write __3__ in the ones place.

Write __1__ above the tens column.

Step 4 Add the tens column.

__1__ $+ 6 + 2 = $ __9__

Write this sum in the tens place.

tens	ones
☐	
6	8
+ 2	5
9	3

Answer $68 + 25 = $ __93__

Copyright © Macmillan/McGraw-Hill • Glencoe, a division of The McGraw-Hill Companies, Inc.

Intervention Strategy   Kinesthetic Learners

Materials: money (pennies and dimes)

1. Give each pair of students $0.27 (2 dimes and 7 pennies). Then give each student $0.18 (1 dime and 8 pennies).

- **How much money do you have?** $0.45; 3 dimes and 15 pennies

2. Write on the board: $27 + 18 = 45$.

- **What is another way to show $0.45?** regroup the 15 pennies as 1 dime and 5 pennies; 4 dimes and 5 pennies also shows $0.45.

3. Explain that when 10 pennies are regrouped as 1 dime, it is the same as regrouping 10 ones as 1 ten.

Repeat the activity using different examples to reinforce the concept of regrouping.

▶ Guided Practice

Find each sum.

1   16 + 23

tens	ones
1	6
+ 2	3
3	9

2   43 + 11

tens	ones
4	3
+ 1	1
5	4

3   32 + 46

tens	ones
3	2
4	6
7	8

4   64 + 27

tens	ones
☐	
6	4
+ 2	7
9	1

5   59 + 26

tens	ones
☐	
5	9
+ 2	6
8	5

6   27 + 17

tens	ones
☐	
2	7
+ 1	7
4	4

7

☐ 5	4
+ 2	7
8	1

8
```
   18
 + 51
 ┌────┐
 │ 69 │
 └────┘
```

9
```
   53
 + 25
 ┌────┐
 │ 78 │
 └────┘
```

③ Practice

Guided Practice

Direct students to complete Exercises 1–9 in Guided Practice.

Exercises 4–7 Have base-ten blocks available for students to use.

Using Manipulatives

Base-Ten Blocks   Have students model two-digit addition problems using base ten blocks. Have students justify when and why they need to regroup.

On-Hand Manipulatives   Students can use popsicle sticks (single sticks and groups of 10), money, or cards labeled tens and ones to model regrouping and adding two-digit numbers.

⚠ Common Error *Alert*

Forgetting to Add the New Ten

When regrouping, some students might forget to add the regrouped ones to the tens column before adding the tens. Have students use base-ten blocks to model how 10 ones cubes must be exchanged for 1 tens rod. Ask students to explain how their answer would differ if they forgot to add the regrouped ten. Sample answer: The answer would be 10 less than the correct answer.

Lesson 1-5 Add Two-Digit Numbers **26**

Problem-Solving Practice

Guide students through the four-step problem-solving plan to complete Exercise 10.

- **What are the key words?** 58 stickers, 18 more stickers, how many

- **When we add, why is it important to align the ones and tens on a place value chart?** Sample answer: If you write 18 in the tens column, you are writing 180, which is 18 tens, not 18.

Ask students to check their work using the strategy suggested in the Check step. Students can use a hundred chart to solve the problem.

Practice on Your Own

Direct students to pp. 27–28 in their student books. Have students complete Exercises 11–18 independently. You may need to review the directions of each section before students begin.

Problem-Solving Practice

10 Michelle has <u>58 stickers</u>. She buys <u>18 more stickers</u>. <u>How many</u> stickers does Michelle have?

Understand Underline key words.

Plan Use a place-value chart.

Solve

$$\begin{array}{r} {}^{1} \\ 5\ 8 \\ +\ 1\ 8 \\ \hline 7\ 6 \end{array}$$

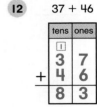

Michelle has ___76___ stickers.

Check Use a hundred chart. Start at 56. Count on 18.

▶ Practice on Your Own

Find each sum.

11 24 + 62

tens	ones
2	4
+ 6	2
8	6

12 37 + 46

tens	ones
¹	
3	7
+ 4	6
8	3

13 71 + 19

$$\begin{array}{r} {}^{1} \\ 7\ 1 \\ +\ 1\ 9 \\ \hline 9\ 0 \end{array}$$

 GO on

Chapter 1   Lesson 5

twenty-seven **27**

Are They Getting It? ❓

Check students' understanding of adding two-digit numbers by writing these exercises on the board. Ask students to point out the correct and incorrect answers and explain their reasoning.

1. 37 + 15 = 412 This is incorrect. The sum is 52.

2. 62 + 9 = 71 This is correct.

3. 27 + 56 = 83 This is correct.

4. 44 + 29 = 63 This is incorrect. The sum is 73.

14 Lilla has 33 acorns. She finds 12 more. How many acorns does Lilla have?

$$\begin{array}{r} 3\,|\,3 \\ +\,1\,|\,2 \\ \hline 4\,|\,5 \end{array}$$

Lilla has __45__ acorns.

15 In the first half of a basketball game, Lin's team scored 37 points. In the second half, they scored 49 points. How many points did Lin's team score in all?

$$\begin{array}{r} \fbox{1} \\ 3\,|\,7 \\ +\,4\,|\,9 \\ \hline 8\,|\,6 \end{array}$$

Lin's team scored __86__ points in all.

16 **WRITING IN ▸ MATH** LaToya solved the following problem, 46 + 38. Is LaToya correct? Solve and explain.

$$\begin{array}{r} 4\,|\,6 \\ +\,3\,|\,8 \\ \hline 7\,|\,14 \end{array}$$

$$\begin{array}{r} \fbox{1} \\ 4\,|\,6 \\ +\,3\,|\,8 \\ \hline 8\,|\,4 \end{array}$$

__No, LaToya did not regroup.__
__The sum is 84.__

Vocabulary Check   Complete.

Look at the number.

17 The 7 is in the __ones__ place.

18 The 2 is in the __tens__ place.

 27

STOP

28 twenty-eight

Copyright © Macmillan/McGraw-Hill • Glencoe, a division of The McGraw-Hill Companies, Inc.

Math Challenge

Find the Sum

Materials: spinner labeled 1–4, spinner labeled 5–9, pencil

- Students work in pairs. Student 1 spins each spinner and uses the numbers to create a two-digit number less than 50. Repeat to create a second number.

- Student 1 adds the numbers and records the sum.

- Student 2 repeats the steps.

- The student with the greater sum receives 1 point. The first student to earn 5 points wins.

See It, Do It, Say It, Write It

Step 1 Write the addition problem 42 + 37 = _____ on the board. Ask students to read the problem, but not solve it.

Step 2 Have students model the problem using base–ten blocks or other manipulatives.

Step 3 Ask students to explain how they solved the problem using the manipulatives.

Step 4 Tell students to write the addition sentence on their papers and solve.

Looking Ahead: Pre-teach

In the next lesson, students will learn how to subtract two-digit numbers.

Example

Find 45 − 21.

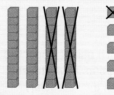
24

Have students find each difference.

1.

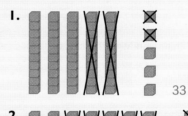
33

2.

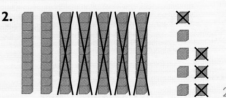
24

Lesson Notes

Lesson Planner

Math Objective   Subtract two-digit numbers.

Vocabulary   tens, ones, regroup

Materials/Manipulatives   base-ten blocks, number cubes, money

Chapter Resource Masters

- **CRM** Vocabulary and English Language Development (p. A25)
- **CRM** Skill Practice (p. A26)
- **CRM** Problem-Solving Practice (p. A27)
- **CRM** Homework Practice (p. A28)

1 Introduce

Vocabulary

Extend Vocabulary   Assign each pair of students a vocabulary word: *ones, tens,* or *regroup.* Have students write a rule or phrase that describes the vocabulary word. Sample answers: ones-write me on the right; regroup-some people call me trading, renaming, borrowing, or carrying; tens-one of me equals 10 ones.

Have each pair share their work with the class.

2 Teach

Key Concept

Foundational Skills and Concepts   After students have read through the Key Concept box, guide them through the following questions.

- **How many crayons were there?** 35
- **How many crayons were crossed out?** 12
- **How many crayons are left?** 23
- **How many tens in are 23? Ones?** 2 tens; 3 ones

Name _____

Subtract Two-Digit Numbers

Key Concept

Look at the crayons. There were 35. Then 12 were crossed out. How many are left?

$$\begin{array}{r} 35 \\ -\ 12 \\ \hline \end{array}$$

There are 3 **ones** left.
There are 2 **tens** left.

tens	ones
2	3

Vocabulary

tens   a place value of a number
The number 23 has 2 tens.

ones   a place value of a number
The number 23 has 3 ones.

regroup   take apart a number to write it in a new way
1 ten + 2 ones becomes 12 ones.

When you subtract two-digit numbers, you can regroup 1 ten as 10 ones.

Chapter 1   Lesson 6   twenty-nine **29**

English Learner Strategy

Subtraction Song

Help English language learners remember how to regroup when subtracting. Teach students the following subtraction song, to the tune of "Head, Shoulders, Knees, and Toes."

Subtract, regroup, from the tens to the ones,
Subtract, regroup, from the tens to the ones,
Take ten away, give to the ones, hip-hooray!
Subtract, regroup, from the tens to the ones!

Repeat several times adding hand motions or using a place-value chart as a prop.

Find 57 — 32.

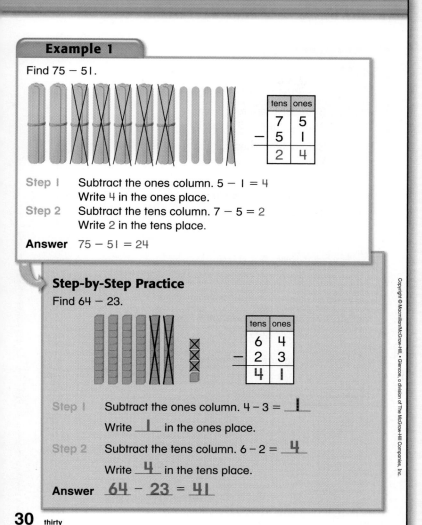

tens	ones
5	7
− 3	2
2	5

Step 1 Subtract the ones column.
$7 - 2 = 5$
Write 5 in the ones place.

Step 2 Subtract the tens column.
$5 - 3 = 2$
Write 2 in the tens place.

Answer $57 - 32 = 25$

Math Coach Notes

Study Skills Allow students to write two-digit subtraction problems on graph paper. The boxes help students correctly align the digits in the tens and ones columns.

Example 1

Find 75 — 51.

tens	ones
7	5
− 5	1
2	4

Step 1   Subtract the ones column. $5 - 1 = 4$
Write 4 in the ones place.
Step 2   Subtract the tens column. $7 - 5 = 2$
Write 2 in the tens place.

Answer $75 - 51 = 24$

Step-by-Step Practice

Find 64 — 23.

tens	ones
6	4
− 2	3
4	1

Step 1   Subtract the ones column. $4 - 3 = \underline{1}$

Write $\underline{1}$ in the ones place.

Step 2   Subtract the tens column. $6 - 2 = \underline{4}$

Write $\underline{4}$ in the tens place.

Answer $\underline{64} - \underline{23} = \underline{41}$

Intervention Strategy

Naturalist/ Linguistic Learners

Create Models and Problems   Take students on a walking field trip through the school. Ask students to record any objects or situations they could use for subtraction problems. Encourage students to notice numbers, objects, shapes, and situations. When they return to the classroom, allow time for students to write, draw, and create their subtraction problems. Have students share their problems with the class.

Additional *Example 2*

Find 87 − 38.

tens	ones
⁷ 8̶	¹⁷ 7̶
− 3	8
4	9

Step 1 8 is greater than 7. Regroup.

Step 2 Subtract 1 ten from 8 tens.
$8 - 1 = 7$
Add 10 ones to 7 ones.
$10 + 7 = 17$

Step 3 Subtract the ones.
$17 - 8 = 9$
Write 9 in the ones place.

Step 4 Subtract the tens columns.
$7 - 3 = 4$
Write 4 in the tens place.

Answer $87 - 38 = 49$

Math Coach Notes

Neatness

Begin the lesson by showing students two different subtraction problems.

Write one problem with extremely messy handwriting and misaligned numbers.

Write the second problem using neat handwriting, emphasizing spacing between numbers.

Point out that 4s and 9s and 1s and 7s can easily be confused if care is not taken in writing the numbers correctly.

Example 2

Find 88 − 29.

Step 1 9 is greater than 8. Regroup.

Step 2 Subtract 1 ten from 8 tens. $8 - 1 = 7$
Add 10 ones to 8 ones. $10 + 8 = 18$

Step 3 Subtract the ones column. $18 - 9 = 9$
Write 9 in the ones place.

Step 4 Subtract the tens column. $7 - 2 = 5$
Write 5 in the tens place.

Answer $88 - 29 = 59$

tens	ones
⁷ 8̶	¹⁸ 8̶
− 2	9
5	9

Step-by-Step Practice

Find 71 − 26.

Step 1 6 is greater than 1. Regroup.

Step 2 Subtract 1 ten from 7 tens. $7 - 1 = \underline{6}$
Add 10 ones to 1 one. $10 + 1 = \underline{11}$

Step 3 Subtract the ones column.
$\underline{11} - \underline{6} = \underline{5}$
Write $\underline{5}$ in the ones place.

Step 4 Subtract the tens column.
$\underline{6} - \underline{2} = \underline{4}$
Write $\underline{4}$ in the tens place.

Answer $71 - 26 = \underline{45}$

tens	ones
⁶ 7̶	¹¹ 1̶
− 2	6
4	5

Intervention Strategy   Kinesthetic Learners

Materials: base-ten blocks

1. Give each student pair 6 tens rods and 2 ones cubes. Then, ask students to subtract 5.

2. Students may be able to do this, but will be unable to demonstrate.

3. **Can you subtract 5 from 2? Explain.** No; I have to regroup so there are more than 2 ones. Help students regroup by exchanging 1 tens rod for 10 ones cubes to make 12 ones cubes in all.

4. Have students complete the subtraction problem.

5. Repeat the activity using different examples.

Name _____

▶ Guided Practice

Find each difference.

1   65 − 22

tens	ones
6	5
− 2	2
4	3

2   79 − 14

tens	ones
7	9
− 1	4
6	5

3   55 − 31

tens	ones
5	5
− 3	1
2	4

4   32 − 14

tens	ones
[2]	[12]
3̷	2̷
− 1	4
1	8

5   65 − 29

tens	ones
[5]	[15]
6̷	5̷
− 2	9
3	6

6   84 − 36

tens	ones
[7]	[14]
8̷	4̷
− 3	6
4	8

7

[2]	[17]
3̷	7̷
− 1	8
1	9

8

```
   74
 − 33
┌──────┐
│  41  │
└──────┘
```

9

[4]	[11]
5̷	1̷
− 3	6
1	5

32 thirty-two

---

③ Practice

Guided Practice

Direct students to complete Exercises 1–9 in Guided Practice.

Exercises 1–9 Make base-ten blocks available for those students who need to use a manipulative to complete subtraction.

Using Manipulatives

Money   Give students a handful of dimes and at least 19 pennies. Have students practice problems that require regrouping. For example: 34 − 18.

Hundred Chart   Have students place a marker on the first number in the subtraction problem and count back to the second number to find the difference. The number they land on is the difference.

On-Hand Manipulatives   Use strips of colored paper to represent tens rods and small squares of paper to represent ones cubes.

⚠ Common Error *Alert*

Forgetting to Add the New Ones

When regrouping some students forget that they need to add the 10 regrouped ones to the ones column before they can subtract.

Have students use base-ten blocks to help them remember to add the ones before subtracting.

Problem-Solving Practice

Guide students through the four-step problem-solving plan to complete Exercise 10.

- **What are the key words?** 33 blocks, 16 blocks, how many, left

- **How did you regroup?** Take 1 ten from the tens column and regroup it as 10 ones in the ones column.

- **How many blocks are left?** 17

Ask students to check their work using the strategy suggested in the Check step. Students can use a hundred chart to solve the problem.

Practice on Your Own

Direct students to pp. 33–34 in their student books. Have students complete Exercises 11–17 independently. You may need to review the directions of each section before students begin.

Problem-Solving Practice

10 There were 33 blocks on the floor. Imena picked up 16 blocks. How many blocks are left on the floor?

Understand Underline key words.

Plan Use a model.

Solve Use base-ten blocks to regroup.
Cross out 16. How many are left?

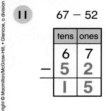

There are __17__ blocks left on the floor.

Check Use a hundred chart. Start at 33. Count back 16.

▶ Practice on Your Own

Find each difference.

11 67 − 52

tens	ones
6	7
− 5	2
1	5

12 75 − 28

tens	ones
6	15
7̶	5̶
− 2	8
4	7

13 88 − 39

tens	ones
7	18
8̶	8̶
− 3	9
4	9

GO on

Are They Getting It?

Check students understanding of subtracting two-digit numbers by writing these exercises on the board. Ask students to point out the correct and incorrect answers and explain their reasoning.

1. 47 − 24 = 23 This is correct.

2. 36 − 19 = 27 This is incorrect. The difference is 17.

3. 55 − 29 = 26 This is correct.

4. 43 − 16 = 33 This is incorrect. The difference is 27.

14 Pam counted 43 birds.
Then 21 birds flew away.
How many birds are left?

$$\begin{array}{c|c} 4 & 3 \\ -\ 2 & 1 \\ \hline 2 & 2 \end{array}$$

There are ___22___ birds left.

15 Ryan has 21 goldfish in his tank.
He gives 13 of them to his brother.
How many fish does Ryan have left?

$$\begin{array}{c|c} \boxed{1} & \boxed{11} \\ \cancel{2} & \cancel{1} \\ -\ 1 & 3 \\ \hline 0 & 8 \end{array}$$

Ryan has ___8___ fish left.

16 **WRITING IN ▶MATH**   Explain how to subtract
57 − 18 using a place-value chart. Complete
the place-value chart.

$$\begin{array}{c|c} \boxed{4} & \boxed{17} \\ \cancel{5} & \cancel{7} \\ -\ 1 & 8 \\ \hline 3 & 9 \end{array}$$

8 is greater than 7. Regroup 1 ten
as 10 ones. Subtract the ones: 17 − 8 = 9.
Subtract the tens: 4 − 1 = 3.
The difference is 39.

Vocabulary Check   Complete.

17 When you ___regroup___, you take apart a number to
write it in a new way.

 STOP

34 thirty-four

4 Assess

See It, Do It, Say It, Write It

Step 1 Write the subtraction problem 43 − 27
= _____ on the board. Read the problem to
the class.

Step 2 Have students model the problem using
base-ten blocks or other manipulatives.

Step 3 Have students present their strategies for
solving the problem to the class or a partner.

Step 4 Have students write the steps they took to
solve the problem. Make sure the explanation
includes the regrouping step.

Math Challenge

99 and Out!

Materials: base-ten blocks, two number cubes

Place students in pairs or small groups.

- Give each student 99 in base-ten blocks.

- Students take turns rolling two number cubes and forming a
two-digit number. For example: rolling a 3 and 4 make the
number 34 or 43.

- The student subtracts their number from 99 and shows the
difference using base-ten blocks.

- The player who runs out of base-ten blocks first wins.

Chapter 1 Progress Check 3

Formative Assessment

Use the Progress Check to assess students' mastery of the previous lessons. Have students review the lesson indicated for the problems they answered incorrectly.

⚠ Common Error *Alert*

Some students might have trouble regrouping. Remind students that in addition, regrouping occurs in the ones place where groups of ten are made and placed in the tens column. In subtraction, regrouping occurs in the tens place where tens are taken and regrouped as ones in the ones column.

If students have trouble regrouping, have them use base-ten blocks to represent each number.

Exercise 7 After completing three subtraction problems, some students might overlook "in all" and try to subtract. Point out that students need to add.

Name _____

Progress Check 3 (Lessons 1-5 and 1-6)

Find each sum.

1 34 + 53

tens	ones
3	4
+ 5	3
8	7

2 67 + 18

tens	ones
[1]	
6	7
+ 1	8
8	5

3

```
   [1]
    6   9
 +  2   3
 ─────────
    9   2
```

Find each difference.

4 79 − 34

tens	ones
7	9
− 3	4
4	5

5 83 − 29

tens	ones
[7]	[13]
8̶	3̶
− 2	9
5	4

6

```
    57
 − 35
 ──────
    22
```

7 There are 19 students in Miss Charnick's third-grade math class. Mr. Cruz has 24 students in his third-grade math class. How many math students are there in all?

43 math students in all

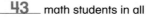

Data-Driven Decision Making

Students missing Exercises . . .	Have trouble with . . .	Should review and practice . . .
1–3	adding two-digit numbers.	**SSG** Lesson 1-5, p. 23 **CRM** Skills Practice, p. A22
4–6	subtracting two-digit numbers without regrouping.	**SSG** Lesson 1-6, p. 29 **CRM** Skills Practice, p. A26
7	problem-solving that involves adding two-digit numbers	**SSG** Lesson 1-5, p. 27 **CRM** Problem-Solving Practice, p. A23

Name _____

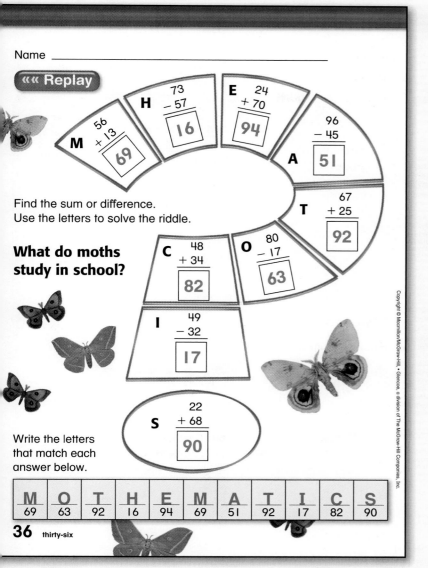

«« Replay

Find the sum or difference.
Use the letters to solve the riddle.

What do moths study in school?

M
56
+ 13
69

H
73
− 57
16

E
24
+ 70
94

96
− 45

A **51**

67
+ 25

T **92**

C
48
+ 34
82

O
80
− 17
63

I
49
− 32
17

S
22
+ 68
90

Write the letters that match each answer below.

M	O	T	H	E	M	A	T	I	C	S
69	63	92	16	94	69	51	92	17	82	90

Replay

Use the Replay activity to review and reinforce the concepts and skills presented in Lessons 1-5 and 1-6.

Instructions

Have students read the directions on the left side of the student page.

Be sure students understand how to enter the letters to solve the riddle. Make sure students realize that if a sum or difference does not appear at the bottom of the page, they have made a mistake.

Student Technology

Students can use the following technology resources to reinforce chapter content.

- StudentWorks™ Plus
- Math Online > macmillanmh.com
- eGlossary

Vocabulary

If students have difficulty answering Exercises 1–3, use the page references below to review the vocabulary words, or refer them to the glossary.

difference (p. 13)
regroup (p. 23)
sum (p. 3)

Vocabulary Review Strategies

Vocabulary Flashcards   Have students fold a sheet of notebook paper into fourths and cut the paper into cards. On the front side of the card, they should list a vocabulary word. On the back side of the card, they provide a definition or summary for the term. They should also provide an example or picture to illustrate their understanding of the word.

Concepts

The exercises in this section are grouped to cover content from each lesson in the chapter. The first exercise of each set is partially completed for the student in order to show the method for solving the other exercise(s) in the set.

Exercise 4: Lesson 1-1 (p. 3)
Exercise 5: Lesson 1-5 (p. 23)
Exercise 6: Lesson 1-6 (p. 29)
Exercises 7–9: Lesson 1-5 (p. 23)
Exercises 10–12: Lesson 1-6 (p. 29)
Exercise 13: Lesson 1-5 (p. 23)

Find **Extra Practice** for these concepts in the Practice Worksheets, pp. A5–A28.

Name _____

Review

Vocabulary

Word Bank	Use the Word Bank to complete.
difference **regroup** **sum**	1 $9 + 1 = 10$ <u>sum</u>
	2 $25 - 13 = 12$ <u>difference</u>
	3 = <u>regroup</u>

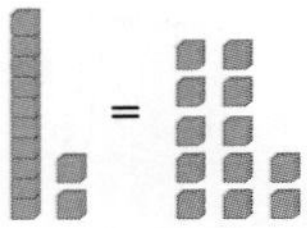

▶ Concepts

Find each sum or difference.

4 +

    <u>3</u> + <u>4</u> = <u>7</u>

5   +

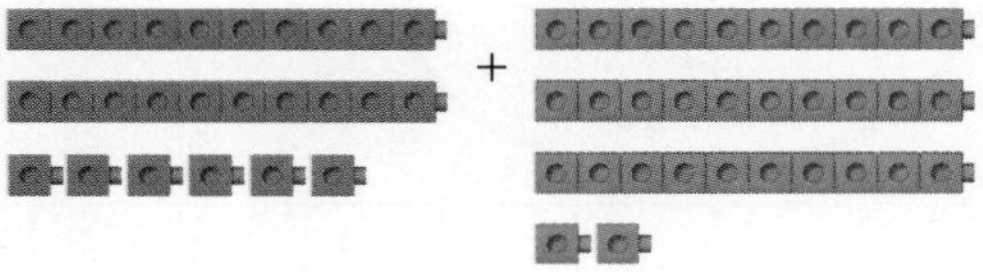

    <u>26</u> + <u>32</u> = <u>58</u>

GO on

Find each sum or difference.

6

$45 - 23 = 22$

7 $49 + 28$

tens	ones
☐ 1	
4	9
+ 2	8
7	7

8 $52 + 34$

$$\begin{array}{c|c} 5 & 2 \\ + 3 & 4 \\ \hline 8 & 6 \end{array}$$

9 $56 + 19$

$$\begin{array}{r} \boxed{1} \\ 5\,6 \\ + 1\,9 \\ \hline 7\,5 \end{array}$$

10 $48 - 19$

tens	ones
3	18
4	8
− 1	9
2	9

11 $51 - 33$

$$\begin{array}{c|c} \boxed{4} & \boxed{11} \\ 5 & 1 \\ - 3 & 3 \\ \hline 1 & 8 \end{array}$$

12 $74 - 26$

$$\begin{array}{r} \boxed{6}\ \boxed{14} \\ 7\,4 \\ - 2\,6 \\ \hline 4\,8 \end{array}$$

13 Miguel recycles cans. He collects 28 cans one week and 35 cans the next week. How many cans does Miguel collect in all?

Miguel collects __63__ cans in all.

tens	ones
☐ 1	
2	8
+ 3	5
6	3

STOP

FOLDABLES® **Dinah Zike's**
Study Organizer **Foldables®**

Have students use the Foldable they created at the beginning of the chapter to review and reinforce the concepts and skills they learned during the chapter. (See Chapter Resource Masters p. A1 for instructions.)

Intervention Strategy

Use this Intervention Strategy activity at any point during the chapter to reinforce the concepts and skills presented in the chapter.

If the teacher decides to use this Intervention Strategy, he or she must set up a ticket program, in which teams are created and awarded tickets for completing tasks.

Buy Extra Recess

Step 1 Divide students into teams. Help each team create an organizer to chart the team's total for each day of the week.

Step 2 Each group will be responsible for adding their team's tickets on a daily basis.

Step 3 On Friday, each team should share their results with the class.

Step 4 The class can add all of the team's tickets together.

- **What can you conclude from the data collected?** When they have enough tickets to buy an extra recess.

Classroom Management

Materials Management Each day as students finish using the money manipulatives or base-ten blocks, have them sort the manipulatives into groups of ten in baggies or envelopes. Not only will this build responsibility and help students practice making tens and counting, it will also help organize your materials before the next use. Advanced students can even regroup, trading tens rods for hundreds blocks or ones cubes for tens rods, depending on student ability and how you want your materials organized.

Chapter Resource Masters

Additional forms of the Chapter Test are available.

Test Format	Where to Find it
Chapter Test	Math Online macmillanmh.com
Blackline Masters	Assessment Masters, p. 12

ExamView®
Assessment Suite

Customize and create multiple versions of your chapter test and their answer keys. All of these questions from the chapter tests are available on ExamView® Assessment Suite.

Online Assessment and Reporting
macmillanmh.com

This online assessment tool allows teachers to track student progress with easily accessible, comprehensive reports available for every student. Assess students using any internet-ready computer.

Alternative Assessment

Use Portfolios Give students an addition and subtraction problem. Have the students solve each of these problems and explain the strategies used. Strategies could include pictorial representations, number lines, hundreds grids, manipulatives, or using the opposite operation.

Name _____

Chapter Test

Find each sum or difference.

1 $4 + 5 =$ _9_

2 $10 - 7 =$ _3_

3 $24 + 10 =$ _34_

4 $18 - 11 =$ _7_

5
tens	ones
1	
5	5
+ 2	8
8	3

6
tens	ones
7	9
− 3	6
4	3

7
tens	ones
7	13
8	3
− 3	9
4	4

8

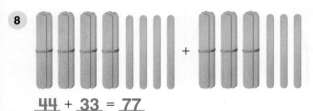

_44_ + _33_ = _77_

9

_28_ − _13_ = _15_

GO on

Chapter 1 Test

thirty-nine 39

10 Who is Correct?

Emma and Jorgé solved the problem $81 - 57 =$ ____.

81 − 57 = 36

81 − 57 = 24

Emma   Jorgé

Circle the correct answer. Explain.

Jorgé is correct. He regrouped before
subtracting. Emma did not regroup.

---

11 Karim found 19 ladybugs in the grass.
He found 23 more ladybugs on a tree.
How many ladybugs did Karim find in all?

<u>19</u> + <u>23</u> = <u>42</u>

Karim found ___42___ ladybugs in all.

```
  [1]
  1  9
+ 2  3
─────
  4  2
```

12 Nicholas had 34 pictures of butterflies.
He gave 26 pictures to his sister.
How many butterfly pictures does
Nicholas have left?

<u>34</u> − <u>26</u> = <u>8</u>

Nicholas has ___8___ butterfly pictures left.

```
 [2] [14]
  3   4
−  2   6
─────
      8
```

STOP

40 forty

Who Is Correct?
Diagnostic Teaching

- Emma says 81 − 57 is 36. This is not correct. Emma did not regroup correctly. In the ones place, instead of recognizing that 1 − 7 required regrouping, Emma inverted the problem and subtracted 7 − 1 which is 6. Then she subtracted the tens column.

- Jorgé says 81 − 57 = 24. This is correct. He was able to regroup and subtract.

Learning from Mistakes

Missed Questions Review commonly missed questions as a small group or class. Ask students to share their methods of answering each question. Try to point out when any errors occur and take corrective measures.

Data-Driven Decision Making

Students missing Exercises . . .	Have trouble with . . .	Should review and practice . . .
1	finding sums 0 to 10.	**SSG** Lesson 1-1, p. 3 **CRM** Skills Practice, p. A6
2	subtracting numbers from 0 to 10.	**SSG** Lesson 1-3, p. 13 **CRM** Skills Practice, p. A14
3, 5, 8	adding two-digit numbers.	**SSG** Lesson 1-5, p. 23 **CRM** Skills Practice, p. A22
4	subtracting numbers through 18.	**SSG** Lesson 1-4, p. 17 **CRM** Skills Practice, p. A22
6, 7, 9, 10	subtracting two-digit numbers.	**SSG** Lesson 1-6, p. 29 **CRM** Skills Practice, p. A26
11, 12	problem-solving that involves adding and subtracting two-digit numbers.	**SSG** Lesson 1-5, p. 27 **CRM** Problem-Solving Practice, p. A23 **SSG** Lesson 1-6, p. 33 **CRM** Problem-Solving Practice, p. A27

Test Practice Notes

⚠ Diagnose Student Errors

Survey student responses for each item. Class trends may indicate common errors and misconceptions.

1. 0: does not understand how to regroup tens
   7: does not understand how to regroup tens
   17: does not understand how to regroup tens
   70: correct

2. The sum is 69:   does not understand the term *sum*
   52 is being added to 17: does not understand an addition sentence
   17 is an addend: does not understand the term *addend*
   The sum is 52:   correct

3. 5: does not understand how to regroup tens
   15: does not understand how to regroup tens
   50: correct
   55: does not understand how to regroup tens

4. +: correct
   −: does not understand the symbol for addition
   =: does not understand the symbol for addition
   <: does not understand the symbol for addition

5. $15 − 9 = 6$: misread the number line
   $15 − 6 = 9$: correct
   $9 + 6 = 15$: confused counting back with counting on
   $6 + 9 = 15$: confused counting back with counting on

6. =: does not understand the symbol for subtraction
   <: does not understand the symbol for subtraction
   +: does not understand the symbol for subtraction
   −: correct

7. $4 − 3 = 1$:   confused addition with subtraction
   $7 − 3 = 4$:   does not understand the picture
   $4 + 3 = 7$:   correct
   $3 + 4 = 12$: multiplied 3 and 4 instead of adding 3 and 4

8. 73: subtracted instead of adding
   79: subtracted the tens instead of adding them
   96: incorrectly added the ones
   99: correct

9. 5: forgot to subtract the tens
   15: correct
   26: subtracted incorrectly
   99: confused subtraction with addition

10. <: does not understand regrouping
    >: does not understand regrouping
    +: does not understand regrouping
    =: correct

11. 13: correct
    25: subtracted incorrectly
    27: did not regroup and inversed the ones to subtract
    89: confused subtraction with addition

12. 38: confused subtraction with addition
    62: added incorrectly
    76: correct
    616: did not regroup the ones

Name _____

Test Practice

Choose the correct answer.

1 How many ones does 7 tens equal?

    0   7   17   70
    ○   ○   ○   ●

2 Which of the following is **NOT** true about the addition sentence?

$$52 + 17 = 69$$

○ The sum is 69.
○ 52 is being added to 17.
○ 17 is an addend.
● The sum is 52.

3 How many ones does 5 tens equal?

    5   15   50   55
    ○   ○   ●   ○

4 Which symbol tells you to join sets together?

    +   −   =   <
    ●   ○   ○   ○

5 Which number sentence does the number line show?

6   5   4   3   2   1

8 ⑨ 10 11 12 13 14 15 16

○ $15 − 9 = 6$
● $15 − 6 = 9$
○ $9 + 6 = 15$
○ $6 + 9 = 15$

6 Which symbol tells you to separate sets?

    =   <   +   −
    ○   ○   ○   ●

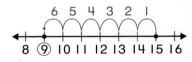

Chapter 1   Test Practice

forty-one **41**

7 Which number sentence is shown by this picture?

+

○ 4 − 3 = 1
○ 7 − 3 = 4
● 4 + 3 = 7
○ 3 + 4 = 12

8 What is the sum of 13 and 86?

73	79	96	99
○	○	○	●

9 Complete the subtraction sentence.

57 − 42 = _____

5	15	26	99
○	●	○	○

10 What symbol best compares these amounts?

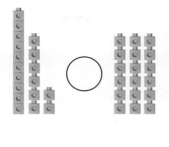

<	>	+	=
○	○	○	●

11 What is the difference of 51 and 38?

13	25	27	89
●	○	○	○

12 Complete the addition sentence.

57 + 19 = _____

38	62	76	616
○	○	●	○

Diagnosing Student Errors and Misconceptions

Multiple Choice Standardized tests ask multiple choice questions. Instruct students to narrow down their choices.

Remind students to think about what the problem is asking and what operation they must perform. For example, many addition multiple choice problems have an answer choice that is the correct difference of the two numbers even though the problem asks students to add. Encourage students to look at the answer choices carefully.

Chapter Overview

Chapter-at-a-Glance

Lesson	Math Objective	State/Local Standards
2-1 Equal Groups (pp. 45–48)	Find the total in equal groups.	
2-2 Repeated Addition and Skip Counting (pp. 49–52)	Find totals using repeated addition and skip counting.	
Progress Check 1 (p. 53)		
2-3 Arrays (pp. 55–58)	Use arrays to represent multiplication.	
2-4 Area Models (pp. 59–62)	Use area models to represent multiplication.	
Progress Check 2 (p. 63)		
2-5 Multiply by 0 and 1 (pp. 65–68)	Multiply by 0 and 1.	
2-6 Multiply by 2 and 5 (pp. 69–72)	Multiply by 2 and 5.	
Progress Check 3 (p. 73)		

Content-at-a-Glance

The diagram below summarizes and unpacks Chapter 2 content.

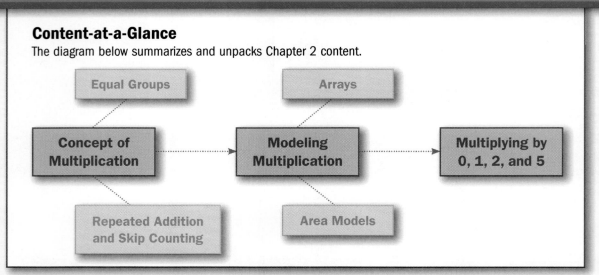

Chapter Assessment Manager

Diagnostic   Diagnose students' readiness.

	Student Study Guide/ Teacher Editions	Assessment Masters	Technology
Course Placement Test		1	⊙ ExamView® Assessment Suite
Book 1 Pretest		6	⊙ ExamView® Assessment Suite
Chapter Pretest		20	⊙ ExamView® Assessment Suite
Get Ready	SSG 44		Math Online ▷ macmillanmh.com StudentWorks™ Plus

Formative   Identify students' misconceptions of content knowledge.

	Student Study Guide/ Teacher Editions	Assessment Masters	Technology
Progress Checks	SSG 53, 63, 73		Math Online ▷ macmillanmh.com StudentWorks™ Plus
Vocabulary Review	SSG 48, 52, 58, 62, 68, 72, 75		Math Online ▷ macmillanmh.com
Lesson Assessments			⊙ ExamView® Assessment Suite
Are They Getting It?	TE 47, 51, 57, 61, 67, 71		

Summative   Determine student success in learning the concepts in the lesson, chapter, or book.

	Student Study Guide/ Teacher Editions	Assessment Masters	Technology
Chapter Test	SSG 77	23	⊙ ExamView® Assessment Suite
Test Practice	SSG 79	26	⊙ ExamView® Assessment Suite
Alternative Assessment	TE 77	29	
See It, Do It, Say It, Write It	TE 48, 52, 58, 62, 68, 72		
Book 1 Test		42	⊙ ExamView® Assessment Suite

Back-mapping and Vertical Alignment **McGraw-Hill's** *Math Triumphs* intervention program was conceived and developed with the final result in mind: student success in grade-level mathematics, including Algebra 1 and beyond. The authors, using the **NCTM Focal Points and Focal Connections** as their guide, developed this brand-new series by back-mapping from grade-level and Algebra 1 concepts, and vertically aligning the topics so that they build upon prior skills and concepts and serve as a foundation for future topics.

Teacher Works Plus™
All-In-One Planner and Resource Center

	Lesson 2-1	**Lesson 2-2**	**Lesson 2-3**	**Lesson 2-4**
Concept	Equal Groups	Repeated Addition and Skip Counting	Arrays	Area Models
Objective	Find the total in equal groups.	Find totals using repeated addition and skip counting.	Use arrays to represent multiplication.	Use area models to represent multiplication.
Math Vocabulary	equal groups	repeated addition skip count	array multiplication sentence product	area model factor
Lesson Resources	**Materials** • 1-minute timer/ stopwatch • paper • group of nature photos **Manipulatives** • spinner with numbers 1–10 • counters • base-ten blocks **Other Resources** CRM Vocabulary and English Language Development CRM Skills Practice CRM Problem-Solving Practice CRM Homework Practice	**Materials** • bell • hundred chart **Manipulatives** • counters • base-ten blocks **Other Resources** CRM Vocabulary and English Language Development CRM Skills Practice CRM Problem-Solving Practice CRM Homework Practice	**Materials** • index cards **Manipulatives** • counters **Other Resources** CRM Vocabulary and English Language Development CRM Skills Practice CRM Problem-Solving Practice CRM Homework Practice	**Materials** • grid/graph paper **Manipulatives** • base-ten blocks **Other Resources** CRM Vocabulary and English Language Development CRM Skills Practice CRM Problem-Solving Practice CRM Homework Practice
Technology	**Math Online** macmillanmh.com StudentWorks™ Plus ⊙ ExamView® Assessment Suite	**Math Online** macmillanmh.com StudentWorks™ Plus ⊙ ExamView® Assessment Suite	**Math Online** macmillanmh.com StudentWorks™ Plus ⊙ ExamView® Assessment Suite	**Math Online** macmillanmh.com StudentWorks™ Plus ⊙ ExamView® Assessment Suite

Lesson 2-5	Lesson 2-6	
Multiply by 0 and 1	Multiply by 2 and 5	**Concept**
Multiply by 0 and 1.	Multiply by 2 and 5.	**Objective**
factor multiply (multiplication) product	multiply (multiplication) product	**Math Vocabulary**
Materials • grid paper	**Materials** • number lines	**Lesson Resources**
Manipulatives • counters • coins • small cups • base-ten blocks	**Manipulatives** • connecting cubes • nickels • counters • base-ten blocks	

Other Resources
CRM Vocabulary and
  English Language
  Development
CRM Skills Practice
CRM Problem-Solving
  Practice
CRM Homework Practice
	Other Resources
	CRM Vocabulary and
	  English Language
	  Development
	CRM Skills Practice
	CRM Problem-Solving
	  Practice
	CRM Homework Practice	

Math Online ▷
macmillanmh.com
StudentWorks™ Plus
💿 ExamView®
  Assessment Suite
	Math Online ▷
	macmillanmh.com
	StudentWorks™ Plus
	💿 ExamView®
	  Assessment Suite
		Technology

Chapter Notes

Home Connection

Read the Home Connection letter with students and have them write their names in the space below.

Read and explain the activity under Help at Home. If time allows, complete a portion of the activity so students can introduce the activity to a parent or other caregiver.

Have students:

- skip count pairs of socks by 2s. Skip count the five-minute intervals around a clock face by 5s.

- find examples of items already in an array or area model, such as cookies laid out on a cookie sheet or a tiled countertop. Arrange small objects or finger foods in arrays.

Real-World Applications

Counting Coins   Show students a jar full of pennies. Then show them a roll of pennies. Explain that every roll has an equal number of pennies: 50 pennies, or 50 cents.

- **How would putting the pennies from the jar into rolls help you count the pennies?** You can count the number of rolls of pennies and then multiply by 50 cents.

English   **Spanish**

Dear Family,
Today our class started **Chapter 2, Introduction to Multiplication.** In this chapter, I will learn about equal groups and skip counting. I will also learn about arrays and area models. I will use these strategies to multiply numbers by 0, 1, 2, and 5.

Love, _____

Estimada Familia:
Hoy en clase empezó **el Capítulo 2, Introducción a la multiplicación.** En este capítulo voy a aprender sobre los grupos iguales y a brincar salteado. También aprenderé sobre los arreglos (arrays) y los modelos de área. Usaré estas estrategias para aprender a multiplicar por cero, 1, 2, y 5.

Cariños, _____

Help at Home

You can practice skip counting with your child at home. Line up pairs of shoes. Skip count by 2s to find the number of shoes in all. Find other objects that can be counted by 2s or 5s, and use skip counting to find how many objects in all.

Math Online ⟩ Take the chapter Get Ready quiz at macmillanmh.com.

Ayude en casa

Usted puede practicar contar salteado con su niño en casa. Puede alinear pares de zapatos. Cuente salteado, de 2 en 2, para calcular el número total de zapatos. Busque otros objetos que puedan ser contados de 2 en 2, de 5 en 5, y cuente salteado para calcular el total de objetos.

Chapter 2   **forty-three** **43**

Key Vocabulary

Find interactive definitions in 13 languages in the **eGlossary** at macmillanmh.com.

English   Español *Introduce the most important vocabulary terms from Chapter 2.*

equal groups   grupos iguales

each group has the same number of objects (p. 45)

repeated addition   suma repetida

add the same number more than one time (p. 49)

$6 + 6 + 6 + 6 = 24$

skip count   contar salteado

count objects in equal groups of two or more   2, 4, 6, 8, 10 (p. 49)

array   arreglo

objects shown in rows and columns (p. 55)

product   producto

the answer to a multiplication problem (p. 55)

$4 \times 2 = 8$ ◄— product

multiplication sentence   enunciado de multiplicación

a math sentence that has a multiplication sign in it (p. 55)

area model   modelo del área

a grid that models a multiplication sentence (p. 59)

factor   factor

a number that is multiplied by another number (p. 59)

multiply (multiplication) multiplicar (multiplicación)

the operation of repeated addition of the same number (p. 65)

Name _____

Get Ready

Count. Write how many.

1 There are __2__ rows of buttons.

There are __4__ buttons in each row.

There are __8__ buttons in all.

2 There are __3__ rows of stickers.

There are __3__ stickers in each row.

There are __9__ stickers in all.

3 The rectangle has __2__ rows.

Each row has __5__ squares.

There are __10__ squares in all.

4 The square has __3__ rows.

Each row has __4__ small squares.

There are __12__ small squares in all.

Find each sum.

5 $2 + 2 + 2 =$ __6__

6 $4 + 4 =$ __8__

7 $3 + 3 =$ __6__

8 $5 + 5$ ... __15__

STOP

44 forty-four

Get Ready

Have students complete Get Ready to assess readiness for the chapter concepts and skills. Refer to the lessons below for additional support for prerequisite skills.

1-1 Addition Facts 0 to 10 (p. 3)
1-2 Addition Facts through 18 (p. 7)

You may also assess student readiness with the following resources:

Math Online Online Readiness quiz at macmillanmh.com

Assessment Masters: Chapter Pretest (p. 20)

FOLDABLES®
Study Organizer **Dinah Zike's Foldables®**

Guide students through the directions on p. A29 in the Chapter Resource Masters to create their own Foldable graphic organizer for use with this chapter.

Professional Development

Targeted professional development has been articulated throughout **McGraw-Hill's** *Math Triumphs* intervention program. **The McGraw-Hill Professional Development Video Library** provides short videos that support the **NCTM Focal Points and Focal Connections.**
For more information, visit macmillanmh.com.

Model Lessons   Instructional Strategies

Voc...

Present th... ...roups, skip count, ...a model. Use ... meanings of ... ...t for other two-wor...

mea...
over s...

means to pass over s... ...e counting to find how many

Lesson 2-1

Lesson Notes

Lesson Planner

Objective   Find the total in equal groups.

Vocabulary   equal groups

Materials/Manipulatives   counters, base-ten blocks, spinner with numbers 1–10, 1-minute timer/stopwatch, group of nature photos, paper

Chapter Resource Masters

- CRM Vocabulary and English Language Development (p. A32)
- CRM Skills Practice (p. A33)
- CRM Problem-Solving Practice (p. A34)
- CRM Homework Practice (p. A35)

1 Introduce

Vocabulary

Explore Vocabulary   Write "Which has equal groups?" on the board. Put 2 rows of 3 circles on the board. Then to the right of that group, make 1 row of 4 circles and 1 row of 2 circles. Ask students to identify the set with equal groups. Discuss the meaning of *equal groups.*

Ask students to model equal groups.

2 Teach

Key Concept

Foundational Skills and Concepts   After students have read through the Key Concept box, guide them through the following questions.

- **How many equal groups are there?** 2
- **How many buttons are in each group?** 4
- **How many buttons are there in all?** 8

45 Chapter 2 Introduction to Multiplication

Lesson 2-1

Name _____

Equal Groups

> **Key Concept**
>
> Alicia has 8 buttons.
>
>
>
> Alicia can place the buttons in 2 **equal groups**. There are 4 buttons in each group.
>
>
>
> 4   4
>
> 2 groups of 4   =   8 buttons in all

Vocabulary

equal groups   each group has the same number of objects

There are 2 equal groups of counters.

There are 4 cubes on each side. There are 8 cubes in all.

There are 4 counters in each group. There are 8 counters in all.

Chapter 2   Lesson 1   forty-five **45**

Copyright © Macmillan/McGraw-Hill, · Glencoe, a division of The McGraw-Hill Companies, Inc.

English Learner Strategy

Describe Equal Groups

1. Write "equal groups" on the board.

2. Discuss equal groups:

   - **The word equal means the same.**

   - **When you have equal groups, you have groups of the same number of objects.** Model the following:

     ▢▢▢▢ = ▢▢▢▢

3. Place the same number of counters in each box. Explain that these are equal groups because there is the same number of counters in each group.

4. Provide students with counters. Ask them to create equal groups. Have students present and explain the groups.

Example

Write how many in all.

| 3 | 3 | 3 |

3 groups of 3   9 cowboy hats in all

Step 1   Count the number of groups. 3
Step 2   Count how many in each group. 3
Step 3   Find the total. 9
Answer   There are 9 cowboy hats in all.

Step-by-Step Practice

Write how many in all.

____5____   ____5____

__2__ groups of __5__   __10__ cowboy boots in all

Step 1   Count the number of groups. __2__
Step 2   Count how many in each group. __5__
Step 3   Find the total. __10__
Answer   There are __10__ cowboy boots in all.

Additional *Example*

Write how many in all.

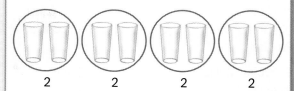

| 2 | 2 | 2 | 2 |

4 goups of 2   8 glasses in all

Step 1 Count the number of groups. 4

Step 2 Count how many in each group. 2

Step 3 Find the total. 8

Answer There are 8 glasses in all.

⚠ Common Error *Alert*

Equal Groups   Students may confuse the number of groups with the number of objects in each group. When students model equal groups, have them write out the meaning of each number. For example, when modeling 4 groups of 3 counters, have them write: "There are 4 equal groups. Each group has 3 counters." They can use the sentences to check their models.

Math Coach Notes

Multiplication   Explain that working with equal groups will help students understand the concept of multiplication.

Students will find that knowing the number of equal groups and the number of objects in each group will make counting a large number of objects easier.

Intervention Strategy   Naturalist Learners

Materials: paper; photographs of poison ivy, dogwood blossoms, spiders, and insects

Divide students into groups of 3 or 4. Ask them to look at the photographs and identify objects that occur in equal groups. 3 leaves on poison ivy, 4 petals on dogwood blossoms, 8 legs on spiders, 6 legs on insects

Ask students to choose one photograph and draw 4 of that plant or animal on a piece of paper.

- **How many equal groups of [leaves, petals, or legs] do you see?**
  4 groups

- **How many [leaves, petals, or legs] are in each group?** Sample answers: 3, 4, 8, 6

- **What is the total number of [leaves, petals, or legs]?** Sample answers: 12, 16, 32, 24

Practice

Guided Practice

Direct students to complete Exercises 1–2 in Guided Practice.

Exercise 2 Make sure students understand that there are 4 groups of 3, not 3 groups of 4.

Problem-Solving Practice

Guide students through the four-step problem-solving plan to complete Exercise 3.

- **How many movies are in each equal group?** 4

- **How could a picture help you solve the problem?**
  I can draw 4 equal groups of 4 movies and then count the total number of movies.

Ask students to check their work using the strategy suggested in the Check step. Students can skip count by 4s to solve the problem.

Using Manipulatives

Base-Ten Blocks Students may use base-ten blocks to model equal groups.

Counters Counters can be used to make equal groups and find a total.

On-Hand Manipulatives Use dried beans, coins, or other common objects to make equal groups and find the total.

Name _____

▶ Guided Practice

Write how many in all.

1.
   __2__ groups of __2__   __4__ umbrellas in all

2.
   __4__ groups of __3__   __12__ rain hats in all

Problem-Solving Practice

3. Vincent watches movies on a rainy day. He has 4 types of movies. He has 4 movies of each type. How many movies does Vincent have in all?

Understand Underline key words.

Plan Draw a picture.

Solve Draw __4__ groups of __4__ rectangles.

Vincent has __16__ movies in all.

Check Circle each group of rectangles. Skip count by 4s to check your answer.

GO on

Are They Getting It?

Check students' understanding of equal groups by writing these statements on the board. Ask students to point out the correct and incorrect statements and their reasoning.

1. There are 4 groups of 3 stars. This is incorrect. There are 3 groups of 3 stars.

2. There are 9 stars in all. This is correct.

3. There is a total of 10 birds in 3 groups of 5 birds. This is incorrect. There is a total of 15 birds in 3 groups of 5 birds.

▶ Practice on Your Own

Write how many in all.

4

___3___ groups of __4__   __12__ paint cans in all

5

___4___ groups of __2__   __8__ paint rollers in all

---

6 **WRITING IN ▶MATH**   Elaine has 10 paintbrushes. Can Elaine place the paintbrushes in equal groups? How do you know?

Sample answer: Yes, Elaine can place the paintbrushes in 2 equal groups of 5.

Vocabulary Check   Complete.

7 When each group has the same number of objects, they are __equal groups__.

STOP

48   forty-eight

Math Challenge

Equal Group Brainstorm

Materials: spinner with numbers 1–10, 1-minute timer/stopwatch

Divide students into small groups. Players take turns using the spinner and keeping time.

One player spins and lands on a number. This number represents how many objects are in each equal group. The players have 1 minute to write things that model equal groups of that number. For example, if 8 is spun, a player may write *octopus* (8 legs), *hot dogs* (package has 8), and *spider* (8 legs).

The player who writes the greatest number of correct objects in 1 minute wins one point. Students play until everyone in the group has had a turn keeping time. The player with the most points wins the game.

Practice on Your Own

Direct students to p. 48 in their student books. Have students complete Exercises 4–7 independently. You may need to review the directions of each section before students begin.

④ Assess

See It, Do It, Say It, Write It

Step 1 Draw 4 groups of 3 circles on the board. Ask students how many are in each group and how many groups in all.

Step 2 Students work in pairs to model 3 groups of 5 with counters.

Step 3 Tell students to describe the equal groups they modeled. For example, they may say "3 groups of 5 counters = 15 counters in all."

Step 4 Draw 4 groups of 2 objects on the board. Have students write two sentences to describe the equal groups.

Looking Ahead: Pre-teach

In the next lesson, students will learn about skip counting.

Example

Skip count to find the sum.

There are 6 pears in all.

Have students skip count to find each sum.

1.

10

2.

12

3.
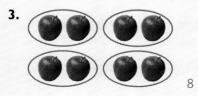
8

Lesson Notes

Lesson Planner

Objective   Find totals using repeated addition and skip counting.

Vocabulary   repeated addition, skip count

Materials/Manipulatives   counters, bell, hundred chart, base-ten blocks

Chapter Resource Masters

- CRM Vocabulary and English Language Development (p. A36)
- CRM Skill Practice (p. A37)
- CRM Problem-Solving-Practice (p. A38)
- CRM Homework Practice (p. A39)

 **1 Introduce**

Vocabulary

Compare Vocabulary   Write *repeated addition* and *skip count* on the board. Draw 10 stars. Demonstrate repeated addition. Circle 2 stars at a time and add them: 2 + 2 + 2 + 2 + 2 = 10. Demonstrate skip counting by 2s: 2, 4, 6, 8, 10. Discuss the similarities and differences between the two methods.

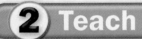 **2 Teach**

Key Concept

Foundational Skills and Concepts   After students have read through the Key Concept box, guide them through the following questions.

- **What is repeated addition?** Adding the same number more than one time.

- **What addition sentence shows repeated addition?** 2 + 2 + 2 + 2 = 8

- **What does the *skip* in *skip counting* mean?** You skip numbers as you count.

- **How can you skip count by 2s from 0 to 8?** 2, 4, 6, 8

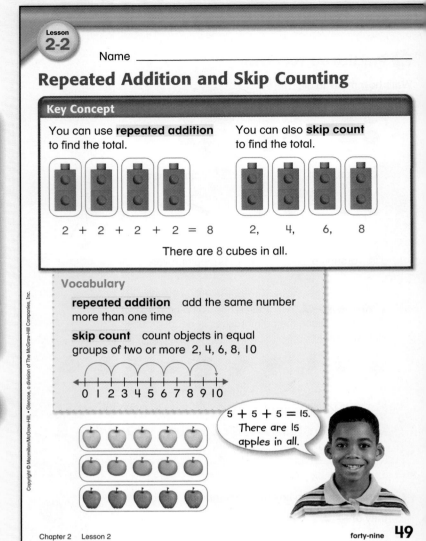

Name _____

Repeated Addition and Skip Counting

Key Concept

You can use **repeated addition** to find the total.

2 + 2 + 2 + 2 = 8

You can also **skip count** to find the total.

2,   4,   6,   8

There are 8 cubes in all.

Vocabulary

repeated addition   add the same number more than one time

skip count   count objects in equal groups of two or more 2, 4, 6, 8, 10

0 1 2 3 4 5 6 7 8 9 10

5 + 5 + 5 = 15.
There are 15 apples in all.

Chapter 2   Lesson 2   **forty-nine 49**

English Learner Strategy

Practice Skip Counting   Students can skip count out loud to become familiar with the multiples of 2, 3, and 5. Provide each student with a set of counters.

- Have students make 8 groups of 2 counters.

- Have students skip count out loud by 2s while pointing to each group of counters. Then have students skip count again, writing the numbers as they count.

- Repeat the activity, with groups of 3 and 5 counters. Each time, have students skip count out loud at least three times.

Example

Skip count to find the sum.

Step 1	Count the number in each group. 2
Step 2	Count the number of groups. 5
Step 3	Write an addition sentence.
	$2 + 2 + 2 + 2 + 2 = 10$
Step 4	Skip count to find the sum. 2, 4, 6, 8, 10
Answer	There are 10 frogs in all.

Step-by-Step Practice

Skip count to find the sum.

Step 1	Count the number in each group. __4__
Step 2	Count the number of groups. __3__
Step 3	Write an addition sentence.
	__4__ + __4__ + __4__ = __12__
Step 4	Skip count to find the sum. __4__, __8__, __12__
Answer	There are __12__ bees in all.

Additional *Example*

Skip count to find the sum.

Step 1 Count the number in each group. 3

Step 2 Count the number of groups. 2

Step 3 Write an addition sentence.
$3 + 3 = 6$

Step 4 Skip count to find the sum.
3, 6

Answer There are 6 snails in all.

⚠ **Common Error** *Alert*

Skip Counting Students might struggle to skip count by 3 and 4. They are more likely to leave out numbers than to name the wrong one. For example, students may count: 3, 6, 9, 12, 18 or 4, 8, 16, 20. Number lines can help students count the missing numbers.

Math Coach Notes

Study Tip Encourage students to write the numbers as they skip count. This is especially helpful when counting over a large range of numbers.

Intervention Strategy — Auditory Learners

Materials: bell

Students will write addition sentences and skip count from ringing patterns. Stand so that students cannot see you. Ring the bell clearly in groups of a given number, such as 2 rings, pausing in between groups of rings. Have students translate the ringing groups into an addition sentence and a skip counting list.

For example:

ring ring (pause) ring ring (pause) ring ring (end)

| 2 | + | 2 | + | 2 | = 6 |

| 2, | | 4, | | 6 |

Repeat for several different ringing patterns.

Guided Practice

Direct students to complete Exercise 1 in
Guided Practice.

Exercise 1 Tell students that the row with the plus
signs is for repeated addition and the row with the
commas is for skip counting.

Problem-Solving Practice

Guide students through the four-step problem-solving
plan to complete Exercise 2.

- **Why is *in each box* part of the key words?** It tells
  me how many are in each group.

- **How do you know how many fives will be in the
  addition sentence?** Alfonso has 5 boxes of crayons,
  so five is added 5 times.

Ask students to check their work using the strategy
suggested in the Check step. Students can skip count
by 5s to solve the problem.

Using Manipulatives

Base-Ten Blocks   Students can use the ones
cubes from a set of base-ten blocks to help them skip
count and write repeated addition sentences.

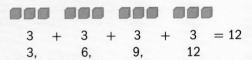

$$3 \quad + \quad 3 \quad + \quad 3 \quad + \quad 3 \quad = 12$$
$$3, \qquad 6, \qquad 9, \qquad 12$$

Counters   Students can use counters to help them
skip count and write repeated addition sentences.

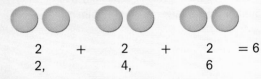

$$2 \quad + \quad 2 \quad + \quad 2 \quad = 6$$
$$2, \qquad 4, \qquad 6$$

On-Hand Manipulatives   Use beans or
other common objects to help students model
equal groups that they can skip count or add
repeatedly.

Name _____

▶ Guided Practice

1   Use repeated addition and skip counting to find the sum.

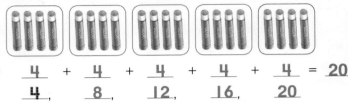

$$\underline{4} \quad + \quad \underline{4} \quad + \quad \underline{4} \quad + \quad \underline{4} \quad + \quad \underline{4} \quad = \underline{20}$$
$$\underline{4}, \qquad \underline{8}, \qquad \underline{12}, \qquad \underline{16}, \qquad \underline{20}$$

There are __20__ glue sticks in all.

Problem-Solving Practice

2   Alfonso has <u>5 boxes</u> of crayons.
There are <u>5 crayons in each box</u>.
<u>How many crayons</u> does Alfonso
have <u>in all</u>?

Understand   Underline key words.

Plan   Write an addition sentence.

Solve   Find the sum.

$$\underline{5} \; + \; \underline{5} \; + \; \underline{5} \; + \; \underline{5} \; + \; \underline{5} \; = \underline{25}$$

Alfonso has __25__ crayons in all.

Check   Skip count by 5s.

 GO on

Are They Getting It?

Check students' understanding of skip counting and repeated addition
by writing these exercises on the board. Ask students to point out the
correct and incorrect answers and explain their reasoning.

1. 2, 4, 7, 8 This is incorrect. 2, 4, 6, 8

2. 3, 6, 9, 12, 15 This is correct.

3. 5, 10, 15, 20 This is correct.

4. $4 + 4 + 4 = 16$ This is incorrect. $4 + 4 + 4 = 12$

▶ Practice on Your Own

Use repeated addition and skip counting to find each sum.

3

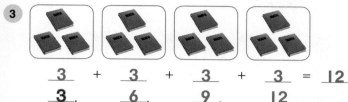

$$\underline{3} + \underline{3} + \underline{3} + \underline{3} = 12$$
$$\underline{3}, \quad \underline{6}, \quad \underline{9}, \quad \underline{12}$$

There are __12__ math books in all.

4

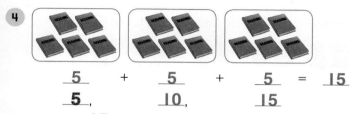

$$\underline{5} + \underline{5} + \underline{5} = \underline{15}$$
$$\underline{5}, \quad \underline{10}, \quad \underline{15}$$

There are __15__ reading books in all.

5 ◀WRITING IN ▶MATH Domingo put 10 books on each of 3 shelves. How many books did he put on the shelves in all? Explain.

Domingo put 30 books on the shelves.
Sample answer: I used repeated addition.
10 + 10 + 10 = 30

Vocabulary Check   Complete.

6 You can ____**skip count**____ to count objects in equal groups of two or more.   🛑 STOP

52 fifty-two

Math Challenge

Skip Counting Challenges

Materials: hundred chart

- Give each group of students a hundred chart. Ask them to skip count by 2s beginning with the number 2 until they get to the end of the chart.

  - **What was the last number you landed on?** 100

  - **If you continue to skip count by 2s, what number comes next?** 102

- Have students use the chart to skip count by 2s beginning with any number except 2. Observe how long they can skip count without reverting back to the familiar list of 2, 4, 6, 8, . . .

Practice on Your Own

Direct students to p. 52 in their student books. Have students complete Exercises 3–6 independently. You may need to review the directions of each section before students begin.

See It, Do It, Say It, Write It

Step 1 Draw 3 groups of 5 squares on the board. Write 5 + 5 + 5 = 15 and 5, 10, 15 under the squares.

Step 2 Have students use ones cubes to make 4 groups of 4 cubes. Have them work in pairs. One student writes a repeated addition sentence while the other student writes a skip counting list.

Step 3 Have each student explain to their partner how they found the total.

Step 4 Have students write an explanation of how to find the total number of cubes using repeated addition and skip counting.

Looking Ahead: Pre-teach

In the next lesson, students will learn how to use arrays to represent multiplication.

Example

Write a multiplication sentence and find the product.

◯◯◯◯
◯◯◯◯ $2 \times 4 = 8$

Have students write a multiplication sentence and find the product.

1.
◯◯◯◯◯ $1 \times 5 = 5$

2.
◯◯◯
◯◯◯ $2 \times 3 = 6$

3.
◯
◯
◯ $3 \times 1 = 3$

Lesson 2-2 Repeated Addition and Skip Counting **52**

Progress Check 1

Formative Assessment

Use the Progress Check to assess students' mastery of the previous lessons. Have students review the lesson indicated for the problems they answered incorrectly.

 Common Error *Alert*

Number of Groups Students may confuse the number of groups with the number of objects in each group. Explain that the first number represents the number of groups and the second number represents the number of objects in each group.

Exercise 2 Make sure students understand that the number of bears in each group will be added repeatedly. The blanks separated by commas are for skip counting.

Exercise 3 Make sure students understand the vocabulary in the problem. If they need assistance, read the problem aloud.

Name _____

Progress Check 1 (Lessons 2-1 and 2-2)

1 Write how many in all.

__4__ groups of __3__   There are __12__ deer in all.

---

2 Use repeated addition and skip counting to find the sum.

__2__ + __2__ + __2__ + __2__ + __2__ = __10__

__2__, __4__, __6__, __8__, __10__

There are __10__ bears in all.

---

3 There are 6 exhibits of monkeys at a zoo. There are 3 monkeys in each exhibit. How many monkeys are on exhibit in all? Explain.

There are 18 monkeys on exhibit in all. Sample answer: I used repeated addition.

$3 + 3 + 3 + 3 + 3 + 3 = 18$

Chapter 2   Progress Check   fifty-three **53**

Data-Driven Decision Making

Students missing Exercises . . .	Have trouble with . . .	Should review and practice . . .
1	finding totals of equal groups.	SSG Lesson 2-1, p. 45 — CRM Skills Practice, p. A33
2	skip counting or using repeated addition to find totals.	SSG Lesson 2-2, p. 49 — CRM Skills Practice, p. A37
3	problem-solving that involves skip counting or repeated addition.	SSG Lesson 2-2, p. 51 — CRM Problem-Solving Practice, p. A38

Name _____

Code Combination

Use skip counting and repeated addition to find the secret code and unlock the gym locker.

Kofi's football team made 5 field goals.
A field goal is worth 3 points.

Skip count. __3__, __6__, __9__, __12__, __15__ points

The team scored ☐ 15 ☐ points from field goals.

The team made 3 touchdowns. A touchdown is worth 6 points.

Use repeated addition. __6__ + __6__ + __6__ = __18__ points

The team scored ☐ 18 ☐ points from touchdowns.

How many points did the team score in all? Add.

__15__ + __18__ = __33__

The team scored

☐ 33 ☐ points

from touchdowns.

Arrange the points to find the secret code.

The secret code is:

15 · 18 · 33

Replay

Use the Replay activity to review and reinforce the concepts and skills presented in Lessons 2-1 and 2-2.

Instructions

Have students read the directions at the top of the student page carefully.

Make sure students understand that the secret code is formed by each total they place in the boxes. Students should place these numbers in order in the boxes at the bottom of the student page to find the secret code.

Student Technology

Students can use the following technology resources to reinforce chapter content.

- ⊕ StudentWorks™ Plus

- Math Online ⟩ macmillanmh.com

- eGlossary

Lesson Notes

Lesson Planner

Objective   Use arrays to represent multiplication.

Vocabulary   array, product, multiplication sentence

Materials/Manipulatives   counters, index cards

Chapter Resource Masters

- 📄 Vocabulary and English Language Development (p. A40)
- 📄 Skill Practice (p. A41)
- 📄 Problem-Solving-Practice (p. A42)
- 📄 Homework Practice (p. A43)

① Introduce

Vocabulary

Relationships   Draw an array of 3 rows with 2 triangles in each row. Write $3 \times 2 = 6$ under the array. Explain the connection between the number of rows and columns in the array and the numbers 3 and 2. Explain that the product of 6 represents the total number of triangles in the array.

② Teach

Key Concept

Foundational Skills and Concepts   After students have read through the Key Concept box, guide them through the following questions.

- **How many rows are in the array?** 2

- **How many are in each row?** 4

- **What multiplication sentence represents the array?** $2 \times 4 = 8$

- **What is the answer to a multiplication sentence?** product

---

Name _____

Arrays

Key Concept

You can use an **array** to show multiplication.

There are 2 rows.
There are 4 in each row.
The **product** is 8.

$$2 \quad \times \quad 4 \quad = \quad 8$$
number of rows   number in each row   in all

Vocabulary

array   objects shown in rows and columns

row →
↑
column

product   the answer to a multiplication problem

$3 \times 4 = 12$
↑

multiplication sentence   a math sentence that has a multiplication sign in it

$5 \times 4 = 20$

You can check multiplication with repeated addition.

$$4 \times 6 = 24$$
$$4 + 4 + 4 + 4 + 4 + 4 = 24$$

Chapter 2   Lesson 3

fifty-five **55**

English Learner Strategy

Arrays   Help students become familiar with the word *array* and its definition.

1. Write *array* on the board. Next to it write *arrange*. Say both words so students hear the similarity. **When you arrange objects, you put them in a special order. When we draw an array of objects we put them in row and columns.**

2. Draw an array for $3 \times 6 = 18$ on the board. Point to the three rows. **The objects are arranged in rows and columns. The array shows 3 rows with 6 in each row.**

3. Draw other arrays on the board. Call on students to describe each array in terms of how the objects are arranged.

4. Ask students to say the multiplication sentence represented by each array.

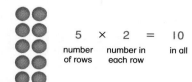

Example

Write a multiplication sentence. Find the product.

$$5 \times 2 = 10$$
number of rows   number in each row   in all

Step 1   Count the number of rows. 5
Step 2   Count the number in each row. 2
Step 3   Find the product. 10
Answer   The product of 5×2 is 10.

Step-by-Step Practice

Write a multiplication sentence. Find the product.

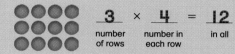

$$\underline{3} \times \underline{4} = \underline{12}$$
number of rows   number in each row   in all

Step 1   Count the number of rows. __3__
Step 2   Count the number in each row. __4__
Step 3   Find the product. __12__
Answer   The product of __3__ × __4__ is __12__.

56 fifty-six

Additional *Example*

Write a multiplication sentence. Find the product.

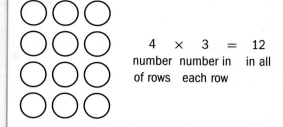

$$4 \times 3 = 12$$
number of rows   number in each row   in all

Step 1 Count the number of rows. 4

Step 2 Count the number in each row. 3

Step 3 Find the product. 12

Answer The product of 4×3 is 12.

⚠ Common Error *Alert*

Confusing Multiplication and Addition
Students might write sentences such as $5 \times 5 = 10$. Explain the difference between repeated addition and multiplication, as well as the difference between the multiplication and addition symbols.

Math Coach Notes

Strategies Demonstrate the connection between repeated addition and a multiplication sentence. Point out that the first number in a multiplication sentence tells you how many times to add the second number.

For example: $4 \times 3 = 12$ means you should add 3 to itself 4 times: $3 + 3 + 3 + 3 = 12$.

Have students practice writing repeated addition sentences for multiplication sentences and vice versa.

Intervention Strategy

Kinesthetic/ Visual Learners

Materials: counters

1. Give each pair of students a set of counters. Write the multiplication sentence $2 \times 5 = 10$ on the board.

2. Explain that the sentence can be represented by an array of 2 rows with 5 counters in each row.

3. Have students work together to make an array that represents the multiplication sentence. Using the vocabulary words, they can explain to each other how the array represents the multiplication sentence.

4. Write another multiplication sentence on the board and have students repeat the steps.

Practice

Guided Practice

Direct students to complete Exercises 1–2 in Guided Practice.

Exercises 1 and 2 To help students understand that the rows of the array form equal groups, have students circle each row.

Problem-Solving Practice

Guide students through the four-step problem-solving plan to complete Exercise 3.

- **What does one picnic basket represent?** one group of 6 bananas

- **Describe the array that models this problem.** The array has 3 rows, one for each basket. Each row has 6 circles to represent the bananas in each basket.

Ask students to check their work using the strategy suggested in the Check step. Students can use repeated addition to solve the problem.

Using Manipulatives

Base-Ten Blocks Have students create arrays with ones cubes to represent a variety of multiplication sentences.

$4 \times 3 = 12$

Counters Have students create arrays with counters to represent a variety of multiplication sentences.

$3 \times 3 = 9$

On-Hand Manipulatives Dried beans, paper clips, or other common objects can be used to make arrays.

Name _____

▶ Guided Practice

Write a multiplication sentence. Find each product.

1

$\underline{2} \times \underline{3} = \underline{6}$
rows   in each row   in all

2

$\underline{3} \times \underline{5} = \underline{15}$
rows   in each row   in all

Problem-Solving Practice

3 There are 3 picnic baskets. There are 6 bananas in each basket. How many bananas are there in all?

Understand   Underline key words.

Plan   Draw an array.

Solve

Write a multiplication sentence.

$\underline{3} \times \underline{6} = \underline{18}$

There are $\underline{18}$ bananas in all.

Check   Use repeated addition to check your answer.

GO on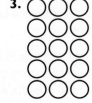

Copyright © Macmillan/McGraw-Hill. • Glencoe, a division of The McGraw-Hill Companies, Inc.

Chapter 2   Lesson 3   fifty-seven **57**

Are They Getting It? ❓

Check students' understanding of arrays by writing these exercises on the board. Have students point out the correct and incorrect answers and explain their reasoning.

1. ⭕⭕⭕⭕
⭕⭕⭕⭕
⭕⭕⭕⭕
⭕⭕⭕⭕

$4 \times 4 = 16$ This is correct.

2. ⭕⭕⭕⭕
⭕⭕⭕⭕
⭕⭕⭕⭕

$3 \times 3 = 9$ This is incorrect. $3 \times 4 = 12$

3. ⭕⭕⭕
⭕⭕⭕
⭕⭕⭕
⭕⭕⭕
⭕⭕⭕

$5 \times 3 = 15$
This is correct.

57 Chapter 2 Introduction to Multiplication

► Practice on Your Own

Write a multiplication sentence. Find each product.

4

$$\underline{4} \times \underline{3} = \underline{12}$$

5

$$\underline{5} \times \underline{5} = \underline{25}$$

6

$$\underline{3} \times \underline{2} = \underline{6}$$

7

$$\underline{3} \times \underline{3} = \underline{9}$$

8 **WRITING IN ►MATH** There are 4 rows of desks in Mr. Oliver's classroom. There are 6 desks in each row. Molly says there are 10 desks in all. Is Molly correct? How do you know?

<u>No, Molly is not correct. She added.</u>
<u>4 + 6 = 10 She should have multiplied.</u>
<u>4 × 6 = 24 There are 24 desks in all.</u>

Vocabulary Check Complete.

9 In 2 × 3 = 6, 6 is the <u>product</u>.

10 An <u>array</u> shows objects in rows and columns.

Math Challenge

Making Arrays

Materials: index cards, counters

Give 8 index cards and a set of counters to each pair of students. Each student writes a multiplication sentence on each of 4 cards. Each problem should have one factor greater than 5. For example, one problem could be 3 × 7 = _____.

Have the pair use counters to make an array and solve each problem. They should fill in the product on each index card. Ask pairs to share their completed multiplication sentences with the class.

Practice on Your Own

Direct students to p. 58 in their student books. Have students complete Exercises 4–10 independently. You may need to review the directions of each section before students begin.

④ Assess

See It, Do It, Say It, Write It

Step 1 Draw an array for 4 × 5 = 20 on the board. Describe what you are doing as you draw the columns and rows of the array.

Step 2 Choose 10 students to stand up and arrange themselves in an array. Write the multiplication sentence for the array of students on the board.

Step 3 Ask students to explain how the array shows a multiplication sentence. Be sure students are using the correct vocabulary.

Step 4 Have students draw an array and write the multiplication sentence represented by the array.

Looking Ahead: Pre-teach

In the next lesson, students will learn how to use area models to show multiplication.

Example

Shade the area model. Find each product.

$$\underset{\substack{\text{number} \\ \text{of rows}}}{4} \times \underset{\substack{\text{number in} \\ \text{each row}}}{2} = \underset{\substack{\text{in all}}}{\underline{8}}$$

Have students shade the area model. Find the product.

1.

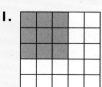

$$3 \times 3 = \underline{9}$$

Lesson Planner

Objective Use area models to represent multiplication.

Vocabulary area model, factor

Materials/Manipulatives base-ten blocks, grid/graph paper

Chapter Resource Masters

- [CRM] Vocabulary and English Language Development (p. A44)
- [CRM] Skills Practice (p. A45)
- [CRM] Problem-Solving Practice (p. A46)
- [CRM] Homework Practice (p. A47)

1 Introduce

Vocabulary

Vocabulary Preview Discuss the meaning of *area* as a covering, of paint on a wall. Display an area model of 2 rows with 3 squares in each row. Explain that the area is covered by 6 squares. Explain the connection between the rows and columns of the area model to the factors 2 and 3 and the product 6.

Show another area model and its corresponding multiplication sentence. Ask students to label the factors and product.

2 Teach

Key Concept

Foundational Skills and Concepts After students have read through the Key Concept box, guide them through the following questions.

- **How many rows are shaded?** 3
- **How many squares are shaded in each row?** 4
- **What do the shaded squares in the area model show?** a product of 12

59 Chapter 2 Introduction to Multiplication

Area Models

Key Concept

You can use an **area model** to show multiplication.

$$3 \times 4 = 12$$

number of rows — number in each row — in all

There are 3 shaded rows.
There are 4 shaded squares in each row.
There are 12 shaded squares in all.
The product is 12.

Vocabulary

area model a grid that models a multiplication sentence
$$3 \times 5 = 15$$

factor a number that is multiplied by another number

$$3 \times 5 = 15$$
↑   ↑

Peyton collects state quarters.
She has filled 3 rows of quarters, with 4 quarters in each row.
Peyton has collected 12 state quarters in all.

Chapter 2   Lesson 4   **fifty-nine 59**

English Learner Strategy

Area Models Explain to students that an area model is like an array made of squares.

1. Arrange 15 ones cubes to cover 5 rows and 3 columns on graph or grid paper. Explain that the cubes create an array.

2. Have students shade each square with a cube. Explain that the shading creates an area model.

   - **What problem can you write from this model?** 5×3
   - **What is the product?** 15

3. Have students model 4×4 using an array and an area model. Have them identify the factors and the product.

Example

Shade the area model.
Find the product.

Step 1   The first factor is 4.

Step 2   The second factor is 2.

Step 3   Shade 4 rows.
                 Shade 2 squares in each row.

Step 4   Count the shaded squares to
                 find the product.

Answer $4 \times 2 = 8$

Step-by-Step Practice

Shade the area model.
Find the product.

Step 1   The first factor is __2__.

Step 2   The second factor is __3__.

Step 3   Shade __2__ rows.

               Shade __3__ squares in
               each row.

Step 4   Count the shaded squares to
                 find the product.

Answer $2 \times 3 = $ __6__

Additional *Example*

Shade the area model. Find the product.

5×2

Step 1 The first factor is 5.

Step 2 The second factor is 2.

Step 3 Shade 5 rows.
           Shade 2 squares in each row.

Step 4 Count the shaded squares to find
           the product.

Answer $5 \times 2 = 10$

⚠ Common Error *Alert*

Students may look at the blank 5×5 grids and conclude that all products are 25. Be sure that students shade the correct number of squares to represent each multiplication sentence. Remind students to count the shaded squares to find the product.

Intervention Strategy   Interpersonal Learners

Divide students into small groups. Give each group a different set of 4 area models. Have students work together to write a multiplication sentence for each area model. They should identify the factors and product in each multiplication sentence.

When all groups have finished, have them present their area models and multiplication sentences.

Math Coach Notes

Strategies   To explore multiplication in greater depth, draw different area models that show the same product. For example, $3 \times 4 = 12$, $4 \times 3 = 12$, $2 \times 6 = 12$, $6 \times 2 = 12$, $1 \times 12 = 12$, and $12 \times 1 = 12$. Discuss how area models show that the order of the factors does not change the product.

Practice

Guided Practice

Direct students to complete Exercises 1–2 in Guided Practice.

Exercises 1 and 2 Remind students that the first factor tells the number of rows to shade. The second factor tells how many shaded squares in each row.

Problem-Solving Practice

Guide students through the four-step problem-solving plan to complete Exercise 3.

- **What does one glass represent in the area model?** one row of the area model

- **What do the ice cubes represent in the area model?** the number of shaded squares in each row

Ask students to check their work using the strategy suggested in the Check step. Students can skip count by 5s to solve the problem.

Using Manipulatives

Base-Ten Blocks Students can use ones cubes to create area models on grid or graph paper.

Connecting Cubes Students can use connecting cubes to create area models on grid or graph paper.

On-Hand Manipulatives Use small rectangular sticky notes or other common objects to create area models.

Name _____

▶ **Guided Practice**

Shade the area model. Find each product.

1 3 rows of 5

$3 \times 5 = \underline{15}$

2 5 rows of 2

$5 \times 2 = \underline{10}$

Problem-Solving Practice

3 Shawn fills 5 glasses with ice cubes. He puts 5 ice cubes in each glass. How many ice cubes does Shawn use in all?

Understand Underline key words.

Plan Use an area model.

Solve

$\underline{5}$ glasses × $\underline{5}$ ice cubes in each = $\underline{25}$

Shawn uses $\underline{25}$ ice cubes in all.

Check Skip count by 5s.

Chapter 2   Lesson 4

sixty-one **61**

Are They Getting It? ❓

Check students' understanding of area models by writing these exercises on the board. Show students area models that go with the exercises. Ask students to point out the correct and incorrect multiplication sentences and explain their reasoning.

1. 5 × 2

This is incorrect.
4 × 2

2. 3 × 2

This is correct.

3. 1 × 4

This is incorrect.
5 × 1

Copyright © Macmillan/McGraw-Hill • Glencoe, a division of The McGraw-Hill Companies, Inc.

61 Chapter 2 Introduction to Multiplication

▶ Practice on Your Own

Shade the area model. Find each product.

4. __2__ rows of __4__

$2 \times 4 =$ __8__

5. __2__ rows of __2__

$2 \times 2 =$ __4__

6. __4__ rows of __4__

$4 \times 4 =$ __16__

7. __5__ rows of __3__

$5 \times 3 =$ __15__

8. **WRITING IN ▶MATH** Look at the area model. Write a multiplication sentence. Explain.

__$5 \times 4 = 20$ There are 5 rows shaded. There are 4 squares shaded in each row. There are 20 squares shaded in all.__

Vocabulary Check Complete.

9. This __area model__ shows $3 \times 2 = 6$.

 STOP

Math Challenge

Larger Area Models

Materials: graph or grid paper

Outline four 10 × 10 areas on a sheet of graph or grid paper and make copies for students. Write these multiplication sentences on the board. Direct students to make area models to find each product. When students are finished, have them present their area models and answers to the class.

1. $7 \times 5 =$ _____ 35

2. $3 \times 8 =$ _____ 24

3. $9 \times 2 =$ _____ 18

4. $4 \times 7 =$ _____ 28

Practice on Your Own

Direct students to p. 62 in their student books. Have students complete Exercises 4–9 independently. You may need to review the directions of each section before students begin.

④ Assess

See It, Do It, Say It, Write It

Step 1 Write 4 × 5 on the board. Draw an area model to represent the multiplication sentence. Ask a volunteer to point to each row as you skip count by 5s count until you reach the last row and the product, 20.

Step 2 Ask students to shade an area model for 3 × 4. Have them skip count to find the product.

Step 3 Have students say the multiplication sentence for the model.

Step 4 Have students write, using the vocabulary words, how an area model relates to a multiplication sentence.

Looking Ahead: Pre-teach

In the next lesson, students will multiply by 0 and 1. A number multiplied by 0 is 0. A number multiplied by 1 is that number.

Example

$3 \times 1 = 1$

Find the product.

1. 4×0 0

2. 4×1 4

3. 3×0 0

4. 3×1 3

Progress Check 2

Formative Assessment

Use the Progress Check to assess students' mastery of the previous lessons. Have students review the lesson indicated for the problems they answered incorrectly.

Common Error *Alert*

Factors If students are not identifying the factors correctly, review how factors relate to the model. One factor tells the number of equal groups or rows. The other factor tells the number of items in each group or row.

Exercises 1–2 Make sure students understand that multiplication sentences have a multiplication sign.

Exercise 5 Remind students they can use the "draw a picture" strategy from the problem-solving plan to solve other problems.

Name _____

Progress Check 2 (Lessons 2-3 and 2-4)

Write a multiplication sentence. Find each product.

1.

   $\underline{2} \times \underline{3} = \underline{6}$

2.

   $\underline{1} \times \underline{7} = \underline{7}$

Shade the area model. Find each product.

3. $\underline{4}$ rows of $\underline{1}$

   $4 \times 1 = \underline{4}$

4. $\underline{3}$ rows $\underline{3}$

   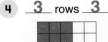

   $3 \times 3 = \underline{9}$

5. Miss Sung creates a bulletin board. She makes 4 rows of photos. She places 5 photos in each row. How many photos does Miss Sung use in all? How do you know?

   Miss Sung uses 20 photos in all. She created 4 rows of 5. $4 \times 5 = 20$

6. Marisol models $4 \times 3 = 12$. Does he shade the area model correctly? Explain.

   Yes, there are 4 rows of 3 squares shaded. There are 12 squares shaded in all.

Chapter 2 Progress Check   sixty-three **63**

Data-Driven Decision Making

Students missing Exercises . . .	Have trouble with . . .	Should review and practice . . .
1–2	using an array to represent multiplication.	SSG Lesson 2-3, p. 55 CRM Skills Practice, p. A41
3–4	using an area model to represent multiplication.	SSG Lesson 2-4, p. 59 CRM Skills Practice, p. A45
5–6	problem-solving that involves using arrays and area models	SSG Lesson 2-3, p. 57 CRM Problem-Solving Practice, p. A42 SSG Lesson 2-4, p. 61 CRM Problem-Solving Practice, p. A46

Name _____

«« Replay **Array Match**

Draw a line to match each number sentence with the correct array. Find each product.

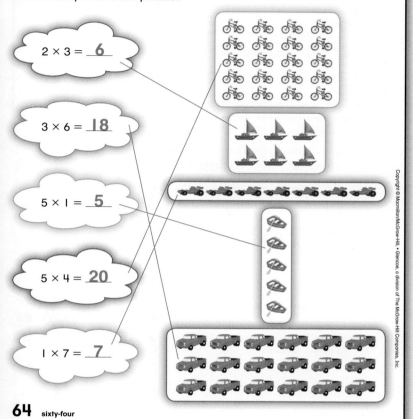

$2 \times 3 =$ __6__

$3 \times 6 =$ __18__

$5 \times 1 =$ __5__

$5 \times 4 =$ __20__

$1 \times 7 =$ __7__

64 sixty-four

Use the Replay activity to review and reinforce the concepts and skills presented in Lessons 2-3 and 2-4.

Instructions

Have students read the directions at the top of the student page carefully.

Remind students that the first factor represents the number of rows in an array.

Student Technology

Students can use the following technology resources to reinforce chapter content.

- 💿 StudentWorks™ Plus

- **Math Online** > macmillanmh.com

- eGlossary

Lesson Notes

Lesson Planner

Objective   Multiply by 0 and 1.

Vocabulary   multiply (multiplication), product, factor

Materials/Manipulatives   small cups, coins, counters, base-ten blocks, grid paper

Chapter Resource Masters

- **CRM** Vocabulary and English Language Development (p. A48)
- **CRM** Skills Practice (p. A49)
- **CRM** Problem-Solving Practice (p. A50)
- **CRM** Homework Practice (p. A51)

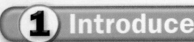 **Introduce**

Vocabulary

Nonexamples   Write 3 × 4 = 12 and 4 + 4 + 4 = 12 on the board.

- **Which math sentence is not an example of multiplication? Explain.** 4 + 4 + 4 = 12; multiplication sentences must have a multiplication sign.

- **Which numbers are not examples of products? of factors?** 3 and 4 in 3 × 4 = 12; all the numbers in 4 + 4 + 4 = 12.

Have students work in pairs. Students write number sentences and pose similar questions to a partner.

 **Teach**

Key Concept

Foundational Skills and Concepts   After students have read through the Key Concept box, guide them through the following questions.

- **What is the product when you multiply any number by 1? by 0?** that number, 0

- **What is 3 × 1? 3 × 0?** 3; 0

Name _____

Multiply by 0 and 1

Key Concept

When you **multiply** any number by 1, the **product** is that number.

$3 \times 1 = 3$ The product of 3 × 1 is 3.

When you multiply any number by 0, the product is 0.

$3 \times 0 = 0$ The product of 3 × 0 is 0.

Vocabulary

multiply (multiplication)   the operation of repeated addition of the same number

product   the answer to a multiplication problem

$3 \times 4 = 12$

factor   a number that is multiplied by another number

$3 \times 6 = 18$

When you multiply, you join equal groups.

$$5 \quad \times \quad 1 \quad = \quad 5$$

number of vases   number of flowers in each vase   product

English Learner Strategy

Multiplying by 0 and 1

Have students work in small groups. Give each group 5 cups and 5 coins.

Demonstrate the activity by taking 3 cups and 3 coins. Place 1 coin in each cup. Say: "I am multiplying 3 by 1." Point to each cup in turn and say: "1, 2, 3. The product is 3." Remove the coins from each cup. Say: "I am multiplying 3 by 0. Point to each cup and say: "0. The product is 0." Students should see that the cups represent: 3 groups of 1 and 3 groups of 0.

Have groups model the following problems using their cups and coins. They should explain how to multiply the factors to find the product.

1. 4 × 0 0   **2.** 2 × 1 2   **3.** 3 × 0 0   **4.** 5 × 1 5   **5.** 2 × 0 0

Example

Find the product.

$$6 \quad \times \quad 1 \quad = \quad 6$$

baskets   apple in   product
each basket

Step 1   The first factor tells how many groups. 6

Step 2   The second factor tells how many in
each group. 1

Step 3   Multiply. $6 \times 1 = 6$

Answer   There are 6 apples in all.

Step-by-Step Practice

Find the product.

$$\underline{4} \quad \times \quad \underline{0} \quad = \quad \underline{0}$$

baskets   apples in   product
each basket

Step 1   The first factor tells how many groups. __4__

Step 2   The second factor tells how many in

each group. __0__

Step 3   Multiply. __4__ × __0__ = __0__

Answer   There are __0__ apples in all.

66   sixty-six

Additional *Example*

Find the product.

$$3 \quad \times \quad 0 \quad = \quad 0$$

number of   number in   product
baskets   each basket

Step 1 The first factor tells how many groups. 3

Step 2 The second factor tells how many in each
group. 0

Step 3 Multiply. $3 \times 0 = 0$

Answer There are 0 objects in all.

!   **Common Error** *Alert*

Students may confuse multiplying by 0 with
multiplying by 1, answering $0 \times 5 = 5$ or 1×8
$= 0$. Use concrete and pictorial models to
demonstrate that $0 \times 5 = 0$ and $1 \times 8 = 8$.

Math Coach Notes

Repeated Addition   Use repeated addition to help
students see the logic of multiplying by 0 and 1. Write
$1 \times 5 = 5$ and $1 + 1 + 1 + 1 + 1 = 5$ on the
board. Explain that the multiplication sentence tells you
to add 1 five times.

Write $0 \times 3 = 0$ and $0 + 0 + 0 = 0$. Explain that
the multiplication sentence tells you to add 0 three
times.

Intervention Strategy

**Visual/
Kinesthetic Learners**

Materials: grid paper, base-ten blocks

Have students draw arrays for the multiplication sentences with the
factors 1 and a whole number from 0 to 9. They should write the
multiplication sentence and its equivalent repeated addition sentence
underneath each array.

Then have students model each multiplication sentence with ones
cubes. Explain to students that modeling multiplication sentences will
help them understand the concept of multiplication.

Guided Practice

Direct students to complete Exercises 1–4 in Guided Practice.

Exercise 2 Make sure students understand that the empty circles represent a group.

Problem-Solving Practice

Guide students through the four-step problem-solving plan to complete Exercise 5.

- **How many friends are invited to Keshia's party?** 6

- **How many balloons will each friend receive?** 1

- **What does the array show?** It shows 1 balloon for each friend, or 6 balloons in all.

Ask students to check their work using the strategy suggested in the Check step. Students can use repeated addition to solve the problem.

Using Manipulatives

Counters Students can model multiplication problems using counters.

  $1 \times 4 = 4$

Base-Ten Blocks Students can use ones cubes to model multiplication problems.

  $1 \times 6 = 6$

On-Hand Manipulatives Use small cups or bowls to model problems multiplying by 0. Explain that an empty cup or bowl shows the factor 0.

Name _____

▶ Guided Practice

Find each product.

1

$2 \times 1 = \underline{2}$

number of groups   number in each group   product

2

$5 \times 0 = \underline{0}$

number of groups   number in each group   product

3 $7 \times 1 = \underline{7}$

4 $0 \times 1 = \underline{0}$

Problem-Solving Practice

5 Keshia invites <u>6 friends</u> to her birthday party. She has <u>1 balloon</u> to give each friend. <u>How many balloons</u> does Keshia have?

Understand Underline key words.

Plan Draw an array.

Solve Write a multiplication sentence.

$\underline{6} \times \underline{1} = \underline{6}$

Keshia has __6__ balloons.

Check Use repeated addition to check your answer.

GO on

Chapter 2   Lesson 5   sixty-seven **67**

Are They Getting It?

Check students' understanding of multiplying by 0 and 1 by writing these exercises on the board. Ask students to point out the correct and incorrect answers and explain their reasoning.

1. $5 \times 0 = 0$ This is correct.

2. $4 \times 1 = 1$ This is incorrect. $4 \times 1 = 4$

3. $0 \times 6 = 6$ This is incorrect. $0 \times 6 = 0$

4. $1 \times 2 = 2$ This is correct.

5. $1 \times 1 = 0$ This is incorrect. $1 \times 1 = 1$

6. $0 \times 4 = 0$ This is correct.

▶ Practice on Your Own

Find each product.

6

$$\underline{4} \times \underline{1} = \underline{4}$$

number of groups　number in each group　product

7

$$\underline{2} \times \underline{0} = \underline{0}$$

number of groups　number in each group　product

8 $1 \times 1 = \underline{1}$

9 $0 \times 7 = \underline{0}$

10 $9 \times 1 = \underline{9}$

11 $10 \times 0 = \underline{0}$

12 $1 \times 10 = \underline{10}$

13 $1 \times 3 = \underline{3}$

14 **WRITING IN ▶MATH** Write a multiplication sentence about the dogs. Explain.

$2 \times 1 = 2$ **There are 2 groups. There is 1 dog in each group. There are 2 dogs in all.**

Vocabulary Check　Complete.

15 Look at the multiplication sentence $0 \times 9 = 0$.

The number 9 is a ___**factor**___.

 STOP

Math Challenge

Coin Toss

Materials: coins

Divide students into small groups. Give each group 1 coin. Tell students that heads is 1 and tails is 0.

Students take turns flipping the coin. If it is heads, the player says a multiplication sentence with 1 as a factor. If it is tails, the player says a multiplication sentence with 0 as a factor.

Students must say a new multiplication sentence on each turn. Have students record each multiplication sentence on a sheet of paper.

If the multiplication sentence is new and correct, the player gets 1 point. The player with the most points at the end of the game wins.

Practice on Your Own

Direct students to p. 68 in their student books. Have students complete Exercises 6–15 independently. You may need to review the directions of each section before students begin.

 4 Assess

See It, Do It, Say It, Write It

Step 1 Draw a picture modeling $0 \times 3 = 0$ and write the multiplication sentence on the board. Ask students to identify the factors and the product.

Step 2 Have students draw a picture to model a multiplication problem with 0 or 1 as a factor.

Step 3 Have students present their drawings to the class.

Step 4 Finally, have students write a description of their multiplication sentences and models.

Looking Ahead: Pre-teach

In the next lesson, students will learn how to use skip counting to multiply by 2 and 5.

Example

Have students skip count to find the product.

$$2 \times 4 = \underline{8}$$

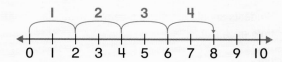

Have students skip count to find each product.

1. $3 \times 5 = \underline{15}$　　**2.** $2 \times 5 = \underline{10}$

3. $5 \times 4 = \underline{20}$　　**4.** $2 \times 2 = \underline{4}$

Lesson Planner

Objective   Multiply by 2 and 5.

Vocabulary   multiply (multiplication), product

Materials/Manipulatives   number lines, nickels, connecting cubes, counters, base-ten blocks

Chapter Resource Masters

- [CRM] Vocabulary and English Language Development (p. A52)
- [CRM] Skills Practice (p. A53)
- [CRM] Problem-Solving Practice (p. A54)
- [CRM] Homework Practice (p. A55)

1 Introduce

Vocabulary

Reenact Vocabulary   Review the definitions of the vocabulary terms. Have students work in small groups.

- Assign one word to each group.
- Have students develop a skit to act out the word.
- Have students present their skits to the class.
- Students should identify the correct vocabulary word from each skit.

2 Teach

Key Concept

Foundational Skills and Concepts   After students have read through the Key Concept box, guide them through the following questions.

- **How do you skip count to solve 4 × 2?**   2, 4, 6, 8
- **What is the product of 4 × 2?**   8
- **How do you skip count to solve 3 × 5?**   5, 10, 15
- **What is the product of 3 × 5?**   15

Name _____

Multiply by 2 and 5

Key Concept

You can use skip counting to **multiply**.

Find the **product** of 4 and 2.   Find the product of 3 and 5.
Skip count by 2s four times.   Skip count by 5s three times.

2, 4, 6, 8   5, 10, 15

$4 \times 2 = 8$ $3 \times 5 = 15$

The product is 8.   The product is 15.

Vocabulary

multiply (multiplication)   the operation of repeated addition of the same number

product   the answer to a multiplication problem

 $3 \times 4 = 12$

I can use a number line to skip count by 2s four times.
$4 \times 2 = 8$

English Learner Strategy

First Language Skip Counting   Write the problems on the board.

2×3 6 5×6 30 8×2 16 4×5 20 2×4 8

Ask students to share how they skip count by 2s and 5s in their first language. Then ask a student to skip count by 2s and 5s in English. Provide assistance as needed.

Below the problems, write out the lists of skip counting numbers:

2   4   6   8   10   12   14   16   18   20
two, four, six, eight, ten, twelve, fourteen, sixteen, eighteen, twenty

5   10   15   20   25   30   35   40   45
five, ten, fifteen, twenty, twenty-five, thirty, thirty-five, forty, forty-five

Have students use the list to solve the problems. They may count in their first language and then in English.

Example

Skip count to find the product. 7 × 2 = _____

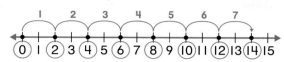

Step 1	Skip count by 2s.
Step 2	Skip count 7 times.
	2, 4, 6, 8, 10, 12, 14
Step 3	Multiply. 2 × 7 = 14
Answer	The product is 14.

Step-by-Step Practice

Skip count to find the product. 6 × 5 = _____

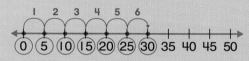

Step 1	Skip count by **5** s.
Step 2	Skip count **6** times.
	5 , **10** , **15** , **20** , **25** , **30**
Step 3	Multiply. 6 × 5 = **30**
Answer	The product is **30** .

70 seventy

Additional *Example*

Skip count to find the product. 3 × 5 = _____

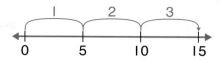

Step 1 Skip count by 5s.

Step 2 Skip count 3 times.
5, 10, 15

Step 3 Multiply. 5 × 3 = 15

Answer The product is 15.

⚠ Common Error *Alert*

Students may start skip counting at the wrong number on the number line. For example:

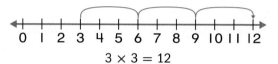

3 × 3 = 12

Make sure students understand to always start skip counting at 0.

Math Coach Notes

Strategies

1. Point out that any multiplication problem with a factor of 2 can be rewritten as an addition problem that adds the other factor to itself. For example, $9 \times 2 = 9 + 9$.

2. When multiplying by 5, the ones place In the product will always be a 5 or a 0. Model several examples so students can see the pattern.

Intervention Strategy   Intrapersonal Learners

Materials: number lines, nickels, connecting cubes

Have students work in pairs. Give each pair of students number lines marked 0 to 50, and 0 to 20, 10 nickels, and 20 connecting cubes. Tell students to use these tools to help them find products.

Have students find each product. When they are finished, ask them to explain how the tools helped find each product.

1. 7 × 5 35	**2.** 2 × 8 16	**3.** 6 × 2 12	**4.** 5 × 5 25
5. 9 × 2 18	**6.** 4 × 2 8	**7.** 2 × 1 2	**8.** 5 × 8 40
9. 4 × 5 20	**10.** 9 × 5 45		

③ Practice

Guided Practice

Direct students to complete Exercises 1 – 2 in Guided Practice.

Exercises 1 and 2 Students should circle the numbers as they skip count. The circles will help them avoid making errors.

Problem-Solving Practice

Guide students through the four-step problem-solving plan to complete Exercise 3. Be sure students realize that a "pair of socks" equals 2 socks.

- **What are the key words?** 8 pairs of socks, how many socks, in all

- **Why do you skip count 8 times?** because Bruce has 8 pairs of socks

Ask students to check their work using the strategy suggested in the Check step. Students can draw a picture and count the socks to solve the problem.

Using Manipulatives

Counters Students can use counters to model skip counting.

4 × 5 = 20

Base-Ten Blocks Students can use ones cubes to model skip counting by 2s or 5s.

4 × 5 = 20

 **On-Hand Manipulatives** Link pairs of paper clips together. Students can use these linked paper clips to help them skip count by 2s or 5s.

71 Chapter 2 Introduction to Multiplication

Name _____

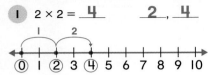 Guided Practice

Skip count to find each product. Use the number line.

1. 2 × 2 = __4__   __2__, __4__

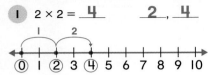

2. 4 × 5 = __20__   __5__, __10__, __15__, __20__

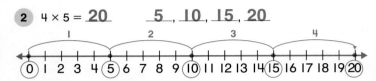

Problem-Solving Practice

3. Bruce has <u>8 pairs of socks</u>.
   <u>How many socks</u> does Bruce have <u>in all</u>?

   Understand   Underline key words.

   Plan   Skip count.

   Solve   Skip count by __2__s eight times.

   __2__, __4__, __6__, __8__, __10__, __12__, __14__, __16__

   __8__ × __2__ = __16__ socks in all

   Check   Draw a picture. Count the socks.

Copyright © Macmillan/McGraw-Hill, • Glencoe, a division of The McGraw-Hill Companies, Inc.

GO on

Chapter 2   Lesson 6   seventy-one **71**

Are They Getting It? ❓

Check students' understanding of multiplying by 2 and 5 by writing these exercises on the board. Have students identify the correct and incorrect statements or answers, and explain their reasoning.

1. To find the product of 5 × 8, skip count by 5s. This is correct.

2. 3 × 2 = 5 This is incorrect. 3 × 2 = 6

3. 5 × 5 = 25 This is correct.

4. The 2 in 2 × 6 = 12 is the product. This is incorrect. The 2 is a factor.

5. 5 × 3 = 15 This is correct.

6. 2 × 7 = 16 This is incorrect. 2 × 7 = 14

▶ Practice on Your Own

Skip count to find each product.

4 $6 \times 2 = \underline{12}$ $\underline{2}, \underline{4}, \underline{6}, \underline{8}, \underline{10}, \underline{12}$

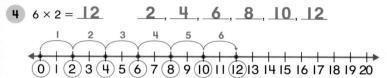

5 $5 \times 5 = \underline{25}$ $\underline{5}, \underline{10}, \underline{15}, \underline{20}, \underline{25}$

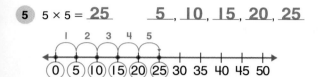

6 $4 \times 2 = \underline{8}$
$\underline{2}, \underline{4}, \underline{6}, \underline{8}$

7 $3 \times 5 = \underline{15}$
$\underline{5}, \underline{10}, \underline{15}$

8 **WRITING IN ▶ MATH** Joel has 10 boxes of books. There are 5 books in each box. How many books does Joel have? Explain.

Joel has 50 books. I skip counted by fives 10 times. 5, 10, 15, 20, 25, 30, 35, 40, 45, 50

Vocabulary Check Complete.

9 You __multiply__ to find a product. STOP

Practice on Your Own

Direct students to p. 72 in their student books. Have them complete Exercises 4–9 independently. You may need to review the directions of each section before students begin.

④ Assess

See It, Do It, Say It, Write It

Step 1 Draw a number line labeled 0 through 10 on the board. Model how to find the product of 4×2 by skip counting on the number line.

Step 2 Solicit several multiplication problems from the class with factors of 2 or 5. Write the problems on the board. Then give students several blank number lines. Have them use the number lines to find each product.

Step 3 Have students show their number lines to a partner. They should discuss how they solved two of the problems.

Step 4 Have students write a description of how they solved one of the problems. Tell them to use as many vocabulary words as possible.

Math Challenge

Multiples of 2 and 5

Have pairs of students work together to think of items that come in groups of 2 or 5. Provide a couple of examples, such as pairs of shoes and 5 fingers on a hand.

Then have each pair write two multiplication word problems. One should be based on items that come in groups of 2, and the other based on items that come in groups of 5.

Have students exchange word problems and solve. After students solve the word problems, have them share the problems and answers with the class.

Chapter 2 Progress Check 3

Formative Assessment

Use the Progress Check to assess students' mastery of the previous lessons. Have students review the lesson indicated for the problems they answered incorrectly.

⚠ Common Error *Alert*

Skip Counting When skip counting more than two or three times, students might miss a number. Encourage them to memorize the first ten numbers when skip counting by 2s and 5s.

Exercise 1 Remind students that empty circles represent groups of 0.

Exercise 7 If students have difficulty with this problem, encourage them to draw an array or area model for both 2 × 5 and 5 × 2. Then they can count each item or square in the models.

Name _____

Progress Check 3 (Lessons 2-5 and 2-6)

Find each product.

1 ○○○○○   5 × 0 = **0**
                number   number in   product
                of groups each group

2 3 × 1 = **3**   **3** 0 × 1 = **0**

Skip count to find each product.

4 5 × 4 = **20**   **5, 10, 15, 20**

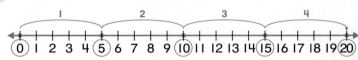

5 2 × 2 = **4**   **2, 4**

6 6 × 5 = **30**   **5, 10, 15, 20, 25, 30**

---

7 The problem 2 × 5 appears on a test.
Nashoba skip counts by 2s to find the product. 2, 4, 6, 8, 10.
Mona skip counts by 5s to find the product. 5, 10.
Who is correct? Explain.

Nashoba and Mona are both correct.
Since 2 and 5 are the factors, you can
skip count by 2s or by 5s.

Chapter 2   Progress Check   seventy-three **73**

Data-Driven Decision Making

Students missing Exercises . . .	Have trouble with . . .	Should review and practice . . .
1–3	multiplying by 0 and 1.	**SSG** Lesson 2-5, p. 65 **CRM** Skills Practice, p. A49
4–6	multiplying by 2 and 5.	**SSG** Lesson 2-6, p. 69 **CRM** Skills Practice, p. A53
7	problem-solving that involves multiplying by 2 and 5.	**SSG** Lesson 2-6, p. 71 **CRM** Problem-Solving Practice, p. A54

Name _____

«« Replay Who am I?

Find the vocabulary term or number that answers each riddle.

Answer Bank		
factor	1	9
multiply	4	10
product	0	7
skip count	5	12

1 I am the answer to a multiplication

problem. Who am I? **product**

2 When any number is multiplied by 0,

I am the product. Who am I? **0**

3 When I am multiplied by another number, the product is always that number.

Who am I? **1**

4 I am a number that is multiplied by another

number. Who am I? **factor**

5 I am the product of 5 × 2.

Who am I? **10**

6 I am the product of 1 × 4.

Who am I? **4**

7 I am the product of 9 × 1.

Who am I? **9**

Use the Replay activity to review and reinforce the concepts and skills presented in Lessons 2-5 and 2-6.

Instructions

Have students read the directions at the top of the student page carefully. Explain that although some answers will be vocabulary words, some answers will also be numbers. Remind students that not all vocabulary terms and numbers in the Answer Bank will be used.

Student Technology

Students can use the following technology resources to reinforce chapter content.

- StudentWorks™ Plus

- **Math Online** > macmillanmh.com

- eGlossary

Review

Vocabulary

If students have difficulty answering Exercises 1–3, use the page references below to review the vocabulary words, or refer them to the glossary.

array (p. 55)
factor (p. 59)
product (p. 55)

Vocabulary Review Strategies

Vocabulary Connections   List all chapter vocabulary terms and definitions on the board. Have students write sentences that describe the connections between the words. For example, *Arrays and area models show both factors in a multiplication problem* and the *product.* Students should use every vocabulary word at least once.

Concepts

The exercises in this section are grouped to cover content from each lesson in the chapter.

Exercise 4: Lesson 2-1 (p. 45)
Exercise 5: Lesson 2-2 (p. 49)
Exercise 6: Lesson 2-3 (p. 55)
Exercise 7: Lesson 2-4 (p. 59)
Exercises 8–10: Lesson 2-5 (p. 65)
Exercises 11–13: Lesson 2-6 (p. 69)

Find **Extra Practice** for these concepts in the Practice Worksheets, pp. A32–A55.

Name _____

Review

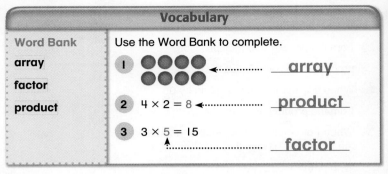

Vocabulary

Word Bank
array
factor
product

Use the Word Bank to complete.

1.  .... __array__

2. $4 \times 2 = 8$ .... __product__

3. $3 \times 5 = 15$ .... __factor__

▶ **Concepts**

4. Write how many in all.

__4__ groups of __3__   __12__ chicks in all

5. Use repeated addition and skip counting to find the sum.

__6__ + __6__ + __6__ = __18__ penguins

__6__ , __12__ , __18__ penguins

GO on

Copyright © Macmillan/McGraw-Hill. • Glencoe, a division of The McGraw-Hill Companies, Inc.

6 Write a multiplication sentence. Find the product.

$\underline{2} \times \underline{5} = \underline{10}$

7 Shade the area model. Find the product.

$4 \times 4 = \underline{16}$

Find each product.

8 $1 \times 4 = \underline{4}$ **9** $0 \times 8 = \underline{0}$ **10** $1 \times 0 = \underline{0}$

Skip count to find each product.

11 $6 \times 2 = \underline{12}$ $\underline{2}, \underline{4}, \underline{6}, \underline{8}, \underline{10}, \underline{12}$

12 $4 \times 5 = \underline{20}$ $\underline{5}, \underline{10}, \underline{15}, \underline{20}$

13 Leslie sees 5 groups of birds. There are 5 birds in each group. How many birds does Leslie see in all? Explain.

<u>Leslie sees 25 birds in all. There are</u>
<u>5 equal groups of 5. Sample answer:</u>
<u>Skip count by 5s. 5, 10, 15, 20, 25</u>

STOP

Dinah Zike's Foldables®

Have students use the Foldable they created at the beginning of the chapter to review and reinforce the concepts and skills they learned during the chapter. (See Chapter Resource Masters p. A29 for instructions.)

Intervention Strategy

Use this Intervention Strategy activity at any point during the chapter to reinforce the concepts and skills presented in the chapter.

Counting Coins

Step 1 Provide each group with a different number of pennies. Be sure students can divide the pennies into equal groups of 5.

Step 2 Tell each group to draw an area model that represents the equal groups of pennies. The area models should have 5 columns to represent the number of pennies in each group.

Step 3 Have students write a multiplication sentence for their pennies. For example, if they have 30 pennies, they should write $6 \times 5 = 30$.

Step 4 Have each group present their area model and multiplication sentence to the class.

- **How could you find out how much 8 nickels are worth?** Skip count 8 times by 5s: 5, 10, 15, 20, 25, 30, 35, 40¢

Chapter 2 Chapter Test

Chapter Resource Masters

Additional forms of the Chapter Test are available.

Test Format	Where to Find it
Chapter Test	**Math Online** macmillanmh.com
Blackline Masters	Assessment Masters, p. 23

ExamView®
Assessment Suite

Customize and create multiple versions of your chapter test and their answer keys. All of these questions from the chapter tests are available on ExamView® Assessment Suite.

Advance TRACKER

Online Assessment and Reporting
macmillanmh.com

This online assessment tool allows teachers to track student progress with easily accessible, comprehensive reports available for every student. Assess students using any internet-ready computer.

Alternative Assessment

Use Portfolios Present the following multiplication problems to students:

3×0 5×6 2×4 7×1

Have students use strategies they learned throughout the chapter to find each product.

Have students present their work with an explanation of how each answer was determined. Students should use a different strategy to solve each problem.

Students can display their work on a poster, foldable, or any other representation they choose.

Name _____

Chapter Test

Write how many in all.

1

_2_ groups of _4_
_8_ cubes in all

2

_3_ groups of _2_
_6_ cubes in all

3 Use repeated addition and skip counting to find the sum.

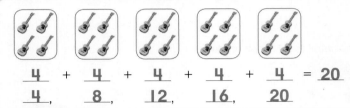

$\underline{4} + \underline{4} + \underline{4} + \underline{4} + \underline{4} = \underline{20}$

_4_, _8_, _12_, _16_, _20_

Write a multiplication sentence. Find each product.

4

$\underline{2} \times \underline{5} = \underline{10}$

5

$\underline{4} \times \underline{3} = \underline{12}$

6 Shade the area model. Find the product.

$5 \times 3 = \underline{15}$

GO on

7 Who is Correct?

Rodolfo and Desta find the product of 0 and 5.

O times 5 equals 5.

Rodolfo

O times 5 equals 0.

Desta

Circle the correct answer. Explain.

Desta is correct. 0 × 5 = 0 When any
number is multiplied by 0, the product is 0.

Find each product.

8 1 × 10 = __10__   **9** 3 × 0 = __0__   **10** 8 × 1 = __8__

Skip count to find each product.

11 4 × 2 = __8__   __2__ , __4__ , __6__ , __8__

12 5 × 5 = __25__   __5__ , __10__ , __15__ , __20__ , __25__

13 The Smith family has 2 fish tanks. There are 5 fish in each tank. How many fish does the Smith family have in all? How do you know?

The Smith family has 10 fish in all.
I used repeated addition. 5 + 5 = 10

STOP

Copyright © Macmillan/McGraw-Hill • Glencoe, a division of The McGraw-Hill Companies, Inc.

78 seventy-eight

Who Is Correct?

Diagnostic Teaching

- Rodolfo says that 0 times 5 equals 5. This is incorrect. He has confused the rule for multiplying by 1 with the rule for multiplying by 0. The product of 0 and any number is always 0.

- Desta says that 0 times 5 equals 0. This is correct.

Learning from Mistakes

Missed Questions Review commonly missed questions as a small group or class. Ask students to share their methods of answering each question. Try to point out when any errors occur and take corrective measures.

Data-Driven Decision Making

Students missing Exercises . . .	Have trouble with . . .	Should review and practice . . .
1–2	finding totals of equal groups.	SSG Lesson 2-1, p. 45 CRM Skills Practice, p. A33
3	skip counting or using repeated addition to find totals.	SSG Lesson 2-2, p. 49 CRM Skills Practice, p. A37
4	using an array to represent multiplication.	SSG Lesson 2-3, p. 55 CRM Skills Practice, p. A41
5–6	using an area model to represent multiplication.	SSG Lesson 2-4, p. 59 CRM Skills Practice, p. A45
7–10	multiplying by 0 and 1.	SSG Lesson 2-5, p. 65 CRM Skills Practice, p. A49
11–12	multiplying by 2 and 5.	SSG Lesson 2-6, p. 69 CRM Skills Practice, p. A53
13	problem-solving that involves muitiplying by 2 and 5.	SSG Lesson 2-6, p. 71 CRM Problem-Solving Practice, p. A54

Chapter 2 Test Practice

Diagnose Student Errors

Survey student responses for each item. Class trends may indicate common errors and misconceptions.

1. 0: does not understand the concept of multiplying by 1
1: does not understand the concept of multiplying by 1
6: correct
7: added the factors instead of multiplying

2. 2: chose a factor as the product
5: chose a factor as the product
7: added the factors instead of multiplying
10: correct

3. 3 groups of 2: correct
4 groups of 2: counted 4 groups instead of 3
2 groups of 3: switched the number of groups with the number in each group
3 groups of 3: counted 3 in each group

4. $2 \times 3 = 5$: added the factors
$1 \times 5 = 5$: correct
$0 \times 5 = 5$: does not understand concept of multiplying by 0
$1 \times 4 = 5$: adds the factors

5. 0: correct
1: does not understand the concept of multiplying by 0
4: does not understand the concept of multiplying by 0
10: does not understand the concept of multiplying by 0

6. 2: did not multiply
4: correct
6: multiplied by 3 instead of 2
8: multiplied by 4 instead of 2

7. $6 \times 2 = 12$: does not understand area models
$12 \times 1 = 12$: does not understand area models
$4 \times 3 = 12$: correct
$2 \times 6 = 12$: does not understand area models

8. 0: does not understand the concept of multiplying by 2
1: does not understand the concept of multiplying by 2
5: added the factors
6: correct

9. 0: does not understand the concept of multiplying by 2
2: does not understand the concept of multiplying by 2
5: does not understand the concept of multiplying by 2
8: correct

10. skip count by 2s: skip counts as if the socks were in pairs
skip count by 4s: skip counts by an incorrect number
skip count by 5s: correct
skip count by 10s: skip counts as if there were 10 socks in each basket

11. $4 \times 2 = 6$: mixed up the number of rows with the number in each row and adds the factors
$2 \times 4 = 6$: added the factors instead of multiplying
$3 \times 5 = 8$: does not understand arrays
$2 \times 4 = 8$: correct

12. 0: correct
1: does not understand the concept of multiplying by 0 or 1
10: does not understand the concept of multiplying by 0 or 1
100: does not understand the concept of multiplying by 0 or 1

Name _____

Test Practice

Choose the correct answer.

1 What is the product of 6×1?

0 ○ 1 ○ 6 ● 7 ○

2 Miss Miller packs for a 5-day trip. She packs 2 shirts for each day. How many shirts does Miss Miller pack in all?

2 ○ 5 ○ 7 ○ 10 ●

3 Which equal groups are modeled?

● 3 groups of 2
○ 4 groups of 2
○ 2 groups of 3
○ 3 groups of 3

4 Which multiplication sentence is true?

○ $2 \times 3 = 5$
● $1 \times 5 = 5$
○ $0 \times 5 = 5$
○ $1 \times 4 = 5$

5 What is the product of 4×0?

0 ● 1 ○ 4 ○ 10 ○

6 Emilio has 2 twin sisters. For their birthday, he wants to buy each sister 2 presents. How many presents should Emilio buy in all?

2 ○ 4 ● 6 ○ 8 ○

GO ON

Chapter 2   Test Practice

seventy-nine **79**

79 Chapter 2 Test Practice

7 Which multiplication sentence does the area model show?

- ○ $6 \times 2 = 12$
- ● $12 \times 1 = 12$
- ● $4 \times 3 = 12$
- ○ $2 \times 6 = 12$

8 Barasa knits scarves. He knits 2 scarves a day for 3 days. How many scarves does Barasa knit in all?

0	1	5	6
○	○	○	●

9 What is the product of 4×2?

0	2	5	8
○	○	○	●

10 Peta has 3 baskets of socks. There are 5 socks in each basket. How should Peta count the socks?

- ○ skip count by 2s
- ○ skip count by 4s
- ● skip count by 5s
- ○ skip count by 10s

11 Which multiplication sentence does the array show?

- ○ $4 \times 2 = 6$
- ○ $2 \times 4 = 6$
- ○ $3 \times 5 = 8$
- ● $2 \times 4 = 8$

12 What is the product of 0×1?

0	1	10	100
●	○	○	○

Diagnosing Student Errors and Misconceptions

Focusing on One Problem at a Time Students may perform better if they focus on one test question at a time. Have students fold a sheet of paper into fourths and then cut away one fourth. Show them how they can use the cut paper to frame the test question on which they are working.

Chapter Overview

Chapter-at-a-Glance

Lesson	Math Objective	State/Local Standards
3-1 Relate Multiplication and Division (pp. 83–86)	Relate multiplication and division.	
3-2 Repeated Subtraction and Skip Counting (pp. 87–90)	Model division with repeated subtraction and skip counting.	
Progress Check 1 (p. 91)		
3-3 Use Arrays to Model Division (pp. 93–96)	Model division with arrays.	
3-4 Use Area Models to Show Division (pp. 97–100)	Model division with area models.	
Progress Check 2 (p. 101)		
3-5 Divide with 0 and 1 (pp. 103–106)	Divide with 0 and 1.	
3-6 Divide by 2 and 5 (pp. 107–110)	Divide by 2 and 5.	
Progress Check 3 (p. 111)		

Content-at-a-Glance

The diagram below summarizes and unpacks Chapter 3 content.

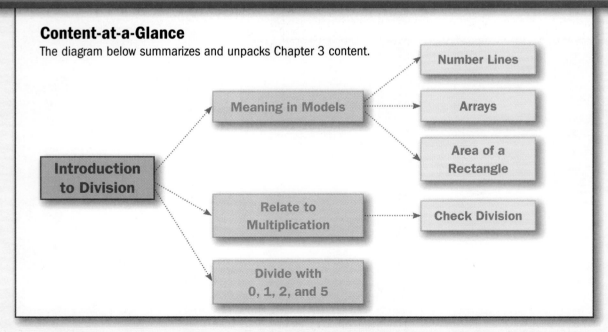

Chapter Assessment Manager

Diagnostic Diagnose students' readiness.

	Student Study Guide/ Teacher Editions	Assessment Masters	Technology
Course Placement Test		1	ExamView® Assessment Suite
Book 1 Pretest		6	ExamView® Assessment Suite
Chapter Pretest		31	ExamView® Assessment Suite
Get Ready	SSG 82		Math Online macmillanmh.com StudentWorks™ Plus

Formative Identify students' misconceptions of content knowledge.

	Student Study Guide/ Teacher Editions	Assessment Masters	Technology
Progress Checks	SSG 91, 101, 111		Math Online macmillanmh.com StudentWorks™ Plus
Vocabulary Review	SSG 86, 90, 96, 100, 106 110, 113		Math Online macmillanmh.com StudentWorks™ Plus
Lesson Assessments			ExamView® Assessment Suite
Are They Getting It?	TE 85, 89, 95, 99, 105, 109		

Summative Determine student success in learning the concepts in the lesson, chapter, or book.

	Student Study Guide/ Teacher Editions	Assessment Masters	Technology
Chapter Test	SSG 115	34	ExamView® Assessment Suite
Test Practice	SSG 117	37	ExamView® Assessment Suite
Alternative Assessment	TE 115	40	
See It, Do It, Say It, Write It	TE 86, 90, 96, 100, 106, 110		
Book 1 Test		42	ExamView® Assessment Suite

Back-Mapping and Vertical Alignment McGraw-Hill's *Math Triumphs* intervention program was conceived and developed with the final result in mind: student success in grade-level mathematics, including Algebra 1 and beyond. The authors, using the **NCTM Focal Points and Focal Connections** as their guide, developed this brand-new series by back-mapping from grade-level and Algebra 1 concepts, and vertically aligning the topics so that they build upon prior skills and concepts and serve as a foundation for future topics.

Chapter Resource Manager

TeacherWorks Plus™
All-In-One Planner and Resource Center

	Lesson 3-1	Lesson 3-2	Lesson 3-3	Lesson 3-4
Concept	Relate Multiplication and Division	Repeated Subtraction and Skip Counting	Use Arrays to Model Division	Use Area Models to Show Division
Objective	Relate multiplication and division.	Model division with repeated subtraction and skip counting.	Model division with arrays.	Model division with area models.
Math Vocabulary	divide (division) multiply (multiplication)	divide (division) repeated subtraction skip count	array	area
Lesson Resources	**Materials** • beans • fact triangle • index cards **Manipulatives** • connecting cubes • pattern blocks • counters **Other Resources** [CRM] Vocabulary and English Language Development [CRM] Skills Practice [CRM] Problem-Solving Practice [CRM] Homework Practice	**Materials** • number lines **Manipulatives** • counters **Other Resources** [CRM] Vocabulary and English Language Development [CRM] Skills Practice [CRM] Problem-Solving Practice [CRM] Homework Practice	**Materials** • poster board **Manipulatives** • counters • base-ten blocks • connecting cubes • geoboards **Other Resources** [CRM] Vocabulary and English Language Development [CRM] Skills Practice [CRM] Problem-Solving Practice [CRM] Homework Practice	**Materials** • inch graph paper • centimeter graph paper • colored pencils • construction paper **Manipulatives** • connecting cubes • base-ten blocks • pattern blocks **Other Resources** [CRM] Vocabulary and English Language Development [CRM] Skills Practice [CRM] Problem-Solving Practice [CRM] Homework Practice
Technology	**Math Online** macmillanmh.com StudentWorks™ Plus ⊙ ExamView® Assessment Suite	**Math Online** macmillanmh.com StudentWorks™ Plus ⊙ ExamView® Assessment Suite	**Math Online** macmillanmh.com StudentWorks™ Plus ⊙ ExamView® Assessment Suite	**Math Online** macmillanmh.com StudentWorks™ Plus ⊙ ExamView® Assessment Suite

Lesson 3-5	Lesson 3-6	
Divide with 0 and 1	Divide by 2 and 5	**Concept**
Divide with 0 and 1.	Divide by 2 and 5.	**Objective**
divide (division)	divide (division)	**Math Vocabulary**
Materials	**Materials** • construction paper • markers/crayons	**Lesson Resources**
Manipulatives • number lines • connecting cubes • base-ten blocks • geoboards • counters • index cards	**Manipulatives** • number lines • connecting cubes • base-ten blocks • geoboards • number cube • index cards • counters	
Other Resources **CRM** Vocabulary and English Language Development **CRM** Skills Practice **CRM** Problem-Solving Practice **CRM** Homework Practice	**Other Resources** **CRM** Vocabulary and English Language Development **CRM** Skills Practice **CRM** Problem-Solving Practice **CRM** Homework Practice	
Math Online macmillanmh.com StudentWorks™ Plus ● ExamView® Assessment Suite	Math Online macmillanmh.com StudentWorks™ Plus ● ExamView® Assessment Suite	**Technology**

Home Connection

Read the Home Connection letter with students and have them write their names in the space below.

Read and explain the activity under Help at Home. If time allows, complete a portion of the activity so students can introduce the activity to a parent or other caregiver.

Have students:

- find food products, boxes of pencils/crayons, battery packs, etc., that are arranged in rows and columns.

- practice multiplying the number of rows by the number of columns to find the number of items in all.

 Real-World Applications

Seating Arrangements Explain this scenario to students: "A tram at a wild life park seats four people per car. The person in charge of the tram uses division to figure out how many tram cars will be needed to fit everyone waiting in line."

- **How could you use division to solve this problem?**
  Divide the number of people in line by 4. If there are 16 people in line, 4 cars are needed since 16 ÷ 4 = 4.

Introduction to Division

English

Dear Family,
Today our class started **Chapter 3, Introduction to Division.** In this chapter, I will learn about different division strategies and models. I will also learn how to divide by 1, 2, and 5.

Love, _____

Spanish

Estimada familia:
Hoy en clase comenzamos el **Capítulo 3, Introducción a la división.** En este capítulo aprenderé sobre las diferentes estrategias y modelos para dividir. También aprenderé a dividir entre 1, 2 y 5.

Cariños, _____

Help at Home

You can help your child by asking him or her to divide common household items into equal groups, such as cereal pieces, paper clips, or crayons. Ask your child how many objects are in each equal group.

Ayude en casa

Usted puede ayudar a su niño pidiéndole que divida objetos comunes en grupos iguales, como trozos de cereal, sujetadores de papel o crayones. Pregúntele a su niño cuántos objetos hay en cada uno de los grupos iguales.

Math Online ▸ Take the chapter Get Ready quiz at macmillanmh.com.

Chapter 3

eighty-one 81

Key Vocabulary

Find interactive definitions in 13 languages in the **eGlossary** at macmillanmh.com.

English **Español** *Introduce the most important vocabulary terms from Chapter 3.*

multiply (multiplication)
multiplicar (multiplicacion)
  to combine equal groups (p. 83)
$$4 \times 2 = 8$$

divide (division)
dividir (division)
  to separate into equal groups (p. 83)
$$9 \div 3 = 3$$

repeated subtraction
  subtract the same number more than one time (p. 87)
$$15 - 5 - 5 - 5 = 0$$

skip count **contar salteado**
  count objects in equal groups of 2 or more (p. 87)

array **arreglo**
  objects displayed in rows and columns (p. 93)

area **área**
  the number of square units needed to cover the inside of an object (p. 97)

Name _____

Get Ready

Subtract.

1 18
    − 6
    12

2 36
    − 9
    27

3 24
    − 8
    16

Write a multiplication sentence.

4

__4__ × __3__ = __12__

5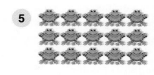

__3__ × __5__ = __15__

Circle each number you count on the number line.

6 Skip count by 4s.

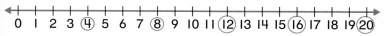
0 1 2 3 ④ 5 6 7 ⑧ 9 10 11 ⑫ 13 14 15 ⑯ 17 18 19 ⑳

7 Skip count by 6s.

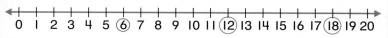
0 1 2 3 4 5 ⑥ 7 8 9 10 11 ⑫ 13 14 15 16 17 ⑱ 19 20

Multiply.

8 2 × 8 = __16__

9 3 × 7 = __21__

10 0 × 9 = __0__

Get Ready

Have students complete Get Ready to assess readiness for the chapter concepts and skills. Refer to the lessons below for additional support for prerequisite skills.

1-6 Subtract Two-Digit Numbers (p. 29)
2-2 Repeated Addition and Skip Counting (p. 49)
2-3 Arrays (p. 55)
2-5 Multiply by 0 and 1 (p. 65)
2-6 Multiply by 2 and 5 (p. 69)

You may also assess student readiness with the following resources:

 Online Readiness quiz at macmillanmh.com

Assessment Masters: Chapter Pretest (p. 31)

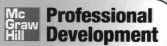 **Dinah Zike's Foldables®**

Guide students through the directions on p. A56 in the Chapter Resource Masters to create their own Foldable graphic organizer for use with this chapter.

Professional Development

Targeted professional development has been articulated throughout **McGraw-Hill's** *Math Triumphs* intervention program. **The McGraw-Hill Professional Development Video Library** provides short videos that support the **NCTM Focal Points and Focal Connections.** For more information, visit macmillanmh.com.

Model Lessons   Instructional Strategies

Vocabulary Preview

Make a list of the chapter's vocabulary terms on the board.

As you go through each lesson, have students identify terms that are new and unfamiliar.

Have student volunteers give definitions and examples of new vocabulary terms in their own words.

At the end of the chapter, have student pairs present three vocabulary terms with examples and definitions in their own words.

Lesson Notes

Lesson Planner

Objective Relate multiplication and division.

Vocabulary multiply (multiplication), divide (division)

Materials/Manipulatives beans, fact triangle, connecting cubes, pattern blocks, counters, index cards

Chapter Resource Masters

- [CRM] Vocabulary and English Language Development (p. A60)
- [CRM] Skills Practice (p. A61)
- [CRM] Problem-Solving Practice (p. A62)
- [CRM] Homework Practice (p. A63)

1 Introduce

Vocabulary

Vocabulary Relationships Write *cold/hot, large/small, inside/outside* on the board.

- **These pairs of words are opposites. What are some other pairs of opposites?** Answers will vary.

In math, multiplication and division are opposite operations. Explain that multiplication can undo division and vice versa.

Use fact families to demonstrate opposite operations.

2 Teach

Key Concept

Foundational Skills and Concepts After students have read through the Key Concept box, guide them through the following questions.

- **How many groups of counters? How many in each group?** 3; 2

- **How many counters in all?** 6

- **What division sentence shows 6 counters divided into 3 groups?** 6 ÷ 3 = 2

- **What are the related multiplication facts?**
  3 × 2 = 6, 2 × 3 = 6

83 Chapter 3 Introduction to Division

Lesson 3-1

Name _____

Relate Multiplication and Division

Key Concept

Multiplication and **division** are related.

There are 3 groups of counters.
There are 2 counters in each group.
There are 3 × 2 = 6 counters in all.

There are 6 counters in all.
They are divided into 3 equal groups of 2.
There are 6 ÷ 3 = 2 counters in each group.

Vocabulary

multiply (multiplication) to combine equal groups
$$4 \times 2 = 8$$
Four groups of two are equal to eight or
$$2 + 2 + 2 + 2 = 8.$$

divide (division) to separate into equal groups

$$9 \div 3 = 3$$

A fact triangle shows the numbers in related multiplication and division sentences.

3 × 2 = 6	2 × 3 = 6
6 ÷ 3 = 2	6 ÷ 2 = 3

English Learner Strategy

Model Multiplication and Division Use beans to model multiplication and division. Explain both operations in a variety of ways.

Have students make the following tables. Instruct them on how to use the beans to explore division and fill in the table.

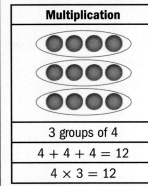

Multiplication
3 groups of 4
4 + 4 + 4 = 12
4 × 3 = 12

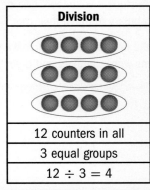

Division
12 counters in all
3 equal groups
12 ÷ 3 = 4

Example

Write related multiplication and division sentences.

Step 1   There are 3 groups of frogs.
Step 2   There are 6 frogs in each group.
Step 3   There are 18 frogs in all.

Answer $3 \times 6 = 18$
$18 \div 3 = 6$

Step-by-Step Practice

Write related multiplication and division sentences.

Step 1   There are __6__ groups of turtles.
Step 2   There are __2__ turtles in each group.
Step 3   There are __12__ turtles in all.

Answer   __6__ × __2__ = __12__
__12__ ÷ __6__ = __2__

Intervention Strategy

Kinesthetic/Interpersonal Learners

Materials: 24 counters

Understanding Related Facts Have students work in pairs. Give 24 counters to each pair. Have students make the following table. Instruct them to use the counters to explore fact families. An example is given.

Multiplying		Dividing
. . . groups of . . .	Multiplication sentence	Division sentences
4 groups of 6	$4 \times 6 = 24$	$24 \div 4 = 6$ $24 \div 6 = 4$

Encourage students to find as many different equal groups and related number sentences as possible using 24 counters.

Additional *Example*

Write related multiplication and division sentences.

Step 1 There are 5 groups of flowers.

Step 2 There are 3 flowers in each group.

Step 3 There are 15 flowers in all.

Answer $5 \times 3 = 15$
$15 \div 5 = 3$

⚠ **Common Error** *Alert*

Strategy   Some students may need assistance organizing the numbers in a fact triangle into math sentences.

On the board draw a fact triangle with the numbers, 2, 9, and 18.

- **What multiplication sentences can be made from this fact triangle?** $2 \times 9 = 18$, $9 \times 2 = 18$

- **Is it important which factor comes first in the multiplication sentence? Explain.** No; you will always get the same answer.

- **What division sentences can be made from this fact triangle?** $18 \div 2 = 9$, $18 \div 2 = 9$

- **Is it important which number comes first in the division sentence? Explain.** Yes; $18 \div 9 = 2$, but $9 \div 18 \neq 2$.

- **Where is the largest number of a fact triangle placed in a division sentence?** It is the first number in the division sentence.

Students might struggle understanding that division can be used to find the number *in each group* or the number of groups. To reinforce this, review the Key Concept, Example, and Additional Example with students.

Practice

Guided Practice

Direct students to complete Exercises 1–2 in Guided Practice.

Exercises 1–2 Remind students that the placement of the numbers in a division sentence is important. Sample answers are given. Students can write other multiplication and division sentences that are part of the fact family.

Problem-Solving Practice

Guide students through the four-step problem-solving plan to complete Exercise 3.

- **What are the key words?** 14 shoes, pairs of 2, how many pairs

- **What do the squares represent?** 14 shoes in groups of 2

- **How many pairs of shoes does Riley have?** 7

Ask students to check their work using the strategy suggested in the Check step. Students can write related multiplication and division sentences to solve the problem.

Using Manipulatives

Connecting Cubes Students can use connecting cubes to show equal groups when modeling multiplication and division sentences.

Counters Students can use counters to show equal groups when modeling multiplication and division sentences.

On-Hand Manipulatives Students can use beans, buttons, craft sticks, or paper squares to model multiplication and division.

Math Coach Notes

Begin this lesson by reviewing multiplication facts. Reinforcing the relationship between multiplication and division will assist students in committing facts to memory.

Name _____

▶ **Guided Practice**

Write related multiplication and division sentences.

1.

$\underline{5} \times \underline{2} = \underline{10}$
$\underline{10} \div \underline{5} = \underline{2}$

2.

$\underline{8} \times \underline{4} = \underline{32}$
$\underline{32} \div \underline{8} = \underline{4}$

Problem-Solving Practice

3. Riley has <u>14 shoes</u> in her closet. She sorted the shoes into <u>pairs of 2</u>. <u>How many pairs</u> of shoes does Riley have?

Understand Underline key words.

Plan Draw a picture.

Solve Draw 14 shoes in groups of 2. Circle each group

Riley has __7__ pairs of shoes.

Check Write related multiplication and division sentences.

$\underline{7} \times 2 = 14$ $14 \div \underline{7} = 2$

GO on

Chapter 3   Lesson 1

eighty-five **85**

Are They Getting It? ?

Check students' understanding of how multiplication relates to division. Write these exercises on the board. Ask students to point out the correct and incorrect answers and explain their reasoning.

1. The following number sentences are related. $3 \times 7 = 21$ and $21 \div 3 = 7$ This is correct.

2. The following number sentences are related. $4 \times 6 = 24$ and $6 \div 24 = 4$ This is incorrect. The related division sentences are $24 \div 6 = 4$ and $24 \div 4 = 6$.

3. The following number sentences form a fact family. $2 \times 9 = 18$, $9 \times 2 = 18$, $18 \div 2 = 9$, $18 \div 9 = 2$ This is correct.

Copyright © Macmillan/McGraw-Hill · Glencoe, a division of The McGraw-Hill Companies, Inc.

85 Chapter 3 Introduction to Division

▶ Practice on Your Own

Write related multiplication and division sentences.

4

Sample answer:

$\underline{5} \times \underline{3} = \underline{15}$

$\underline{15} \div \underline{5} = \underline{3}$

5

Sample answer:

$\underline{3} \times \underline{4} = \underline{12}$

$\underline{12} \div \underline{3} = \underline{4}$

6 24 / 4 6

Sample answer:

$\underline{4} \times \underline{6} = \underline{24}$

$\underline{24} \div \underline{4} = \underline{6}$

7 **WRITING IN ▶MATH** Luis plants 8 flowers in his garden. He makes 4 equal rows. How many flowers are in each row? Explain.

There are 2 flowers in each row.

8 ÷ 4 = 2

Vocabulary Check Complete.

8 You can use ___**division**___ to separate objects into equal groups.

 STOP

86 eighty-six

Copyright © Macmillan/McGraw-Hill • Glencoe, a division of The McGraw-Hill Companies, Inc.

Math Challenge

Go Fish

Materials: index cards

Place students in groups of four. Give each student 4 index cards.

Have each student write four sentences of a fact family, on each index card.

Have groups shuffle the cards and deal 2 cards to each student. Place the other cards face down in a pile.

The game proceeds as the game of "Go Fish." One player asks another player for a number sentence related to one on their card. If this card is available, the card is given. If not, the player picks another card from the pile.

A set of cards is made with 4 cards from the same fact family. The player with the most sets of cards wins.

Practice on Your Own

Direct students to p. 86 in their student books. Have students complete Exercises 4–8 independently. You may need to review the directions of each section before students begin.

 Assess

See It, Do It, Say It, Write It

Step 1 Show the following on the board.

Write $3 \times 2 = 6$. Explain that this means 3 groups of 2 which is 6. Write $6 \div 3 = 2$. Explain that this means 6 divided into 3 groups equals 2 in each group.

Step 2 Have students write a multiplication and division sentence for the following.

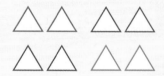

Step 3 Instruct students to say the meaning of each number sentence.

Step 4 Write the numbers 4, 5, and 20 on the board. Have students write a multiplication and division sentence using the numbers on the board.

Looking Ahead: Pre-teach

In the next lesson, students will learn how to use repeated subtraction and skip counting to divide.

Example $14 \div 7 = 2$

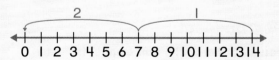

1. Have students divide to find the answer.

$16 \div 4 = $ _____ 4

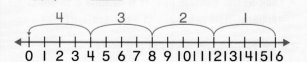

Lesson Notes

Lesson Planner

Objective   Model division with repeated subtraction and skip counting.

Vocabulary   divide (division), repeated subtraction, skip count

Materials/Manipulatives   counters, number lines

Chapter Resource Masters

- CRM Vocabulary and English Language Development (p. A64)
- CRM Skill Practice (p. A65)
- CRM Problem-Solving Practice (p. A66)
- CRM Homework Practice (p. A67)

 Introduce

Vocabulary

Review Vocabulary   Have students review the meaning of *repeated addition*. Relate this to *repeated subtraction*. Give examples of each.

Nonexamples   Give students nonexamples of repeated addition (i.e, $4 + 5 + 4 + 5$). Ask them to explain why this is not repeated addition. Give students nonexamples of repeated subtraction. (i.e, $15 - 5 - 4 - 3 - 2 - 1$). Ask them to explain why this is not repeated subtraction.

 Teach

Key Concept

Foundational Skills and Concepts   After students have read through the Key Concept box, guide them through the following questions.

- **Look at the number line. It is divided into equal sections. How many are in each section?**   Yes; 5

- **How many equal sections are there?**   4

- **What is $20 \div 5$?**   4

87 Chapter 3 Introduction to Division

Name _____

Repeated Subtraction and Skip Counting

Key Concept

How many equal groups of 5 can be made from 20?
The number 20 is shown on the number line.
Count back by 5s until you reach 0.

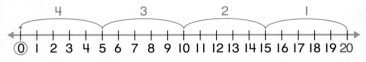

Subtract 5 from 20 until you reach 0.

$20 \div 5 = 4$

$$\begin{array}{cccc} 20 & 15 & 10 & 5 \\ -5 & -5 & -5 & -5 \\ \hline 15 & 10 & 5 & 0 \end{array}$$

Vocabulary

divide (division)   to separate into equal groups

repeated subtraction   subtract the same number more than one time
$15 - 5 - 5 - 5 = 0$

skip count   count objects in equal groups of 2 or more

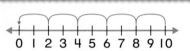

I can use a number line to skip count backward.

Chapter 3   Lesson 2

eighty-seven **87**

English Learner Strategy

Grasping Terms   Make sure students understand the term *repeated subtraction.*

Review the word *repeated.* Remind students that patterns often contain repeating elements. Ask them to identify or create several patterns of repeating elements.

Write the division sentence $12 \div 4 = 12 - 4 - 4 - 4$. Discuss repeated subtraction as subtracting the same number more than one time. Have students identify the repeated subtraction in the example. Explain that division is the same as repeated subtraction.

Have students use repeated subtraction to solve $15 \div 3$. Ask students to explain their answer.

Example

There are 18 students in Mr. Lazo's class.
He wants to divide his students into teams of 3.
How many teams will he have?

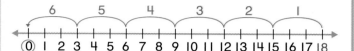

Step 1 Start at 18. Skip count backward by 3s.
Step 2 Subtract 6 times to reach 0.
Step 3 Write the division sentence. $18 \div 3 = 6$

Answer Mr. Lazo will have 6 teams.

Step-by-Step Practice

Molly has 16 toy cars.
She wants to divide the cars onto 4 shelves.
How many cars will be on each shelf?

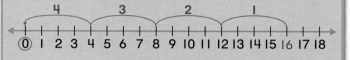

Step 1 Start at **16**. Skip count backward by **4**s.

Step 2 Subtract **4** times to reach 0.

Step 3 Write the division sentence.
$$16 \div 4 = 4.$$

Answer There will be **4** cars on each shelf.

88 eighty-eight

Additional *Example*

Martin has 10 seeds.
He wants to plant the seeds in 2 rows.
How many seeds will be in each row?

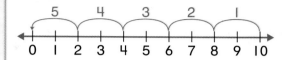

Step 1 Start at 10. Skip count backward by 2s.

Step 2 Subtract 5 times to reach 0.

Step 3 Write the division sentence.
$$10 \div 2 = 5$$

Answer There will be 5 seeds in each row.

Math Coach Notes

Strategy   Many students have difficulty identifying when to use division to solve word problems.

- First, be sure students learn to identify the given total in the problem. (This is a clear indication that division or subtraction is to be performed).

- Second, have them identify the key words that signal division.

- Last, make sure students identify how the total is being divided. If the number of equal groups is given, then you find the number in each group. If the number in each group is given, you find the number of equal groups.

Reinforce this with the Example Step-by-Step, and Additional Example.

Intervention Strategy   Visual Learners

Materials: counters

Vertical Model Show students the vertical form of repeated subtraction for $12 \div 2 = 6$. Demonstrate using counters coinciding with the algorithm. Explain that this method shows how 12 can be divided into groups of 2.

Make sure students understand they are to count the number of times 2 is subtracted until 0 is reached.

Have students solve other division problems using this method.

```
  12
 − 2  ← 1
  10
 − 2  ← 2
   8
 − 2  ← 3
   6
 − 2  ← 4
   4
 − 2  ← 5
   2
 − 2  ← 6
   0
```

Guided Practice

Direct students to complete Exercise 1 in Guided Practice.

Exercise 1 Struggling students can use 21 counters to make equal groups of 7.

Problem-Solving Practice

Guide students through the four-step problem-solving plan to complete Exercise 2.

- **What are the key words?** 25 prizes, 5 prizes to each friend, how many friends

- **At what number should the skip counting begin?** 25

- **By what number should we skip count?** Skip count backward by 5s.

Ask students to check their work using the strategy suggested in the Check step. Students can write a related multiplication sentence to check their division.

Using Manipulatives

Number Lines Students can use number lines to explore how repeated subtraction and skip counting is used to solve division problems.

Counters Students can use counters to model the division of a total into equal groups.

On-Hand Manipulatives Students can use rulers, yard sticks, sentence strips, or a long piece of masking tape, to make number lines.

Students can use beans, buttons, craft sticks, or squares of different colored construction paper as counters to model division.

Name _____

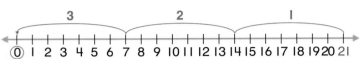 **Guided Practice**

1 Divide. Use the number line.

$21 \div 7 =$ __3__

Problem-Solving Practice

2 Maria bought <u>25 prizes</u> for her birthday party. She gave <u>5 prizes to each friend</u>. <u>How many friends</u> were at Maria's party?

Understand Underline key words.

Plan Use a number line.

Solve Divide. $25 \div 5 =$ __5__

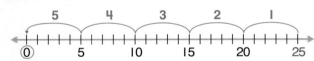

Check Use a related multiplication sentence.

__5__ × 5 = 25

Are They Getting It?

Check students' understanding of repeated subtraction and skip counting by writing the following statements on the board. Ask students to point out the correct and incorrect statements and explain their reasoning.

$18 \div 6 = 3$

1. The number line shows skip counting by 6. This is correct.

2. There are 3 in each group. This is incorrect. There are 6 in each group.

3. The number line does not show repeated subtraction. This is incorrect. On the number line a movement to the left shows subtracting. The number line is showing repeated subtraction of 6.

▶ **Practice on Your Own**

3 Divide. Use the number line.

$14 \div 2 = \underline{7}$

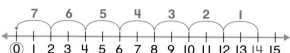

4 Write a division sentence. Use the number line.

$\underline{6} \div \underline{3} = \underline{2}$

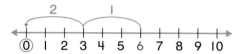

5 ⟨**WRITING IN** ▶**MATH**⟩ Alberto has 8 books. He reads 2 books a week. How many weeks will it take Alberto to read all 8 books? How do you know?

It will take Alberto 4 weeks. I can use a number line and skip count backward by 2s until I reach 0.

Vocabulary Check Complete.

6 When you _____**skip count**_____, you count objects in equal groups of 2 or more.

90 ninety

Math Challenge

Number Line Mania

Materials: number lines

Have students work in pairs. Have pairs model a division problem on a number line.

Have pairs exchange number lines with another pair. Students decide the correct division problem for the number line. The pair that correctly finishes first, wins 1 point.

Repeat the activity 5 times. The team with the most points wins.

Alternative: Have students make division problems and then opposing pairs make the corresponding number line.

Practice on Your Own

Direct students to p. 90 in their student books. Have students complete Exercises 3–6 independently. You may need to review the directions of each section before students begin.

④ Assess

See It, Do It, Say It, Write It

Step 1 Write the following division sentence on the board and explain how to use the number line to solve.

$$9 \div 3 = 3$$

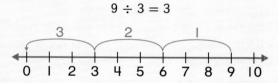

Step 2 Have students model $14 \div 7 = 2$ on a number line.

Step 3 Have students describe their models verbally.

Step 4 Instruct students to explain in writing how to use a number line to solve a division problem.

Looking Ahead: Pre-teach

In the next lesson, students will learn how to use arrays to model division.

Example Write a division sentence.

There are 6 counters.
There are 3 rows.
There are 2 in each row.
$6 \div 3 = 2$

Have students write each division sentence.

1.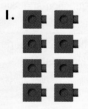

2.

$8 \div 4 = 2$ $6 \div 2 = 3$

Chapter 3

Progress Check 1

Formative Assessment

Use the Progress Check to assess students' mastery of the previous lessons. Have students review the lesson indicated for the problems they answered incorrectly.

Common Error *Alert*

Number Placement Students sometimes do not put the numbers in the correct position in a division sentences. Stress to students the importance of the placement of numbers. Be sure students always put the largest number first in the division sentence.

Name _____

Progress Check 1 (Lessons 3-1 and 3-2)

Write related multiplication and division sentences.

1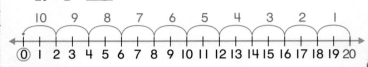

2 × 4 = 8
8 ÷ 2 = 4

2

7 × 8 = 56
56 ÷ 7 = 8

---

3 Divide. Use the number line.

20 ÷ 2 = 10

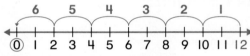

---

4 Rafael scored 12 goals during a soccer season. He scored 2 goals in every game he played. How many games did Rafael play this season?

Rafael played 6 games this season.

Chapter 3   Progress Check

ninety-one **91**

Data-Driven Decision Making

Students missing Exercises . . .	Have trouble with . . .	Should review and practice . . .
1–2	writing related multiplication and division sentences.	SSG Lesson 3-1, p. 83 CRM Skills Practice, p. A61
3	using repeated subtraction and skip counting to divide.	SSG Lesson 3-2, p. 87 CRM Skills Practice, p. A65
4	problem-solving that involves repeated subtraction and skip counting.	SSG Lesson 3-2, p. 89 CRM Problem-Solving Practice, p. A66

Name _____

«« Replay **Felix's Fun Facts!**

Help Felix the Frog leap across the pond!

Find the missing number in each fact triangle below. Use each answer to help you find the missing number in the next triangle.

Start

12 3

24 4

18 6

15 3

40 5

8

4 2

2 2

2 1

Finish

Copyright © Macmillan/McGraw-Hill • Glencoe, a division of The McGraw-Hill Companies, Inc.

92 ninety-two

Replay

Use the Replay activity to review and reinforce the concepts and skills presented in Lessons 3-1 and 3-2.

Instructions

Have students read the directions at the top of the student page.

Student Technology

Students can use the following technology resources to reinforce chapter content.

- StudentWorks™ Plus
- **Math Online** ⟩ macmillanmh.com
- eGlossary

Lesson Notes

Lesson Planner

Math Objective   Model division with arrays.

Vocabulary   array

Materials/Manipulatives   base-ten blocks, counters, connecting cubes, poster board, geoboards

Chapter Resource Masters

- CRM Vocabulary and English Language Development (p. A68)
- CRM Skill Practice (p. A69)
- CRM Problem-Solving Practice (p. A70)
- CRM Homework Practice (p. A71)

 **1** **Introduce**

Vocabulary

Vocabulary Preview   Draw a picture of a batch of cookies on a tray in rows and columns. Identify the rows and the columns. Explain to students when there is an equal number in each column and row, it is called an array. Ask students where they have seen this kind of formation before. participants in a parade, cookies in a box, trees in an orchard, etc.

 **2** **Teach**

Key Concept

Foundational Skills and Concepts   After students have read through the Key Concept box, guide them through the following questions.

- **How many total counters are in the array?**   12
- **How many rows are in the array?**   3
- **How many counters are in each row?**   4
- **What is 12 ÷ 3?**   4

Name _____

Use Arrays to Model Division

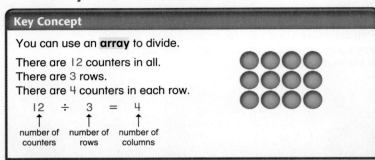

Key Concept

You can use an **array** to divide.

There are 12 counters in all.
There are 3 rows.
There are 4 counters in each row.

$$12 \div 3 = 4$$

number of counters | number of rows | number of columns

Vocabulary

array   objects displayed in rows and columns

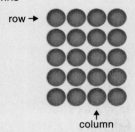

row →

column

The array of red counters has 5 rows and 4 columns.

To make an array, put objects into equal rows and columns.

Chapter 3   Lesson 3   ninety-three **93**

English Learner Strategy

Use Connecting Cubes to Make Arrays   Use connecting cubes to help students understand the term *array*.

Give each student 16 connecting cubes.

Ask students to use all 16 cubes to create several rectangles. Explain and demonstrate the five different possibilities: 1 × 16, 16 × 1, 2 × 8, 8 × 2, 4 × 4. Explain how many cubes to place in each row and column.

Explain that each arrangement is called an array.

Have students continue to explore arrays using different numbers of connecting cubes.

Example

Write a division sentence for the array.

Step 1   There are 15 beach balls in all.

Step 2   There are 3 rows.

Step 3   There are 5 columns.

Answer $15 \div 3 = 5$

Step-by-Step Practice

Write a division sentence for the array.

Step 1   There are **16** soccer balls in all.

Step 2   There are **4** rows.

Step 3   There are **4** columns.

Answer   **16** $\div$ **4** = **4**

94   ninety-four

Additional *Example*

Write a division sentence for the array.

Step 1 There are 10 juice boxes in all.

Step 2 There are 2 rows.

Step 3 There are 5 columns.

Answer $10 \div 2 = 5$

⚠ Common Error *Alert*

Students commonly mix up rows and columns in an array. It might be helpful to display a poster that clearly labels the rows and columns. Students can use the poster as a reference. Make sure students understand the importance of distinguishing columns from rows.

Math Coach Notes

Strategy   For a solid understanding of division and arrays, be sure students can produce a model from a given division sentence.

For example: show $18 \div 9 = 2$ as an array.

Intervention Strategy   Kinesthetic Learners

Materials: base-ten blocks

Give each student 20 ones cubes. Have students copy the following table. Instruct them to assemble all the ones cubes into an array.

Total	÷	Number of rows	=	Number in each row
20	÷	5	=	4

Students should identify the total, the number of rows, and the number in each row of the array. Have students fill in the table to form a division sentence.

Students can repeat the activity modeling a different division sentence.

Guided Practice

Direct students to complete Exercises 1–2 in Guided Practice.

Exercises 1–2 Students might place the numbers of the division sentences in the incorrect order. Remind students to write the total first, followed by the number of rows, followed by the number of columns.

Problem-Solving Practice

Guide students through the four-step problem-solving plan to complete Exercise 3.

- **What is the total?** 18
- **Into how many rows are the pineapples arranged?** 2
- **How many are in each row?** 9

Ask students to check their work using the strategy suggested in the Check step. Students can count the number of columns in the array to solve the problem.

Using Manipulatives

Counters Students can use counters to model arrays.

Connecting Cubes Students can use connecting cubes to model arrays.

Geoboards Students can use geoboards to model arrays.

On-Hand Manipulatives Students can use beans or squares of different colored construction paper to model arrays.

Name _____

▶ Guided Practice

Write a division sentence for each array.

1 ● ● ●
   ● ● ●
   ● ● ●

2 ● ● ● ●
   ● ● ● ●
   ● ● ● ●
   ● ● ● ●
   ● ● ● ●

$\underline{9} \div \underline{3} = \underline{3}$ $\underline{20} \div \underline{5} = \underline{4}$

Problem-Solving Practice

3 Akili works in a grocery store. He put <u>18 pineapples</u> in <u>2 equal rows</u>. <u>How many pineapples are in each row</u>?

Understand Underline key words.

Plan Draw a picture.

Solve Draw an array of 18 pineapples in 2 equal rows.

○ ○ ○ ○ ○ ○ ○ ○ ○
○ ○ ○ ○ ○ ○ ○ ○ ○

There are __9__ pineapples in each row.

Check Count the number of columns in the array.

GO on

Are They Getting It? ❓

Check students' understanding of arrays and division sentences by writing the following exercises on the board. Ask students to point out the correct and incorrect answers and explain their reasoning.

1. This array models $10 \div 2 = 5$.

● ● ● ● ●
● ● ● ● ●

This is correct.

2. This array models $18 \div 6 = 3$.

● ● ●
● ● ●
● ● ●
● ● ●
● ● ●

This is incorrect. The array models $15 \div 5 = 3$.

Practice on Your Own

Write a division sentence for each array.

4

$21 \div 3 = 7$

5 (array of dots)

$15 \div 3 = 5$

6 Draw an array that shows $16 \div 2 = 8$.

(two rows of circles)

7 An array has 12 balloons in 6 equal rows.
How many balloons are in each row? __2__ balloons

8 **WRITING IN ►MATH** Keith put 14 stickers in 2 equal rows. How many stickers are in each row? Explain.

I can draw an array. 14 stickers ÷ 2 rows = 7 stickers in each row.

Vocabulary Check Complete.

9 Objects displayed in rows and columns are called __arrays__.

96 ninety-six

Math Challenge

Words to Sentences

Materials: counters, poster board

Have students work in pairs. Have students reread the division word problems on page 88.

Have students arrange counters into an array that models the division from each problem.

Next, have students write their own division word problem. Have students display the problem, array, and related division problem on a poster.

Students can present and explain their posters.

Practice on Your Own

Direct students to p. 96 in their student books. Have students complete Exercises 4–9 independently. You may need to review the directions of each section before students begin.

See It, Do It, Say It, Write It

Step 1 Show the following array. Explain there are 14 counters in 7 rows, with 2 counters in each row. Ask students what division sentence the counters model. $14 \div 7 = 2$

Step 2 Have students use 10 counters to make an array with a corresponding division sentence.

Step 3 Have students explain their arrays and division sentences.

Step 4 Instruct students to write how division sentences can be represented by arrays.

Looking Ahead: Pre-teach

In the next lesson, students will learn how to use area models to show division.

Example Write a division sentence.

Find how many squares. 6
Find how many rows. 3
There are 2 squares in each row.
$6 \div 3 = 2$

Have students write a division sentence for each area model.

1.  $4 \div 2 = 2$

2. 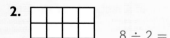 $8 \div 2 = 4$

Lesson 3-3 Use Arrays to Model Division **96**

Copyright © Macmillan/McGraw-Hill • Glencoe, a division of The McGraw-Hill Companies, Inc.

Lesson Notes

Lesson Planner

Objective Model division with area models.

Vocabulary area

Materials/Manipulatives inch graph paper, centimeter graph paper, colored pencils, connecting cubes, base-ten blocks, pattern blocks, construction paper

Chapter Resource Masters

- [CRM] Vocabulary and English Language Development (p. A72)
- [CRM] Skill Practice (p. A73)
- [CRM] Problem-Solving Practice (p. A74)
- [CRM] Homework Practice (p. A75)

1 Introduce

Vocabulary

Vocabulary Interaction Explain how to find the amount of area inside a figure by enclosing a rectangular area on 1-inch graph paper. Ask students to find the amount of space or area in the rectangle by counting the number of squares. Repeat with other size rectangles.

2 Teach

Key Concept

Foundational Skills and Concepts After students have read through the Key Concept box, guide them through the following questions.

- **How many squares are there in all?** 30
- **How many rows are in the area model?** 6
- **How many squares are in each row?** 5
- **Why do you use the area of a rectangle or square to model division?** These shapes show an array.
- **What division sentence is modeled by the area model?** $30 \div 6 = 5$

Use Area Models to Show Division

Key Concept

You can use an **area** model to divide. $30 \div 6 =$ _____

$$\underset{\substack{\text{number of}\\\text{squares}}}{30} \div \underset{\substack{\text{number of}\\\text{rows}}}{6} = \underset{\substack{\text{number in}\\\text{each row}}}{5}$$

There are 30 squares.
There are 6 rows.
There are 5 squares in each row.
$30 \div 6 = 5$

Vocabulary

area the number of square units needed to cover the inside of an object

An area model is similar to an array. Both have equal rows and equal columns.

Chapter 3 Lesson 4   ninety-seven **97**

English Learner Strategy

Tiles Can Show Area Use tiles found on a floor to demonstrate *area*.

Enclose a rectangular area of tiles. Explain that the space inside the rectangle is called the area.

Have students count the number of tiles to find the area.

Have students multiply the number of tiles in each row by the number of columns to find the area.

Demonstrate the relationship between a rectangle and an array.

Repeat the activity with different size rectangles as needed.

Example

Write a division sentence.

Step 1	There are 12 squares in all.
Step 2	There are 4 rows.
Step 3	There are 3 columns.
Step 4	The model shows 12 squares divided into 4 equal rows equals 3 columns of squares.

Answer $12 \div 4 = 3$

Step-by-Step Practice

Write a division sentence.

Step 1	There are **21** squares in all.
Step 2	There are **3** rows.
Step 3	There are **7** columns.
Step 4	The model shows **21** squares divided into **3** equal rows equals **7** columns of squares.

Answer **21** ÷ **3** = **7**

98 ninety-eight

Additional *Example*

Write a division sentence.

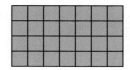

Step 1 There are 28 squares in all.

Step 2 There are 4 rows.

Step 3 There are 7 columns.

Step 4 The model shows 28 squares divided into 4 equal rows equals 7 columns of squares.

Answer $28 \div 4 = 7.$

Math Coach Notes

Strategy Have students do paper weaving to better understand areas that involve rows and columns.

Intervention Strategy

Kinesthetic/Logical Learners

Materials: centimeter graph paper, colored pencils

Give students the materials. Tell them they will use the squares to make larger shapes. Ask them to make a rectangle that is made from 15 squares. Have students lightly color in the area of the rectangle.

- **How many squares are there in all?** 15

Have students lightly circle each row.

- **How many rows are there in all?** Sample answer: 5

- **How many squares in each row?** Sample answer: 3

Have students write a division sentence for their area model.

Repeat with rectangles having different areas.

③ Practice

Guided Practice

Direct students to complete Exercises 1–2 in Guided Practice.

Exercises 1–2 Remind students to correctly count the number of squares.

Problem-Solving Practice

Guide students through the four-step problem-solving plan to complete Exercise 3.

- **What are the key words?** 30 tiles, 3 tiles in each row, how many rows

- **How many rows of tiles does Caroline make?** 10

Ask students to check their work using the strategy suggested in the Check step. Students can count the number of rows, columns, and tiles in all to check their answer.

Using Manipulatives

Connecting Cubes Students can use connecting cubes to form rectangles and display area models.

Base-Ten Blocks Students can use base-ten blocks to form rectangles and display area models.

Pattern Blocks Students can use orange squares to form rectangles and to display area models.

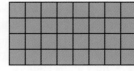**On-Hand Manipulatives** Students can use window panes, floor or wall tiles, graph paper, and squares cut from construction paper to form rectangles and display area models.

Name _____

▶ Guided Practice

Write a division sentence.

 1 **28** squares in all
   4 rows and **7** columns

28 ÷ 4 = 7

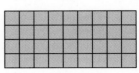 2 **36** squares in all
   4 rows and **9** columns

36 ÷ 4 = 9

Problem-Solving Practice

3 Caroline covers a rectangle with <u>30 tiles</u>. She places <u>3 tiles in each row</u>. <u>How many rows</u> of tiles are made?

Understand Underline key words.

Plan Draw an area model.

Solve Draw rows of **3** tiles.
Add rows until there
are **30** tiles in all.
Caroline makes **10** rows of tiles.

Check Did you draw 30 tiles in equal rows and columns?

GO on

Chapter 3   Lesson 4   ninety-nine **99**

Copyright © Macmillan/McGraw-Hill • Glencoe, a division of The McGraw-Hill Companies, Inc.

Are They Getting It? ❓

Check students' understanding of using area models to write division sentences. Draw the grid and write the following statements on the board. Ask students to point out the correct and incorrect statements and explain their reasoning.

1. The space inside the rectangle is called the area. This is correct.

2. There are 8 rows. This is incorrect. There are 4 rows.

3. There are 4 squares in each row. This is incorrect. There are 8 squares in each row.

4. The model represents the division sentence 32 ÷ 4 = 8. This is correct.

99 Chapter 3 Introduction to Division

Write a division sentence.

4 <u>45</u> squares in all

<u>5</u> rows and <u>9</u> columns

<u>45</u> ÷ <u>5</u> = <u>9</u>

5 <u>42</u> squares in all

<u>6</u> rows and <u>7</u> columns

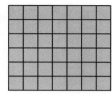

<u>42</u> ÷ <u>6</u> = <u>7</u>

6 An area model has 18 squares in all. There are 2 equal rows of squares.

<u>18</u> ÷ <u>2</u> = <u>9</u>

7 **WRITING IN** ▶**MATH** Thomas places 64 tiles in equal rows of 8. How many rows of tiles does Thomas make? How do you know?

<u>**Sample answer: Thomas makes 8 rows**</u>
<u>**of tiles. I can draw an area model with**</u>
<u>**8 tiles in a row until there are 64 tiles in all.**</u>

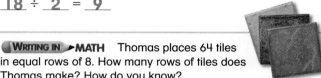

Vocabulary Check Complete.

8 <u>**Area**</u> is the number of square units needed to cover the inside of an object.

100 one hundred

Math Challenge

Growing Area

Material: centimeter graph paper

Have students work in groups of 4. Instruct one student to create a rectangle on graph paper.

The other students write a division sentence modeled by the rectangle. The group compares answers. Correct answers receive a check mark next to the answer.

The graph paper is given to another student who shades additional squares to form a new, larger rectangle.

Play continues giving each student a chance to make a new rectangle. The student with the most check marks at the end wins the challenge.

Practice on Your Own

Direct students to p. 100 in their student books. Have students complete Exercises 4–8 independently. You may need to review the directions of each section before students begin.

4 **Assess**

See It, Do It, Say It, Write It

Step 1 Draw the following on the board.

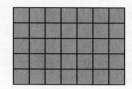

Show how a division sentence is formed by identifying the total, the number of rows, and the number in each row. 35 ÷ 5 = 7

Step 2 Draw the following on the board.

Ask students to find the total the number of rows, and the number in each row to make a division sentence.

Step 3 Ask students to write a division sentence for the model. Have them discuss how they write the division sentence.

Step 4 Have students write directions on how to make a division sentence from an area model.

Looking Ahead: Pre-teach

In the next lesson, students will learn how to divide with 0 and 1.

Example 4 ÷ 1 = 4

The 4 is divided into 1 group. This leaves 4 in the group.

Have students solve each problem.

1. 16 ÷ 1 = ___ 16 **2.** 0 ÷ 25 = ___ 0

Progress Check 2

Formative Assessment

Use the Progress Check to assess students' mastery of the previous lessons. Have students review the lesson indicated for the problems they answered incorrectly.

⚠️ **Common Error** *Alert*

Exercises 2 Students might draw an area model for the division sentence 9 ÷ 3 = 3 instead of an array. Point out that Exercise 1 shows an array and Exercise 3 shows an area model to help them draw the correct type of model.

Exercises 4–5 Remind students that they should make a drawing or use graph paper to help solve the problems.

Name _____

Progress Check 2 (Lessons 3-3 and 3-4)

1 Write a division sentence.

$14 ÷ 2 = 7$

2 Draw an array that matches the division sentence $9 ÷ 3 = 3$.

3 Write a division sentence for the area model.

$32 ÷ 4 = 8$

4 An area model has 25 squares in 5 equal rows. How many squares are in each row? __5__ squares

5 Kwasi arranged 20 recorders for music class in 2 equal rows. How many recorders did Kwasi place in each row? Explain.

Kwasi placed 10 recorders in each row. To make 2 equal rows, 10 recorders must be placed in each row. 20 ÷ 2 = 10

Chapter 3   Progress Check

one hundred one **101**

Copyright © Macmillan/McGraw-Hill, • Glencoe, a division of The McGraw-Hill Companies, Inc.

Data-Driven Decision Making

Students missing Exercises ...	Have trouble with ...	Should review and practice ...
1–2	using arrays to model division.	SSG Lesson 3-3, p. 93 CRM Skills Practice, p. A69
3–4	using area models to show division.	SSG Lesson 3-4, p. 97 CRM Skills Practice, p. A73
5	problem-solving that involves using arrays to model division.	SSG Lesson 3-3, p. 95 CRM Problem-Solving Practice, p. A70

Replay

Name _____

Complete each division sentence. Fill in the letters below to find the answer to the knock-knock joke.

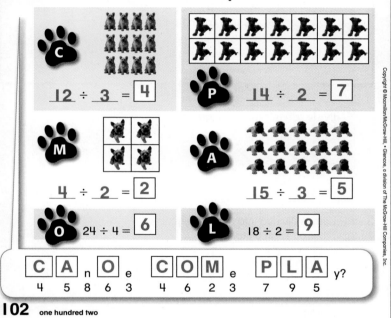

$12 \div 3 = \boxed{4}$ (C)

$14 \div 2 = \boxed{7}$ (P)

$4 \div 2 = \boxed{2}$ (M)

$15 \div 3 = \boxed{5}$ (A)

$24 \div 4 = \boxed{6}$ (O)

$18 \div 2 = \boxed{9}$ (L)

| C | A | n | O | e | C | O | M | e | P | L | A | y? |
| 4 | 5 | 8 | 6 | 3 | 4 | 6 | 2 | 3 | 7 | 9 | 5 | |

102 one hundred two

Copyright © Macmillan/McGraw-Hill • Glencoe, a division of The McGraw-Hill Companies, Inc.

Replay

Use the Replay activity to review and reinforce the concepts and skills presented in Lessons 3-3 and 3-4.

Instructions

Have students read the directions at the top of the student page.

Remind students to be sure the numbers are in the correct spaces in the division sentences.

Student Technology

Students can use the following technology resources to reinforce chapter content.

- StudentWorks™ Plus
- **Math Online** macmillanmh.com
- eGlossary

Lesson Notes

Lesson Planner

Objective   Divide with 0 and 1.

Vocabulary   divide (division)

Materials/Manipulatives   number lines, connecting cubes, base-ten blocks, geoboards, counters, index cards

Chapter Resource Masters

[CRM] Vocabulary and English Language Development (p. A76)

[CRM] Skill Practice (p. A77)

[CRM] Problem-Solving-Practice (p. A78)

[CRM] Homework Practice (p. A79)

1 Introduce

Vocabulary

Vocabulary Review   Review what is meant by division. Write $6 \div 3 = 2$ on the board. Ask students what the number sentence means. Explain that six can be divided into three groups with two in each group. Explain the relationship to $6 \div 2 = 3$.

Ask students to write and explain other division sentences. They should use chapter vocabulary in their explanations.

2 Teach

Key Concept

Foundational Skills and Concepts   After students have read through the Key Concept box, guide them through the following questions.

- **What is the answer if you divide 0 by any number?**   0

- **What is the answer if you divide any number by 1?**   that number

- **What is the answer if you divide any number by itself?**   1

103 Chapter 3 Introduction to Division

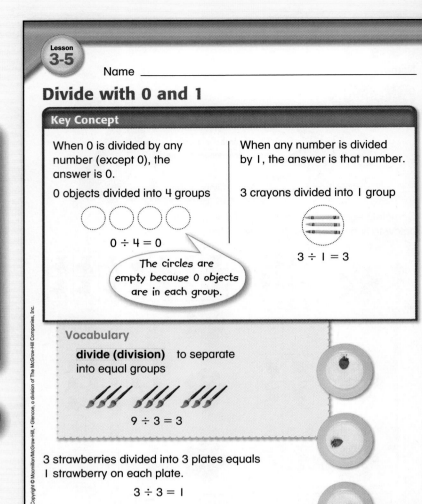

Name _____

Divide with 0 and 1

Key Concept

When 0 is divided by any number (except 0), the answer is 0.

0 objects divided into 4 groups

$0 \div 4 = 0$

The circles are empty because 0 objects are in each group.

When any number is divided by 1, the answer is that number.

3 crayons divided into 1 group

$3 \div 1 = 3$

Vocabulary

divide (division)   to separate into equal groups

$9 \div 3 = 3$

3 strawberries divided into 3 plates equals 1 strawberry on each plate.

$3 \div 3 = 1$

Chapter 3   Lesson 5

one hundred three **103**

Copyright © Macmillan/McGraw-Hill • Glencoe, a division of The McGraw-Hill Companies, Inc.

English Learner Strategy

Connecting Symbols with Words   Students should be able to connect the symbols used in a division sentence with their word meanings.

1. $0 \div 5 = 0$ Explain that if **zero** objects are **divided** into **five** groups there are **zero** objects in each group. Have students draw a model.

2. $5 \div 0$ Explain that this division sentence has no answer because **five** objects **cannot be divided** into **zero** groups. Have students try to find a counter example.

3. $5 \div 1 = 5$ Explain that if **five** objects are **divided** into **one** group, there are **five** objects in each group. Have students draw a model.

4. $4 \div 4 = 1$ Explain that if **four** objects are **divided** into **four** groups, there is **one** object in each group. Have students draw a model.

Example

Write a division sentence.

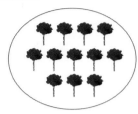

Step 1   There are 12 flowers in all.
Step 2   The flowers are in 1 group.
Step 3   The picture shows 12 flowers divided into
         1 group equals 12 flowers in each group.

Answer   12 ÷ 1 = 12

Step-by-Step Practice

Write a division sentence.

Step 1   There are __8__ leaves in all.

Step 2   The leaves are in __8__ groups.

Step 3   The picture shows __8__ leaves divided into

__8__ groups equals __1__ leaf in each group.

Answer   __8__ ÷ __8__ = __1__

Additional *Example*

Write a division sentence.

Step 1 There are 3 squirrels in all.

Step 2 The squirrels are in 3 groups.

Step 3 The picture shows 3 squirrels divided into 3 groups equals 1 squirrel in each group.

Answer 3 ÷ 3 = 1

 Common Error *Alert*

Students might confuse dividing 0 by a number with dividing a number by 0 when asked to write a division sentence with 0. Remind students that you cannot divide by 0 because you cannot place a group of objects into 0 groups. Model this concept with various groups of objects such as counters, connecting cubes or pencils.

Math Coach Notes

Strategy   Have students use related multiplication facts, number lines, arrays, area models to represent the following:

- 0 divided by a number (except 0) is 0.
- a number divided by 1 is that number.
- a number (except 0) divided by itself is 1.

Study Skills   Encourage students to practice division facts. (Point out that **0 ÷ 1 = 0** can often be a tricky fact.) Use flashcards, tables, or frequently timed drills to assess progress. The more comfortable and automatic these basic facts become, the less difficulty students will encounter when the numbers become larger.

Intervention Strategy

Auditory/Interpersonal Learners

Materials: counters

Division Challenge   Have students work in pairs. Write several division sentences that involve dividing with 0 and 1 and dividing a number by itself. Include a few incorrect answers in the list of division sentences.

Recite each sentence to the class. Ask students to write down the sentences. Challenge them to use counters to determine which sentences are correct.

Have students show models for those sentences that are correct. Have students provide explanations and corrections for those that are incorrect.

Practice

Guided Practice

Direct students to complete Exercises 1–2 in Guided Practice.

Exercises 1–2 Remind students that the first number in a division sentence is the total number of objects.

Problem-Solving Practice

Guide students through the four-step problem-solving plan to complete Exercise 3.

- **What are the key words?** 12 fish, 1 fish tank, how many fish

- **How many fish does Juana have in all?** 12

Ask students to check their work using the strategy suggested in the Check step. Students can draw a picture to solve the problem.

Using Manipulatives

Number Lines Students can use number lines to model division sentences.

Connection Cubes Students can use connecting cubes to model division sentences.

Base-Ten Blocks Students can use ones cubes to model division sentences.

Geoboards Students can use geoboards to model division sentences.

On-Hand Manipulatives Students can use beans, buttons, or squares of different colored construction paper as counters. They can use small tins or bowls as grouping vessels.

Name _____

▶ **Guided Practice**

Write a division sentence.

1 0 crayons in 5 boxes

$\underline{0} \div \underline{5} = \underline{0}$

2 15 books on 1 shelf

$\underline{15} \div \underline{1} = \underline{15}$

Problem-Solving Practice

3 Juana has $\underline{12}$ fish. If she has only $\underline{1}$ fish tank, how many fish are in Juana's tank?

Understand Underline key words.

Plan Use logical reasoning.

Solve Juana has $\underline{12}$ fish in all. She will keep the fish in $\underline{1}$ group. The rule says any number divided by $\underline{1}$ is **that number**.

$\underline{12} \div \underline{1} = \underline{12}$

There are $\underline{12}$ fish in Juana's tank.

Check Draw a picture to check your answer.

 GO on

Chapter 3 Lesson 5   one hundred five **105**

Are They Getting It?

Check students' understanding of dividing with 0 and 1 by writing the following exercises on the board. Ask students to point out the correct and incorrect answers and explain their reasoning.

1. $0 \div 8 = 8$ This is incorrect. $0 \div 8 = 0$

2. $6 \div 6 = 36$ This is incorrect. $6 \div 6 = 1$

3. $0 \div 10 = 0$ This is correct.

4. $0 \div 1 = 0$ This is correct.

Copyright © Macmillan/McGraw-Hill. • Glencoe, a division of The McGraw-Hill Companies, Inc.

▶ Practice on Your Own

Write a division sentence.

4 26 buttons in 1 group

$\underline{26} \div \underline{1} = \underline{26}$

5 0 cookies on 2 plates

$\underline{0} \div \underline{2} = \underline{0}$

6 Draw a picture for $6 \div 6 = 1$.

⊗ ⊗ ⊗ ⊗ ⊗ ⊗

Divide.

7 $32 \div 1 = \underline{32}$

8 $45 \div 45 = \underline{1}$

9 $0 \div 19 = \underline{0}$

10 $0 \div 11 = \underline{0}$

11 **WRITING IN ►MATH** Mrs. Romero has 25 markers. She divides her markers equally among 25 students. How many markers does each student have? How do you know?

<u>Each student has 1 marker. 25 markers</u>
<u>divided into 25 groups equals 1 marker</u>
<u>per group. 25 ÷ 25 = 1</u>

Vocabulary Check Complete.

12 When you ___**divide**___ a number by 1, the answer is that number.

STOP

106 one hundred six

Copyright © Macmillan/McGraw-Hill • Glencoe, a division of The McGraw-Hill Companies, Inc.

Math Challenge

Rule Rhythms

Place students in groups. Have the groups come up with a song or riddle to help memorize the rules of division:

• Zero divided by any number except 0 is 0.

• Any number (except 0) divided by 1 is that number.

• Any number (except 0) divided by itself is 1.

Have groups share their songs or riddles with the class.

Practice on Your Own

Direct students to p. 106 in their student books. Have students complete Exercises 4–12 independently. You may need to review the directions of each section before students begin.

4 Assess

See It, Do It, Say It, Write It

Step 1 Write $6 \div 1 = 6$, $6 \div 6 = 1$, and $0 \div 6 = 0$ on the board. Explain each division sentence.

Step 2 Have students write three similar division sentences using the numbers 0 and 1.

Step 3 Have students verbally explain the meaning of each division sentence.

Step 4 Have students write and list the rules for dividing with 0 and 1.

Looking Ahead: Pre-teach

In the next lesson, students will learn how to divide by 2 and 5.

Example $15 \div 5 = 3$

15 can be divided into 5 equal groups. This leaves 3 in each group.

Have students solve each problem.

1. $10 \div 5 = \underline{}$ 2

2. $8 \div 2 = \underline{}$ 4

3. $25 \div 5 = \underline{}$ 5

Lesson Notes

Lesson
3-6

Name _____

Divide by 2 and 5

Key Concept

A number line can be used to **divide** 20 by 5.

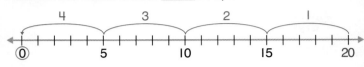

Skip count backward by 5s. Start at 20.
20, 15, 10, 5, 0 skip 4 times to reach 0.
$20 \div 5 = 4$

Vocabulary

divide (division)   to separate into
equal groups

$9 \div 3 = 3$

You can use multiplication to
check division.

$25 \div 5 = 5$
$5 \times 5 = 25$

> There are 25 counters in all. There are 5 groups of counters. So, there are 5 counters in each group.

Copyright © Macmillan/McGraw-Hill • Glencoe, a division of The McGraw-Hill Companies, Inc.

Chapter 3   Lesson 6

one hundred seven   **107**

Lesson Planner

Math Objective   Divide by 2 and 5.

Vocabulary   divide (division)

Materials/Manipulatives   number lines,
connecting cubes, base-ten blocks, geoboards,
construction paper, markers/crayons, number
cube, index cards, counters

Chapter Resource Masters

CRM Vocabulary and English Language
Development (p. A80)

CRM Skill Practice (p. A81)

CRM Problem-Solving-Practice (p. A82)

CRM Homework Practice (p. A83)

1 Introduce

Vocabulary

Model Vocabulary   Write $8 \div 2 = 4$ on the board.
Model the sentence by drawing a number line, array of
circles, and area model. Have students explain how the
division sentence can be represented using each
model. Be sure the word *divide* is incorporated into
the discussion.

2 Teach

Key Concept

Foundational Skills and Concepts   After
students have read through the Key Concept box, guide
them through the following questions.

- **The number line is divided into sections. How
  many equal sections are there?** 4

- **How many tick marks are in each section?** 5

- **At what number do you start skip counting?** 20

- **What is $20 \div 5$?** 4

English Learner Strategy

Guiding Questions   With the conclusion of this chapter, students
who are learning English might need additional help with the
concepts. Use questioning to help solidify and assess students'
understanding of the meaning of division.

Write $10 \div 5 = $ ___ on the board. Read the number sentence out
loud. Then ask the following questions.

- **What kind of sentence is this?** division

- **How do you know?** The sentence has a division symbol.

- **What do the numbers in the sentence mean?** divide 10 into
  5 equal groups

Discuss how to find the answer using manipulatives such as
connecting cubes or counters.

Example

Margaret has 30 connecting cubes.
She places the cubes in 5 equal rows.
How many cubes are in each row?

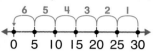

Step 1   Skip count backward by 5s. Start at 30.
Step 2   Skip 6 times. 30, 25, 20, 15, 10, 5, 0
Step 3   The division sentence is $30 \div 5 = 6$.
Answer   There are 6 cubes in each row.

Step-by-Step Practice

Alonso bought a paint set. There are 12 paint colors in all. There are 2 rows of paint colors. How many paint colors are in each row?

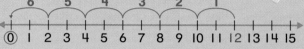

Step 1   Skip count backward by __2__s. Start at __12__.

Step 2   Skip __6__ times.

__12__, __10__, __8__, __6__, __4__, __2__, __0__

Step 3   The division sentence is __12__ $\div$ __2__ = __6__.

Answer   There are __6__ paint colors in each row.

108   one hundred eight

Copyright © Macmillan/McGraw-Hill • Glencoe, a division of The McGraw-Hill Companies, Inc.

Juan has 18 crayons. He has 2 groups of crayons. How many crayons are in each group?

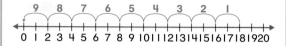

Step 1 Skip count backward by 2s. Start at 18.

Step 2 Skip 9 times. 18, 16, 14, 12, 10, 8, 6, 4, 2, 0

Step 3 The division sentence is $18 \div 2 = 9$.

Answer There are 9 crayons in each group.

⚠ Common Error *Alert*

Students might skip count forward to solve a division problem. Explain that they skip count forward for multiplication, but they skip count backward for division.

Math Coach Notes

Strategies   Have students reread and redo the Example and Step-by-Step using the previously taught skills of using related multiplication facts, repeated subtraction, and arrays to find the answer. This will reinforce and solidify their understanding of division.

Study Skills   Encourage students to practice division facts. Use flashcards, tables, or frequently timed drills to assess progress. The more comfortable and automatic these basic facts become, the less difficulty students will encounter when the numbers become larger.

Intervention Strategy

Auditory/Visual/ Interpersonal Learners

Materials: counters

Explore Division   Write division problems with two-digit dividends and 2 or 5 as divisors on the board. Make sure the quotients will be whole numbers.

Have students work in pairs to solve each division problem.

Have one student choose a division problem from the board and explain how to solve it. Encourage students to use correct vocabulary terms and clear language.

Have the other student model the division sentence with counters.

Have students switch roles and repeat with a different problem.

③ Practice

Guided Practice

Direct students to complete Exercise 1 in Guided Practice.

Exercise 1 Students may need to review how to model division on a number line.

Problem-Solving Practice

Guide students through the four-step Problem-Solving plan to complete Exercise 2.

- **What are the key words?** 35 students, 5 sections, how many students are in each section

- **At what number do you start skip counting on the number line?** 35

Ask students to check their work using the strategy suggested in the Check step. Students can use a related multiplication fact to check their answer.

Using Manipulatives

Connecting Cubes Students can use connecting cube to model division sentences.

Number Lines Students can use number lines to model division sentences.

Base-Ten Blocks Students can use base-ten blocks to model division sentences.

Geoboards Students can use geoboards to model division sentences.

On-Hand Manipulatives Students can use rulers, beans, buttons, or squares of different colored construction paper as counters. They can use small tins or bowls as grouping vessels.

Name _____

▶ Guided Practice

1   Ian divides 15 marbles into 5 equal groups. How many marbles does Ian place in each group?

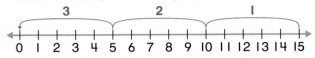

$15 ÷ 5 = 3$ Ian places __3__ marbles in each group.

Problem-Solving Practice

2   There are 35 students in Mr. Lin's music class. He places the students into 5 sections. How many students are in each section?

Understand   Underline key words.

Plan   Use a number line.

Solve   Start at __35__. Skip count backward by 5s until you reach __0__.

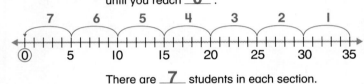

There are __7__ students in each section.

Check   Use a related multiplication fact.

Copyright © Macmillan/McGraw-Hill • Glencoe, a division of The McGraw-Hill Companies, Inc.

GO on

Chapter 3   Lesson 6   one hundred nine **109**

Are They Getting It?

Check students' understanding of dividing by 2 and 5 by writing the following word problem and number lines on the board. Students should decide which number line models the word problem. Ask students to point out the correct and incorrect number line and explain their reasoning.

Melba has 14 crackers. She has 2 birds. How many crackers could each bird get?

1.
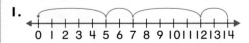

This is incorrect. This does not show repeated subtraction of 2.

2.

This is correct.

▶ Practice on Your Own

3 Kay makes an array of 20 tiles in 4 rows. How many tiles does Kay place in each row?

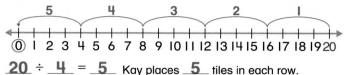

$20 \div \underline{4} = \underline{5}$ Kay places $\underline{5}$ tiles in each row.

4 Skip count backward to divide.

$45 \div 5 = \underline{9}$

45, 40, 35, 30, 25, 20, 15, 10, 5, 0

5 **WRITING IN ▶MATH**   There are 14 cowboy hats in a store. The hats are displayed in 2 groups. How many hats are in each group? Explain.

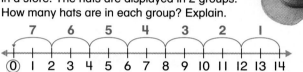

There are 7 hats in each group. I used a number line to skip count backward.

Vocabulary Check   Complete.

6 In this lesson, we learned how to __divide__ objects into equal groups of 2 or 5.

STOP

110   one hundred ten

Math Challenge

Materials: construction paper, markers/crayons, number cube

Division Gaming

Have students work in pairs. Challenge students to create a board game using the division facts learned in this chapter (i.e. dividing by 1, 2, and 5; facts with 0 as the dividend). The board should have a start and finish, and the distance between should be divided into 12 spaces. A division fact, without the answer, should be placed in each space.

To play the game, a number cube is rolled. The player moves this number of spaces and completes the division fact. If correct, the player stays on the space, and the turn moves to the other player. If incorrect, the player moves back to their original space, and the turn moves to the other player. The first player to finish wins.

Practice on Your Own

Direct students to p. 110 in their student books. Have students complete Exercises 3–6 independently. You may need to review the directions of each section before students begin.

Exercises 3–5 Remind students they can check their answers by using a related multiplication fact.

④ Assess

See It, Do It, Say It, Write It

Step 1   Write the following word problem and number line on the board. *Mr. Jeri has 25 markers. Five students need to use them. How many markers should each student get?*

Explain how to find the answer using repeated subtraction and skip counting on the number line.

Step 2   Write the following word problem on the board.

Lin had 12 sheets of paper. She and a friend needed to share the paper. How many sheets did each person get?

Have students make a number line to find the answer.

Step 3   Have students explain how to find the answer using repeated subtraction and skip counting on the number line.

Step 4   Have students write the division sentence that is modeled by the number line.

Chapter 3 Progress Check 3

Formative Assessment

Use the Progress Check to assess students' mastery of the previous lessons. Have students review the lesson indicated for the problems they answered incorrectly.

Remind students of the correct placement of numbers in a division sentence.

Exercises 3–4, 9 Encourage students to draw a model to help with problem-solving

⚠ Common Error *Alert*

Check Your Work to Eliminate Errors
Students should check their answers using related multiplication facts.

Name _____

Progress Check 3 (Lessons 3-5 and 3-6)

1 Write a division sentence for the picture.

$\underline{0} \div \underline{6} = \underline{0}$

2 Draw a picture for $18 \div 1 = 18$.

3 Meg bought 23 stamps. She wants to glue all of the stamps on 1 page of a notebook. How many stamps will be on the page?

$\underline{23} \div \underline{1} = \underline{23}$

$\underline{23}$ stamps

Divide.

4 $40 \div 5 = \underline{8}$

5 $4 \div 2 = \underline{2}$

6 $26 \div 26 = \underline{1}$

7 $50 \div 5 = \underline{10}$

8 Kevin has a package of 6 juice boxes. There are 2 equal rows of boxes. How many juice boxes are in each row? Explain.

There are 3 juice boxes in each row.

$6 \div 2 = 3$

Chapter 3   Progress Check   **one hundred eleven**   **111**

Copyright © Macmillan/McGraw-Hill, • Glencoe, a division of The McGraw-Hill Companies, Inc.

Data-Driven Decision Making

Students missing Exercises . . .	Have trouble with . . .	Should review and practice . . .
1–3, 6	dividing with 0 and 1.	**SSG** Lesson 3-5, p. 103 **CRM** Skills Practice, p. A77
4, 5, 7	dividing by 2 and 5.	**SSG** Lesson 3-6, p. 107 **CRM** Skills Practice, p. A81
8	problem-solving that involves dividing by 2.	**SSG** Lesson 3-6, p. 109 **CRM** Problem–Solving Practice, p. A82

111 Chapter 3 Introduction to Division

Name _____

What is the Mystery Picture?

Solve the division problems in the picture below.
Color the section **orange** when the answer is **0**.
Color the section **blue** when the answer is **any other number**.

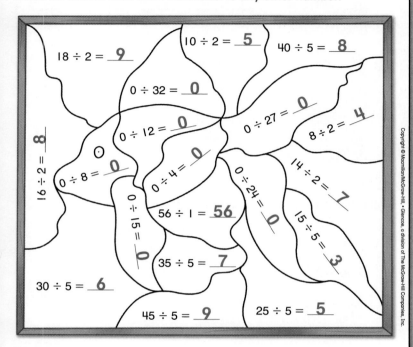

18 ÷ 2 = __9__

10 ÷ 2 = __5__

40 ÷ 5 = __8__

0 ÷ 32 = __0__

0 ÷ 12 = __0__

0 ÷ 27 = __0__

8 ÷ 2 = __4__

16 ÷ 2 = __8__

0 ÷ 8 = __0__

0 ÷ 4 = __0__

0 ÷ 24 = __0__

14 ÷ 2 = __7__

0 ÷ 15 = __0__

56 ÷ 1 = __56__

15 ÷ 5 = __3__

35 ÷ 5 = __7__

30 ÷ 5 = __6__

45 ÷ 5 = __9__

25 ÷ 5 = __5__

Replay

Use the Replay activity to review and reinforce the concepts and skills presented in Lessons 3-5 and 3-6.

Instructions

Have students read the directions at the top of the student page.

After completing the page, students should be able to identify the mystery picture.

Student Technology

Students can use the following technology resources to reinforce chapter content.

- StudentWorks™ Plus

- Math Online   macmillanmh.com

- eGlossary

Review

Vocabulary

If students have difficulty answering Exercises 1–3, use the page references below to review the vocabulary words, or refer them to the glossary.

area (p. 97)
array (p. 93)
skip count (p. 87)

Vocabulary Review Strategies

Remember Vocabulary   Divide the class into small groups. Have groups work together to determine a method for remembering the meanings of the vocabulary terms. The groups should create guidelines or a visual to teach the method to their classmates. Students may choose any of the following (or come up with their own method):

• associate each word with a finger to remember it.

• pair pictures with words to learn vocabulary.

• visualize the word and its definition.

Concepts

The exercises in this section are grouped to cover content from each lesson in the chapter. The first exercise of each set is partially completed for the student in order to show the method for solving the other exercise(s) in the set.

Exercises 4–5: Lesson 3-1 (p. 83)
Exercises 6–7: Lesson 3-2 (p. 87)
Exercise 8: Lesson 3-4 (p. 97)
Exercise 9: Lesson 3-3 (p. 93)
Exercises 10–11: Lesson 3-5 (p. 103)
Exercises 12–14: Lesson 3-6 (p. 107)

Find **Extra Practice** for these concepts in the Practice Worksheets, pp. A60–A83.

Name _____

Review

Vocabulary

Word Bank
area model
array
skip count

Use the Word Bank to complete.

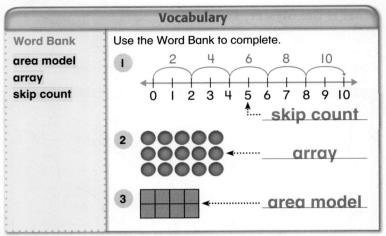

1   skip count

2   array

3   area model

▶ Concepts

Write related multiplication and division sentences.

4
56
7   8

Sample answer:
_7_ × _8_ = _56_
_56_ ÷ _7_ = _8_

5
27
3   9

Sample answer:
_3_ × _9_ = _27_
_27_ ÷ _3_ = _9_

GO on

Chapter 3   Review

one hundred thirteen **113**

Divide.

6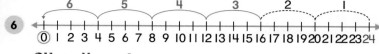

$$24 \div 4 = 6$$

7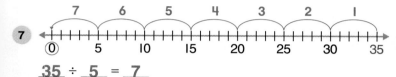

$$35 \div 5 = 7$$

Write a division sentence.

8 $16 \div 4 = 4$

9 $15 \div 3 = 5$

10 8 empty water glasses

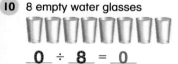

$$0 \div 8 = 0$$

11 10 shells in 1 group

$$10 \div 1 = 10$$

Divide.

12 $12 \div 2 = 6$ **13** $10 \div 5 = 2$ **14** $18 \div 2 = 9$

Copyright © Macmillan/McGraw-Hill • Glencoe, a division of The McGraw-Hill Companies, Inc.

Have students use the Foldable they created at the beginning of the chapter to review and reinforce the concepts and skills they learned during the chapter. (See Chapter Resource Masters p. A56 for instructions.)

Intervention Strategy

Use this Intervention Strategy activity at any point during the chapter to reinforce the concepts and skills presented in the chapter.

Step 1 Place students in groups. Give each group construction paper.

Step 2 Tell students that they can better understand division by forming equal groups.

Step 3 Tell students they need to help come up with ideas on how to arrange the desks. Have students draw an arrangement of 20 desks. Stress the need that desks must be arranged in equal groups, or by rows and columns. Challenge students to find different arrangements.

Step 4 Have students share and explain their drawings with the class.

Classroom Management

Early Finishers Some students will not require as much time to complete their Review. For those students who seem to have a solid understanding of the materials from the chapter, suggest they develop a small quiz from which you can pull additional review questions to be used at a later time. These could be presented to the remaining members of the class who could use the extra practice.

Chapter 3

Chapter Test

Chapter Resource Masters

Additional forms of the Chapter Test are available.

Test Format	Where to Find it
Chapter Test	**Math Online** macmillanmh.com
Blackline Masters	Assessment Masters, p. 34

ExamView®
Assessment Suite

Customize and create multiple versions of your chapter test and their answer keys. All of these questions from the chapter tests are available on ExamView® Assessment Suite.

Online Assessment and Reporting
macmillanmh.com

This online assessment tool allows teachers to track student progress with easily accessible, comprehensive reports available for every student. Assess students using any internet-ready computer.

Alternative Assessment

Use Portfolios Have students represent the following division sentences by creating a model for each.

$$0 \div 6 = 0 \qquad 24 \div 24 = 1 \qquad 30 \div 5 = 6$$

Be sure students give a written explanation of each model. Finally, have students write a related multiplication fact for each division sentence.

Name _____

Chapter Test

1. Write related multiplication and division sentences.

Sample answer:

$\underline{7} \times \underline{6} = \underline{42}$

$\underline{42} \div \underline{7} = \underline{6}$

2. Divide.

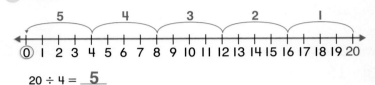

$20 \div 4 = \underline{5}$

Write a division sentence.

3. $\underline{24} \div \underline{4} = \underline{6}$

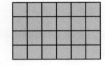

4. $\underline{12} \div \underline{3} = \underline{4}$

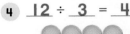

5. Draw a picture for $8 \div 1 = 8$.

GO on

Chapter 3 Test

one hundred fifteen **115**

Copyright © Macmillan/McGraw-Hill, • Glencoe, a division of The McGraw-Hill Companies, Inc.

---

6 Who is Correct?

Juanita and Matthew solve $0 \div 12 =$ _____.

 Juanita

$0 \div 12 = 12$

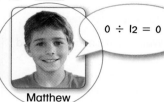 Matthew

$0 \div 12 = 0$

Circle the correct answer. Explain.

Matthew is correct. Zero divided by any number equals 0.

7
Miss Peta owns a bike shop.
She has 16 wheels in stock.
Each bike needs 2 wheels.
How many bikes can she make?

$\underline{16} \div \underline{2} = \underline{8}$ Miss Peta can make $\underline{8}$ bikes.

8
Sarah went to a flower store. She has 25 dollars.
Potted flowers cost 5 dollars each.
How many potted flowers can Sarah buy?

$\underline{25} \div \underline{5} = \underline{5}$ Sarah can buy $\underline{5}$ potted flowers.

Divide.

9 $14 \div 2 = \underline{7}$

10 $30 \div 5 = \underline{6}$

11 $0 \div 18 = \underline{0}$

12 $13 \div 13 = \underline{1}$

STOP

Who Is Correct?

Diagnostic Teaching

- Juanita says the answer is 12. She is incorrect. She thought 0 objects placed into 12 equal groups would equal 12 objects in each group.

- Matthew says the answer is 0. He is correct. Zero objects placed into 12 equal groups equals 0 objects in each group.

Learning from Mistakes

Missed Questions   Review commonly missed questions as a small group or class. Ask students to share their methods of answering each question. Try to point out when any errors occur and take corrective measures.

Data-Driven Decision Making

Students missing Exercises . . .	Have trouble with . . .	Should review and practice . . .	
1	writing related multiplication and division sentences.	SSG Lesson 3-1, p. 83	CRM Skills Practice, p. A61
2	using repeated subtraction and skip counting to divide.	SSG Lesson 3-2, p. 87	CRM Skills Practice, p. A65
3	using area models to show division.	SSG Lesson 3-4, p. 97	CRM Skills Practice, p. A73
4	using arrays to model division.	SSG Lesson 3-3, p. 93	CRM Skills Practice, p. A69
5, 6, 11, 12	dividing with 0 and 1.	SSG Lesson 3-5, p. 103	CRM Skills Practice, p. A77
7–8	problem-solving that involves dividing by 2 and 5.	SSG Lesson 3-6, p. 109	CRM Problem Solving Practice, p. A82
9–10	dividing by 2 and 5.	SSG Lesson 3-6, p. 107	CRM Skills Practice, p. A81

Chapter 3 Test Practice

Survey student responses for each item. Class trends may indicate common errors and misconceptions.

1. $6 \div 3 = 2$:   factors are not in same fact family
   $18 \div 9 = 2$: factors are not in same fact family
   $6 \div 2 = 3$:   factors are not in same fact family
   $18 \div 3 = 6$: correct

2. 4: divided by 4 instead of by 2
   8: correct
   12: does not understand concept of division
   14: subtracted instead of dividing

3. $8 \div 2 = 4$: read model incorrectly
   $5 \div 1 = 5$: does not understand concept of arrays
   $10 \div 2 = 5$: correct
   $2 \times 5 = 10$: chose a multiplication sentence

4. $25 \div 5 = 5$: correct
   $25 \div 5 = 20$: misread operation as subtraction
   $25 \div 5 = 25$: does not understand concept of division
   $25 \div 5 = 30$: misread operation as addition

5. $15 \div 3 = 5$: correct
   $5 \times 3 = 15$: chose a multiplication sentence
   $15 \div 1 = 15$: does not understand concept of area models
   $3 \times 5 = 15$: chose a multiplication sentence

6. $0 \times 3 = 0$: chose a multiplication sentence
   $0 \div 3 = 0$: correct
   $3 \div 3 = 1$: does not understand the model
   $3 \div 1 = 3$: does not understand the model

7. 9: correct
   12: does not understand concept of division
   19: does not understand concept of division
   24: subtracted instead of dividing

8. $14 \div 2 = 7$: correct
   $14 \div 2 = 12$: misread operation as subtraction
   $14 \div 2 = 16$: misread operation as addition
   $14 \div 2 = 28$: misread operation as multiplication

9. $12 \div 3 = 4$: does not understand concept of arrays
   $12 \div 2 = 6$: correct
   $12 \div 1 = 12$: does not understand concept of arrays
   $3 \times 4 = 12$: does not understand concept of arrays

10. $0 \div 4 = 0$: does not understand the model
    $4 \div 2 = 2$: does not understand model.
    $4 \div 1 = 4$: correct
    $1 \times 4 = 4$: chose the related multiplication sentence

11. $3 \times 6 = 18$: factors are not in same fact family
    $6 \times 4 = 24$: factors are not in same fact family
    $8 \times 3 = 24$: correct
    $24 \times 3 = 72$: factors are not in same fact family

12. $5 \div 1 = 5$: does not understand concept of area models
    $30 \div 5 = 6$: correct
    $30 \div 3 = 10$: does not understand concept of area models
    $6 \times 5 = 30$: chose a multiplication sentence

Name _____

Test Practice

Choose the correct answer.

1 Which division fact is related to $6 \times 3 = 18$?
- ○ $6 \div 3 = 2$
- ○ $18 \div 9 = 2$
- ○ $6 \div 2 = 3$
- ● $18 \div 3 = 6$

2 Tegene and Lilla divide 16 strawberries into 2 equal groups. How many strawberries are in each group?

| 4 | 8 | 12 | 14 |
| ○ | ● | ○ | ○ |

3 Which division sentence matches this array?
- ○ $8 \div 2 = 4$
- ○ $5 \div 1 = 5$
- ● $10 \div 2 = 5$
- ○ $2 \times 5 = 10$

4 Which division sentence is true?
- ● $25 \div 5 = 5$
- ○ $25 \div 5 = 20$
- ○ $25 \div 5 = 25$
- ○ $25 \div 5 = 30$

5 Which division sentence matches this area model?

- ● $15 \div 3 = 5$
- ○ $5 \times 3 = 15$
- ○ $15 \div 1 = 15$
- ○ $3 \times 5 = 15$

6 Which division sentence is shown by this picture?

- ○ $0 \times 3 = 0$
- ● $0 \div 3 = 0$
- ○ $3 \div 3 = 1$
- ○ $3 \div 1 = 3$

GO ON ▷

Copyright © Macmillan/McGraw-Hill • Glencoe, a division of The McGraw-Hill Companies, Inc.

7 Craig has 27 marbles. He wants to divide his marbles into 3 equal piles. How many marbles will be in each pile?

9 ● 12 ○
19 ○ 24 ○

8 Which division sentence is true?

● $14 \div 2 = 7$
○ $14 \div 2 = 12$
○ $14 \div 2 = 16$
○ $14 \div 2 = 28$

9 Which division sentence matches this array?

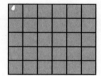

○ $12 \div 3 = 4$
◐ $12 \div 2 = 6$
○ $12 \div 1 = 12$
○ $3 \times 4 = 12$

10 Which division sentence is shown by this picture?

○ $0 \div 4 = 0$
○ $4 \div 2 = 2$
● $4 \div 1 = 4$
○ $1 \times 4 = 4$

11 Which multiplication fact is related to $24 \div 8 = 3$?

○ $3 \times 6 = 18$
○ $6 \times 4 = 24$
● $8 \times 3 = 24$
○ $24 \times 3 = 74$

12 Which division sentence matches this area model?

○ $5 \div 1 = 5$
● $30 \div 5 = 6$
○ $30 \div 3 = 10$
○ $6 \times 5 = 30$

STOP

Test Practice

Diagnosing Student Errors and Misconceptions

Review Sharing the answer key could benefit students. Have students score their own Test Practice and revise their response as needed. After doing so, take an informal class poll in order to determine the number of students missing particular questions. This can help indicate any misconceptions the class may have with the material.

Many of the problems ask students to relate multiplication and division. Be sure students realize that the same three numbers will be used in opposite or related number sentences.

Chapter Overview

Chapter-at-a-Glance

Lesson	Math Objective	Local/State Standards
4-1 Count to 100 (pp. 121–124)	Count numbers less than 100.	
4-2 Expanded Form (pp. 125–128)	Write equivalent representations of numbers.	
Progress Check 1 (p. 129)		
4-3 Round Two-Digit Numbers (pp. 131–134)	Round two-digit numbers to the nearest ten.	
4-4 Whole Number Less Than 10,000 (pp. 135–138)	Model numbers less than 10,000.	
Progress Check 2 (p. 139)		

Content-at-a-Glance

The diagram below summarizes and unpacks Chapter 4 content.

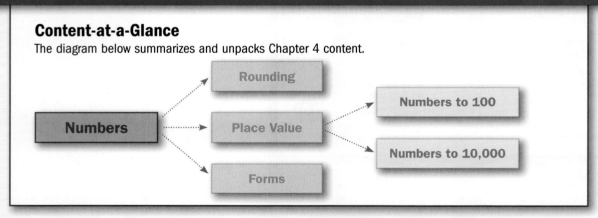

Chapter Assessment Manager

Diagnostic — Diagnose students' readiness.

	Student Study Guide/ Teacher Editions	Assessment Masters	Technology
Course Placement Test		1	ExamView® Assessment Suite
Book 2 Pretest		45	ExamView® Assessment Suite
Chapter Pretest		48	ExamView® Assessment Suite
Get Ready	SSG 120		Math Online macmillanmh.com StudentWorks™ Plus

Formative — Identify students' misconceptions of content knowledge.

	Student Study Guide/ Teacher Editions	Assessment Masters	Technology
Progress Checks	SSG 129, 139		Math Online macmillanmh.com StudentWorks™ Plus
Vocabulary Review	SSG 124, 128, 134, 138, 141		Math Online macmillanmh.com
Lesson Assessments			ExamView® Assessment Suite
Are They Getting It?	TE 123, 127, 133, 137		

Summative — Determine student success in learning the concepts in the lesson, chapter, or book.

	Student Study Guide/ Teacher Editions	Assessment Masters	Technology
Chapter Test	SSG 143	51	ExamView® Assessment Suite
Test Practice	SSG 145	54	ExamView® Assessment Suite
Alternative Assessment	TE 143	57	
See It, Say It, Do It, Write It	TE 124, 128, 134, 138		
Book 2 Test		82	ExamView® Assessment Suite

Back-mapping and Vertical Alignment **McGraw-Hill's** *Math Triumphs* intervention program was conceived and developed with the final result in mind: student success in grade-level mathematics, including Algebra 1 and beyond. The authors, using the **NCTM Focal Points and Focal Connections** as their guide, developed this brand-new series by back-mapping from grade-level and Algebra 1 concepts, and vertically aligning the topics so that they build upon prior skills and concepts and serve as a foundation for future topics.

	Lesson 4-1	**Lesson 4-2**	**Lesson 4-3**	**Lesson 4-4**
Concept	Count to 100	Expanded Form	Round Two-Digit Numbers	Whole Numbers Less Than 10,000
Objective	Count numbers less than 100.	Write equivalent representations of numbers.	Round two-digit numbers to the nearest ten.	Model numbers less than 10,000.
Math Vocabulary	ones standard form tens	expanded form standard form word form	number line round	place-value chart thousands
Lesson Resources	**Materials** • music player **Manipulatives** • base-ten blocks • connecting cubes • number cube • counters **Other Resources** CRM Vocabulary and English Language Development CRM Skills Practice CRM Problem-Solving Practice CRM Homework Practice	**Materials** • index cards • newspapers **Manipulatives** • base-ten blocks • connecting cubes • counters **Other Resources** CRM Vocabulary and English Language Development CRM Skills Practice CRM Problem-Solving Practice CRM Homework Practice	**Materials** • marble • number line • index cards **Manipulatives** • number cubes **Other Resources** CRM Vocabulary and English Language Development CRM Skills Practice CRM Problem-Solving Practice CRM Homework Practice	**Materials** **Manipulatives** • base-ten blocks • number cubes **Other Resources** CRM Vocabulary and English Language Development CRM Skills Practice CRM Problem-Solving Practice CRM Homework Practice
Technology	**Math Online** macmillanmh.com StudentWorks™ Plus ExamView® Assessment Suite	**Math Online** macmillanmh.com StudentWorks™ Plus ExamView® Assessment Suite	**Math Online** macmillanmh.com StudentWorks™ Plus ExamView® Assessment Suite	**Math Online** macmillanmh.com StudentWorks™ Plus ExamView® Assessment Suite

Intervention Strategy

Base-Ten Blocks

Materials: base-ten blocks, centimeter graph paper, sentence strips

Help students become familiar with the base-ten block manipulatives used throughout the chapter. (If not available, use centimeter graph paper and have students make the manipulatives.)

Step 1

Provide students with at least 10 ones cubes and 1 tens rod. Lead them to determine that 10 ones cubes equal 1 tens rod. Write the equivalency on a sentence strip. (10 ones cubes = 1 tens rod) Hang this in the classroom.

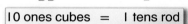

Step 2

Provide students with at least 10 tens rods and 1 hundreds flat. Have students determine how many tens rods equal one hundreds flat. Write the equivalency on a sentence strip. (10 tens rods = 1 hundreds flat) Hang this in the classroom.

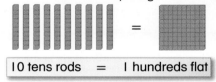

Step 3

Provide students with at least 10 hundreds flats and 1 thousands block. Have students determine how many hundreds flats equal 1 thousands block. Write the equivalency on a sentence strip. (10 hundreds flats = 1 thousands block) Hang this in the classroom.

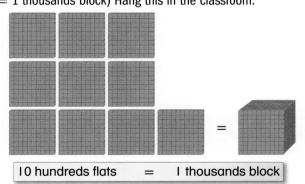

Chapter Notes

Home Connection

Read the Home Connection letter with students and have them write their names in the space below.

Read and explain the activity under Help at Home. If time allows, complete a portion of the activity so students can introduce the activity to a parent or other caregiver.

Have students:

- count the number of windows in the room, tiles on the floor, or steps to the gymnasium.
- find numbers in newspapers and magazines.
- bring examples to class.

Real-World Applications

Calendar Count   Students can count to determine how many days they have been in school. Mark X on each school day on a class calendar.

- **How can you count the number of school days using the calendar?** Count all the days marked X.

CHAPTER 4 Place Value

English

Dear Family,
Today our class started **Chapter 4, Place Value.** In this chapter, I will learn how to count and estimate numbers less than 100. I will also learn to represent numbers in standard form, word form, and expanded form. I will learn how to model numbers to show thousands, hundreds, tens, and ones.

Love, _____

Spanish

Estimada familia:
Hoy en clase comenzamos el **Capítulo 4, Valor posicional.** En este capítulo aprenderé a contar y a calcular números menores de 100. También, aprenderé a representar números en forma estándar, con palabras y en forma desarrollada. Aprenderé a usar los números para mostrar millares, centenas, decenas y unidades.

Cariños, _____

Help at Home

You can help your child learn about place value by identifying place value of digits. Look for numbers in magazines and newspapers. Ask your child how many thousands, hundreds, tens, or ones are in each number.

Ayude en casa

Usted puede ayudar a su hijo(a) a aprender sobre el valor posicional al identificar el valor posicional de los dígitos. Busquen números en revistas y periódicos. Pregunte a su hijo(a) cuántos millares, centenas, decenas y unidades hay en cada número.

Math Online > Take the chapter Get Ready quiz at macmillanmh.com.

Chapter 4   one hundred nineteen **119**

Key Vocabulary

Find interactive definitions in 13 languages in the **eGlossary** at macmillanmh.com.

English   Español *Introduce the most important vocabulary terms from Chapter 4.*

tens   decenas
a place value of a number (p. 121)

ones   unidades
a place value of a number (p. 121)

standard form   forma estándar
the usual way of writing a number that shows only its digits, no words (p. 121)

expanded form   forma desarrollada
the way of writing a number as a sum that shows the value of each digit (p. 125)

word form   escrita con palabras
the way of writing a number in words, no numbers (p. 125)

round   redondear
to find the nearest value of a number based on a given place value (p. 131)

number line   recta numéricarecta numérica
a line with number labels (p. 131)

thousands   millares
a place value of a number (p. 135)

place-value chart   tabla de valor de posición
a chart that represents the place value of digits in a number (p. 135)

Name _____

Get Ready

Write each missing number.

 1. 1, 2, 3, __4__, 5

2. 6, 7, __8__, 9, 10

Write each number shown.

3.

_____1_____

4.

_____10_____

5.

_____100_____

Write each number.

6. two
_____2_____

7. nine
_____9_____

8. four
_____4_____

Write each number name.

9. 3 __three__

10. 6 __six__

Find each sum.

11. 20 + 3 = __23__

12. 80 + 9 = __89__

13. Find each number missing from the number line.

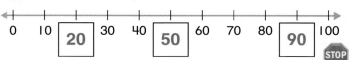

120 **one hundred twenty**

Vocabulary Preview

Make a poster to display the chapter's vocabulary words.

• List the vocabulary words in the word column.

• Ask students to give examples of any of the words they already know. Record examples in the example column.

• As you finish each lesson, revisit the vocabulary poster and have students add examples for words they have learned.

Word	Example

Get Ready

Have students complete Get Ready to assess readiness for the chapter concepts and skills. Refer to the lessons below for additional support for prerequisite skills.

1-1 Addition Facts 0 to 10 (p. 3)
1-2 Addition Facts through 18 (p. 7)
1-5 Add Two-Digit Numbers (p. 23)

You may also assess student readiness with the following resources:

Math Online Online Readiness quiz at macmillanmh.com

Assessment Masters: Chapter Pretest (p. 48)

FOLDABLES Study Organizer **Dinah Zike's Foldables®**

Guide students through the directions on p. A84 in the Chapter Resource Masters to create their own Foldable graphic organizer for use with this chapter.

Professional Development

Targeted professional development has been articulated throughout **McGraw-Hill's Math Triumphs** intervention program. **The McGraw-Hill Professional Development Video Library** provides short videos that support the **NCTM Focal Points and Focal Connections.** For more information, visit www.macmillanmh.com.

Model Lessons | Instructional Strategies

Lesson Notes

Lesson Planner

Objective   Count numbers less than 100.

Vocabulary   tens, ones, standard form

Materials/Manipulatives   base-ten blocks, connecting cubes, counters, number cube, music player

Chapter Resource Masters

- CRM Vocabulary and English Language Development (p. A88)
- CRM Skills Practice (p. A89)
- CRM Problem-Solving Practice (p. A90)
- CRM Homework Practice (p. A91)

① Introduce

Vocabulary

Compare Vocabulary   Write the following numbers on the board: 2, 4, 7, 21, 35, and 88. Discuss one- and two-digit numbers.

- **How are the numbers alike?** They are all numbers.

- **How are the numbers different?** Three numbers are one-digit numbers and three numbers are two-digit numbers.

Have students sort the numbers and add other examples to the groups.

② Teach

Key Concept

Foundational Skills and Concepts   After students have read through the Key Concept box, guide them through the following questions.

- **What digit is in the tens place in 35?** 3

- **How many tens does 35 have?** 3 tens

- **What digit is in the ones place in 35?** 5

- **How many ones does 35 have?** 5 ones

Name _____

Count to 100

Key Concept

There are 35 marbles in all.
There are 3 sets of ten marbles.
There is one set of 5 marbles.

The number 35 has the digit 3 in the **tens** place and the digit 5 in the **ones** place.

tens	ones
3	5

35   **standard form**

Vocabulary

tens   a place value of a number

ones   a place value of a number

standard form   the usual way of writing a number that shows only its digits, no words
537   89   1,642

23
This number has **2** tens and **3** ones.

The number 35 is between 34 and 36.

English Learner Strategy

Use Counters to Model Tens   Use counters to help students understand the relationship between tens and ones.

1. Review that tens are groups of 10 objects and ones are single objects.

2. Place 30 counters on a desk arranged in 3 groups of ten. Point to 1 group.

   - **How many groups of ten?** 3

   - **How many in each group?** 10

   - **How many counters in all?** 30

3. Repeat for the tens 20, 40, and 50.

Write the missing number.
61, 62, 63, _____, 65, 66,

61	62	63	64	65	66	67	68	69	70
71	72	73	74	75	76	77	78	79	80

Step 1 Begin at the first number. 61

Step 2 The ones digit goes up by 1.
61, 62, 63,

Step 3 What number is after 63? 64

Answer The missing number is 64.

Example

Write the missing number.
57, 58, 59, _____, 61, 62

51	52	53	54	55	56	57	58	59	60
61	62	63	64	65	66	67	68	69	70

Step 1   Begin at the first number. 57
Step 2   The ones digit goes up by 1.
          57, 58, 59
Step 3   What number is after 59? 60
Answer   The missing number is 60.

Step-by-Step Practice

Write the missing number.
21, 22, 23, _____, 25, 26

21	22	23	24	25	26	27	28	29	30

Step 1   Begin at the first number. **21**
Step 2   The ones digit goes up by 1.
          21, 22, 23
Step 3   What number is after 23? **24**
Answer   The missing number is **24**.

122 one hundred twenty-two

Math Coach Notes

Strategy   Encourage students to use a hundred chart throughout the lesson.

1. When finding a missing number, have students place their pencils on each number in the list as they count out loud up to the missing number.

2. Have students place their pencils on each number in the hundred chart as they count out loud to find the missing number.

3. After students write the missing number, have them check that their answer matches the number in the chart.

Intervention Strategy   Auditory Learners

Materials: connecting cubes, music player

Give each pair or small group of students 100 connecting cubes. Tell students they will make groups of ten connecting cubes until the music stops playing.

Play music as students make groups of ten connecting cubes. When the music stops ask:

- **How many groups of ten did you make?** Sample answer: 6 groups

- **What number did you make?** Sample answer: 60

Have students pick up a handful (less than 10) of connecting cubes. Have them add these to the tens and determine the number they have now. Sample answer: 64

Repeat the activity.

Guided Practice

Direct students to complete Exercises 1–4 in Guided Practice.

Exercises 1–3 Remind students to look closely at the lists of numbers. Students should count by ones to determine the missing numbers.

Problem-Solving Practice

Guide students through the four-step problem-solving plan to complete Exercise 5.

- **What are the key words?** just after 65, just before 67
- **What numbers come after 60?** 61, 62, 63, 64, 65, 66, 67

Ask students to check their work using the strategy suggested in the Check step. Students can count back from 70 to solve the problem.

Using Manipulatives

Pattern Blocks Students can model numbers with pattern blocks. For example, they can represent tens with squares and ones with triangles.

Money Use dimes and pennies to represent tens and ones.

 23

Base-ten Blocks Use base-ten blocks to represent numbers. Demonstrate how tens rods represent the tens place and unit cubes represent the ones place.

32

On-Hand Manipulatives Use beans, buttons, crayons, or other common objects to model numbers.

Graph Paper Use inch graph paper. Cut out strips of 10 squares to make tens rods and single squares to make ones cubes to model numbers.

Name _____

▶ Guided Practice

Write each missing number.

1.

71	72	73	74	**75**	76	77	78	79	80

2. 84, 85, 86, _87_, 88   3. _94_, 95, 96, 97, 98

4. Match each number with the correct place values.

75   43   21   15

| 7 tens 5 ones | 2 tens 1 one | 1 ten 5 ones | 4 tens 3 ones |

Problem-Solving Practice

5. The mystery number comes <u>just after 65</u> and <u>just before 67</u>. What is the mystery number?

Understand Underline key words.

Plan Count by ones.

Solve Start at 60 and count on by ones.

_60_, _61_, _62_, _63_, _64_, _65_, _66_, _67_

The mystery number is _66_.

Check Count back from 70. Is your answer the same?

GO on

Chapter 4 Lesson 1   one hundred twenty-three **123**

Are They Getting It? ❓

Check students' understanding of counting numbers to 100 by writing these exercises on the board. Ask students to point out the correct and incorrect statements and explain their reasoning.

1. 84, 85, 86, _____, 88, 89
   87 is the missing number. This is correct.

2. The number 75 has 5 tens. This is incorrect. 75 has 7 tens.

3. _____, 25, 26, 27, 28
   24 is the missing number. This is correct.

4. The number 89 has 9 tens and 8 ones. This is incorrect. 89 has 8 tens and 9 ones.

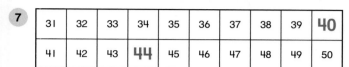

Practice on Your Own

Write each missing number.

6

| 51 | 52 | 53 | 54 | 55 | **56** | 57 | 58 | 59 | 60 |

7

| 31 | 32 | 33 | 34 | 35 | 36 | 37 | 38 | 39 | **40** |
| 41 | 42 | 43 | **44** | 45 | 46 | 47 | 48 | 49 | 50 |

8 _18_, 19, 20, 21, 22

9 77, 78, _79_, 80, 81

10 66, 67, 68, 69, _70_

11 91, 92, _93_, 94, 95

Complete each place value.

12 37 = _3_ tens _7_ ones

13 48 = _4_ tens _8_ ones

14 16 = _1_ ten _6_ ones

15 91 = _9_ tens _1_ one

16 **WRITING IN ▸MATH** Emilio says his house number has 3 tens and 8 ones. Is Emilio correct? Explain.

No, Emilio is not correct.
His house number has 8 tens
and 3 ones.

Vocabulary Check Complete.

17 The number 70 has 7 _tens_ .

STOP

124 one hundred twenty-four

Copyright © Macmillan/McGraw-Hill • Glencoe, a division of The McGraw-Hill Companies, Inc.

Math Challenge

Build a Number

Materials: base-ten blocks, number cube

Have students work with a partner. Student 1 rolls a number cube and takes that many tens rods. Student 2 rolls the number cube and takes that many ones cubes. The students place their tens rods and ones cubes together.

- **How many tens do you have?** Sample answer: 4
- **How many ones do you have?** Sample answer: 2
- **What number did you make?** Sample answer: 42
- **What number comes next?** Sample answer: 43

Have students switch roles and repeat the activity.

Practice on Your Own

Direct students to p. 124 in their student books. Have students complete Exercises 6–17 independently. You may need to review the directions of each section before students begin.

(4) Assess

See It, Do It, Say It, Write It

Step 1 Write the number 96 on the board. Identify the tens and ones.

Step 2 Have students write the number 96. They should circle the tens, underline the ones, then model the number using base-ten blocks.

Step 3 Have students explain to a partner how they modeled the number and what number comes next.

Step 4 Students should write a different number on their paper, draw a model of the number, then write the number that comes next.

Looking Ahead: Pre-teach

In the next lesson, students will learn how to write equivalent representations of numbers.

Example

The number 23 can be written in expanded form or word form: 20 + 3 or twenty-three.

Have students write each number in expanded form and word form.

1. 45 40 + 5; forty-five

2. 39 30 + 9; thirty-nine

3. 70 70 + 0; seventy

Lesson 4-1 Count to 100 **124**

Lesson Notes

Lesson Planner

Objective Write equivalent representations of numbers.

Vocabulary standard form, expanded form, word form

Materials/Manipulatives base-ten blocks, connecting cubes, index cards, newspapers, counters

Chapter Resource Masters

- **CRM** Vocabulary and English Language Development (p. A92)
- **CRM** Skills Practice (p. A93)
- **CRM** Problem-Solving Practice (p. A94)
- **CRM** Homework Practice (p. A95)

① Introduce

Vocabulary

Vocabulary Match Write the following on the board:

```
87          70 + 8
36          sixty-three
78          80 + 7
63          thirty-six
```

Have students match the number on the left with the equivalent form on the right. Discuss the similarities and differences among the numbers.

② Teach

Key Concept

Foundational Skills and Concepts After students have read through the Key Concept box, guide them through the following questions.

- **How many tens rods and ones cubes show 25?**
  2 tens rods and 5 ones cubes

- **How is 25 written in expanded form and word form?** 20 + 5 and twenty-five

---

Expanded Form

Key Concept

Numbers can be written in different forms.

20 + 5 = 25

The picture shows 2 tens rods and 5 ones cubes. The picture shows 25 blocks in all.

standard form	25
expanded form	20 + 5
word form	twenty-five

Vocabulary

standard form the usual way of writing a number that shows only its digits, no words

expanded form the way of writing a number as a sum that shows the value of each digit

word form the way of writing a number in words, no numbers

Use a hyphen to separate two or more tens from the ones. twenty-one

Use an addition sign to show the tens plus the ones. 21 = 20 + 1

> I use a hyphen in the word form of a number. I use an addition sign in the expanded form of a number.

Chapter 4 Lesson 2

one hundred twenty-five **125**

English Learner Strategy

Understanding Terms Students will benefit from exploring the terms standard and expanded. These terms may be unfamiliar to students but they can be explained using synonyms.

Explain that standard means normal or typical and expanded means to stretch out or make longer.

Draw the table and have students offer other synonyms.

Term	Synonyms
standard	normal, typical, regular, usual, ordinary
expanded	stretched, longer, bigger

Example

Complete the table.

Step 1   How many tens? 3
What is the value of the tens? 30

Step 2   How many ones? 7
What is the value of the ones? 7

Step 3   Write the values as a sum. 30 + 7

Step 4   Write the number and number name of the values. 37, thirty-seven

standard form	37
expanded form	30 + 7
word form	thirty-seven

Step-by-Step Practice

Complete the table.

Step 1   How many tens? __5__
What is the value of the tens? __50__

Step 2   How many ones? __8__
What is the value of the ones? __8__

Step 3   Write the values as a sum. __50 + 8__

Step 4   Write the number and number name of the values. __58__, __fifty-eight__

standard form	**58**
expanded form	**50 + 8**
word form	**fifty-eight**

126   one hundred twenty-six

Intervention Strategy

Linguistic/Kinesthetic Learners

Materials: newspapers, magazines, other printed material

Have students collect numbers between 1 and 100 from newspapers, magazines, or other printed material.

Have students tape the numbers on a sheet of paper and write the numbers in equivalent forms.

Example: ninety-three
Equivalent forms: 90 + 3; 93

Additional *Example*

Complete the table.

Step 1   How many tens? 4
What is the value of the tens? 40

Step 2   How many ones? 6
What is the value of the ones? 6

Step 3   Write the values as a sum. 40 + 6

Step 4   Write the number and number name of the values. 46, forty-six

standard form	46
expanded form	40 + 6
word form	forty-six

⚠ Common Error *Alert*

Students might write the tens digit rather than the value of the tens when writing a number in expanded form. Review skip counting by 10s to help students understand the value of the tens. Write the number 74 on the board.

- **How many tens?** 7
- **Skip count by 10s 7 times.**
  10, 20, 30, 40, 50, 60, 70
- **What is the value of the tens?** 70
- **What is 74 written in expanded form?** 70 + 4

Math Coach Notes

Study Skills   Encourage students to reference the table in the Key Concept box throughout the lesson. The table models each equivalent representation of a number.

Guided Practice

Direct students to complete Exercises 1–2 in Guided Practice.

Exercises 1–2 Students can use a place-value chart if necessary.

Problem-Solving Practice

Guide students through the four-step problem-solving plan to complete Exercise 3.

- **What are the key words?** greater than 50, less than 60, 5 tens, 4 ones

Remind students that working backward means to start with the last information given.

Ask students to check their work using the strategy suggested in the Check step. Students can use base-ten blocks to solve the problem.

Using Manipulatives

Base-Ten Blocks   Students can model two-digit numbers using base-ten blocks.

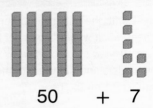

$$50 \quad + \quad 7$$

Connecting Cubes   Make trains of ten connecting cubes to model the tens and ones cubes to model the ones.

On-Hand Manipulatives   Use beans, buttons, crayons, or other common objects to model numbers.

Graph Paper   Use inch graph paper. Cut out strips of 10 squares to make tens rods and single squares to make ones cubes to model numbers.

Name _____

▶ **Guided Practice**

Complete each table.

1

standard form	17
expanded form	10 + 7
word form	seventeen

2

standard form	62
expanded form	60 + 2
word form	sixty-two

Problem-Solving Practice

3   I am greater than 50, but less than 60.
I have 5 tens and 4 ones. What number am I?

Understand   Underline key words.

Plan   Work backward.

Solve   5 tens = __50__

4 ones = __4__

__50__ + __4__ = 54

The number is __54__.

Check   Use place-value blocks to check your answer.

GO on

Are They Getting It?

Check students' understanding of representing numbers in equivalent form by writing these statements on the board. Ask students to point out the correct and incorrect statements and explain their reasoning.

1. Sixty-one in standard form is 60 + 1. This is incorrect. The standard form of sixty-one is 61.

2. In expanded form, 13 is 10 + 3. This is correct.

3. 7 groups of ten and 8 ones is the standard form of 87. This is incorrect. 7 groups of ten and 8 ones is 78.

4. Fifty-six is equivalent to 65. This is incorrect. Fifty-six is equivalent to 56 or 50 + 6.

 **Practice on Your Own**

Write each number in expanded form.

4 74 = __70__ + __4__

5 53 = __50__ + __3__

Complete each table.

6

standard form	92
expanded form	90 + 2
word form	ninety-two

7

standard form	43
expanded form	40 + 3
word form	forty-three

8

standard form	21
expanded form	20 + 1
word form	twenty-one

9

standard form	69
expanded form	60 + 9
word form	sixty-nine

10 **WRITING IN ▶MATH** Marcos wants to write 99 in expanded form. He writes 9 + 9. Is Marcos correct? Explain.

__No, 9 + 9 does not equal 99. The number 99 in expanded form is 90 + 9.__

Vocabulary Check Complete.

11 The __expanded__ form of 38 is 30 + 8.

STOP

128 one hundred twenty-eight

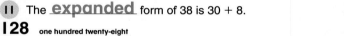

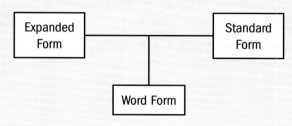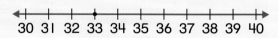

Math Challenge

Concentration

Materials: index cards

Students work in groups of 3 or 4. Assign each student a two-digit number. Give each student four index cards. Have students represent their number in four equivalent forms, one per index card: model using base-ten blocks, word form, standard form, and expanded form.

Have students shuffle the cards and arrange them in an array. Students take turns turning over two cards trying to make a match. A match is any two cards that represent the same number. The student with the most matches at the end of the game wins.

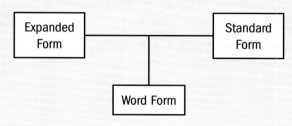

Practice on Your Own

Direct students to p. 128 in their student books. Have students complete Exercises 4–11 independently. You may need to review the directions of each section before students begin.

4 **Assess**

See It, Do It, Say It, Write It

Step 1 Draw a word web outline on the board. Model the number 99 with base-ten blocks.

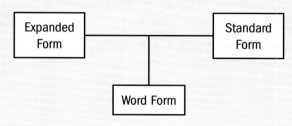

Step 2 Ask student volunteers to write the number in the three equivalent forms.

Step 3 Have students explain how to write the number in the three equivalent forms.

Step 4 Have students choose their own number to model with base-ten blocks and complete in word web. Make sure students write the number in three forms.

Looking Ahead: Pre-teach

In the next lesson, students will learn how to round two-digit numbers to the nearest ten.

Example

Round 33 to the nearest ten. Use a number line.

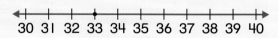

33 is closer to 30. It rounds down to 30.

Have students use a number line to round each number to the nearest ten.

1. 47 50   **2.** 71 70   **3.** 14 10

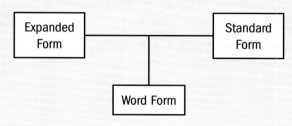

Chapter 4

Progress Check 1

Formative Assessment

Use the Progress Check to assess students' mastery of the previous lessons. Have students review the lesson indicated for the problems they answered incorrectly.

⚠ **Common Error** *Alert*

Place-Value Chart Remind students that the tens place is on the left and the ones place is on the right in a place-value chart.

Exercises 3 and 4 If students have trouble writing the number in expanded form, have them use base-ten blocks to model the numbers.

Name _____

Progress Check 1 (Lessons 4-1 and 4-2)

Write each missing number.

1

| 31 | 32 | 33 | 34 | **35** | 36 | 37 | 38 | 39 | 40 |

2

| 41 | 42 | **43** | 44 | 45 | 46 | 47 | 48 | 49 | 50 |

Complete each table.

3

standard form	**67**
expanded form	**60 + 7**
word form	sixty-seven

4

standard form	**91**
expanded form	90 + 1
word form	**ninety-one**

Write each number in standard form.

5 twenty-one ___**21**___   **6** sixty-eight ___**68**___

Write each number in word form.

7 75 ___**seventy-five**___   **8** 86 ___**eighty-six**___

9 I am a number greater than 30 but less than 40. I have 3 tens and 8 ones. What number am I? How do you know?

___**The number is 38. Thirty-eight has 3 tens and 8 ones.**___

Chapter 4 Progress Check   one hundred twenty-nine **129**

Data-Driven Decision Making

Students missing Exercises . . .	Have trouble with . . .	Should review and practice . . .
1–2	counting numbers less than 100.	SSG Lesson 4-1, p. 121 CRM Skills Practice, p. A89
3–8	writing equivalent representations of numbers.	SSG Lesson 4-2, p. 125 CRM Skills Practice, p. A93
9	problem-solving that involves counting numbers less than 100.	SSG Lesson 4-1, p. 124 CRM Problem-Solving Practice, p. A90

Name _____

What comes after A?

Connect the dots from 50 to 100 to find the answer.

130 one hundred thirty

Replay

Replay

Use the Replay activity to review and reinforce the concepts and skills presented in Lessons 4-1 and 4-2.

Instructions

Have students read the directions at the top of the student page.

Student Technology

Students can use the following technology resources to reinforce chapter content.

- 💿 StudentWorks™ Plus
- Math Online > macmillanmh.com
- eGlossary

Lesson Planner

Objective   Round two-digit numbers to the nearest ten.

Vocabulary   round, **number line**

Materials/Manipulatives   marble, number line, index cards, number cubes

Chapter Resource Masters

- [CRM] Vocabulary and English Language Development (p. A96)
- [CRM] Skills Practice (p. A97)
- [CRM] Problem-Solving Practice (p. A98)
- [CRM] Homework Practice (p. A99)

 **Introduce**

Vocabulary

Vocabulary Interactions   Draw a large number line from 0 to 40 on the board. Mark and label only the tick marks at 0, 10, 20, 30, and 40. Call out a number. Ask a student to come to the board and identify where the number would go on the number line. Have students explain their reasoning.

 **Teach**

Key Concept

Foundational Skills and Concepts   After students have read through the Key Concept box, guide them through the following questions.

- **What numbers are shown on the number line?**
  20 to 30

- **Is 28 closer to 20 or 30?**   30

- **Should 28 be rounded down to 20 or up to 30?**
  up to 30

Round Two-Digit Numbers

Key Concept

You can **round** numbers to the nearest ten.
Look at 28 on the **number line**.

28 is between 20 and 30.
Is 28 closer to 20 or 30?

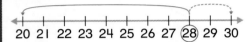

28 is 8 away from 20.
28 is 2 away from 30.
28 is closer to 30, so it rounds up to 30.

Vocabulary

round   to find the nearest value of a number based on a given place value
24 rounded to the nearest ten is 20.

number line   a line with number labels

> When a number has a 5 in the ones place, it rounds up. 25 rounds up to 30.

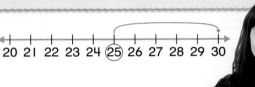

Copyright © Macmillan/McGraw-Hill, • Glencoe, a division of The McGraw-Hill Companies, Inc.

Chapter 4   Lesson 3   one hundred thirty-one   **131**

English Learner Strategy

Nearest, Closer, and Farthest   Help students understand the relationship between numbers on a number line.

1. Have 5 students stand in a line facing the door of the classroom.

2. Assign the students numbers 1–5, Student 1 being nearest to the door and Student 5 being farthest from the door.

   - **Is Student 2 closer to the door or the back of the line? Why?**   Sample answer: Student 2 is closer to the door because they are second in line.

   - **Which student is farthest from the door?**   Sample answer: Student 5 is farthest from the door because they are last in line.

3. Have students switch positions and renumber. Have students identify their positions using the items nearest, closer, or farther.

Example

There are 34 soup cans on a shelf. About how many soup cans are on the shelf? Round to the nearest ten.

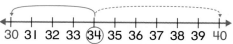

Step 1   34 is between 30 and 40. Circle 34.
Step 2   The nearest ten to the left of 34 is 30.
Step 3   The nearest ten to the right of 34 is 40.
Step 4   34 is closer to 30.

Answer   There are about 30 soup cans on the shelf.

Step-by-Step Practice

Mary bakes 67 cookies for a bake sale. About how many cookies does Mary bake? Round to the nearest ten.

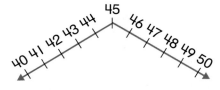

Step 1   67 is between __60__ and __70__. Circle 67.
Step 2   The nearest ten to the left of 67 is __60__.
Step 3   The nearest ten to the right of 67 is __70__.
Step 4   67 is closer to __70__.

Answer   Mary bakes about __70__ cookies.

132 one hundred thirty-two

Additional *Example*

There are 48 flowers in a garden. About how many flowers are in the garden? Round to the nearest ten.

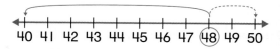

Step 1 48 is between 40 and 50. Circle 48.

Step 2 The nearest ten to the left of 48 is 40.

Step 3 The nearest ten to the right of 48 is 50.

Step 4 48 is closer to 50.

Answer There are about 50 flowers in the garden.

Math Coach Notes

Strategy Be certain students understand that rounding always involves a given place value. In this lesson, students round to the nearest ten.

1. Point out to students that the number line in the Example shows the ten less than 34 (30) and the ten greater than 34 (40). Looking at the number line, students can see which ten is closer.

2. If students have difficulty rounding when a number line is not provided in the problem, give them a blank number line to label with numbers from the problem.

3. The word *about* is a cue for students to use or find estimates. Emphasize the use of *about* while completing this lesson with students.

Intervention Strategy   Visual/Tactile Learners

Materials: index card and marble

The Marble Test   Have students create a folded number line on an index card and label with the numbers 40 to 50 (45 should be written on the peak).

45
40 41 42 43 44   46 47 48 49 50

The peak of the number line shows the number that is half way between 40 and 50. Have students place a marble on different numbers, and decide which way the marble will roll. Tell students that if the marble is on the peak number, it will always roll towards the greater ten.

Guided Practice

Direct students to complete Exercises 1–2 in Guided Practice.

Exercises 1–2 Remind students to examine the number line, fill in the tens at the ends of the number line, and then round the number.

Problem-Solving Practice

Guide students through the four-step problem-solving plan to complete Exercise 3.

- **What are the key words?** about 70, rounds, nearest ten, 62, 64, or 66

Ask students to check their work using the strategy suggested in the Check step. Students can use a number line labeled from 60 to 70 to solve the problem.

Using Manipulatives

Number Line and Connecting Cubes Give students a number line from 40 to 50. Have students circle the number they are to round. Have students connect red cubes from 40 up to the number to be rounded. Have students connect blue cubes from the number up to 50. Students count the cubes to determine which set of cubes is shorter, then round to the ten that is the shorter distance.

On-Hand Manipulatives Repeat the activity above, using different colored beans or buttons.

Name _____

▶ Guided Practice

Use the number line to round each number.

1 73 rounds to **70**

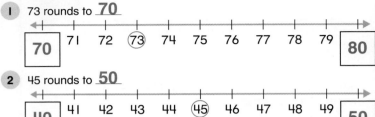

| 70 | 71 72 (73) 74 75 76 77 78 79 | 80 |

2 45 rounds to **50**

| 40 | 41 42 43 44 (45) 46 47 48 49 | 50 |

Problem-Solving Practice

3 Simon has <u>about 70</u> baseball cards when he <u>rounds</u> to the <u>nearest ten</u>. Could Simon have <u>62, 64, or 66</u> baseball cards?

Understand Underline key words.

Plan Count backward.

Solve 70, 69, 68, **67**, **66**, **65**, **64**, **63**, **62**, **61**, **60**

66 is closest to 70. It rounds to 70.

Simon could have **66** baseball cards.

Check Use a number line.

 GO on

Chapter 4   Lesson 3   one hundred thirty-three **133**

Are They Getting It? ▸?

Check students' understanding of rounding two-digit numbers to the nearest ten by writing these statements on the board. Ask students to point out correct and incorrect statements and explain their reasoning.

Draw a number line from 60 to 70 on the board.

1. 63 rounded to the nearest ten is 70. This is incorrect. 63 rounds to 60.

2. 68 rounded to the nearest ten is 70. This is correct.

3. 65 rounded to the nearest ten is 70. This is correct.

4. Tina has 28 pairs of earrings. Tina has about 20 pairs of earrings. This is incorrect. She has about 30 pairs of earrings.

▶ **Practice on Your Own**

Use the number line to round each number.

4 32 rounds to __30__

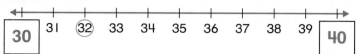

30 | 31 | ③② | 33 | 34 | 35 | 36 | 37 | 38 | 39 | 40

5 56 rounds to __60__

50 | 51 | 52 | 53 | 54 | 55 | ⑤⑥ | 57 | 58 | 59 | 60

Fill in the blanks.

6 23 is between __20__ and __30__. 23 rounds to __20__.

7 62 is between __60__ and __70__. 62 rounds to __60__.

8 ▸**WRITING IN** ▸**MATH** Halima has about 90 photos when she rounds to the nearest ten. Could Halima have 81, 84, or 88 photos? Explain.

Halima could have 88 photos. 81 and 84 round to 80. 88 rounds to 90.

Vocabulary Check   Complete.

9 When you __round__ a number, you find the nearest value of the number based on a given place value.

 STOP

134   one hundred thirty-four

Math Challenge

Rolling and Rounding

Materials: 2 number cubes

Students work in pairs. Provide each pair of students with two number cubes. Draw the table on the board for students to copy.

Number	Rounds to . . .

One partner rolls the number cubes to make a number. For example: 63 or 36. Partners write the number in the table and round to the nearest ten. Partners switch roles and repeat the activity.

Practice on Your Own

Direct students to p. 134 in their student books. Have students complete Exercises 4–9 independently. You may need to review the directions of each section before students begin.

④ Assess

See It, Do It, Say It, Write It

Step 1 Have students open their math books to page 58.

Step 2 Have students count out loud the pages back to 50, and then forward to 60.
57, 56, 55, 54, 53, 52, 51, 50, 59, 60

Step 3 Ask students if the page is closer to page 50 or 60. page 60

Step 4 Have students write how to round the number 55 to the nearest ten.

Looking Ahead: Pre-teach

In the next lesson, students will learn how to model numbers less than 10,000.

Example

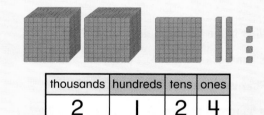

thousands	hundreds	tens	ones
2	1	2	4

Have students write the number.

1.

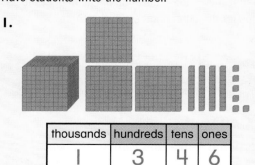

thousands	hundreds	tens	ones
1	3	4	6

Lesson Notes

Lesson Planner

Objective   Model numbers less than 10,000.

Vocabulary   thousands, place-value chart

Materials/Manipulatives   base-ten blocks, place-value charts, number cubes

Chapter Resource Masters

CRM Vocabulary and English Language Development (p. A100)

CRM Skills Practice (p. A101)

CRM Problem-Solving Practice (p. A102)

CRM Homework Practice (p. A103)

 **Introduce**

Vocabulary

Nonexamples   Display a place-value chart with ones, tens, hundreds, and thousands. Remind students that place value is the value given to a digit by its place in a number. Write the following numbers in the chart: 784, 3,204, 605, 1,008.

- **What is the hundreds digit in 784?** 7

- **Is hundreds the greatest place value in 784?** yes

- **What is the hundreds digit in 3,204?** 2

- **Is hundreds the greatest place value in 3,204?**
  No, thousands is the greatest place value.

Explain that 3 is in the thousands place. Repeat the questions for the other numbers in the chart.

 **Teach**

Key Concept

Foundational Skills and Concepts   After students have read through the Key Concept box, guide them through the following questions.

- **What is the value of 1 thousands block?** 1,000

- **What is the value of 2 thousands blocks?** 2,000

135 Chapter 4 Place Value

Name _____

Whole Numbers Less Than 10,000

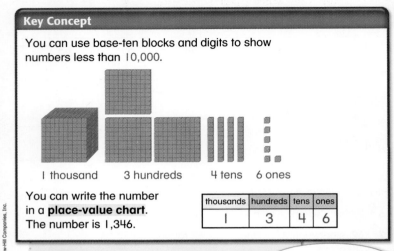

Key Concept

You can use base-ten blocks and digits to show numbers less than 10,000.

| 1 thousand | 3 hundreds | 4 tens | 6 ones |

You can write the number in a **place-value chart**. The number is 1,346.

thousands	hundreds	tens	ones
1	3	4	6

Vocabulary

thousands   a place value of a number

1,253

The 1 is in the thousands place.
place-value chart   a chart that represents the place value of digits in a number

thousands	hundreds	tens	ones
1	2	5	3

You separate the thousands digit and hundreds digit with a comma.

Chapter 4   Lesson 4   one hundred thirty-five **135**

English Learner Strategy

Model Hundreds and Thousands   Use base-ten blocks to practice counting by 100s and 1,000s.

1. Give a hundreds flat to three students. Have the students line up in front of the class.

2. Have the class count out loud by 100s to find the total value.
   100, 200, 300

3. Repeat the activity with other students and differing amounts of hundreds blocks until students are comfortable counting by 100s.

4. Repeat the activity with thousands blocks.

Example

Write the number.

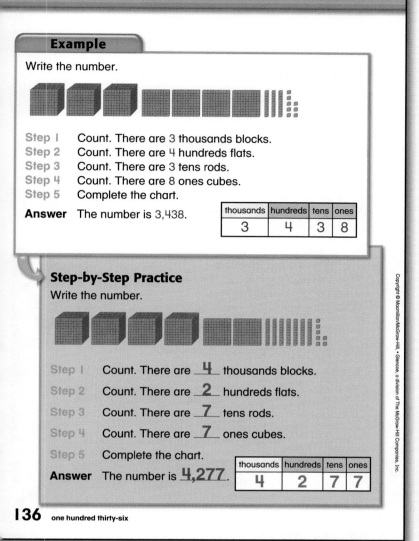

Step 1   Count. There are 3 thousands blocks.
Step 2   Count. There are 4 hundreds flats.
Step 3   Count. There are 3 tens rods.
Step 4   Count. There are 8 ones cubes.
Step 5   Complete the chart.

Answer   The number is 3,438.

thousands	hundreds	tens	ones
3	4	3	8

Step-by-Step Practice

Write the number.

Step 1   Count. There are _4_ thousands blocks.
Step 2   Count. There are _2_ hundreds flats.
Step 3   Count. There are _7_ tens rods.
Step 4   Count. There are _7_ ones cubes.
Step 5   Complete the chart.

Answer   The number is _4,277_.

thousands	hundreds	tens	ones
4	2	7	7

136   one hundred thirty-six

Write the number.

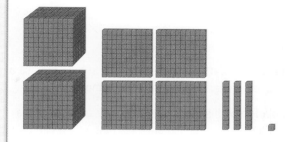

Step 1 Count. There are 2 thousands blocks.

Step 2 Count. There are 4 hundreds flats.

Step 3 Count. There are 3 tens rods.

Step 4 Count. There is 1 ones cube.

Step 5 Complete the chart.

thousands	hundreds	tens	ones
2	4	3	1

Answer The number is 2,431.

Math Coach Notes

Strategy   To help students correctly place commas in four-digit numbers, write a four-digit number on the board without a comma. For example: 4603. Ask students to clap three times as you point to the ones, tens, and hundreds places. After three claps, write the comma in the number: 4,603.

Repeat for other numbers: clap three times and write the comma.

Intervention Strategy

Kinesthetic/Visual Learners

Materials: base-ten blocks, place-value chart

Modeling a Number   Write the number 1,286 in a place-value chart. Have students model the number with base-ten blocks.

Write the number 1,826 in a place-value chart. Have students model the number with base-ten blocks.

• **How are the models alike?** Both have 1 thousands block and 6 ones cubes.

• **How are the models different?** One number has 2 hundreds flats and 8 tens rods. The other number has 8 hundreds flats and 2 tens rods.

Emphasize the direct connection between the digits in the numbers and how many blocks, flats, rods, and cubes are used in the models.

Guided Practice

Direct students to complete Exercise 1–2 in Guided Practice.

Exercises 1–2 Remind students that they can use a place-value chart to help write the number.

Exercise 1 Instruct students to look carefully at the base-ten blocks. Remind students that if there are no blocks representing a certain place value, they need to use a zero as a place holder.

Problem-Solving Practice

Guide students through the four-step problem-solving plan to complete Exercise 3.

- **What are the key words?** 8 thousands, 6 hundreds, 5 tens, and 1 one, what is the number

Ask students to check their work using the strategy suggested in the Check step. Students can model the number using base-ten blocks to solve the problem.

Using Manipulatives

Base-ten Blocks Use base-ten blocks to model numbers that include the digit 0.

 On-Hand Manipulatives Use play money to model numbers. Be sure the money includes 1, 10, 100, and 1,000 dollar bills.

Grid Paper Cut a sheet of grid paper into different sizes to represent different place values.

One entire sheet can represent a thousands block.
A 10 by 10 square can represent a hundreds flat.
A 10 by 1 strip can represent a tens rod.
Individual squares can represent ones cubes.

Name _____

▶ Guided Practice

Write each number.

1. __6,206__

2. A number has 5 thousands, 2 tens, and 8 ones.
   What is the number? __5,028__

Problem-Solving Practice

3. Theo rides the bus to school.
   The number of the bus he rides has
   8 thousands, 6 hundreds, 5 tens, and 1 one.
   What is the number of Theo's bus?

Understand   Underline key words.

Plan   Use a place-value chart.

Solve   Write each clue in the place-value chart.

thousands	hundreds	tens	ones
8	6	5	1

The number of Theo's bus is __8,651__.

Check   Use base-ten blocks to model the number.

GO on

Copyright © Macmillan/McGraw-Hill • Glencoe, a division of The McGraw-Hill Companies, Inc.

Are They Getting It? ?

Check students' understanding of modeling numbers less than 10,000 by writing these exercises on the board. Ask students to point out the correct and incorrect answers and explain their reasoning.

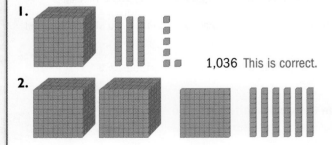

1.   1,036 This is correct.

2.   2,016 This is incorrect. The number modeled is 2,160. There is 1 hundreds flat and 0 ones cubes.

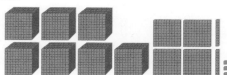

4 Write the number.

__7,423__

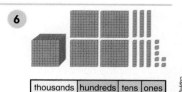

5 A number has 9 thousands, 4 hundreds, 5 tens, and 1 one. What is the number?

thousands	hundreds	tens	ones
9	4	5	1

6

thousands	hundreds	tens	ones
1	4	6	7

7 **WRITING IN ▶MATH** How many tens are in 4,307? Explain.

__There are 0 tens in 4,307 because there is a 0 in the tens place.__

Vocabulary Check Complete.

8 In 3,867, the digit 3 is in the __thousands__ place.

STOP

138 one hundred thirty-eight

Practice on Your Own

Direct students to p. 138 in their student books. Have students complete Exercises 4–8 independently. You may need to review the directions of each section before students begin.

④ Assess

See It, Do It, Say It, Write It

Step 1 Model the number 5,067 by displaying the following.

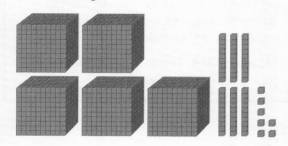

Step 2 Have students determine the value of the model. Write the number 5,067 in a place-value chart.

Step 3 Have students say the value of the model out loud.

Step 4 Have students write the number modeled below in a place-value chart and explain in writing how they found its value.

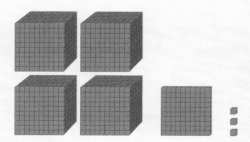

Math Challenge

Materials: 4 number cubes

Greatest Number Place students in groups of four, and give each group 4 number cubes. Have each student draw 4 lines on a piece of paper. They should place a comma between the first two lines.

____ , ____ ____ ____

• Students take turns rolling the 4 number cubes and creating the greatest number possible.

• After each student has rolled the cubes and created a number, the student with the greatest number gets a point.

• The first student with 5 points wins.

Variation: Have students make the least number.

Progress Check 2

Formative Assessment

Use the Progress Check to assess students' mastery of the previous lessons. Have students review the lesson indicated for the problems they answered incorrectly.

⚠️ **Common Error** *Alert*

Place-Value Chart   Review the place-value chart with the students. Be sure students can identify the thousands, hundreds, tens, and ones places within a given number.

Exercises 4–5   Remind students that they will need to use a 0 as a place holder.

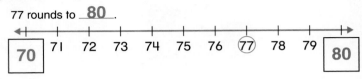

Name _____

Progress Check 2 (Lessons 4-3 and 4-4)

1   Use the number line to round the number.

77 rounds to __80__.

Fill in the blanks.

2   81 is between __80__ and __90__. 81 rounds to __80__.

3   95 is between __90__ and __100__. 95 rounds to __100__.

4   Write the number.

__5,096__

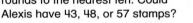

5   Complete the place-value chart. A number has 8 thousands, 7 hundreds, and 3 ones. What is the number?

thousands	hundreds	tens	ones
8	7	0	3

6   Alexis has about 50 stamps when she rounds to the nearest ten. Could Alexis have 43, 48, or 57 stamps?

Alexis could have __48__ stamps.

Copyright © Macmillan/McGraw-Hill, • Glencoe, a division of The McGraw-Hill Companies, Inc.

Data-Driven Decision Making

Students missing Exercises . . .	Have trouble with . . .	Should review and practice . . .
1–3	rounding two-digit numbers to the nearest ten.	**SSG** Lesson 4-3, p. 131 **CRM** Skills Practice, p. A97
4, 5	representing numbers less than 10,000.	**SSG** Lesson 4-4, p. 135 **CRM** Skills Practice, p. A101
6	problem-solving that involves rounding two-digit numbers to the nearest ten.	**SSG** Lesson 4-3, p. 133 **CRM** Problem-Solving Practice, p. A98

Name _____

«« Replay **Ready to Round Game**

How to Play

1 Players 1 and 2 take turns rolling the number cubes to make a two-digit number.

2 Round each number to the nearest ten. Record the answers on the score card.

3 Circle the greater rounded number. The player with the greater rounded number earns one point. The first player to earn three points wins!

Materials
score card
number cube 1– 6
blank number cube
(label sides 4 – 9)

Ready to Round Game	Player 1		Player 2	
	number	Round to the Nearest 10	number	Round to the Nearest 10
Roll 1				
Roll 2				
Roll 3				
Roll 4				
Roll 5				
Score				

I rolled the numbers 4 and 8. I can make the number 84, which rounds to 80.

140 one hundred forty

Replay

Use the Replay activity to review and reinforce the concepts and skills presented in Lessons 4-3 and 4-4.

Instructions

Have students read the directions on the student page.

Make sure students follow the directions in the correct order.

Students should independently notice that different two-digit numbers can often be created. If a student rolls a 4 and 8, they could create the number 48 or 84. Since they earn a point for the greater estimate, the student should use the two-digit number 84.

Student Technology

Students can use the following technology resources to reinforce chapter content.

- StudentWorks™ Plus
- Math Online macmillanmh.com
- eGlossary

Chapter 4 Review

Vocabulary

If students have difficulty answering Exercises 1–4, use the page references below to review the vocabulary words, or refer them to the glossary.

expanded form (p. 125)
round (p. 131)
standard form (p. 121)
word form (p. 125)

Vocabulary Review Strategies

Game Time Have students work in pairs or small groups and quiz each other, using the Vocabulary portion of the Practice on Your Own pages. For example, one student may say: "In the number 83, there are 8 of these." The other student would answer: "tens."

Concepts

The exercises in this section are grouped to cover content from each lesson in the chapter.

Exercises 5–6 : Lesson 4-1 (p. 121)
Exercises 7–13: Lesson 4-2 (p. 125)
Exercises 14–16: Lesson 4-3 (p. 131)
Exercises 17–18: Lesson 4-4 (p. 135)
Exercise 19: Lesson 4-3 (p. 131)

Find **Extra Practice** for these concepts in the Practice Worksheets, pp. A88–A103.

Name _____

Review

Vocabulary

Word Bank	Use the Word Bank to complete.
expanded form	1 eighty-two __word form__
round	2 67 __standard form__
standard form	3 26 → 30 __round__
word form	4 40 + 5 __expanded form__

▶ Concepts

Write each missing number.

5

71	72	73	74	75	76	**77**	78	79	80

6

81	82	83	84	85	86	87	88	**89**	90

Complete each table.

7

standard form	68
expanded form	**60 + 8**
word form	**sixty-eight**

8

standard form	**35**
expanded form	30 + 5
word form	**thirty-five**

GO on

Write each number in standard form.

9 seventy-three __73__

10 twenty-nine __29__

11 forty-eighty __48__

Write each number in expanded form.

12 75 __70 + 5__

13 86 __80 + 6__

Fill in the blanks.

14 67 is between __60__ and __70__. 67 rounds to __70__.

15 75 is between __70__ and __80__. 75 rounds to __80__.

16 I am a number greater than 70 but less than 80.
I have 7 tens and 3 ones. What number am I? __73__

Write each number in a place-value chart.

17

thousands	hundreds	tens	ones
2	0	7	6

18 A number has 7 thousands, 8 hundreds, 1 ten, and 4 ones. What is the number?

thousands	hundreds	tens	ones
7	8	1	4

19 Thomas has about 80 buttons when he rounds to the nearest ten. Could Thomas have 72, 75, or 86 buttons? Explain.

__Thomas could have 75 buttons. 72 rounds to 70, and 86 rounds to 90. 75 rounds to 80.__

142 one hundred forty-two

Review

FOLDABLES® Study Organizer **Dinah Zike's Foldables®**

Have students use the Foldable they created at the beginning of the chapter to review and reinforce the concepts and skills they learned during the chapter. (See Chapter Resource Masters p. A84 for instructions.)

Intervention Strategy

Use this Intervention Strategy activity at any point during the chapter to reinforce the concepts and skills presented in the chapter.

Calendar Count

Step 1 Divide students into groups. Have each group determine the following:

- number of days since the first day of school.
- number of days of summer break.
- number of Tuesdays since the first day of school.
- number of months in the school year with 5 Fridays.

Step 2 Have students write the numbers in standard, word, and expanded form.

Step 3 Have students round the numbers to the nearest ten.

Step 4 Have each group make a poster displaying the information.

Classroom Management

Partners Teach Partner a student who has a strong understanding of the material with another student who needs additional support. Have the partners take turns asking each other questions based on the examples in the Review. If necessary, after a question is answered, have the author give an explanation of the answer and approach.

Chapter Resource Masters

Additional forms of the Chapter Test are available.

Test Format	Where to Find it
Chapter Test	**Math Online** macmillanmh.com
Blackline Masters	Assessment Masters, p. 51

ExamView®
Assessment Suite

Customize and create multiple versions of your chapter test and their answer keys. All of these questions from the chapter tests are available on ExamView® Assessment Suite.

Advance

Online Assessment and Reporting
macmillanmh.com

This online assessment tool allows teachers to track student progress with easily accessible, comprehensive reports available for every student. Assess students using any internet-ready computer.

Alternative Assessment

Use Portfolios Ask students to model the numbers 13, 64, and 87. Ask them to write each number in expanded and word form, and then round each to the nearest ten.

Ask students to model the numbers 3,407 and 5,019 with base-ten blocks.

Name _____

Chapter Test

Write each missing number.

1   46, 47, 48, __49__, 50   2   __31__, 32, 33, 34, 35

3   73, __74__, 75, 76, __77__   4   __96__, 97, 98, 99, __100__

Complete each table.

5
standard form	63
expanded form	60 + 3
word form	**sixty-three**

6
standard form	85
expanded form	**80 + 5**
word form	**eighty-five**

Fill in the blanks.

7   43 is between __40__ and __50__. 43 rounds to __40__.

8   25 is between __20__ and __30__. 25 rounds to __30__.

Write each number. Fill in the place-value chart.

9
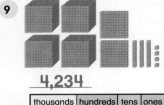

__4,234__

thousands	hundreds	tens	ones
4	2	3	4

10   A number has 2 thousands, 3 tens, and 4 ones. What is the number?

__2,034__

thousands	hundreds	tens	ones
2	0	3	4

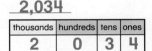
GO on

Copyright © Macmillan/McGraw-Hill, • Glencoe, a division of The McGraw-Hill Companies, Inc.

Chapter 4 Test   one hundred forty-three   **143**

11 Who is Correct?

Juanita and Matt write the number shown.

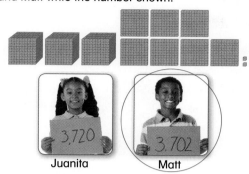

Juanita   Matt

Circle the correct answer. Explain.

Matt is correct. The number is 3,702.
Juanita mixed up the tens and ones digits.

Fill in the blanks.

12 The players line up by number. Which player is missing?

Player number **30** is missing.

13 I am a number greater than 80 but less than 90. I have 5 ones and I round to 90. What number am I? **85**

14 Vickie has about 20 crayons when she rounds to the nearest ten. Could Vickie have 14, 22, or 28 crayons? Explain.

Vickie could have 22 crayons.
14 rounds to 10 and 28 rounds to 30.

STOP

Who is Correct?
Diagnostic Teaching

- Juanita says the number is 3,720. This is incorrect. Juanita counted the ones cubes as tens. She did not understand that there are 0 tens in the number.

- Matt says the number is 3,702. This is correct. This can be checked by placing each digit in a place-value chart. He recognized that there are 0 tens in the number.

Learning from Mistakes

Missed Questions   Review commonly missed questions as a small group or class. Ask students to share their methods of answering each question. Try to point out when any errors occur and take corrective measures.

Data-Driven Decision Making

Students missing Exercises . . .	Have trouble with . . .	Should review and practice . . .
1–4, 12	counting numbers less than 100.	SSG Lesson 4-1, p. 121 CRM Skills Practice, p. A89
5–6	writing equivalent representations of numbers.	SSG Lesson 4-2, p. 125 CRM Skills Practice, p. A93
7–8	rounding two-digit numbers to the nearest ten.	SSG Lesson 4-3, p. 131 CRM Skills Practice, p. A97
9–11	representing numbers less than 10,000.	SSG Lesson 4-4, p. 135 CRM Skills Practice, p. A101
13–14	problem-solving that involves rounding two-digit numbers to the nearest ten.	SSG Lesson 4-3, p. 133 CRM Problem-Solving Practice, p. A98

Chapter 4

Test Practice

⚠ Diagnose Student Errors

Survey student responses for each item. Class trends may indicate common errors and misconceptions.

1. 34: mixed up the digits
41: does not understand counting
43: correct
46: does not understand counting

2. 69: mixed up the digits
91: does not understand counting
95: does not understand counting
96: correct

3. 129: disregarded the tens place
1,029: mixed up the hundreds and tens places
1,209: correct
1,290: mixed up the tens and ones places

4. 40: rounded down
45: does not understand rounding
50: correct
60: does not understand rounding

5. 10: does not understand rounding
20: correct
30: rounded up
40: does not understand rounding

6. 8 + 6: does not understand expanded form
8 + 60: mixed up the place values
80 + 6: correct
80 + 60: does not understand expanded form

7. 47: correct
74: mixed up the place values
407: does not understand standard form
704: does not understand standard form

8. 463: disregarded the hundreds place and mixed up the tens and ones place
4,036: correct
4,306: mixed up the hundreds and tens places
4,360: mixed up the place values

9. forty-nine: incorrectly worded the tens
fifty: did not include the ones
fifty-nine: correct
ninety-five: mixed up the place values

10. 20: does not understand counting
22: does not understand counting
26: correct
29: does not understand counting

11. 1,025: correct
1,205: mixed up the hundreds and tens places
1,250: does not understand place value
125: does not understand place value

12. 2 + 5: does not understand expanded form
2 + 50: mixed up the place values
20 + 5: correct
20 + 50: does not understand expanded form

Name _____

Test Practice

Choose the correct answer.

1 What is the missing number?

40, 41, 42, ____, 44, 45

| 34 | 41 | 43 | 46 |
| ○ | ○ | ● | ○ |

2 What is the missing number?

93, 94, 95, ____, 97, 98

| 69 | 91 | 95 | 96 |
| ○ | ○ | ○ | ● |

3 Bernard uses base-ten blocks to model his favorite number. What is Bernard's favorite number?

| 129 | 1,029 | 1,209 | 1,290 |
| ○ | ○ | ● | ○ |

4 Polly sold 48 boxes of cookies for a fundraiser. About how many boxes did Polly sell? Round to the nearest ten.

| 40 | 45 | 50 | 60 |
| ○ | ○ | ● | ○ |

5 What is 21 rounded to the nearest ten?

| 10 | 20 | 30 | 40 |
| ○ | ● | ○ | ○ |

6 Ryan wants to write the expanded form of the number 86 for his little brother. What should Ryan write?

○ 8 + 6   ○ 8 + 60
● 80 + 6   ○ 80 + 60

GO ON →

Copyright © Macmillan/McGraw-Hill • Glencoe, a division of The McGraw-Hill Companies, Inc.

Chapter 4   Test Practice

one hundred forty-five **145**

7 What is the standard form of 40 + 7?

47   74   407   704
●   ○   ○   ○

8 What number is shown?

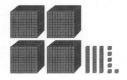

○ 463
● 4,036
○ 4,306
○ 4,360

9 Arnaldo is counting his money. He has 50 + 9 pennies. What is this number in word form?

○ forty-nine   ○ fifty
● fifty-nine   ○ ninety-five

10 What is the missing number?

23, 24, 25, _____, 27, 28

20   22   26   29
○   ○   ●   ○

11 Which model shows 1,025?

12 Chloe scored 25 points in a basketball game. What is this number in expanded form?

○ 2 + 5   ○ 2 + 50
● 20 + 5   ○ 20 + 50

STOP

Diagnosing Student Errors and Misconceptions

Place-Value Charts For students who are struggling with place values and their meanings, encourage them to memorize the place-value chart. Provide students with blank place-value charts so they can practice recalling the names and values of each place. Students should fill in a blank place-value chart each day until they can visualize the chart without having it in front of them.

Chapter Overview

Chapter-at-a-Glance

Lesson	Math Objective	Local/State Standards
5-1 Equal Parts (p. 149–152)	Identify equal parts of a whole.	
5-2 One-Half, One-Third, and One-Fourth (p. 153–156)	Name a fraction that identifies part of a whole.	
Progress Check 1 (p. 157)		
5-3 Parts of a Whole (p. 159–162)	Name a fraction that identifies part of a whole.	
5-4 Parts of a Set (p. 163–166)	Name a fraction that identifies part of a set.	
Progress Check 2 (p. 167)		
5-5 Model Fractions (p. 169–172)	Model fractions.	
5-6 Fractions on a Number Line (p. 173–176)	Identify fractions on a number line.	
Progress Check 3 (p. 177)		

Content-at-a-Glance

The diagram below summarizes and unpacks Chapter 5 content.

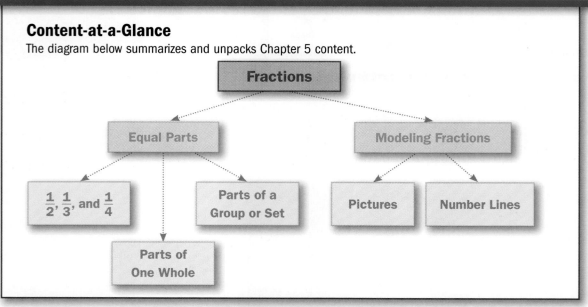

Chapter Assessment Manager

Diagnostic   Diagnose students' readiness.

	Student Study Guide/ Teacher Editions	Assessment Masters	Technology
Course Placement Test		1	ExamView® Assessment Suite
Book 2 Pretest		45	ExamView® Assessment Suite
Chapter Pretest		60	ExamView® Assessment Suite
Get Ready	SSG 148		Math Online macmillanmh.com StudentWorks™ Plus

Formative   Identify students' misconceptions of content knowledge.

	Student Study Guide/ Teacher Editions	Assessment Masters	Technology
Progress Checks	SSG 157, 167, 177		Math Online macmillanmh.com StudentWorks™ Plus
Vocabulary Review	SSG 152, 156, 162, 166, 172, 176, 179		Math Online macmillanmh.com
Lesson Assessments			ExamView® Assessment Suite
Are They Getting It?	TE 151, 155, 161, 165, 171, 175		

Summative   Determine student success in learning the concepts in the lesson, chapter, or book.

	Student Study Guide/ Teacher Editions	Assessment Masters	Technology
Chapter Test	SSG 181	63	ExamView® Assessment Suite
Test Practice	SSG 183	66	ExamView® Assessment Suite
Alternative Assessment	TE 181	69	
See It, Do It, Say It, Write It	TE 152, 156, 162, 166, 172, 176		
Book 2 Test		82	ExamView® Assessment Suite

Back-mapping and Vertical Alignment McGraw-Hill's *Math Triumphs* intervention program was conceived and developed with the final result in mind: student success in grade-level mathematics, including Algebra 1 and beyond. The authors, using the **NCTM Focal Points and Focal Connections** as their guide, developed this brand-new series by back-mapping from grade-level and Algebra 1 concepts, and vertically aligning the topics so that they build upon prior skills and concepts and serve as a foundation for future topics.

Chapter Resource Manager

Teacher Works™ Plus
All-In-One Planner and Resource Center

	Lesson 5-1	Lesson 5-2	Lesson 5-3	Lesson 5-4
Concept	Equal Parts	One-Half, One-Third, and One-Fourth	Parts of a Whole	Parts of a Set
Objective	Identify equal parts of a whole.	Name a fraction that identifies part of a whole.	Name a fraction that identifies part of a whole.	Name a fraction that identifies part of a set.
Math Vocabulary	equal parts whole	denominator fraction numerator	denominator fraction numerator	denominator fraction numerator
Lesson Resources	**Materials** • paper • pictures of flowers: impatiens, forget-me-nots, a flowering pear tree leaf • tracing paper • construction paper • index cards	**Materials** • sentence strips • construction paper • index cards	**Materials** • index cards • colored construction paper	**Materials** • beans or buttons • crayons or colored pencils
	Manipulatives • pattern blocks • fraction tiles • geoboards	**Manipulatives** • fraction circles • fraction tiles	**Manipulatives** • fraction circles • fraction tiles • connecting cubes	**Manipulatives** • counters • connecting cubes • pattern blocks
	Other Resources [CRM] Vocabulary and English Language Development [CRM] Skills Practice [CRM] Problem-Solving Practice [CRM] Homework Practice	**Other Resources** [CRM] Vocabulary and English Language Development [CRM] Skills Practice [CRM] Problem-Solving Practice [CRM] Homework Practice	**Other Resources** [CRM] Vocabulary and English Language Development [CRM] Skills Practice [CRM] Problem-Solving Practice [CRM] Homework Practice	**Other Resources** [CRM] Vocabulary and English Language Development [CRM] Skills Practice [CRM] Problem-Solving Practice [CRM] Homework Practice
Technology	**Math Online** macmillanmh.com StudentWorks™ Plus ⊚ ExamView® Assessment Suite	**Math Online** macmillanmh.com StudentWorks™ Plus ⊚ ExamView® Assessment Suite	**Math Online** macmillanmh.com StudentWorks™ Plus ⊚ ExamView® Assessment Suite	**Math Online** macmillanmh.com StudentWorks™ Plus ⊚ ExamView® Assessment Suite

Lesson 5-5	Lesson 5-6	
Model Fractions	Fractions on a Number Line	**Concept**
Model fractions.	Identify fractions on a number line.	**Objective**
denominator fraction numerator	fraction number line	**Math Vocabulary**
Materials • science/library books with nature pictures • apples • oranges • index cards that show the fractions $\frac{2}{5}, \frac{3}{6}, \frac{5}{8}, \frac{4}{5}, \frac{5}{6}, \frac{6}{8}$ as whole and set **Manipulatives** • connecting cubes • pattern blocks	**Materials** • ruler or yard stick • sentence strip • straightedge • measuring cup • weight scale • index cards • number line **Manipulatives** • flexible ruler	**Lesson Resources**
Other Resources **CRM** Vocabulary and English Language Development **CRM** Skills Practice **CRM** Problem-Solving Practice **CRM** Homework Practice	**Other Resources** **CRM** Vocabulary and English Language Development **CRM** Skills Practice **CRM** Problem-Solving Practice **CRM** Homework Practice	
▷ **Math Online** ▷ macmillanmh.com StudentWorks™ Plus 💿 ExamView® Assessment Suite	▷ **Math Online** ▷ macmillanmh.com StudentWorks™ Plus 💿 ExamView® Assessment Suite	**Technology**

Home Connection

Read the Home Connection letter with students and have them write their names in the space below.

Read and explain the activity under Help at Home. If time allows, complete a portion of the activity so students can introduce the activity to a parent or other caregiver.

Have students:

- identify the markings on a measuring cup such as $\frac{1}{4}$, $\frac{1}{2}$, and 1 whole.
- identify the markings on wrenches such as $\frac{1}{4}$, $\frac{1}{2}$, and 1 whole.
- identify the markings on a grocer's scale such as $\frac{1}{4}$, $\frac{1}{2}$, and 1 whole.

Real-World Applications

Baking Present the students with several baking recipes. Identify the fractions within the recipes. Discuss the implications of using a part of a whole amount.

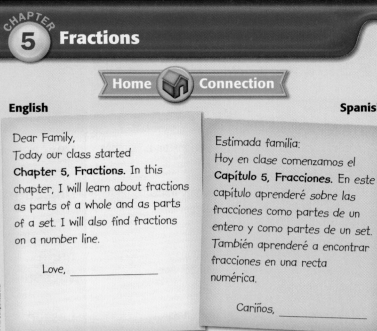

CHAPTER
5 Fractions

Home Connection

English

Dear Family,
Today our class started **Chapter 5, Fractions.** In this chapter, I will learn about fractions as parts of a whole and as parts of a set. I will also find fractions on a number line.

Love, _____

Spanish

Estimada familia:
Hoy en clase comenzamos el **Capítulo 5, Fracciones.** En este capítulo aprenderé sobre las fracciones como partes de un entero y como partes de un set. También aprenderé a encontrar fracciones en una recta numérica.

Cariños, _____

Help at Home
You can help your child learn about fractions. Have your child fold or cut a paper plate or another household item into equal parts. Have him or her identify different fractions of the whole.

Ayude en casa
Usted puede ayudar a su hijo(a) a aprender sobre las fracciones. Pida a su niño que doble y corte en partes iguales un plato de cartón u otra cosa que tenga en casa. Pídale que identifique las diferentes fracciones de un entero.

Math Online > Take the chapter Get Ready quiz at macmillanmh.com.

Chapter 5

one hundred forty-seven **147**

Copyright © Macmillan/McGraw-Hill • Glencoe, a division of The McGraw-Hill Companies, Inc.

Key Vocabulary

Find interactive definitions in 13 languages in the **eGlossary** at macmillanmh.com.

English   Español *Introduce the most important vocabulary terms from Chapter 5.*

whole   el toda
the entire amount or object (p. 149)

equal parts   grupos iguales
each part is the same size (p. 149)

fraction   fracción
a number that represents part of a whole or part of a set (p. 153)

numerator   part of the fraction that tells how many equal parts are being used (p. 153)

denominator   part of the fraction that tells the total number of equal parts (p. 153)

number line   recta numericarecta numerica
a line with number labels (p. 173)

Name _____

Get Ready

Count. Write how many.

1. ▬▬▬▬▬▬▬▬▬ __10__

2. ● ● ● ● ● ● ● ● __8__

Write equal or unequal.

3. __unequal__

4. __equal__

5. __unequal__

6. __equal__

Draw a model for each number.

7. 5 ○ ○ ○ ○ ○

8. 7 X X X X X X X

Complete each number line.

9. 0 1 2 3 4 5 [6] 7

10. 0 1 [2] 3 4 5 6 [7] 8 9

STOP

148 one hundred forty-eight

Vocabulary Preview

Make a poster to display the chapter's vocabulary words.

- List the vocabulary words in the word column.

- Ask students to give examples of any of the words they already know.

- As you finish each lesson, revisit the vocabulary poster and have students add examples to describe the new words they have learned.

Word	Example

Get Ready

Have students complete Get Ready to assess readiness for the chapter concepts and skills. Refer to the lesson below for additional support for prerequisite skills.

2-1 Equal Groups (p. 45)

You may also assess student readiness with the following resources:

 Online Readiness quiz at macmillanmh.com

Assessment Masters: Chapter Pretest (p. 60)

FOLDABLES Study Organizer **Dinah Zike's Foldables®**

Guide students through the directions on p. A104 in the Chapter Resource Masters to create their own Foldable graphic organizer for use with this chapter.

McGraw Hill Professional Development

Targeted professional development has been articulated throughout **McGraw-Hill's Math Triumphs** intervention program. **The McGraw-Hill Professional Development Video Library** provides short videos that support the **NCTM Focal Points and Focal Connections.** For more information, visit macmillanmh.com.

Model Lessons   Instructional Strategies

Lesson Notes

Lesson Planner

Objective Identify equal parts of a whole.

Vocabulary whole, equal parts

Materials/Manipulatives paper, pattern blocks, pictures of flowers (impatiens, forget-me-nots, a flowering pear tree leaf), tracing paper, construction paper, index cards, fraction tiles, geoboards

Chapter Resource Masters

CRM Vocabulary and English Language Development (p. A107)

CRM Skill Practice (p. A108)

CRM Problem-Solving-Practice (p. A109)

CRM Homework Practice (p. A110)

1 Introduce

Vocabulary

Compare Vocabulary Write *whole* and *equal parts* on the board. Ask students to compare the terms.

- **Do I need to start with equal parts to have a whole amount? Explain.** Sample answer: No; puzzle pieces are not equal parts and they form one whole.

- **Do I need to start with a whole amount to have equal parts?** Yes; equal parts are made by dividing one whole into same-sized smaller parts.

2 Teach

Key Concept

Foundational Skills and Concepts After students have read through the Key Concept box, guide them through the following questions.

- **Does the left rectangle have equal parts? Explain.** Yes; all the parts are the same size.

- **Does the right rectangle not have equal parts? Explain.** No; its parts have different sizes.

149 Chapter 5 Fractions

Name _____

Equal Parts

Key Concept

You can divide an object into parts.

  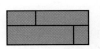

The orange rectangle is divided into 4 **equal parts**.

The blue rectangle is divided into 4 unequal parts.

Vocabulary

whole the entire amount or object

equal parts each part is the same size

This sandwich is cut into 2 equal parts.

You can fold a piece of paper to show equal parts.

Place one part on top of another to show the parts are equal.

Chapter 5   Lesson 1   one hundred forty-nine **149**

English Learner Strategy

Use Pattern Blocks to Model. Use patterns blocks to model one whole and equal parts.

1. Trace one hexagon. Cut the figure out. Write the term "One Whole" in the middle of the figure.

2. Trace one whole hexagon. Fold the hexagon in half. Cut the hexagon out. Then cut on the fold to create equal parts. Write the term "Equal Part" on each of the two pieces.

   - **Show one whole.** Student holds up one whole

   - **Show two equal parts.** Student holds up both equal parts.

3. Repeat with other pattern blocks. Allow students to use the models as a reference.

Example

Circle the figure that shows equal parts.
Write how many equal parts.

Step I   Look at the parts of each figure.

Step 2   Circle the figure with equal parts.

Step 3   Count the number of equal parts. 1, 2, 3

Answer   There are 3 equal parts.

Step-by-Step Practice

Circle the figure that shows equal parts.
Write how many equal parts.

Step I   Look at the parts of each figure.

Step 2   Circle the figure with equal parts.

Step 3   Count the number of equal parts.

     _1_ , _2_ , _3_ , _4_

Answer   There are _4_ equal parts.

150 one hundred fifty

Additional *Example*

Circle the figure that shows equal parts.
Write how many parts.

Step 1 Look at the parts of each figure.

Step 2 Circle the figure with equal parts.

Step 3 Count the number of equal parts. 1, 2, 3, 4

Answer There are 4 equal parts.

Math Coach Notes

Explain to students that to prove parts are equal, place one part on top of another to see if they match exactly. However, students cannot physically place parts on top of one another when working in a textbook so they need to visualize placing one part on top of another to determine if they are equal.

To be sure students do not miss or recount parts, have them place a check mark in each part as they count.

Intervention Strategy

Naturalist/Intrapersonal Learners

Materials: pictures of flowers (impatiens, forget-me-nots, and flowering pear tree leaf), tracing paper

Place students in pairs. Give each pair tracing paper and pictures. Have one partner trace an item. Have students decide how the drawing could be divided into equal parts. Students should fold the drawing to see if the parts are the same size and conclude whether the parts are equal.

- **What other ways can you make the same number of equal parts?** Answers will vary. Check students' answers.

Have students repeat this activity with the other items.

③ Practice

Guided Practice

Direct students to complete Exercises 1–4 in Guided Practice.

Exercises 3–4 Remind students to carefully count the number of equal parts.

Problem-Solving Practice

Guide students through the four-step problem-solving plan to complete Exercise 5.

- **What are the key words?** 4 equal parts, show

- **How could a picture help you solve the problem?** You could draw a sandwich, and divide it into 4 equal parts.

Ask students to check their work using the strategy suggested in the Check step. Students can fold the picture to be sure the parts are equal.

Using Manipulatives

Pattern Blocks Use blocks to show different ways to make equal parts.

Geoboard Use geoboards to show different ways to make equal parts.

Fraction Tiles Use the backside of fraction tiles to show different ways to make equal parts.

On-Hand Manipulatives Use two different colored pieces of construction paper to show equal parts.

Name _____

▶ Guided Practice

Circle each figure that shows equal parts.

1   2

How many equal parts are there?

3   4

___6___ equal parts   ___5___ equal parts

Problem-Solving Practice

5   Jeremy wants to cut his sandwich into 4 equal parts. <u>Show</u> how Jeremy should cut his sandwich.

Understand Underline key words.

Plan Draw a picture.

Solve Draw lines to show __4__ equal parts.

Check Look at the parts of the sandwich. Are they equal?

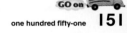 GO on

---

Are They Getting It?

Check students' understanding of identifying equal parts by drawing these figures on the board. Ask students to point out correct and incorrect statements and explain their reasoning.

1.   **This shows equal parts.** This is correct.

2.   **This shows equal parts.** This is incorrect. The parts are not equal.

3.   **This shows 6 equal parts.** This is incorrect. It shows 8 equal parts.

Practice on Your Own

Circle each object that shows equal parts.

6.

7.

How many equal parts are there?

8.

   __5__ equal parts

9.

   __3__ equal parts

10. **WRITING IN** ▸**MATH** Mrs. Thomas wants to cut a pie into 8 equal slices. How can you show this?

I can draw lines over the pie to show 8 equal parts.

Vocabulary Check Complete.

11. An object with same size parts is divided into __equal parts__.

STOP

152 one hundred fifty-two

Practice on Your Own

Direct students to p. 152 in their student books. Have students complete Exercises 6–11 independently. You may need to review the directions of each section before students begin.

 (4) Assess

See It, Do It, Say It, Write It

Step 1 Draw a rectangle divided into four equal parts. Have students point to and identify the parts as equal parts.

Step 2 Have students trace a whole pattern block. Have them fold the tracing to create equal parts.

Step 3 Have students show their tracings and say how many equal parts the figure is divided into.

Step 4 Tell students to write what is meant by equal parts using words, numbers, and drawings.

Looking Ahead: Pre-teach

In the next lesson, students will model unit fractions.

Example

What fraction names the shaded part?

 $\frac{1}{2}$

There are 2 parts and 1 part is shaded.

Have students write the fraction that names the shaded part.

1. $\frac{1}{3}$

2. $\frac{1}{2}$

3. $\frac{1}{4}$

Math Challenge

Equal or Unequal

Materials: index cards

Place students in groups of 3 or 4. Have each player draw 3 figures on index cards. (They can trace pattern blocks or make larger figures with the pattern blocks.) Each figure should be divided into equal or unequal parts.

Next, place the index cards face down in the middle of group. The first player picks a card and tells whether the parts are equal and the number of parts. If the group decides that he or she is correct, the player receives a point. Play continues to the next student. The player with the most points, after all cards have been picked, wins.

Lesson Notes

Lesson Planner

Objective Name a fraction that identifies part of a whole.

Vocabulary fraction, numerator, denominator

Materials/Manipulatives fraction circles, fraction tiles, sentence strips, construction paper, index cards

Chapter Resource Masters

- [CRM] Vocabulary and English Language Development (p. A111)
- [CRM] Skill Practice (p. A112)
- [CRM] Problem-Solving-Practice (p. A113)
- [CRM] Homework Practice (p. A114)

① Introduce

Vocabulary

Relationships Write the following statements on the board. Ask students which statement best describes how the vocabulary words relate to each other.

- A numerator has a fraction and a denominator.
- A fraction has a numerator and a denominator.
- A denominator has a numerator and a fraction.

② Teach

Key Concept

Foundational Skills and Concepts After students have read through the Key Concept box, guide them through the following questions.

- **How many equal parts in the first figure?** 2
- **What is another way to describe 2 equal parts?** halves
- **What is another way to describe 3 equal parts?** thirds
- **How many equal parts in the last figure?** 4

153 Chapter 5 Fractions

Name _____

One-Half, One-Third, and One-Fourth

Key Concept

You can use a **fraction** to name part of a whole.

one-half or $\frac{1}{2}$	one-third or $\frac{1}{3}$	one-fourth or $\frac{1}{4}$
1 out of 2 parts is blue.	1 out of 3 parts is red.	1 out of 4 parts is green.

Vocabulary

fraction a number that represents part of a whole or part of a set

numerator part of the fraction that tells how many equal parts are being used

$$\frac{5}{6} \longleftarrow \text{numerator}$$

denominator part of the fraction that tells the total number of equal parts

$$\frac{5}{6} \longleftarrow \text{denominator}$$

$\dfrac{1}{2}$
The **numerator** tells the number of shaded parts.
The **denominator** tells the number of equal parts.

Chapter 5   Lesson 2

one hundred fifty-three **153**

English Learner Strategy

Connections Write *number* on the board. Write *numerator* underneath number.

number
numerator

- **Look at the words *number* and *numerator*. How are the words alike?** They look the same in the beginning.

- **You can remember numerator because it looks like number. The numerator is the number of parts being used in the whole.**

- **The numerator always goes on the top in a fraction.**

- **How many parts are shaded?** 1

The fraction that names the shaded part is $\frac{1}{4}$.

Example

Write the fraction that names the shaded part.

Step 1   Are the parts equal? yes

Step 2   The numerator tells the number of shaded parts. The numerator is 1.

Step 3   The denominator tells the number of equal parts. The denominator is 3.

Answer   The fraction is $\frac{1}{3}$.

Step-by-Step Practice

Write the fraction that names the shaded part.

Step 1   Are the parts equal? **yes**

Step 2   The numerator tells the number of shaded parts.

The numerator is __1__.

Step 3   The denominator tells the number of equal parts.

The denominator is __4__.

Answer   The fraction is $\frac{1}{4}$.

154   one hundred fifty-four

Additional *Example*

Write the fraction that names the shaded part.

Step 1 Are the parts equal? yes

Step 2 The numerator tells the number of shaded parts. The numerator is 1.

Step 3 The denominator tells the number of equal parts. The denominator is 2.

Answer The fraction is $\frac{1}{2}$.

Math Coach Notes

Strategies

1. Begin the lesson by asking when fractions are used in everyday life. Some examples include cutting a pizza or apple in equal parts or dividing a package of pencils evenly.

2. Have students model the problems in the lesson with fraction tiles or fraction circles.

Intervention Strategy   Visual Learners

Draw a vertical rectangle that is divided into 3 equal parts with 1 part shaded.

Tell the students that another way of thinking about a fraction is to think of it as a building. The denominator is "the basement" and the numerator is the "1st floor".

To build a building, as a fraction, start with the basement, then build on the 1st floor. Start with the basement, or the denominator, and find the total number of equal parts in the figure, which is 3. Then build on the 1st floor, or numerator, and find the number of shaded parts which is 1.

1st floor (number of shaded parts) ⟶ ☐
basement (number of equal parts) ⟶ ☐

So, the fraction is $\frac{1}{3}$.

Guided Practice

Direct students to complete Exercises 1–3 in Guided Practice.

Exercises 1–3 Remind students to think about the following questions:

• How many equal parts are there in all?

• How many equal parts are shaded?

After each exercise, have the students say how many parts the figures are divided into and the fraction name.

Problem-Solving Practice

Guide students through the four-step problem-solving plan to complete Exercise 4.

• **What are the key words?** color $\frac{1}{2}$ of a banner red

• **How could a model help you solve the problem?** I could divide it into 2 equal parts to create halves. Then, shade in one part to show one-half.

Ask students to check their work using the strategy suggested in the Check step. Students should be sure the shaded part is equal to the unshaded part.

Using Manipulatives

Fraction Circles After tracing 1 whole circle on the board three times, divide the circles into halves, thirds, and fourths. Place within the whole to show parts shaded.

Fraction Tiles After tracing the 1- whole tile on the board three times. Divide up the tiles into halves, thirds, and fourths. Place $\frac{1}{2}$, $\frac{1}{3}$, and $\frac{1}{4}$ within the wholes to show parts shaded.

On-Hand Manipulatives Use 3 sentence strips of the same length. Divide them into halves, thirds, and fourths respectively.

Name _____

▶ Guided Practice

Write the fraction that names each shaded part.

1   2   3

$\frac{1}{3}$ $\frac{1}{4}$ $\frac{1}{3}$

Problem-Solving Practice

4   Devon wants to color $\frac{1}{2}$ of a banner red. Show what the banner will look like.

 red

Understand   Underline key words.

Plan   Use a model.

Solve   Divide the banner into
$\underline{2}$ equal parts.
Color $\underline{1}$ part red.

Check   Is the shaded part of the banner equal to the unshaded part?

GO on

Are They Getting It? ❓

Check students' understanding of naming fractions that identify equal parts by drawing the following figures on the board. Ask students to point out correct and incorrect statements and explain their reasoning.

1. The triangle is divided into equal parts. This is incorrect. The triangle is divided into unequal parts.

2. The rectangle is divided into equal parts. This is correct.

3. The rectangle is divided into halves. This is incorrect. The rectangle is divided into thirds.

4. $\frac{1}{4}$ of the rectangle is shaded. This is incorrect. $\frac{1}{3}$ of the rectangle is shaded.

▶ Practice on Your Own

Write the fraction that names each shaded part.

5
$$\frac{1}{2}$$

6
$$\frac{1}{4}$$

7
$$\frac{1}{2}$$

8
$$\frac{1}{3}$$

9
$$\frac{1}{2}$$

10
$$\frac{1}{4}$$

11 **WRITING IN ▶MATH** Caitlyn is making a sign.

She wants to shade $\frac{1}{3}$ of the sign blue.
Show what this will look like. Explain.

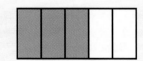

I can divide the sign into
3 equal parts and shade one part blue.

Vocabulary Check Complete.

12 A **fraction** is a number that represents part of a whole.

156 one hundred fifty-six

STOP

Math Challenge

Fraction Match

Materials: index cards

- Divide students into groups of 4. Give each student 6 index cards.
- On 3 of the cards, students draw a picture of each of the fractions $\frac{1}{2}$, $\frac{1}{3}$ and $\frac{1}{4}$.
- On the other 3 cards, students write each of the fractions $\frac{1}{2}$, $\frac{1}{3}$ and $\frac{1}{4}$.
- Next, shuffle the index cards and place them face down. The first player picks two cards and determines if a match has been made. (a match consists of a matching picture and fraction). If a match is made, the player keeps the cards, otherwise the cards are placed face down again.
- The game continues until all matches have been made. The player with the most matches wins.

Practice on Your Own

Direct students to p. 156 in their student books. Have students complete Exercises 5–12 independently. You may need to review the directions of each section before students begin.

④ Assess

See It, Do It, Say It, Write It

Step 1 Draw the figure on the board. Have students point to and identify the four equal parts, or fourths.

Step 2 Have students draw 3 squares and shade them to show $\frac{1}{2}$, $\frac{1}{3}$, and $\frac{1}{4}$.

Step 3 Have students describe to the class how they made their drawings, and then say the word form of the fraction.

Step 4 Tell students to write what is meant by $\frac{1}{2}$, $\frac{1}{3}$, and $\frac{1}{4}$ using words, numbers, and pictures.

Looking Ahead: Pre-teach

In the next lesson, students will write the fraction for the shaded part.

Example

Name the fraction for the shaded part.

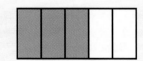
$$\frac{3}{5}$$

1.
$$\frac{2}{6}$$

2.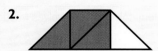
$$\frac{3}{4}$$

Lesson 5-2 One-Half, One-Third, and One-Fourth **156**

Progress Check 1

Formative Assessment

Use the Progress Check to assess students' mastery of the previous lessons. Have students review the lesson indicated for the problems they answered incorrectly.

Common Error *Alert*

Exercises 4, 5, and 6 Students may confuse the numerator and denominator. Review the parts of a fraction and what each represents.

Exercise 7 Students might answer that 1 part of the cookie has been eaten. Remind students they are to represent the answer as a fraction.

Name _____

Progress Check 1 (Lessons 5-1 and 5-2)

1 Circle the figure that shows equal parts.

How many equal parts are there?

2

__6__ equal parts

3

__4__ equal parts

Write the fraction that names each shaded part.

4

$\dfrac{1}{2}$

5

$\dfrac{1}{4}$

6

$\dfrac{1}{3}$

7 **WRITING IN ▶MATH** Kofi cut a large round cookie into 3 equal parts and ate 1 part. How much of the cookie did Kofi eat?

Kofi ate one-third, or $\dfrac{1}{3}$, of the cookie.

Chapter 5   Progress Check   one hundred fifty-seven **157**

Copyright © Macmillan/McGraw-Hill, • Glencoe, a division of The McGraw-Hill Companies, Inc.

Data-Driven Decision Making

Students missing Exercises . . .	Have trouble with . . .	Should review and practice . . .
1–3	identifying equal parts.	SSG Lesson 5-1, p. 149 CRM Skills Practice, p. A108
4–6	naming the fraction for a shaded part.	SSG Lesson 5-2, p. 153 CRM Skills Practice, p. A112
7	problem solving that involves fractions.	SSG Lesson 5-2, p. 155 CRM Problem-Solving Practice, p. A113

Name _____

The hot air balloon is missing its ropes!
Draw a line from each shape to the fraction that
matches the shaded parts.

Copyright © Macmillan/McGraw-Hill • Glencoe, a division of The McGraw-Hill Companies, Inc.

$\frac{1}{3}$ $\frac{1}{2}$ $\frac{1}{4}$

Replay

Use the Replay activity to review and reinforce the
concepts and skills presented in Lessons 5-1 and 5-2.

Instructions

Have students read the directions at the top of
the student page.

Student Technology

Students can use the following technology resources to
reinforce chapter content.

- 💿 StudentWorks™ Plus

- **Math Online** ⟩ macmillanmh.com

- eGlossary

Lesson Notes

Lesson Planner

Objective Name a fraction that identifies part of a whole.

Vocabulary fraction, numerator, denominator

Materials/Manipulatives fraction circles, fraction tiles, index cards, colored construction paper, connecting cubes

Chapter Resource Masters

- [CRM] Vocabulary and English Language Development (p. A115)
- [CRM] Skill Practice (p. A116)
- [CRM] Problem-Solving-Practice (p. A117)
- [CRM] Homework Practice (p. A118)

1 Introduce

Vocabulary

Vocabulary Interface Write *numerator* and *denominator* on the board. Ask students to compare the terms.

- **Which describes the number of equal parts?**
  denominator

- **Which describes the number of shaded parts?**
  numerator

Write a fraction on the board. Have students label the numerator and denominator.

2 Teach

Key Concept

Foundational Skills and Concepts After students have read through the Key Concept box, guide them through the following questions.

- **How many shaded parts in the rectangle?** 2
  What fraction names the shaded parts? $\frac{2}{3}$

- **How many equal parts in the hexagon?** 6
  What fraction names the shaded parts? $\frac{2}{6}$

Name _____

Parts of a Whole

Key Concept

Fractions can name more than one equal part of a whole.

two-thirds or $\frac{2}{3}$ ← numerator, denominator

two-sixths or $\frac{2}{6}$ ← numerator, denominator

The denominator shows that there are 3 equal parts.

The numerator shows that 2 of the 3 parts are shaded.

There are 6 equal parts.
2 of the 6 parts are shaded.
4 of the 6 parts are unshaded.

Vocabulary

fraction a number that represents part of a whole or part of a set

numerator part of the fraction that tells how many equal parts are being used
$\frac{5}{6}$ ← numerator

denominator part of the fraction that tells the total number of equal parts
$\frac{5}{6}$ ← denominator

Chapter 5 Lesson 3

one hundred fifty-nine 159

English Learner Strategy

Use Fraction Circles Use 8 index cards.

Label the cards: $\frac{2}{3}, \frac{2}{4}, \frac{3}{4}, \frac{2}{6}, \frac{4}{6}, \frac{5}{6}, \frac{2}{8},$ and $\frac{6}{8}$.

- Display the chart: ☐ ← number of parts being used
  ☐ ← total number of parts

- Show students a fraction circle that matches one of the cards.

- Have students count aloud the total number of parts and the number of shaded parts. Fill in the chart. Have students say the fraction.

- Ask students to pick the card that names the fraction circle.

Repeat activity with other fractions. Emphasize that counting out loud will help name fractions.

Example

Write the fraction that names the shaded part.

Step 1 Are the parts equal? yes

Step 2 The numerator tells the number of shaded parts. The numerator is 5.

Step 3 The denominator tells the number of equal parts. The denominator is 6.

Answer The fraction is $\dfrac{5}{6}$.

Step-by-Step Practice

Write the fraction that names the shaded part.

Step 1 Are the parts equal? __yes__

Step 2 The numerator tells the number of shaded parts.
The numerator is __3__.

Step 3 The denominator tells the number of equal parts.
The denominator is __8__.

Answer The fraction is $\dfrac{3}{8}$.

160 one hundred sixty

Additional *Example*

Write the fraction that names the shaded part.

Step 1 Are the parts equal? yes

Step 2 The numerator tells the number of shaded parts. The numerator is 3.

Step 3 The denominator tells the number of equal parts. The denominator is 5.

Answer The fraction is $\dfrac{3}{5}$.

Math Coach Notes

Study Skills For the Example and the Additional Example, ask students to name the fraction for the unshaded parts.

Ask students what fractions would name the shaded part if all the equal parts in the examples were shaded. $\dfrac{6}{6}$ and $\dfrac{5}{5}$

Ask students what fractions would name the shaded part if none of the equal parts in the examples were shaded. $\dfrac{0}{6}$ and $\dfrac{0}{5}$

- **Which part of the fractions changed?**
  numerator

- **Which part of the fractions did not change?**
  denominator

Intervention Strategy   Interpersonal Learners

Place students in pairs. Student 1 should draw a picture of a figure divided into equal parts, and then shade some of the parts.

Student 2 takes the drawing and writes the fraction that names the shaded part.

Together the students should count the total number of equal parts and the number of shaded parts to determine the numerator and denominator of the fraction that names the shaded part. If the students agree the answer is correct they switch roles and complete the activity again as time allows.

Copyright © Macmillan/McGraw-Hill • Glencoe, a division of The McGraw-Hill Companies, Inc.

Guided Practice

Direct students to complete Exercises 1–3 in Guided Practice.

Exercises 1–3 Remind students that the numerator names the number of parts being used.

Problem-Solving Practice

Guide students through the four-step problem-solving plan to complete Exercise 4.

- **What are the key words?** Sonia and three friends, which pizza, each girl gets 1 slice

- **Why is the first pizza the wrong choice?** There are only 2 slices of pizza for the 4 girls. There are not enough slices for each girl.

Ask students to check their work using the strategy suggested in the Check step. Students can shade parts of the pizzas to solve the problem.

Using Manipulatives

Fraction Circle Students can use fraction circles to model fractions.

Fraction Tiles Students can use fraction tiles to model fractions.

Connecting Cubes Students can use connecting cubes to model fractions.

On-Hand Manipulatives Use the tiles on a classroom floor and colored paper (the paper should be large enough to cover a tile). Section off a group of tiles to form squares or rectangles. Model different fractional amounts.

Name _____

▶ Guided Practice

Write the fraction that names each shaded part.

1    $\dfrac{3}{4}$

2 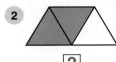 $\dfrac{2}{3}$

3 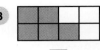 $\dfrac{5}{8}$

Problem-Solving Practice

4   Sonia and three friends want to share a pizza. Which pizza can the girls share so that each girl gets 1 slice?

Understand   Underline key words.

Plan   Guess and check.

Solve   There are ___4___ girls in all.

Which pizza has ___4___ slices? Circle the pizza the girls can share equally.

Check   Shade 1 part of the pizza you circled for each girl. Is there 1 part for each girl?

GO on

161

Chapter 5   Lesson 3   one hundred sixty-one

Are They Getting It?

Check students' understanding of parts of a whole by drawing the following figures on the board. Ask students to point out correct and incorrect statements and explain their reasoning.

1. The shaded part is $\dfrac{2}{3}$. This is incorrect. The shaded part is $\dfrac{2}{5}$.

2. The shaded part is $\dfrac{5}{6}$. This is correct.

3.   The shaded part is $\dfrac{2}{6}$. This is incorrect. The shaded part is $\dfrac{3}{6}$.

Copyright © Macmillan/McGraw-Hill • Glencoe, a division of The McGraw-Hill Companies, Inc.

161 Chapter 5 Fractions

▶ Practice on Your Own

Write the fraction that names each shaded part.

5

$\frac{2}{4}$

6

$\frac{3}{3}$

7

$\frac{3}{5}$

8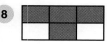

$\frac{4}{6}$

9

$\frac{7}{9}$

10

$\frac{5}{8}$

---

11 **WRITING IN ▶MATH**   Nashoba and two friends ate a small apple pie. Each boy ate an equal number of slices. Which pie could the boys have eaten? Explain.

I circled the pie divided into 3 equal slices so that each boy could have I slice.

Vocabulary Check   Complete.

12 The **denominator** is the part of the fraction that tells the total number of equal parts.

162   one hundred sixty-two

Practice on Your Own

Direct students to p. 162 in their student books. Have students complete Exercises 5–12 independently. You may need to review the directions of each section before students begin.

See It, Do It, Say It, Write It

Step 1   Display this figure.

Have students point to and count the 8 equal parts of the octagon. Then have them point to and count the 6 shaded parts. $\frac{6}{8}$ of the figure is shaded.

Step 2   Display this figure.

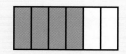

Have students name the fraction that identifies the shaded part.

Step 3   Ask students to explain the fraction from the previous step to a partner.

Step 4   Have students write, in their own words, how to find the fraction for the shaded part of the figure.

Looking Ahead: Pre-teach

In the next lesson, students will write fractions that name parts of a group or set.

Example

Name the fraction of blue birds. $\frac{2}{6}$

1. Have students name the fraction of yellow buttons.

 $\frac{1}{6}$

Lesson 5-3 Parts of a Whole **162**

Math Challenge

Modeling Fractions

Materials: index cards, fraction tiles, fraction circles

Prepare several index cards with fractions written on them. Place students in pairs and then assign two pairs to a group.

Have one student choose a fraction index card. One pair models the fraction using fraction tiles. The other pair models the fraction using fraction circles. The students compare and discuss their results.

Repeat the activity with the other fraction index cards.

Lesson 5-4 — Lesson Notes

Lesson Planner

Objective Name a fraction that identifies part of a set.

Vocabulary numerator, denominator

Materials/Manipulatives
counters, connecting cubes, pattern blocks, beans or buttons, crayons or colored pencils

Chapter Resource Masters
- [CRM] Vocabulary and English Language Development (p. A119)
- [CRM] Skill Practice (p. A120)
- [CRM] Problem-Solving-Practice (p. A121)
- [CRM] Homework Practice (p. A122)

1 Introduce

Vocabulary

Review Vocabulary Write the vocabulary words on the board. Ask students to draw a rectangle that has four equal parts with three shaded parts. Have them describe the picture using the vocabulary words.

2 Teach

Key Concept

Foundational Skills and Concepts After students have read through the Key Concept box, guide them through the following questions.

- **How many buttons are blue?** 3
- **What fraction of the buttons are blue?** $\frac{3}{4}$
- **How many counters are yellow?** 3
- **What fraction of the counters are yellow?** $\frac{3}{5}$

Lesson 5-4

Name _____

Parts of a Set

Key Concept

Fractions can name part of a group or set.

What fraction of the buttons are red?

 1 red button
4 buttons in the set

The fraction $\frac{1}{4}$ tells how many buttons are red.

What fraction of the counters are yellow?

3 yellow counters
5 counters in the set

The fraction $\frac{3}{5}$ tells how many counters are yellow.

Vocabulary

numerator part of the fraction that tells how many equal parts are being used

$\frac{5}{6}$ ← numerator

denominator part of the fraction that tells the total number of equal parts

$\frac{5}{6}$ ← denominator

The fraction $\frac{2}{7}$ tells how many leaves are green.

Chapter 5   Lesson 4   one hundred sixty-three **163**

Copyright © Macmillan/McGraw-Hill, • Glencoe, a division of The McGraw-Hill Companies, Inc.

English Learner Strategy

Model Fractions with Groups Have students form groups of 3, 4, or 5. Students will use their group members to answer these questions.

- **How many students are in your group?** 3, 4, or 5

Explain that this will be the denominator in the fraction that describes the group.

- **How many in your group are wearing sneakers?** Answers will vary.

Explain that this number will be the numerator in the fraction that names how many people are wearing sneakers.

- **What fraction of your group is wearing sneakers?** Answers will vary.

Repeat activity. Ask other questions that students can answer with a fraction.

Example

Name the fraction of orange leaves.

Step 1   There are 3 orange leaves.

Step 2   There are 4 leaves in the set.

Step 3   In the set, 3 out of 4 leaves are orange.

Answer   The fraction is $\frac{3}{4}$.

Step-by-Step Practice

Name the fraction of red flowers.

Step 1   There are __2__ red flowers.

Step 2   There are __6__ flowers in the set.

Step 3   In the set, __2__ out of __6__ flowers are red.

Answer   The fraction is $\dfrac{2}{6}$.

Additional *Example*

Name the fraction of blue pencils.

Step 1 There are 2 blue pencils.

Step 2 There are 5 pencils in the set.

Step 3 In the set, 2 out of 5 pencils are blue.

Answer The fraction is $\frac{2}{5}$.

Math Coach Notes

For extra practice, have students identify other fractions in the Example and Step-by-Step.

• Name the fraction of green leaves. $\frac{1}{4}$

• Name the fraction of yellow flowers. $\frac{4}{6}$

Intervention Strategy

Interpersonal/Visual/Logical/Kinesthetic Learners

Materials: purple and green counters

Fractions of Purple

Place students in pairs. Give each pair a small pile of counters. Have students write the following:

$$\frac{\text{purple}}{\text{purple and green}} = \underline{\qquad}$$

Have students sort the counters by color. Then, complete the fraction above to name the fraction of purple counters.

Repeat the activity with different groups of counters.

 **Practice**

Guided Practice

Direct students to complete Exercises 1–2 in Guided Practice.

Exercises 1–2 Remind students to count the objects in each exercise carefully before answering.

Problem-Solving Practice

Guide students through the four-step problem-solving plan to complete Exercise 3.

- **What are the key words?** 8 apples, 4 red apples, color the part of the apples that are red, name the fraction

- **How many apples should be red?** 4

- **How many apples are there all together?** 8

Ask students to check their work using the strategy suggested in the Check step. Students can count the number of red apples and number of apples in all to solve the problem.

Using Manipulatives

Connecting Cubes Students can use two different colored connecting cubes to display a variety of fractional amounts.

Colored Counters Students can use two different colored counters to display a variety of fractional amounts.

Pattern Blocks Students can use two different shaped blocks to display a variety of fractional amounts.

On-Hand Manipulatives Use different kinds of beans or buttons to display a variety of fractional amounts.

Name _____

▶ **Guided Practice**

Name each fraction.

1

$\dfrac{3}{7}$ of the fruit are pears.

2

$\dfrac{2}{3}$ of the fruit are oranges.

Problem-Solving Practice

3 Molly's mom buys <u>8 apples</u> at the store. She buys <u>4 red apples</u>. <u>Color the part of the apples that are red.</u> <u>Name the fraction.</u>

Understand	Underline key words.
Plan	Color a picture.
Solve	Color __4__ out of __8__ apples red.
	$\dfrac{4}{8}$ of the apples are red.
Check	Count the number of red apples. This is the numerator. Count the number of apples in the set. This is the denominator.

Copyright © Macmillan/McGraw-Hill, • Glencoe, a division of The McGraw-Hill Companies, Inc.

GO on

Chapter 5　Lesson 4　　　　　　one hundred sixty-five **165**

Are They Getting It? ?

Check students understanding of naming parts of a set by displaying the following on the board. Ask students to point out correct and incorrect statements and explain their reasoning.

1. The fraction of squares is $\dfrac{2}{3}$. This is incorrect. The fraction of squares is $\dfrac{2}{5}$.

2. The fraction of circles is $\dfrac{3}{5}$. This is correct.

Practice on Your Own

Name each fraction.

4

$\dfrac{2}{4}$ of the animals are giraffes.

5

$\dfrac{1}{3}$ of the birds are blue.

6

$\dfrac{5}{6}$ of the dogs have red collars.

7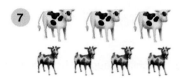

$\dfrac{3}{7}$ of the farm animals are cows.

8 **WRITING IN → MATH** Rafi has 4 cats. Of the cats, 1 is black. What fraction of the cats are black? How can you show this? Explain.

$\dfrac{1}{4}$ of the cats are black. I can draw a picture of 4 cats and color 1 black.

Vocabulary Check Complete.

9 The ___numerator___ is the part of the fraction that tells how many equal parts are being used.

166 one hundred sixty-six

Practice on Your Own

Direct students to p. 166 in their student books. Have students complete Exercises 4–9 independently. You may need to review the directions of each section before students begin.

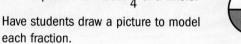 **4 Assess**

See It, Do It, Say It, Write It

Step 1 Display the following: Count aloud the total number of counters and write this as the denominator. Count aloud the number of red counters and write this as the numerator.

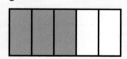

Step 2 Have students write the fraction of yellow counters.

Step 3 Have students explain how they found their answer.

Step 4 Have students write the process for naming the fraction of red counters.

Looking Ahead: Pre-teach

In the next lesson, students will learn about modeling fractions.

Example

Draw a picture to model $\dfrac{3}{4}$ of a whole.

Have students draw a picture to model each fraction.

1. $\dfrac{3}{5}$ of a whole

2. $\dfrac{3}{5}$ as a set

Math Challenge

Apple Coloring

Materials: crayons or colored pencils

Draw 12 apples on the board.

Students should copy the drawing. Challenge students to color the apples accordingly.

- Color $\dfrac{3}{12}$ red.
- Of the remaining, color $\dfrac{3}{9}$ green.
- Of that remaining, color $\dfrac{1}{2}$ yellow.
- Color the remaining $\dfrac{3}{3}$ pink.

Chapter 5 Progress Check 2

Formative Assessment

Use the Progress Check to assess students' mastery of the previous lessons. Have students review the lesson indicated for the problems they answered incorrectly.

⚠ Common Error *Alert*

Exercises 1–4 Remind student to find the fraction of the shaded part.

Exercises 1–6 Students may confuse the numerator and denominator. Review the parts of a fraction and what each represents.

Exercises 5–6 Remind students to count all object in each exercise carefully before answering.

Name _____

Progress Check 2 (Lessons 5-3 and 5-4)

Write the fraction that names each shaded part.

1    $\dfrac{1}{3}$

2    $\dfrac{3}{4}$

3    $\dfrac{4}{6}$

4    $\dfrac{6}{8}$

Name each fraction.

5 Jennifer bought 2 balls and 3 bones for her dog. What fraction of the items are balls?

In the set, $\dfrac{2}{5}$ of the items are balls.

6 Tony bought 1 bed and 2 bowls for his dog. What fraction of the items are bowls?

In the set, $\dfrac{2}{3}$ of the items are bowls.

Copyright © Macmillan/McGraw-Hill • Glencoe, a division of The McGraw-Hill Companies, Inc.

Data-Driven Decision Making

Students missing Exercises . . .	Have trouble with . . .	Should review and practice . . .
1–4	naming parts of a whole.	Lesson 5-3, p. 159 Skills Practice, p. A116
5	naming parts of a group or set.	Lesson 5-4, p. 163 Skills Practice, p. A120
6	Problem–solving that involves identifying parts of a group or set.	Lesson 5-4, p. 165 Problem-Solving Practice, p. A121

Name _____

«« Replay **Sea of Fractions**

Complete the fractions to name each shaded part. Place your answers in order in the boxes below. Use the key to solve the riddle.

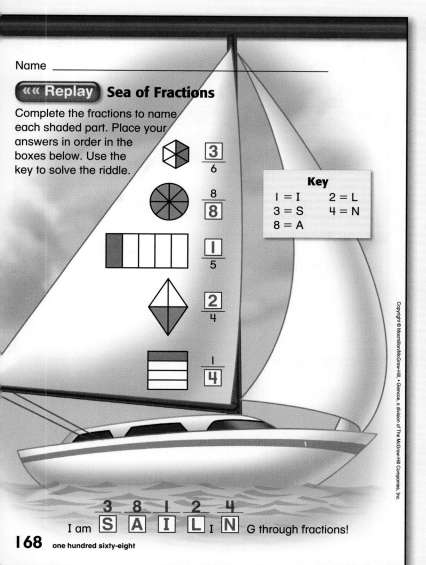

$\frac{3}{6}$

$\frac{8}{8}$

$\frac{1}{5}$

$\frac{2}{4}$

$\frac{1}{4}$

Key

1 = I	2 = L
3 = S	4 = N
8 = A	

I am $\frac{3}{S}$ $\frac{8}{A}$ $\frac{1}{I}$ $\frac{2}{L}$ $\frac{4}{N}$ G through fractions!

Copyright © Macmillan/McGraw-Hill • Glencoe, a division of The McGraw-Hill Companies, Inc.

Use the Replay activity to review and reinforce the concepts and skills presented in Lessons 5-3 and 5-4.

Instructions

Have students read the directions at the top of the student page.

Explain to students that after each number is written to complete a fraction, the numbers should also be written (in order) in the blanks at the bottom of the page. Students should use the key to determine what letter is represented by each number and solve the riddle.

Student Technology

Students can use the following technology resources to reinforce chapter content.

- StudentWorks™ Plus
- **Math Online** > macmillanmh.com
- eGlossary

Lesson Notes

Lesson Planner

Objective   Model fractions.

Vocabulary   fraction, numerator, denominator

Materials/Manipulatives   science library books with nature pictures, connecting cubes, pattern blocks, apples, oranges, index cards that show the fractions $\frac{2}{5}, \frac{3}{6}, \frac{5}{8}, \frac{4}{5}, \frac{5}{6}, \frac{6}{8}$ as a whole and set

Chapter Resource Masters

📖 Vocabulary and English Language Development (p. A123)

📖 Skill Practice (p. A124)

📖 Problem-Solving-Practice (p. A125)

📖 Homework Practice (p. A126)

① Introduce ⏱

Vocabulary

Reenact Vocabulary   Write the following on the board. Have students identify the numerator and denominator in each.

1.  ⟵ numerator
   ⟵ denominator

2. **4 out of 6 equal parts**   4: numerator; 6: denominator

② Teach ⏱

Key Concept

Foundational Skills and Concepts   After students have read through the Key Concept box, guide them through the following questions.

- **What does the denominator represent?**
  The number of parts in a whole or the total number in a group or set.

- **What does the numerator represent?**   The number of shaded parts or the number of parts in a group

---

Name _____

Model Fractions

Key Concept

You can model parts of a whole by drawing a picture.

$\frac{3}{4}$ ⟶ number of parts shaded
⟶ total number of parts in the whole

The **fraction** $\frac{3}{4}$ is modeled by the picture.

You can model parts of a set using counters.

$\frac{3}{4}$ ⟶ number of yellow counters
⟶ total number of counters

The fraction $\frac{3}{4}$ is modeled by the counters.

Vocabulary

fraction   a number that represents part of a whole or part of a set

numerator   part of the fraction that tells how many equal parts are being used

$\frac{5}{6}$ ⟵ numerator

denominator   part of the fraction that tells the total number of equal parts

$\frac{5}{6}$ ⟵ denominator

Chapter 5   Lesson 5   one hundred sixty-nine **169**

English Learner Strategy

Understanding Vocabulary   Write the words *whole* and *set* on the board.

- Discuss the concept of one whole. Show the students one whole apple, box, book, etc. Tell students that one whole object can be split into parts.

- Discuss the concept of one set. Show the students a set of baseball cards, playing cards, chess pieces, etc. Tell students that one set of objects has several pieces.

- Make a chart: whole | set

- Ask students for examples of objects that are one whole and objects that come in a set. Sample answers: group of coins, whole loaf of bread

Example

Mercedes ate $\frac{2}{6}$ of a chicken pot pie.
Draw a picture to model the fraction.

Step 1   Draw 1 circle to represent the whole pie.

Step 2   Explain $\frac{2}{6}$.

     $\dfrac{2}{6}$ $\longrightarrow$ number of parts eaten
     $\phantom{\dfrac{2}{6}}$ $\longrightarrow$ total number of parts in the whole

Step 3   Divide the pie into 6 equal parts.

Step 4   Shade 2 parts.

Answer

Step-by-Step Practice

Alan ate $\frac{4}{9}$ of the berries.
Draw a picture to model the fraction.

Step 1   Draw __9__ circles to represent the berries.

Step 2   Explain $\frac{4}{9}$.

     $\boxed{4}$ $\longrightarrow$ number of berries eaten
     $\boxed{9}$ $\longrightarrow$ total number of berries

Step 3   Shade __4__ circles.

Answer   

170   one hundred seventy

Additional *Example*

Ben planted beans in $\frac{2}{3}$ of his garden. Draw a picture to model the fraction.

Step 1 Draw 1 rectangle to represent the whole garden.

Step 2 Explain $\frac{2}{3}$.

     $\dfrac{2}{3}$ $\longrightarrow$ $\dfrac{\text{number of parts planted with beans}}{\text{total number of parts in the whole}}$

Step 3 Divide the garden into 3 equal parts.

Step 4 Shade 2 parts.

Answer

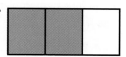

⚠ **Common Error** *Alert*

Students may divide a whole incorrectly. Remind students to look at the denominator of the fraction they are modeling. Students must divide the whole into the total number of equal parts shown by the denominator.

Intervention Strategy

Naturalistic/Interpersonal Learners

Materials: science library books with nature pictures

Fraction Find   Place students in groups.

- Students search through books to find pictures of trees, flowers, birds, and animals that show fractional amounts.

- Have students write the examples they find. For example, they may write "three of six birds are blue." Then have them write the fraction $\frac{3}{6}$.

- Have students explain the fractional amounts they found. They should discuss which is the whole or the set and which is the part of the whole.

③ Practice

Guided Practice

Direct students to complete Exercises 1–3 in Guided Practice.

Exercises 1–3 Remind students to read each exercise carefully. Determine if the fraction is referring to a whole or a set. Then draw the figure(s) according to the numbers in the numerator and the denominator.

Problem-Solving Practice

Guide students through the four-step problem-solving plan to complete Exercise 4.

- **What are the key words?** $\frac{3}{7}$ of the stickers are yellow, other stickers are red, show Ama's stickers

- **Does the fraction refer to a whole or set?** set

Ask students to check their work using the strategy suggested in the Check step. Students can count the number of yellow counters and number of counters in all to solve the problem.

Using Manipulatives

Connecting Cubes Students can use two different colored connecting cubes to display a fraction as a whole or set.

Pattern Blocks Students can use two different shaped blocks to display a fraction as a whole or set.

On-Hand Manipulatives Students can use slices of apples or oranges to display a fraction as a whole or set.

Name _____

▶ Guided Practice

Draw a picture to model each fraction.

1 $\frac{2}{3}$ of a circle is shaded.

2 $\frac{4}{5}$ of a square is shaded.

3 $\frac{3}{8}$ of the stamps are animals.

Problem-Solving Practice

4 Ama has 7 stickers in her sticker book. $\frac{3}{7}$ of the stickers are yellow. The <u>other stickers are red</u>. <u>Show Ama's stickers</u>.

Understand Underline key words.

Plan Use a model.

Solve Model the fraction using counters.

There are __7__ stickers in all.

There are __3__ yellow stickers.

There are __4__ red stickers.

Check How many yellow counters did you use?
How many counters did you use in all?

GO on

Chapter 5 Lesson 5   one hundred seventy-one **171**

Are They Getting It?

Check students' understanding of modeling fractions by drawing the following on the board. Ask students to point out the correct and incorrect statements and explain their reasoning.

1. $\frac{1}{3}$ of the rectangle is white. This is incorrect. $\frac{1}{4}$ of the rectangle is white.

2. $\frac{3}{4}$ of the set is red. This is correct.

3. $\frac{1}{3}$ of the set is yellow. This is incorrect. $\frac{1}{4}$ of the set is yellow.

4. $\frac{3}{1}$ of the rectangle is green. This is incorrect. $\frac{3}{4}$ of the rectangle is green.

171 Chapter 5 Fractions

Copyright © Macmillan/McGraw-Hill • Glencoe, a division of The McGraw-Hill Companies, Inc.

Draw a picture to model each fraction.

5 $\frac{1}{3}$

6 $\frac{2}{4}$

Sample answer:

Sample answer:

Draw circles to model each fraction.

7 $\frac{3}{6}$ ○○○●●●

8 $\frac{1}{4}$ ○○○●

9 $\frac{2}{5}$ ○○○●●

10 $\frac{6}{6}$ ●●●●●●

11 **WRITING IN ►MATH** George has 10 baseball cards. His favorite player is shown on $\frac{6}{10}$ of the cards. How can you model this fraction using counters?

I can model the fraction using 6 yellow and 4 red counters. The yellow counters are the numerator.

Vocabulary Check Complete.

12 The ____numerator____ is the number above the bar in a fraction.

172 one hundred seventy-two

STOP

Math Challenge

Materials: 12 index cards that shows the fractions $\frac{2}{5}, \frac{3}{6}, \frac{5}{8}, \frac{4}{5}, \frac{5}{6}, \frac{6}{8}$ as a whole and set

Model Matching Place students in pairs. Give students the 12 index cards. Have them place the cards face down in an array. The first player picks two cards. If the cards model the same fraction, the player keeps the match. Otherwise, the cards are returned face down. Play moves to the next student and continues until all the matches have been found. The player with the most matches wins.

Practice on Your Own

Direct students to p. 172 in their student books. Have students complete Exercises 5–12 independently. You may need to review the directions of each section before students begin.

See It, Do It, Say It, Write It

Step 1 Display the following on the board.

Whole		Set	
$\frac{3}{4}$	◔	$\frac{3}{4}$	●● ●○

Step 2 Students add another row to the chart by modeling $\frac{2}{5}$ of a whole and a set.

Step 3 Students show and discuss their fraction models to the class.

Step 4 Have students write how to model $\frac{2}{3}$ of a whole and a set.

Looking Ahead: Pre-teach

In the next lesson, students learn how to identify fractions on a number line.

Example

Label $\frac{3}{5}$ on the number line.

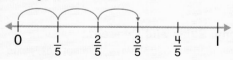

1. Have students identify $\frac{2}{4}$ on the number line.

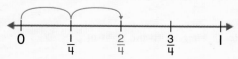

Lesson Notes

Lesson Planner

Objective Identify fractions on a number line.

Vocabulary fraction, number line

Materials/Manipulatives ruler or yard stick, sentence strip, straightedge, flexible ruler, measuring cup, weight scale, index cards, number line

Chapter Resource Material

- [CRM] Vocabulary and English Language Development (p. A127)
- [CRM] Skill Practice (p. A128)
- [CRM] Problem-Solving-Practice (p. A129)
- [CRM] Homework Practice (p. A130)

① Introduce

Vocabulary

Vocabulary Interaction Show students a ruler or yard stick. Tell them they can be used as a number line. Have students observe the whole numbers on the ruler/yard stick and how the distance from the end of the ruler to 1 is divided into equal parts.

② Teach

Key Concept

Foundational Skills and Concepts After students have read through the Key Concept box, guide them through the following questions.

- **What is the first number line divided into? Explain.**
  sixths; there are 6 equal sections on the number line.

- **How many tick marks to the right of 0 is $\frac{4}{6}$?** 4

Name _____

Fractions on a Number Line

Key Concept

You can show **fractions** on a **number line**.

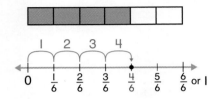

The space between the tick marks is $\frac{1}{6}$.

$\frac{4}{6}$ is 4 tick marks to the right of 0.

Vocabulary

fraction a number that represents part of a whole or part of a set

number line a line with number labels

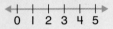

Count the tick marks between 0 and 1. Each tick mark shows the numerator. The denominator stays the same.

Chapter 5 Lesson 6

one hundred seventy-three **173**

English Learner Strategy

Using Prior Knowledge Display a number line from 0 to 20. Point to each number and count out loud from 0 to 20.

- Remind students that when they count on the number line, they count one number at a time.

- Display a number line divided into fifths.

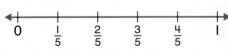

- Emphasize that counting on a fraction number line is similar to counting on a whole number line. Point to the first mark and say, "one-fifth." Point to the next mark and say, "two-fifths." Emphasize the similarity between counting whole numbers and fractions: 1, 2, 3 and $\frac{1}{5}, \frac{2}{5}, \frac{3}{5}$.

- Repeat the activity with a number line divided into sixths.

Example

Bernice has a ribbon that is $\frac{3}{4}$-yard long.

Find the fraction on the number line.

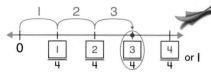

Step 1 Start at 0. Count each jump until you reach 3.

Step 2 Complete each fraction on the number line.

Step 3 Circle $\frac{3}{4}$ on the number line.

Step-by-Step Practice

Lee needs a $\frac{7}{8}$-inch toothpick for a craft project.

Find the fraction on the number line.

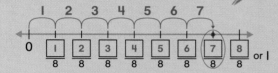

Step 1 Start at 0. Count each jump until you reach ___7___ .

Step 2 Complete each fraction on the number line.

Step 3 Circle $\frac{7}{8}$ on the number line.

174 one hundred seventy-four

Additional *Example*

Toby found a toad that was $\frac{3}{5}$-units long.

Find the fraction on the number line.

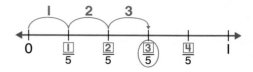

Step 1 Start at 0. Count each jump until you reach 3.

Step 2 Complete each fraction on the number line.

Step 3 Circle $\frac{3}{5}$ on the number line.

Math Coach Notes

Strategies

1. Be sure students understand that a fraction with the same number in the numerator and the denominator refers to the whole or entire group or set.

2. Get the students physically involved by making a number line on the classroom floor. Have students jump or hop along the number line to find the answers to the Example and Step-by-Step.

Intervention Strategy   Naturalistic Learners

Nature's Fractions

• Have students work in small groups.

• Take a walk around the school grounds. Tell students to identify three representations of fractions. Examples may include types of trees, flowers or bushes, stones or pebbles or leaves, and colors of birds.

• Instruct each group to write their examples down. For instance, they might write, "three of the five flowers are red."

• Have each group present their fraction observations to the class. Students should describe the whole or the set and the part.

3 Practice

Guided Practice

Direct students to complete Exercises 1–2 in Guided Practice.

Exercises 1 and 2 Be sure students understand that in past lessons, fractions were shown with shading or, in some cases, no shading. Explain that the problems model fractions in terms of length on a number line.

Exercises 1 and 2 Remind students to identify and write the fractions that make up the number line. Then move from 0 to the given fraction.

Problem-Solving Practice

Guide students through the four-step problem-solving plan to complete Exercise 3.

- **What are the key words?** 4 hats, 2 are baseball caps, what fraction of Miguel's hats are baseball caps

- **How is the number line used to solve the problem?** The number line is divided into four equal sections. Each section represents one hat.

Ask students to check their work using the strategy suggested in the Check step. Students can draw a picture to solve the problem.

Using Manipulatives

Flexible Ruler Use the flexible ruler to show the different fractions within the interval 0–1: halves, fourths, and eighths.

On-Hand Manipulatives Use rulers, sentence strips, measuring cups, and a grocer's scale to show number lines and how the interval from 0–1 can be divided into fractions.

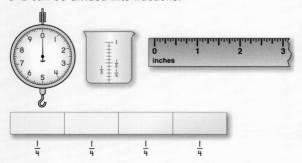

175 Chapter 5 Fractions

Name _____

▶ Guided Practice

Complete each fraction on the number line.
Circle the given fraction.

1 $\frac{3}{5}$

2 $\frac{2}{6}$

Problem-Solving Practice

3 Miguel has 4 hats. Of his hats, 2 are baseball caps. What fraction of Miguel's hats are baseball caps?

Understand Underline key words.

Plan Use a number line.

Solve Start at 0. Count until you reach ___2___.

$\frac{2}{4}$ of Miguel's hats are baseball caps.

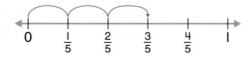

Check Draw a picture. Draw a circle with 4 equal parts. Shade 2 parts. What fraction is modeled?

GO on

Chapter 5   Lesson 6

one hundred seventy-five **175**

Are They Getting It? ❓

Check students' understanding of identifying fractions on a number by drawing the following number line on the board. Ask students to point out the correct and incorrect statements and explain their reasoning.

1. **The number line is divided into fifths.** This is correct.

2. **There are 10 equal parts on the number line.** This is incorrect. There are 5 equal parts on the number line.

3. **The arrow points to the fraction $\frac{3}{5}$.** This is correct.

Practice on Your Own

Complete each fraction on the number line.
Circle the given fraction.

4

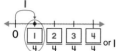

0 $\frac{1}{4}$ $\frac{2}{4}$ $\frac{3}{4}$ $\frac{4}{4}$ or 1

5

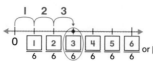

0 $\frac{1}{6}$ $\frac{2}{6}$ $\frac{3}{6}$ $\frac{4}{6}$ $\frac{5}{6}$ $\frac{6}{6}$ or 1

6 $\frac{2}{5}$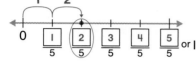

0 $\frac{1}{5}$ $\frac{2}{5}$ $\frac{3}{5}$ $\frac{4}{5}$ $\frac{5}{5}$ or 1

7 **WRITING IN ►MATH** Desta sees eight frogs. Five are on lily pads. What fraction of the frogs are on lily pads? How can you use a number line to show your answer? Explain.

$\frac{5}{8}$ of the frogs are on lily pads. I can count jumps from 0 to 5 and label the fraction.

Vocabulary Check Complete.

8 A _**number line**_ is a line with number labels. It is divided by tick marks into equal parts.

STOP

176 one hundred seventy-six

Math Challenge

Missing Fractions

Materials: index cards

In advance, make index cards with number lines divided into halves, fourths, and eighths. The number lines should show tick marks at each fractional interval. Place a red dot on one tick mark on each number line. The fraction at the red dot should be marked on the back of the card.

Place students in pairs. Give each pair a set of index cards. Place the cards in a pile with the number lines facing up. One partner picks a card and identifies the fraction represented by the red dot. If it is correct, they keep the card. If it is not, it is returned to the pile. Play continues until the pile is gone. The player with the most cards wins.

Practice on Your Own

Direct students to p. 176 in their student books. Have students complete Exercises 4–8 independently. You may need to review the directions of each section before students begin.

Exercises 4–6 Remind students that they must complete the number line and then identify the given fraction.

Exercise 7 Review the Problem-Solving Practice to help find the answer.

See It, Do It, Say It, Write It

Step 1 Draw the number line on the board.

0 $\frac{1}{7}$ $\frac{2}{7}$ $\frac{3}{7}$ $\frac{4}{7}$ $\frac{5}{7}$ $\frac{6}{7}$ 1

Point to each interval while naming the fraction it represents.

Step 2 Have the students identify $\frac{6}{7}$ on the number line.

Step 3 Have students discuss how they identified the fraction.

Step 4 Tell students to write how to find $\frac{5}{6}$ on a number line. Students can use an illustration to help explain their writing.

Chapter 5 Progress Check 3

Formative Assessment

Use the Progress Check to assess students' mastery of the previous lessons. Have students review the lesson indicated for the problems they answered incorrectly.

Exercises 1–4 Remind students to look at the denominator first to find how many parts in the whole or objects in a set. Then complete the model by looking at the numerator. Remind students they can model the fractions in 2 ways.

Common Error Alert

Be sure that students do not confuse the terms *numerator* and *denominator.* Be sure they know the definition of each. Also, students should be able to identify the position of the numerator and denominator in a fraction.

Be sure students are following a systematic method to model fractions.

Name _____

Progress Check 3 (Lessons 5-5 and 5-6)

Draw a picture to model each fraction.

1. $\frac{1}{3}$

2. $\frac{6}{8}$ Sample answer:

Draw circles to model each fraction.

3. $\frac{3}{4}$ 4. $\frac{2}{5}$

Complete each fraction on the number line. Circle the given fraction.

5. $\frac{5}{6}$ 6. $\frac{4}{7}$

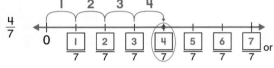

7. Maggie ate $\frac{2}{8}$ of a pizza. Draw a picture to model the amount Maggie ate.

Data-Driven Decision Making

Students missing Exercises ...	Have trouble with ...	Should review and practice ...
1–4	modeling fractions.	Lesson 5-5, p. 169 / Skills Practice, p. A124
5–6	identifying fractions on a number line.	Lesson 5-6, p. 173 / Skills Practice, p. A128
7	problem-solving that involves modeling fractions.	Lesson 5-5, p. 171 / Problem-Solving Practice, p. A125

Name _____

«« Replay Fraction Blast Off

Draw a line to match each fraction with the correct model.

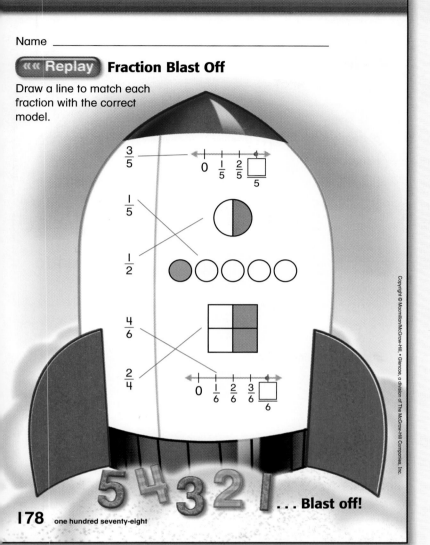

$\frac{3}{5}$

$\frac{1}{5}$

$\frac{1}{2}$

$\frac{4}{6}$

$\frac{2}{4}$

5 4 3 2 1 . . . Blast off!

178 one hundred seventy-eight

Use the Replay activity to review and reinforce the concepts and skills presented in Lessons 5-5 and 5-6.

Instructions

Have students read the direction at the top of the student page.

Student Technology

Students can use the following technology resources to reinforce chapter content.

- StudentWorks™ Plus
- Math Online macmillanmh.com
- eGlossary

Vocabulary

If students have difficulty answering Exercises 1–4, use the page references below to review the vocabulary words, or refer them to the glossary.

denominator (p. 153)
equal parts (p. 149)
number line (p. 173)
numerator (p. 153)

Vocabulary Review Strategies

Vocabulary Flashcards   Students should fold a sheet of notebook paper in fourths. The sections of the paper can be cut into cards. On the front side of the card, list the vocabulary word. On the back side of the card, write a definition or summary of the term. Students can also provide an example or picture to illustrate their understanding of the word.

Concepts

The exercises in this section are grouped to cover content from each lesson in the chapter.

Exercise 5: Lesson 5-1 (p. 149)
Exercise 6: Lesson 5-5 (p. 169)
Exercises 7–9: Lesson 5-3 (p. 159)
Exercises 10–11: Lesson 5-4 (p. 163)
Exercises 12–13: Lesson 5-6 (p. 173)

Find **Extra Practice** for these concepts in the Practice Worksheets, pp. A107–A130.

Name _____

Review

Vocabulary

Word Bank

denominator

equal parts

number line

numerator

Use the Word Bank to complete.

1. $\frac{2}{5}$ ◄·········· **numerator**

2. $0 \quad \frac{1}{4} \quad \frac{2}{4} \quad \frac{3}{4} \quad \frac{4}{4}$ or 1   **number line**

3. $\frac{1}{4}$ ◄·········· **denominator**

4.   **equal parts**

Concepts

5. Circle the figure that shows equal parts.

6. Draw circles to model the fraction.
   $\frac{2}{4}$

GO on

Copyright © Macmillan/McGraw-Hill. • Glencoe, a division of The McGraw-Hill Companies, Inc.

Write the fraction that names each shaded part.

7 $\dfrac{1}{2}$ **8** $\dfrac{4}{4}$ **9** $\dfrac{3}{5}$

Name each fraction.

10 $\dfrac{2}{3}$ of the shirts are green.

11  $\dfrac{3}{6}$ of the pants are blue.

Complete each fraction on the number line.
Circle the given fraction.

12 $\dfrac{4}{7}$ 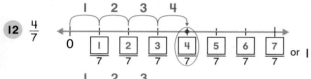 or I

13 $\dfrac{3}{8}$ 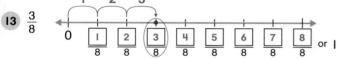 or I

180 one hundred eighty

Review

 **Dinah Zike's Foldables**

Have students use the Foldable they created at the beginning of the chapter to review and reinforce the concepts and skills they learned during the chapter. (See Chapter Resource Masters p. A104 for instructions.)

Intervention Strategy

Use this Intervention Strategy activity at any point during the chapter to reinforce the concepts and skills presented in the chapter.

Baking

Step 1 Place students in groups. Give each group a set of recipes. Ask students to circle the fractions within the recipes.

Step 2 Provide fraction strips and circles. Ask students to model the fractions that they identified in the recipes.

Step 3 Create a recipe box by having students bring in recipes with fractions. Students can find and model the fractions from the recipes when they have finished their class work.

Classroom Management

Partners Teach Partner a student who has a strong understanding of the material with a student who needs additional support. Have the partners give each other questions based on the exercises in the Review. If necessary, after a question is answered, have the author give an explanation of the answer and approach.

Chapter Resource Masters

Additional forms of the Chapter Test are available.

Test Format	Where to Find it
Chapter Test	**Math Online** ▸ macmillanmh.com
Blackline Masters	Assessment Masters, (p. 63)

Customize and create multiple versions of your chapter test and their answer keys. All of these questions from the chapter tests are available on ExamView® Assessment Suite.

Online Assessment and Reporting
macmillanmh.com

This online assessment tool allows teachers to track student progress with easily accessible, comprehensive reports available for every student. Assess students using any internet-ready computer.

Alternative Assessment

Use Portfolios Write the fraction $\frac{1}{6}$. Have students model the fraction as part of a whole, part of a group or set, and on a number line. Students should organize the models in a way that best suits them, such as a table, list, poster or Foldable. Ask students to explain each model verbally or in writing.

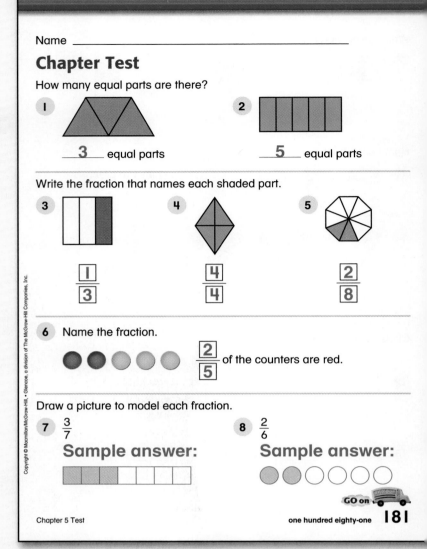

Name _____

Chapter Test

How many equal parts are there?

1. ___3___ equal parts

2. ___5___ equal parts

Write the fraction that names each shaded part.

3. $\frac{1}{3}$

4. $\frac{4}{4}$

5. $\frac{2}{8}$

6. Name the fraction.

$\frac{2}{5}$ of the counters are red.

Draw a picture to model each fraction.

7. $\frac{3}{7}$ **Sample answer:**

8. $\frac{2}{6}$ **Sample answer:**

GO on

Chapter 5 Test   one hundred eighty-one **181**

9 **Who is Correct?**

Esi and Ethan write the fraction shown on the number line.

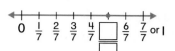

$0 \quad \frac{1}{7} \quad \frac{2}{7} \quad \frac{3}{7} \quad \frac{4}{7} \quad \boxed{} \quad \frac{6}{7} \quad \frac{7}{7}$ or I

The number line shows $\frac{5}{7}$.

Esi

Ethan

The number line shows $\frac{5}{6}$.

Circle the correct answer. Explain.

<u>Esi is correct. The number line is divided</u>

<u>into sevenths, not sixths.</u>

---

10 Samantha ate $\frac{2}{3}$ of a sub sandwich. The sandwich was cut into 3 equal pieces. How many pieces did Samantha eat?

__2__ pieces

11 In a bouquet of 8 flowers, $\frac{6}{8}$ are yellow. Draw circles to model this fraction.

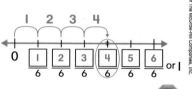

12 Ricardo has 4 red connecting cubes and 2 blue connecting cubes. What fraction of Ricardo's cubes are red? Show your answer on the number line.

$0 \quad \frac{1}{6} \quad \frac{2}{6} \quad \frac{3}{6} \quad \frac{4}{6} \quad \frac{5}{6} \quad \frac{6}{6}$ or I

STOP

182 one hundred eighty-two

Chapter 5 Test

Who Is Correct?
Diagnostic Teaching

- Esi says that $\frac{5}{7}$ is correct. This is correct because the number line is divided into sevenths, and from 0 you count over 5 tick marks to $\frac{5}{7}$.

- Ethan says that the fraction is $\frac{5}{6}$. This is not correct. The number line is divided into sevenths not, sixths.

Learning from Mistakes

Missed Questions Review commonly missed questions as a small group or class. Ask students to share their methods of answering each question. Try to point out when any errors occur and take corrective measures.

Data-Driven Decision Making

Students missing Exercises . . .	Have trouble with . . .	Should review and practice . . .	
1–2	identifying equal parts.	SSG Lesson 5-1, p. 149	CRM Skills Practice, p. A108
3-5	naming parts of a whole.	SSG Lesson 5-2, p. 153 SSG Lesson 5-3, p. 159	CRM Skills Practice, p. A112 CRM Skills Practice, p. A116
6	naming parts of a group or set.	SSG Lesson 5-4, p. 163	CRM Skills Practice, p. A120
7-8	modeling fractions.	SSG Lesson 5-5, p. 169	CRM Skills Practice, p. A124
9	identifying fractions on a number line.	SSG Lesson 5-6, p. 173	CRM Skills Practice, p. A128
10-12	problem-solving that involves naming parts of a whole, modeling fractions, and identifying fractions on a number line.	SSG Lesson 5-3, p. 161 SSG Lesson 5-5, p. 171 SSG Lesson 5-6, p. 175	CRM Skills Practice, p. A117 CRM Skills Practice, p. A125 CRM Skills Practice, p. A129

Test Practice Notes

Diagnose Student Errors

Survey student responses for each item. Class trends may indicate common errors and misconceptions.

1. ⬭: does not understand equal parts
   ⊞: does not understand equal parts
   ▽: chose figure that shows 3 equal parts
   ◇: correct

2. $\frac{1}{3}$: correct
   $\frac{1}{2}$: chose fraction with incorrect denominator
   $\frac{2}{3}$: chose fraction with incorrect numerator
   $\frac{3}{1}$: mixed up the numerator and denominator

3. $\frac{1}{4}$: chose fraction with incorrect denominator
   $\frac{1}{3}$: chose fraction with incorrect denominator
   $\frac{1}{2}$: correct
   $\frac{2}{3}$: does not understand fractions

4. ◓: chose model with incorrect denominator
   ☰: correct
   ▭: chose model that does not have equal parts
   ◩: chose model with incorrect numerator

5. $\frac{3}{4}$ correct
   $\frac{4}{4}$ chose fraction with incorrect numerator
   $\frac{4}{3}$ mixed up the numerator and denominator
   $\frac{3}{1}$ chose fraction with incorrect denominator

6. $\frac{1}{5}$ incorrectly counted the number dimes
   $\frac{2}{5}$ chose fraction that represents the number of nickels.
   $\frac{3}{5}$ correct
   $\frac{2}{3}$ chose fraction that represents the number of nickles

7. $\frac{2}{8}$ incorrectly counted the number of shaded parts
   $\frac{3}{8}$ correct
   $\frac{5}{8}$ counted the number of unshaded parts
   $\frac{6}{8}$ incorrectly counts the number of shaded parts

8. $\frac{2}{6}$ does not understand fractions on a number line
   $\frac{3}{6}$ does not understand fractions on a number line
   $\frac{4}{6}$ correct
   $\frac{4}{5}$ miscounted the number of tick marks on the number line

9. $\frac{1}{8}$ does not understand word form of fractions
   $\frac{1}{7}$ does not understand word form of fractions
   $\frac{7}{8}$ correct
   $\frac{8}{7}$ mixed up the numerator and denominator

10. $\frac{1}{4}$ correct
    $\frac{1}{3}$ chose fraction that represents the number of baseballs over the number of basketballs
    $\frac{3}{1}$ does not understand fractions as part of a set
    $\frac{4}{1}$ mixed up the numerator and denominator

183 Chapter 5 Test Practice

Name _____

Test Practice

Choose the correct answer.

1 Which figure shows 4 equal parts?

○   ○   ○   ●

2 One-third of Jay's books are new. Which fraction shows one-third?

● $\frac{1}{3}$ ○ $\frac{1}{2}$ ○ $\frac{2}{3}$ ○ $\frac{3}{1}$

3 What fraction names the shaded part?

○ $\frac{1}{4}$ ○ $\frac{1}{3}$ ● $\frac{1}{2}$ ○ $\frac{2}{3}$

4 Which model shows $\frac{1}{4}$?

○   ●   ○   ○

5 Three out of four students ride the bus. Which fraction shows 3 out of 4?

● $\frac{3}{4}$ ○ $\frac{4}{4}$ ○ $\frac{4}{3}$ ○ $\frac{3}{1}$

6 Karl has 3 dimes and 2 nickels. What fraction of his coins are dimes?

○ $\frac{1}{5}$ ○ $\frac{2}{5}$ ● $\frac{3}{5}$ ○ $\frac{2}{3}$

GO ON

Chapter 5   Test Practice

one hundred eighty-three **183**

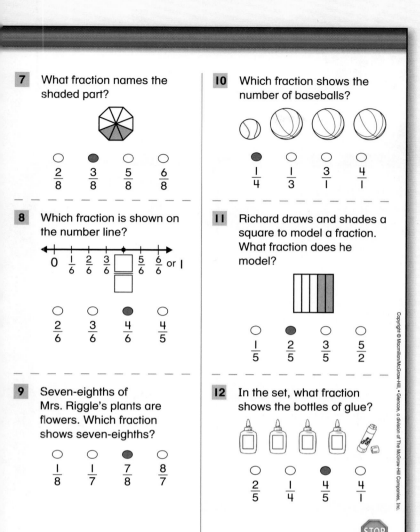

7 What fraction names the shaded part?

○ 2/8　● 3/8　○ 5/8　○ 6/8

8 Which fraction is shown on the number line?

0　1/6　2/6　3/6　☐　5/6　6/6 or 1

○ 2/6　○ 3/6　● 4/6　○ 4/5

9 Seven-eighths of Mrs. Riggle's plants are flowers. Which fraction shows seven-eighths?

○ 1/8　○ 1/7　● 7/8　○ 8/7

10 Which fraction shows the number of baseballs?

● 1/4　○ 1/3　○ 3/1　○ 4/1

11 Richard draws and shades a square to model a fraction. What fraction does he model?

○ 1/5　● 2/5　○ 3/5　○ 5/2

12 In the set, what fraction shows the bottles of glue?

○ 2/5　○ 1/4　● 4/5　○ 4/1

STOP

Diagnosing Student Errors and Misconceptions

Fraction Identification　For students who are struggling with identifying or modeling fractions, have them develop a systematic method for writing and modeling fractions. This method should be written down in a portfolio and memorized. Ask students to recite and perform this method each day until they are comfortable with the process. Review and reinforce throughout the school year to maintain mastery.

11.　1/5　miscounted number of shaded parts

　　　2/5　correct

　　　3/5　counted the number of unshaded parts

　　　5/2　mixed up the numerator and denominator

12.　2/5　miscounted the number of bottles

　　　1/4　chose a fraction that represents the number of glue sticks over the number of bottles

　　　4/5　correct

　　　4/1　does not understand fractions as part of a set

Chapter Overview

Chapter-at-a-Glance

Lesson	Math Objective	Local/State Standards
6-1 Fractions Equal to 1 (pp. 187–190)	Name a fraction for one whole.	
6-2 Comparing Fractions (pp. 191–194)	Compare fractions.	
Progress Check 1 (p. 195)		
6-3 Equivalent Fractions (pp. 197–200)	Write equivalent fractions.	
6-4 Fractions and Measurement (pp. 201–204)	Measure length to the nearest half-inch.	
Progress Check 2 (p. 205)		
6-5 Common Denominators (pp. 207–210)	Compare fractions with common denominators.	
6-6 Common Numerators (pp. 211–214)	Compare fractions with common numerators.	
Progress Check 3 (p. 215)		

Content-at-a-Glance

The diagram below summarizes and unpacks Chapter 6 content.

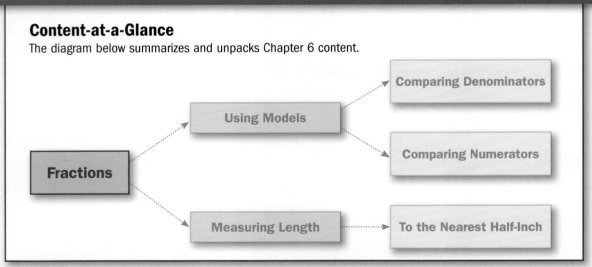

Chapter Assessment Manager

Diagnostic — Diagnose students' readiness.

	Student Study Guide/ Teacher Editions	Assessment Masters	Technology
Course Placement Test		1	💿 ExamView® Assessment Suite
Book 2 Pretest		45	💿 ExamView® Assessment Suite
Chapter Pretest		71	💿 ExamView® Assessment Suite
Get Ready	SSG 186		Math Online ▷ macmillanmh.com StudentWorks™ Plus

Formative — Identify students' misconceptions of content knowledge.

	Student Study Guide/ Teacher Editions	Assessment Masters	Technology
Progress Checks	SSG 195, 205, 215		Math Online ▷ macmillanmh.com StudentWorks™ Plus
Vocabulary Assessments	SSG 190, 194, 200, 204, 210, 214, 217		Math Online ▷ macmillanmh.com
Lesson Assessments			💿 ExamView® Assessment Suite
Are They Getting It?	TE 189, 193, 199, 203, 209, 213		

Summative — Determine student success in learning the concepts in the lesson, chapter, or book.

	Student Study Guide/ Teacher Editions	Assessment Masters	Technology
Chapter Test	SSG 219	74	💿 ExamView® Assessment Suite
Test Practice	SSG 221	77	💿 ExamView® Assessment Suite
Alternative Assessment	TE 219	80	
See It, Do It, Say It, Write It	TE 190, 194, 200, 204, 210, 214		
Book 2 Test		82	💿 ExamView® Assessment Suite

Back-Mapping and Vertical Alignment McGraw-Hill's *Math Triumphs* intervention program was conceived and developed with the final result in mind: student success in grade-level mathematics, including Algebra 1 and beyond. The authors, using the **NCTM Focal Points and Focal Connections** as their guide, developed this brand-new series by back-mapping from grade-level and Algebra 1 concepts, and vertically aligning the topics so that they build upon prior skills and concepts and serve as a foundation for future topics.

	Lesson 6-1	**Lesson 6-2**	**Lesson 6-3**	**Lesson 6-4**
Concept	Fractions Equal to 1	Comparing Fractions	Equivalent Fractions	Fractions and Measurement
Objective	Name a fraction for one whole.	Compare fractions.	Write equivalent fractions.	Measure length to the nearest half-inch.
Math Vocabulary	fraction	is greater than (>) is less than (<)	equivalent fractions	inch length measure
Lesson Resources	**Materials** • index cards • paper **Manipulatives** • fraction circles • fraction tiles • pattern blocks **Other Resources** CRM Vocabulary and English Language Development CRM Skills Practice CRM Problem-Solving Practice CRM Homework Practice	**Materials** • paper • index cards **Manipulatives** • fraction tiles • fraction circles • counters **Other Resources** CRM Vocabulary and English Language Development CRM Skills Practice CRM Problem-Solving Practice CRM Homework Practice	**Materials** • measuring cups • empty pint and half-gallon containers • water • paper towels • index cards **Manipulatives** • fraction circles • fraction tiles • counters **Other Resources** CRM Vocabulary and English Language Development CRM Skills Practice CRM Problem-Solving Practice CRM Homework Practice	**Materials** • paper **Manipulatives** • rulers **Other Resources** CRM Vocabulary and English Language Development CRM Skills Practice CRM Problem-Solving Practice CRM Homework Practice
Technology	**Math Online** macmillanmh.com StudentWorks™ Plus ExamView® Assessment Suite	**Math Online** macmillanmh.com StudentWorks™ Plus ExamView® Assessment Suite	**Math Online** macmillanmh.com StudentWorks™ Plus ExamView® Assessment Suite	**Math Online** macmillanmh.com StudentWorks™ Plus ExamView® Assessment Suite

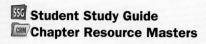

SSG Student Study Guide **TE** Teacher Edition
CRM Chapter Resource Masters 💿 DVD

Lesson 6-5	Lesson 6-6	
Common Denominators	Common Numerators	**Concept**
Compare fractions with common denominators.	Compare fractions with common numerators.	**Objective**
common denominator denominator numerator	denominator is greater than (>) is less than (<) numerator	**Math Vocabulary**
Materials • fraction cards (teacher made) • index cards	**Materials**	**Lesson Resources**
Manipulatives • fraction tiles • pattern blocks	**Manipulatives** • fraction circles • fraction tiles • number cubes	
Other Resources **CRM** Vocabulary and English Language Development **CRM** Skills Practice **CRM** Problem-Solving Practice **CRM** Homework Practice	**Other Resources** **CRM** Vocabulary and English Language Development **CRM** Skills Practice **CRM** Problem-Solving Practice **CRM** Homework Practice	
Math Online macmillanmh.com StudentWorks™ Plus 💿 ExamView® Assessment Suite	**Math Online** macmillanmh.com StudentWorks™ Plus 💿 ExamView® Assessment Suite	**Technology**

Chapter Notes

Home Connection

Read the Home Connection letter with students and have them write their names in the space below.

Read and explain the activity under Help at Home. If time allows, complete a portion of the activity so students can introduce the activity to a parent or other caregiver.

Have students:

- fold paper and compare the size of the paper on each side of the fold. Help students identify equal parts (halves, fourths, eighths . . .).

- look through recipes, newspapers, and magazines to find examples of fractions. Bring examples to class.

 ## Real-World Applications

Now We're Cooking Bring in a recipe for trail mix, marshmallow squares, or another non-cook snacks. Students can use fractions to understand how much of each ingredient needs to be added to make the recipe.

- **Why are fractions important?** They tell us how much of each ingredient to use. If you use too much or too little of an ingredient, it won't taste as it should.

CHAPTER 6 Fraction Equivalence

Home Connection

English   **Spanish**

Dear Family,
Today our class started **Chapter 6, Fraction Equivalence.** In this chapter, I will learn about equivalent fractions. I will also learn how to compare fractions and use fractions in measurement.

Love, _____

Estimada familia:
Hoy en clase comenzamos el **Capítulo 6, Equivalencia de fracciones.** En este capítulo aprenderé sobre las fracciones equivalentes. También aprenderé cómo comparar fracciones y a usar fracciones en la medición.

Cariños, _____

Help at Home
You can compare fractions with your child at home. Have your child identify objects that show equal parts. Then, use fractions to name the objects. Ask your child to compare the fractions using the terms greater than and less than.

Ayude en casa
Usted puede practicar comparando fracciones con su hijo(a) en casa. Haga que identifique objetos que muestren partes iguales. Luego, use fracciones para nombrar los objetos. Pídale que compare las fracciones usando los términos mayor que y menor que.

Math Online Take the chapter Get Ready quiz at macmillanmh.com.

Chapter 6   one hundred eighty-five **185**

Key Vocabulary

Find interactive definitions in 13 languages in the **eGlossary** at macmillanmh.com.

English   Español *Introduce the most important vocabulary terms from Chapter 6.*

fraction   fraccion

a number that represents part of a whole or part of a set (p. 187)

is greater than (>)   es mayor que

5 is greater than 1 $5 > 1$ (p. 191)

is less than (<)   es menor que

2 is less than 10 $2 < 10$ (p. 191)

**equivalent fractions
fracciones equivalentes**

fractions that equal the same amount (p. 197)

measure   medir

to find the length, height, or weight of an object (p. 201)

length   longitud

how long something is (p. 201)

inch   pulgada

a customary unit for measuring length
The plural is *inches*. (p. 201)

**common denominator
común denominador**

the same denominator in two fractions (p. 207)
$\frac{2}{6}$ $\frac{3}{6}$

numerator   numerador

the top number in a fraction (p. 207)

denominator   denominador

the bottom number in a fraction (p. 207)

Name ______________________

Get Ready

Write the fraction for each shaded part.

1 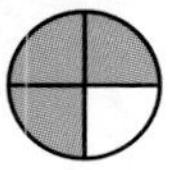

$\frac{3}{4}$

2 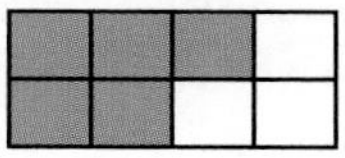

$\frac{5}{8}$

3 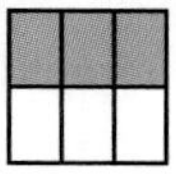

$\frac{3}{6}$

Compare. Write >, <, or =.

4 8 (>) 3 5 4 (=) 4 6 5 (<) 9 7 2 (>) 1

Measure to the nearest inch.

8 __4__ inches

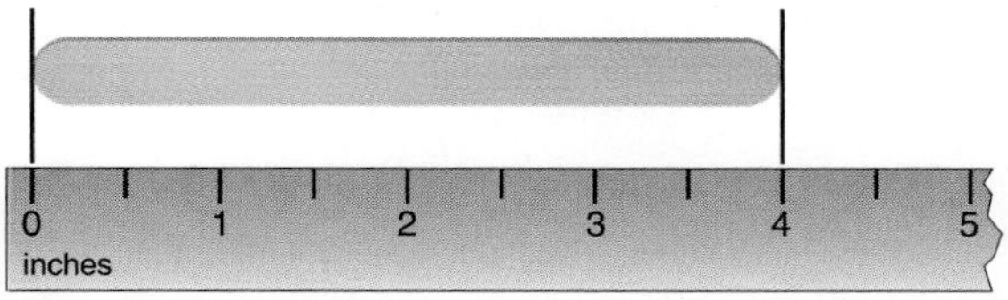

9 __3__ inches

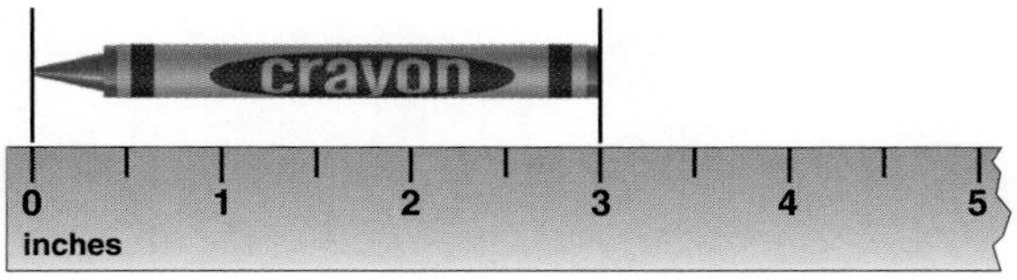

Vocabulary Preview

Make a poster to display the chapter's vocabulary words.

- Make a poster with two columns. Write each vocabulary word and its definition in the left column. Leave the right column empty for student examples.
- Make a small copy of the poster for each student.

After reviewing the definitions with the class, have student pairs develop examples for the vocabulary words they know. They can record their work on their individual copies.

After each lesson, have students add examples for words they have learned. They can also add more examples for other words.

At the conclusion of the chapter, have student volunteers write their examples on the class vocabulary poster. Use the poster as a review.

Get Ready

Have students complete Get Ready to assess readiness for the chapter concepts and skills.
Refer to the lessons below for additional support for prerequisite skills.

Lesson 5-1: Equal Parts (p. 149)
Lesson 5-3: Parts of a Whole (p. 159)
Grade 2, Lesson 3-1: Compare Numbers 0 to 50 (p. 99)
Grade 2, Lesson 8-2: Measure Inches (p. 305)

You may also assess student readiness with the following resources:

Math Online Online Readiness quiz at macmillanmh.com

Assessment Masters: Chapter Pretest (p. 71)

FOLDABLES® Study Organizer

Dinah Zike's Foldables®

Guide students through the directions on p. A131 in the Chapter Resource Masters to create their own Foldable graphic organizer for use with this chapter.

Mc Graw Hill

Professional Development

Targeted professional development has been articulated throughout **McGraw-Hill's *Math Triumphs*** intervention program. **The McGraw-Hill Professional Development Video Library** provides short videos that support the **NCTM Focal Points and Focal Connections.** For more information, visit macmillanmh.com.

Model Lessons

Instructional Strategies

Lesson 6-1

Lesson Notes

Lesson Planner

Objective   Name a fraction for one whole.

Vocabulary   fraction

Materials/Manipulatives   index cards, fraction circles, fraction tiles, paper, pattern blocks

Chapter Resource Masters

- [CRM] Vocabulary and English Language Development (p. A134)
- [CRM] Skill Practice (p. A135)
- [CRM] Problem-Solving-Practice (p. A136)
- [CRM] Homework Practice (p. A137)

1 Introduce

Vocabulary

Explore Vocabulary   Review the word fraction and its definition with the class. Write fractions and other numbers on the board. Have students identify the fractions and tell what each fraction represents. Use numbers around the classroom as well.

2 Teach

Key Concept

Foundational Skills and Concepts   After students have read through the Key Concept box, guide them through the following questions.

- **How many equal parts on the wheel?**   6
- **How many equal parts make 1 wheel?**   6
- **What fraction equals 1 whole?** $\frac{6}{6}$

Lesson 6-1

Name _____

Fractions Equal to 1

Key Concept

Name a **fraction** for one whole.

Look at the wheel. There are 6 equal parts.

All 6 parts make up 1 wheel.

So, $\frac{6}{6}$ equals 1 whole wheel.

$\frac{6}{6} = 1$

Vocabulary

fraction   a number that represents part of a whole or part of a set

$\left(\frac{1}{2}\right), \left(\frac{1}{3}\right), \left(\frac{1}{4}\right), \left(\frac{3}{4}\right)$

A fraction with the same numerator and denominator is equal to 1, or one whole.

There are 9 equal window panes.

All 9 panes make up 1 whole window.

$\frac{9}{9} = 1$

Copyright © Macmillan/McGraw-Hill • Glencoe, a division of The McGraw-Hill Companies, Inc.

English Learner Strategy

Homonyms, Homophones, Synonyms and Vocabulary

Part and *whole* are two words commonly used to describe fractions. *Part* has multiple meanings such as a role in a play.

"Whole" is easily confused with "hole." Be sure students understand "part" and "whole" as they relate to fractions.

1. Give each student an index card. Draw a fraction bar horizontally through the center of the card.

2. Have students write synonyms for "part" above the fraction bar (examples include portion, slice, cut, amount, piece) and synonyms for "whole" below the fraction bar (examples include total, sum, complete, full).

3. Display these alternative definitions in the classroom.

Example

Circle the fraction that equals 1.

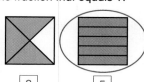

$$\frac{3}{4} \qquad \frac{5}{5}$$

Step 1   Write each fraction.

Step 2   Circle the fraction with the same numerator and denominator.

Answer $\frac{5}{5} = 1$

Step-by-Step Practice

Circle the fraction that equals 1.

Step 1   Write each fraction.

Step 2   Circle the fraction with the same numerator and denominator.

Answer $\frac{4}{4} = \underline{1}$

$$\frac{4}{4} \qquad \frac{2}{8}$$

188   one hundred eighty-eight

Additional *Example*

Circle the fraction that equals 1.

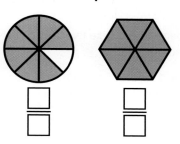

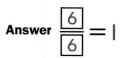

Step 1 Write each fraction.

Step 2 Circle the fraction with the same numerator and denominator.

Answer $\frac{6}{6} = 1$

⚠ **Common Error** *Alert*

Students might write fractions for the unshaded part of a model. Be sure students understand that their answer represents the shaded part of the model unless a problem specifies otherwise.

Intervention Strategy

Auditory/ Kinesthetic Learners

Materials: fraction circles

Fraction Song: Sung to the Tune of "Doe, a Deer," lines correspond to the note in front of each line.

Make a poster with the following lyrics on it. As the students sing the lyrics, have them use fraction circles to model.

(Do)   One half, two halves, they make one whole,
(Re)   One third, two thirds, three thirds make one whole,
(Mi)   One fourth, two fourths, three fourths, four fourths,
(Fa)   Look, they make another whole,
(So)   One fifth, two fifths, three fifths, four fifths
(La)   Five fifths, one whole, one sixth, two sixths
(Ti)   Three sixths, four sixths, five sixths, six sixths
That will bring us back to whole, whole, whole, whole
Repeat.

Guided Practice

Direct students to complete Exercises 1–5 in Guided Practice.

Exercises 4 and 5 Some students may need to represent each fraction using manipulatives.

Problem-Solving Practice

Guide students through the four-step problem-solving plan to complete Exercise 6.

- **What are the key words?** 7 pieces, what fraction shows the whole cake

- **What will the picture look like?** It will have 7 shaded equal parts.

  Note: A circle divided into 7 equal parts may be very difficult for a 3rd grade student to draw, recommend students draw a rectangle.

- **What fraction does your picture show?** $\frac{7}{7}$

Ask students to check their work using the strategy suggested in the Check step. Students can look at the numerator and denominator of the fraction to be sure they are the same.

Using Manipulatives

Fraction Tiles Give each student fraction tiles showing values from $\frac{1}{6}$ through 1 whole. Have students trace a fraction tile and label its value. Then have students use the same tile to make 1 whole (students will draw adjacent shapes until they form 1 whole).

Students should label each piece. (Values from $\frac{1}{8}$ through $\frac{1}{12}$ can be given to more advanced students).

On-Hand Manipulatives Students can fold paper circles, squares, or rectangles to form 1 whole divided into equal parts.

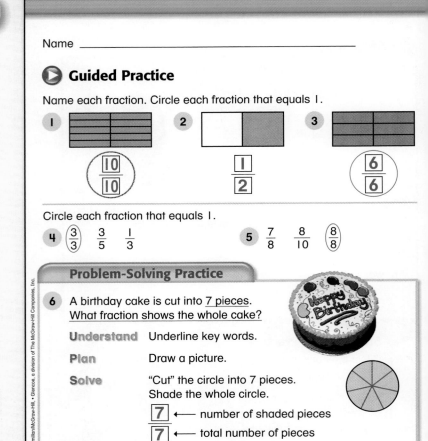

Name _____

▶ **Guided Practice**

Name each fraction. Circle each fraction that equals 1.

1. $\frac{10}{10}$ 2. $\frac{1}{2}$ 3. $\frac{6}{6}$

Circle each fraction that equals 1.

4. $\left(\frac{3}{3}\right)$ $\frac{3}{5}$ $\frac{1}{3}$ 5. $\frac{7}{8}$ $\frac{8}{10}$ $\left(\frac{8}{8}\right)$

Problem-Solving Practice

6. A birthday cake is cut into <u>7 pieces</u>. <u>What fraction shows the whole cake?</u>

Understand	Underline key words.
Plan	Draw a picture.
Solve	"Cut" the circle into 7 pieces. Shade the whole circle.

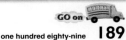 ← number of shaded pieces

 ← total number of pieces

Check	Does the fraction have the same numerator and denominator?

GO on

Copyright © Macmillan/McGraw-Hill • Glencoe, a division of The McGraw-Hill Companies, Inc.

Chapter 6   Lesson 1   one hundred eighty-nine **189**

Are They Getting It? ❓

Check students' understanding of fractions equal to 1 whole by writing these exercises on the board. Ask students to point out the correct and incorrect answers and explain their reasoning.

1. $\frac{3}{4} = 1$ This is incorrect. $\frac{3}{4}$ is not equal to 1 whole.

2. $\frac{5}{5} = 1$ This is correct.

3. $\frac{2}{2} = 1$ This is correct.

4. $\frac{6}{8} = 1$ This is incorrect. $\frac{6}{8}$ is not equal to 1 whole.

Practice on Your Own

Name each fraction. Circle each fraction that equals 1.

7

$$\dfrac{2}{2}$$ (circled)

8

$$\dfrac{4}{6}$$

9

$$\dfrac{12}{12}$$ (circled)

Circle each fraction that equals 1.

10 $\dfrac{6}{7}$ $\left(\dfrac{7}{7}\right)$ $\dfrac{7}{8}$

11 $\dfrac{10}{14}$ $\left(\dfrac{14}{14}\right)$ $\dfrac{12}{14}$

Shade each model to show 1. Name each fraction.

12 $\dfrac{8}{8}$

13 $\dfrac{3}{3}$

14 **WRITING IN ▸MATH** Look at the model. Name the fraction in two ways. Explain.

$\dfrac{4}{4}$ or I whole 4 out of 4 parts are shaded. I whole is shaded.

Vocabulary Check Complete.

15 A **fraction** names part of a whole or part of a set.

STOP

190 one hundred ninety

Math Challenge

Not all pieces look the same!

On the board, draw a picture of a heart. Shade $\dfrac{1}{2}$ of the heart.

- **Are the halves the same size?** yes

- **Do they look exactly the same?** No; one side is shaded.

Give pairs of students 4 square sheets of construction paper.

Have students divide the paper into 4 equal pieces. Each piece of paper should be divided differently. Have students color in one part of the paper and label that part. $\dfrac{1}{4}$

Possible answers:

Have students share their fraction models.

Direct students to p. 190 in their student books. Have students complete Exercises 7–15 independently. You may need to review the directions of each section before students begin.

4 Assess

See It, Do It, Say It, Write It

Step 1 Write the equation $\dfrac{6}{6} = 1$ whole on the board in number form. Read the fraction to the class and then draw a model to show $\dfrac{6}{6}$.

Step 2 Have pairs of students write the equation $\dfrac{5}{5} = 1$ on a sheet of paper and then draw a model.

Step 3 Have pairs present their models and explain their strategy to the class. (Drawings will likely include a circle, square, or rectangle divided into 5 equal parts).

Step 4 Have students work alone to write the statement $\dfrac{8}{8} = 1$ and draw a model representing the fraction.

Looking Ahead: Pre-teach

In the next lesson, students will learn how to compare fractions.

Example

Which fraction is greater?

$\dfrac{3}{4} > \dfrac{2}{4}$

Have students compare the fractions. Write >, <, or =.

1. $\dfrac{1}{2}$ $\left(<\right)$ $\dfrac{2}{2}$

2. $\dfrac{4}{5}$ $\left(>\right)$ $\dfrac{1}{5}$

Lesson 6-1 Fractions Equal to 1 **190**

Lesson Notes

Lesson Planner

Objective Compare fractions.

Vocabulary is greater than (>), is less than (<)

Materials/Manipulatives paper, fraction tiles, fraction circles, counters, index cards

Chapter Resource Masters

- **CRM** Vocabulary and English Language Development (p. A138)
- **CRM** Skills Practice (p. A139)
- **CRM** Problem-Solving Practice (p. A140)
- **CRM** Homework Practice (p. A141)

1 Introduce

Vocabulary

Nonexamples The number 30 is greater than 5. Five is not greater than 30. Ask students to give other nonexamples of numbers greater than other numbers. Then, repeat the process using less than.

2 Teach

Key Concept

Foundational Skills and Concepts After students have read through the Key Concept box, guide them through the following questions.

- **How many equal pieces in each pie?** 3

- **What fraction names the shaded section in the first pie?** $\frac{2}{3}$

- **What fraction names the shaded section in the second pie?** $\frac{1}{3}$

- **Is $\frac{2}{3}$ greater than or less than $\frac{1}{3}$?** greater than

---

Name _____

Compare Fractions

Key Concept

You can compare fractions using models.

 $\frac{2}{3}$ $>$ $\frac{1}{3}$

$\frac{2}{3}$ of a pie is more than $\frac{1}{3}$ of a pie.
The fraction $\frac{2}{3}$ **is greater than** the fraction $\frac{1}{3}$.

Vocabulary

is greater than (>) 5 is greater than 1

$$5 > 1$$

$\frac{3}{4}$ is greater than $\frac{1}{4}$.

is less than (<) 2 is less than 10

$$2 < 10$$

The denominators are the same, so compare the numerators. 5 > 2

$\frac{5}{9} > \frac{2}{9}$ ← numerator
← denominator

Chapter 6   Lesson 2   one hundred ninety-one   **191**

English Learner Strategy

Understanding Vocabulary

1. Make a T chart with students. On the left of the chart write "Is Greater Than (>)" on the right write "Is Less Than (<)".

2. Under each heading help students develop examples of greater than and less than.

   Is Greater Than (>)  >

   Is Less Than (<)

3. Display this poster in the classroom.

Example

Compare the fractions. Write >, <, or =.

$$\frac{2}{8} \; \boxed{<} \; \frac{5}{8}$$

Step 1   Shade the first fraction. Shade 2 out of 8 parts.
Step 2   Shade the second fraction. Shade 5 out of 8 parts.
Step 3   Compare the numerators. 2 < 5

Answer $\frac{2}{8} \boxed{<} \frac{5}{8}$ $\frac{2}{8}$ is less than $\frac{5}{8}$.

Step-by-Step Practice

Compare the fractions. Write >, <, or =.

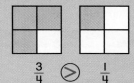

$$\frac{3}{4} \; \boxed{>} \; \frac{1}{4}$$

Step 1   Shade the first fraction.

Shade __3__ out of __4__ parts.

Step 2   Shade the second fraction.

Shade __1__ out of __4__ parts.

Step 3   Compare the numerators. __3__ ⬭> __1__

Answer $\frac{3}{4} \boxed{>} \frac{1}{4}$ $\frac{3}{4}$ is **greater** than $\frac{1}{4}$.

192   one hundred ninety-two

Intervention Strategy

Visual/ Kinesthetic Learners

Materials: chairs

1. On the left of the classroom have 4 students line up their chairs. On the right have 4 more students line up their chairs. Have the students stand in front of their chairs.

2. Have 1 student on the left sit down and 2 students on the right sit down.

   • **What fraction of the students on the left are sitting?** $\frac{1}{4}$

   • **What fraction of the students on the right are sitting?** $\frac{2}{4}$

   • **Which is greater?** $\frac{2}{4}$

3. Repeat by having a different number of students sit down. When students understand the concept have 5 or 6 students line up chairs and work with fractions having denominators of 5 and 6.

Additional *Example*

Compare. Write >, <, or =.

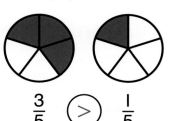

$$\frac{3}{5} \; \boxed{>} \; \frac{1}{5}$$

Step 1 Shade the first fraction.
Shade 3 out of 5 parts.

Step 2 Shade the second fraction.
Shade 1 out of 5 parts.

Step 3 Compare the numerators. 3 > 5

Answer $\frac{3}{5} \boxed{>} \frac{1}{5}$ $\frac{3}{5}$ is greater than $\frac{1}{5}$.

Math Coach Notes

Strategies

1. Have students begin the lesson by comparing whole numbers. For example, 4 > 2.

2. Use models to show students how to compare fractions with the same denominator. Two out of 5 parts, or $\frac{2}{5}$, is less than 4 out of 5 parts, or $\frac{4}{5}$.

3. Let students continue to use models such as fraction circles or fraction tiles to compare fractions.

③ Practice

Guided Practice

Direct students to complete Exercises 1–2 in Guided Practice.

Exercises 1 and 2 Remind students to shade the fraction models before comparing. The models will help them identify the greater or lesser fraction.

Problem-Solving Practice

Guide students through the four-step problem-solving plan to complete Exercise 3.

- **What are the key words?** $\frac{1}{5}, \frac{1}{2}$, farther
- **What fraction bars will be needed?** 1 whole, $\frac{1}{2}$, and $\frac{1}{5}$

Ask students to check their work using the strategy suggested in the Check step. Students can draw a picture to solve the problem.

- **What picture could you draw?** Sample answer: I could draw and shade $\frac{1}{5}$ and $\frac{1}{2}$ of a circle, rectangle, or set.

Using Manipulatives

Fraction Tiles or Fraction Circles Have students use fraction tiles to make comparisons. For example show one-third and one-half fraction tiles.

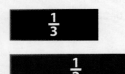

- **Which tile is greater?** one-half
- **How do you know?** It is a larger part of a whole tile.

On-Hand Manipulatives Students can draw fraction comparison models, use strips of paper to make fraction tiles, or fold circles to make models of fraction circles.

Name _____

▶ **Guided Practice**

Shade and compare the fractions. Write >, <, or =.

1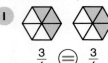

$\frac{3}{6} \bigcirc= \frac{3}{6}$

2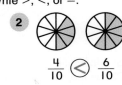

$\frac{4}{10} \bigcirc< \frac{6}{10}$

Problem-Solving Practice

3 José jogged $\frac{1}{5}$ of a mile. Shawon jogged $\frac{1}{2}$ of a mile. Who jogged <u>farther</u>?

Understand Underline key words.

Plan Use fraction bars.

Solve

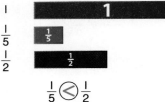

$\frac{1}{5} \bigcirc< \frac{1}{2}$

__Shawon__ jogged farther.

Check Draw a picture. Which fraction has a greater area shaded?

Chapter 6   Lesson 2   one hundred ninety-three **193**

Copyright © Macmillan/McGraw-Hill, • Glencoe, a division of The McGraw-Hill Companies, Inc.

Are They Getting It?

Check students' understanding of comparing fractions by writing these exercises on the board. Ask students to point out the correct and incorrect answers and explain their reasoning.

1. $\frac{2}{4} > \frac{1}{4}$ This is correct.

2. $\frac{4}{5} < \frac{2}{5}$ This is incorrect. $\frac{4}{5}$ is greater than $\frac{2}{5}$.

3. $\frac{3}{6} > \frac{5}{6}$ This is incorrect. $\frac{3}{6}$ is less than $\frac{5}{6}$.

Practice on Your Own

Compare the fractions. Write >, <, or =.

4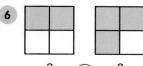

$\frac{3}{3}$ $>$ $\frac{2}{3}$

5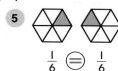

$\frac{1}{6}$ $=$ $\frac{1}{6}$

Shade and compare the fractions. Write >, <, or =.

6

$\frac{2}{4}$ $<$ $\frac{3}{4}$

7

$\frac{3}{7}$ $>$ $\frac{1}{7}$

8 **WRITING IN MATH** Benito says $\frac{1}{3}$ is greater than $\frac{1}{2}$. Is he correct? Explain.

No, Benito is not correct. The $\frac{1}{3}$ fraction bar is shorter than the $\frac{1}{2}$ bar, so $\frac{1}{3} < \frac{1}{2}$.

Vocabulary Check Complete.

9 The symbol > means is ___**greater**___ than.

10 The symbol < means is ___**less**___ than.

STOP

194 one hundred ninety-four

Math Challenge

Materials: paper, fraction tiles, fraction circles

1. Have students work in pairs. Ask each student to write a short fraction story with illustrations of the fractions. In the stories, the main character(s) should compare fractions. Remind students that fractions can be part of a set and do not have to be "part of a pie."

2. Ask students to share their stories with the class.

3. Students should identify the fractions in their classmates' stories.

Practice on Your Own

Direct students to p. 194 in their student books. Have students complete Exercises 4–10 independently. You may need to review the directions of each section before students begin.

4 Assess

See It, Do It, Say It, Write It

Step 1 Write the comparison $\frac{3}{8}$ ◯ $\frac{6}{8}$ on the board. Model how to represent each fraction. Write the < sign.

Step 2 Ask students to write the comparison $\frac{3}{5}$ ◯ $\frac{4}{5}$ on a piece of paper. Have students model and compare the fractions.

Step 3 Have students work in pairs. Write the comparison $\frac{9}{10}$ ◯ $\frac{4}{10}$ on the board. Tell students to discuss how to represent and compare the fractions.

Step 4 Have students work alone. Have them compare the fractions $\frac{7}{12}$ ◯ $\frac{9}{12}$. Tell them to include a model.

Looking Ahead: Pre-teach

In the next lesson, students will learn how to write equivalent fractions.

Example

$\frac{2}{6} = \frac{1}{3}$

Make fraction tiles available to the students. Have students write an equivalent fraction.

1. $\frac{1}{2} = \frac{\boxed{2}}{4}$ **2.** $\frac{4}{5} = \frac{\boxed{4}}{5}$

3. $\frac{2}{3} = \frac{\boxed{4}}{6}$ **4.** $\frac{2}{8} = \frac{\boxed{1}}{4}$

Progress Check 1

Formative Assessment

Use the Progress Check to assess students' mastery of the previous lessons. Have students review the lesson indicated for the problems they answered incorrectly.

 Common Error *Alert*

Some students use the incorrect symbol when comparing numbers. Remind students that the less than symbol always points to the smaller number.

Exercises 7–8 Make sure students shade both models before comparing.

Name _____

Progress Check 1 (Lessons 6-1 and 6-2)

Name each fraction. Circle each fraction that equals 1.

1. ⬡ $\boxed{\dfrac{6}{6}}$

2. △ $\boxed{\dfrac{3}{3}}$

3. ◻ $\dfrac{1}{2}$

Shade each model to show 1. Write the fraction.

4. ▭ $\dfrac{3}{3}$

5. ⬠ $\dfrac{5}{5}$

6. ▱ $\dfrac{7}{7}$

Shade and compare the fractions. Write >, <, or =.

7. $\dfrac{3}{4}$ ⊜ $\dfrac{2}{4}$ → $>$

8. $\dfrac{5}{6}$ ⊜ $\dfrac{3}{6}$ → $>$

9. Sam drank $\dfrac{1}{5}$ of a juice box.

Reid drank $\dfrac{3}{5}$ of a juice box.

Who drank more juice?

Reid drank more juice.

Chapter 6   Progress Check   one hundred ninety-five **195**

Data-Driven Decision Making

Students missing Exercises . . .	Have trouble with . . .	Should review and practice . . .
1–6	naming and modeling fractions for one whole.	SSG Lesson 6-1, p. 187 CRM Skills Practice, p. A135
7–8	comparing fractions.	SSG Lesson 6-2, p. 191 CRM Skills Practice, p. A139
9	problem-solving that involves comparing fractions.	SSG Lesson 6-2, p. 193 CRM Problem-Solving Practice, p. A140

«« Replay Greater Fraction Game

Materials
2 game pieces
number cube labeled 1–6
blank number cube
(label the sides 8, 8, 10, 10, 12, 12)
eighth, tenth, and twelfth fraction strips

Start

Finish

How to Play

Listen as your teacher reads the instructions.

Replay

Use the Replay activity to review and reinforce the concepts and skills presented in Lessons 6-1 and 6-2.

Instructions

Present the instructions to the students.

- Player 1 rolls the number cubes to create a fraction.

- The lesser number is the numerator and the greater number is the denominator.

- Player 2 rolls the number cube (1–6) to create a different fraction with the same denominator.

- Players compare fractions.

- The player with the greater fraction moves one space. If the fractions are the same, both players move one space.

- The first player to Finish wins.

Student Technology

Students can use the following technology resources to reinforce chapter content.

- StudentWorks™ Plus

- Math Online macmillanmh.com

- eGlossary

Lesson Notes

Lesson Planner

Math Objective   Write equivalent fractions.

Vocabulary   equivalent fractions

Materials/Manipulatives   measuring cups, empty pint and half-gallon containers, water, paper towels, fraction tiles, fraction circles, counters, index cards

Chapter Resource Masters

- **[CRM]** Vocabulary and English Language Development (p. A142)
- **[CRM]** Skill Practice (p. A143)
- **[CRM]** Problem-Solving-Practice (p. A144)
- **[CRM]** Homework Practice (p. A145)

① Introduce

Vocabulary

Vocabulary Match   Discuss the definition of equivalent fractions. Draw the following fraction bars on the board. $\frac{2}{8}, \frac{1}{2}, \frac{2}{3}, \frac{4}{8}, \frac{4}{6}$ and $\frac{1}{4}$. Have students match the equivalent fractions and justify how they know they are equivalent.

② Teach

Key Concept

Foundational Skills and Concepts   After students have read through the Key Concept box, guide them through the following questions.

- **What are equivalent fractions?** fractions that represent equal amounts

- **What fraction is equivalent to $\frac{1}{2}$?** $\frac{2}{4}$

Name _____

Equivalent Fractions

Key Concept

Equivalent fractions represent an *equal* amount.

Use fraction bars to find equivalent fractions.

$\frac{1}{2} = \frac{2}{4}$

Vocabulary

equivalent fractions   fractions that equal the same amount

$\frac{1}{2} = \frac{2}{4}$

$\frac{1}{2}$ is the same as $\frac{2}{4}$.

The same area is shaded in $\frac{1}{2}$ and in $\frac{2}{4}$.
The fractions $\frac{1}{2}$ and $\frac{2}{4}$ are equivalent.

English Learner Strategy

Equivalent Fractions in the Kitchen   Bring in several measuring cups, as well as empty pint and half-gallon containers. Have water or rice available and paper towels on hand.

1. If students are from countries where the metric system is used, the teacher should introduce cups, pints, and gallons as part of America's measurement system.

2. Allow students to identify equivalent measures and record the results.

   For example, $\frac{1}{4}$ - cup of water $+ \frac{1}{4}$ - cup of water $= \frac{1}{2}$ - cup of water, so $\frac{2}{4} = \frac{1}{2}$.

3. Have the students share their findings.

Example

Write an equivalent fraction.

Step 1   Shade the top fraction bar. Shade 1 out of 3 parts.

Step 2   Shade an equal amount of the bottom fraction bar.

Step 3   There are 2 parts shaded on the bottom fraction bar.

Step 4   Write the equivalent fraction.

$\dfrac{1}{3}$

$\dfrac{2}{6}$

Answer $\dfrac{1}{3} = \dfrac{2}{6}$

Step-by-Step Practice

Write an equivalent fraction.

Step 1   Shade the top fraction bar. Shade **3** out of **4** parts.

Step 2   Shade an equal amount of the bottom fraction bar.

Step 3   There are **6** parts shaded on the bottom fraction bar.

Step 4   Write the equivalent fraction.

$\dfrac{3}{4}$

$\dfrac{6}{8}$

Answer $\dfrac{3}{4} = \dfrac{\boxed{6}}{8}$

198   one hundred ninety-eight

Write an equivalent fraction

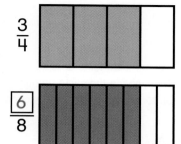

$\dfrac{3}{4}$

$\dfrac{\boxed{6}}{8}$

Step 1   Shade the top fraction bar. Shade 3 out of 4 parts.

Step 2   Shade an equal amount of the bottom fraction bar.

Step 3   There are 6 parts shaded on the bottom fraction bar.

Step 4   Write the equivalent fraction.

Answer $\dfrac{3}{4} = \dfrac{6}{8}$

Math Coach Notes

Have students begin the lesson by using fraction tiles or fraction circles to identify equivalent fractions. Remind students that the smaller the denominator, the larger the fraction will be. This will help students understand comparing fractions and how to make equivalents.

Intervention Strategy

Visual/ Kinesthetic Learners

Materials: fraction circles

1. Distribute the $\dfrac{1}{2}$ and $\dfrac{1}{6}$ parts of the fraction circles to each student.

2. Have students lay down one of the half circles. Ask students to put $\dfrac{1}{6}$ parts on top of the half circle until the pieces cover the half circle exactly. Ask them how many $\dfrac{1}{6}$ pieces cover the half circle. 3 Have students write a fraction with a denominator of 6 that is equivalent to $\dfrac{1}{2}$. $\dfrac{3}{6}$

3. Have students repeat the activity by covering a half circle with $\dfrac{1}{8}$ parts and then write a fraction with a denominator of 8 that is equivalent to $\dfrac{1}{2}$. $\dfrac{4}{8}$

Guided Practice

Direct students to complete Exercises 1 – 2 in Guided Practice.

Exercise 2 Remind students to shade the given fraction first. Then, shade the same amount of the bottom fraction to find the equivalent fraction.

Problem-Solving Practice

Guide students through the four-step problem-solving plan to complete Exercise 3.

- **What are the key words?** $\frac{1}{2}$, blue, how many parts should she color

- **How many parts of the fraction bar need to be colored?** 5

Ask students to check their work using the strategy suggested in the Check step. Students can compare the shaded areas to determine equivalent fractions.

- **How do you know that the shaded areas are equal?** Sample answer: When both fraction bars are compared, the shading covers equal areas.

Using Manipulatives

Fraction Tiles, Fraction Circles, and Counters Students can use the manipulatives to identify and model equivalent fractions.

Ask the students to find as many equivalent fractions as they can for the fractions $\frac{1}{2}$, $\frac{1}{4}$, and $\frac{1}{3}$.

For each fraction, the student should model and record as many fractions equivalent to the original as possible.

On-Hand Manipulatives Students can draw models of equivalent fractions, use strips of paper to make fraction tiles, or fold circles to make examples of fraction circles.

Name _____

▶ Guided Practice

Write an equivalent fraction.

1

$$\frac{4}{5} = \frac{\boxed{8}}{10}$$

2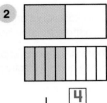

$$\frac{1}{2} = \frac{\boxed{4}}{8}$$

Problem-Solving Practice

3 Mercedes wants to color $\frac{1}{2}$ of the figure <u>blue</u>. <u>How many parts should she color?</u>

Understand Underline key words.

Plan Use fraction bars to find an equivalent fraction.

Solve Mercedes should color

__5__ parts blue. $\frac{1}{2} = \frac{\boxed{5}}{10}$

Check Are the shaded areas equal?

GO on

Copyright © Macmillan/McGraw-Hill • Glencoe, a division of The McGraw-Hill Companies, Inc.

Are They Getting It? ❓

Check students' understanding of equivalent fractions by writing these comparisons on the board. Ask students to point out the correct and incorrect comparisons and explain their reasoning.

1. $\frac{2}{4} = \frac{3}{8}$ This is incorrect. The shading does not cover the same area. When $\frac{2}{4}$ is shaded, it covers more area than $\frac{3}{8}$.

2. $\frac{2}{5} = \frac{4}{10}$ This is correct.

3. $\frac{2}{6} = \frac{2}{3}$ This is incorrect. The shading does not cover the same area. When $\frac{2}{6}$ is shaded, it covers less area than $\frac{2}{3}$.

4. $\frac{1}{2} = \frac{6}{12}$ This is correct.

▶ Practice on Your Own

Write an equivalent fraction.

4

$$\frac{3}{4} = \frac{\boxed{6}}{8}$$

5

$$\frac{1}{2} = \frac{\boxed{3}}{6}$$

6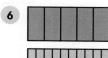

$$\frac{5}{5} = \frac{\boxed{10}}{10}$$

7

$$\frac{2}{3} = \frac{\boxed{8}}{12}$$

8

$$\frac{2}{4} = \frac{\boxed{6}}{12}$$

9

$$\frac{3}{5} = \frac{\boxed{6}}{10}$$

10 **WRITING IN ►MATH**   Rita ran $\frac{4}{5}$ of a mile.
Ed ran $\frac{8}{10}$ of a mile. Who ran farther? Explain.

__They ran the same distance.__ $\dfrac{4}{5} = \dfrac{8}{10}$

Vocabulary Check   Complete.

11 Fractions that equal the same amount are
____**equivalent fractions**____ . STOP

200 two hundred

Math Challenge

Equivalent Fraction Memory

Have students write each of the following fractions on an index card.

$$\frac{1}{2}, \frac{3}{6}, \frac{1}{2}, \frac{2}{4}, \frac{1}{2}, \frac{4}{8}, \frac{1}{3}, \frac{2}{6}, \frac{1}{4}, \frac{2}{8}, \frac{2}{5}, \frac{4}{10}$$

Shuffle the cards and place them face down in an array.

Students take turns flipping over two cards, trying to match two equivalent fractions. Students keep the cards of any matches they make.

Make fraction circles and fraction tiles available for students to use as a resource.

Practice on Your Own

Direct students to p. 200 in their student books. Have students complete Exercises 4–11 independently. You may need to review the directions of each section before students begin.

④ Assess

See It, Do It, Say It, Write It

Step 1 Write the equation $\frac{3}{6} = \frac{?}{12}$ on the board. Read the equation out loud to the class.

Step 2 Have the students work in pairs to find the equivalent fraction.

Step 3 Have students present their answer and strategy (which may include pictures, manipulatives, or knowledge of fractions) to the class.

Step 4 Have students complete the problem $\frac{2}{4} = \frac{?}{8}$ on their own. Make sure students include a model of how they solved the problem.

Looking Ahead: Pre-teach

In the next lesson, students will learn how to measure length to the nearest half-inch.

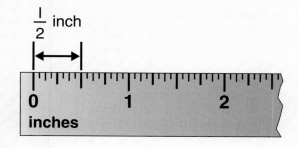

Distribute rulers to the students. Ask students to point to each of the following locations on the ruler. (Teacher should verify locations for correctness.)

1. $2\frac{1}{2}$ inches

2. 3 inches

3. $4\frac{1}{2}$ inches

Lesson Notes

Lesson Planner

Math Objective   Measure length to the nearest half-inch.

Vocabulary   measure, **length**, **inch**

Materials/Manipulatives   rulers, paper

Chapter Resource Masters

- CRM Vocabulary and English Language Development (p. A146)
- CRM Skill Practice (p. A147)
- CRM Problem-Solving-Practice (p. A148)
- CRM Homework Practice (p. A149)

① Introduce ⏱

Vocabulary

Compare Vocabulary   Write the words *measure*, *length*, and *inch* on the board. Ask students to compare the terms.

- **How are they the same?** All the words relate to finding out how long something is.

- **How are they different?** Each term is more specific than the next. To measure is to find any unit of measurement. Length is a specific type of measurement. An inch is a specific unit of length.

② Teach ⏱

Key Concept

Foundational Skills and Concepts   After students have read through the Key Concept box, guide them through the following questions.

- **The end of the crayon is between what two numbers?** 3 and 4

- **What fraction shows a place exactly between two numbers?** $\frac{1}{2}$

- **How long is the crayon?** $3\frac{1}{2}$ inches

Name _____

Fractions and Measurement

Key Concept

You can **measure length** to the nearest half-**inch**.

$3\frac{1}{2}$ inches

The length is halfway between the 3 and the 4.
The crayon is $3\frac{1}{2}$ inches long.

Vocabulary

measure   to find the length, height, or weight of an object

length   how long something is

inch   a customary unit for measuring length
The plural is *inches*.

length

The marks on a ruler are similar to a number line. Use the marks to find the length of an object.

Chapter 6   Lesson 4

two hundred one 201

English Learner Strategy

Understanding Customary Units of Measure   Many English language learners and their parents may be more familiar with metric units than customary units. Help students relate the two types of measurements by creating a Venn diagram. Label the left circle "Customary Units," the right circle "Metric Units," and the overlapping section "Both."

Ask students to share what they know about each and fill in the students' ideas on the Venn diagram. Have a ruler on hand to demonstrate differences and give examples.

Information on the Venn diagram may include the following. *Customary Units:* "inches," "used often in America," and a labeled example of an inch. *Metric Units:* "meter," "centimeter," "millimeter," and "used in many other countries." *Both:* "units of measurement" and "ways to measure length."

Display the Venn diagram in the classroom as a student resource.

Example

Measure to the nearest half-inch.

Step 1   Line up one end of the object with 0.

Step 2   Find the half-inch mark that is closest to the end of the object. $2\frac{1}{2}$ inches

Step 3   Write the length to the nearest half-inch.

$2\frac{1}{2}$ inches

Answer   The feather is $2\frac{1}{2}$ inches long.

? inches

Step-by-Step Practice

Measure to the nearest half-inch.

Step 1   Line up one end of the object with 0.

Step 2   Find the half-inch mark that is closest to the end of the object.

    __2__ inches

Step 3   Write the length to the nearest half-inch.

    __2__ inches

Answer   The fish is __2__ inches long.

? inches

Additional *Example*

Measure to the nearest half-inch.

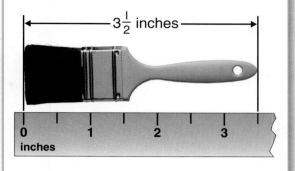

$3\frac{1}{2}$ inches

Step 1   Line up one end of the object with 0.

Step 2   Find the half-inch mark that is closest to the end of the object. $3\frac{1}{2}$ inches

Step 3   Write the length to the nearest half-inch.

$3\frac{1}{2}$ inches

Answer   The paintbrush is $3\frac{1}{2}$ inches long.

⚠ Common Error *Alert*

Students will often start measuring an object at the edge of the ruler rather than at the 0 mark. Make sure students understand to line up the beginning of the object being measured with the 0 mark on the ruler.

Intervention Strategy

Visual/Naturalist/ Kinesthetic Learners

Materials: rulers

Have students copy the following table onto a sheet of paper.

Nature's Measures

Object	Length to the nearest half-inch

Have students work in pairs. Take students outside to measure different objects to the nearest half-inch. Examples might include: leaves, blades of grass, insects, small sticks.

③ Practice

Guided Practice

Direct students to complete Exercises 1 – 2 in Guided Practice.

Exercises 1 and 2 Remind students they are measuring to the nearest half-inch.

Problem-Solving Practice

Guide students through the four-step problem-solving plan to complete Exercise 3.

- **What are the key words?** measures, length, nearest half-inch.

- **What should one end of the carrot line up with?** The 0 mark on the ruler.

- **How long is the carrot?** $4\frac{1}{2}$ inches

Ask students to check their work using the strategy suggested in the Check step. Students should be sure they have lined up one end of the carrot with 0.

Using Manipulatives

Ruler Model how to measure with a ruler. Point out the inch and $\frac{1}{2}$ inch marks. Point out that a ruler is like a number line and when measuring to the nearest half-inch, sometimes the measurement will be a whole number.

 On-Hand Manipulatives Have students use strips of paper to make their own rulers.

Name _____

▶ Guided Practice

Measure to the nearest half-inch.

1   __2__ inches

2   $1\frac{1}{2}$ inches

Copyright © Macmillan/McGraw-Hill • Glencoe, a division of The McGraw-Hill Companies, Inc.

Problem-Solving Practice

3   Obike <u>measures</u> the <u>carrot</u>. What is the <u>length</u> to the <u>nearest half-inch</u>?

Understand   Underline key words.

Plan   Use a ruler.

Solve

The carrot is ___$4\frac{1}{2}$___ inches long.

Check   Does one end of the carrot line up with 0?

GO on

Chapter 6   Lesson 4

two hundred three **203**

Are They Getting It?

Check students' understanding of fractions and measurement by drawing these exercises on the board. Ask students to point out the correct and incorrect answer and explain their reasoning.

1. 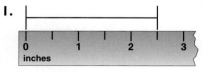   The line is 3 inches long. This is incorrect. The line is $2\frac{1}{2}$ inches long.

2. 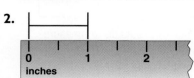   This line is 1 inch long. This is correct.

▶ Practice on Your Own

Measure to the nearest half-inch.

4 ___2___ inches

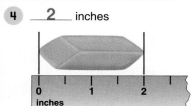

5 $\dfrac{1}{2}$ inch

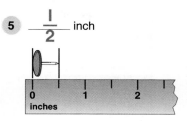

---

6 **WRITING IN** ▶**MATH** Glen says the scissors are 4 inches long to the nearest half-inch. Is Glen correct? Explain.

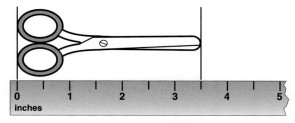

No, Glen measured incorrectly. The scissors are 3$\frac{1}{2}$ inches long.

Vocabulary Check Complete.

7 ___Length___  is how long something is.

STOP

204 two hundred four

Practice on Your Own

Direct students to p. 204 in their student books. Have students complete Exercises 4–7 independently. You may need to review the directions of each section before students begin.

4 Assess

See It, Do It, Say It, Write It

Step 1 Draw a large ruler with inch and half-inch marks on the board. Have student volunteers label the ruler. Draw a figure above the ruler and demonstrate how to measure the object.

Step 2 Hand out a blank ruler and have students fill in the inch and half-inch marks. Then have students draw a figure above the ruler.

Step 3 Have students trade papers and determine the length of the figure. Have students explain to their partner how they measured the figure.

Step 4 Have students in writing explain how to measure the length of an object to the nearest half-inch.

Looking Ahead: Pre-teach

In the next lesson, students will learn how to compare fractions with common denominators.

Example

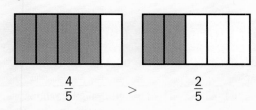

$$\frac{4}{5} \quad > \quad \frac{2}{5}$$

Have students compare.

1. $\dfrac{1}{3}$ $\boxed{<}$ $\dfrac{2}{3}$ **2.** $\dfrac{7}{8}$ $\boxed{>}$ $\dfrac{5}{8}$ **3.** $\dfrac{7}{10}$ $\boxed{>}$ $\dfrac{5}{10}$

Math Challenge

Ruler Art

Have students work independently to draw a picture using only lines that measure $\dfrac{1}{2}$ inch, 1 inch, 1$\dfrac{1}{2}$ inches, 2 inches, 2$\dfrac{1}{2}$ inches, 3 inches, 3$\dfrac{1}{2}$ inches, 4 inches, and 4$\dfrac{1}{2}$ inches long. Have students label the lines lightly as they create their pictures.

Progress Check 2

Formative Assessment

Use the Progress Check to assess students' mastery of the previous lessons. Have students review the lesson indicated for the problems they answered incorrectly.

Common Error Alert

Some students will shade the fractions incorrectly. Be sure students understand to use the shaded portion of each graphic as the numerator of their fraction.

Exercises 5 and 6 Remind students to measure to the nearest half-inch.

Name _____

Progress Check 2 (Lessons 6-3 and 6-4)

Write an equivalent fraction.

1 $\dfrac{2}{3} = \dfrac{\boxed{8}}{12}$

2 $\dfrac{1}{2} = \dfrac{\boxed{4}}{8}$

3 $\dfrac{2}{4} = \dfrac{\boxed{3}}{6}$

4 $\dfrac{4}{5} = \dfrac{\boxed{8}}{10}$

---

5 Measure to the nearest half-inch.

$2\dfrac{1}{2}$ inches

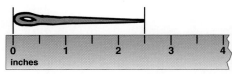

---

6 Adeola drew a green line. Use a ruler to measure the line to the nearest half-inch.

_3_ inches

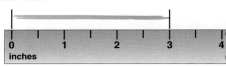

Chapter 6   Progress Check   two hundred five **205**

Data-Driven Decision Making

Students missing Exercises . . .	Have trouble with . . .	Should review and practice . . .
1–4	writing equivalent fractions.	SSG Lesson 6-3, p. 197 CRM Skills Practice, p. A143
5	measuring length to the nearest half-inch.	SSG Lesson 6-4, p. 201 CRM Skills Practice, p. A147
6	problem-solving that involves measuring length to the nearest half-inch.	SSG Lesson 6-4, p. 203 CRM Problem-Solving Practice, p. A148

Name _____

«« Replay **What kind of worm can measure?**

Measure each object to the nearest half-inch.
Fill in the letters to answer the riddle.

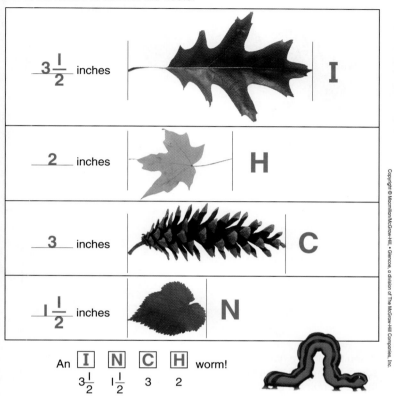

$3\frac{1}{2}$ inches   I

2 inches   H

3 inches   C

$1\frac{1}{2}$ inches   N

An ⬚I⬚ ⬚N⬚ ⬚C⬚ ⬚H⬚ worm!
  $3\frac{1}{2}$ $1\frac{1}{2}$ 3   2

Replay

Use the Replay activity to review and reinforce the concepts and skills presented in Lessons 6-3 and 6-4.

Instructions

Have students read the directions at the top of the student page.

Provide each student with a ruler.

Be sure students realize that if they measure incorrectly, the number will not appear at the bottom of the page in the answer to the riddle.

Student Technology

Students can use the following technology resources to reinforce chapter content.

- 💿 StudentWorks™ Plus
- Math Online ⟩ macmillanmh.com
- eGlossary

Lesson Notes

Lesson Planner

Math Objective Compare fractions with common denominators.

Vocabulary common denominator, numerator, denominator

Materials/Manipulatives fraction cards (teacher made), fraction tiles, pattern blocks, index cards

Chapter Resource Masters

CRM Vocabulary and English Language Development (p. A150)

CRM Skill Practice (p. A151)

CRM Problem-Solving-Practice (p. A152)

CRM Homework Practice (p. A153)

① Introduce

Vocabulary

Reenact Vocabulary Have students who are wearing sneakers stand.

- **What fraction of students in the classroom are wearing sneakers?** Answers will vary.

Write the fraction on the board. Have students identify the numerator (students standing) and the denominator (all students).

Repeat the activity. Have a different group of students stand.

② Teach

Key Concept

Foundational Skills and Concepts After students have read through the Key Concept box, guide them through the following questions.

- **What fraction of the coins on the left are quarters? on the right?** $\frac{2}{5}$; $\frac{4}{5}$

- **Is $\frac{2}{5}$ greater than or less than $\frac{4}{5}$?** less than

---

Name _____

Common Denominators

Key Concept

You can compare fractions with **common denominators.**

$\frac{2}{5}$ are quarters.

$\frac{4}{5}$ are quarters.

$$2 < 4$$
$$\text{So, } \frac{2}{5} < \frac{4}{5}.$$

Vocabulary

common denominator the same denominator in two fractions

$\frac{2}{6}$ $\frac{3}{6}$

6 is greater than 2, so $\frac{6}{7} > \frac{2}{7}$.

numerator the top number in a fraction

denominator the bottom number in a fraction

$\frac{3}{5}$ ← numerator
$\frac{3}{5}$ ← denominator

When the denominators are the same, the fractions are divided into the same number of equal parts.

Chapter 6   Lesson 5

two hundred seven 207

English Learner Strategy

Vocabulary Practice

Numerator and *denominator* are long words that are easily confused. Help students practice with this game:

1. Divide students into two teams and ask both teams to line up across the front of the room.

2. Ask the first student in each line to stand near the board and tap the board when they know the answer.

3. Hold up a fraction card (a card displaying a fraction in number form) and point to either the top or bottom number.

4. The first student who taps the board is called on to answer whether that number is the *numerator* or *denominator.*

5. Repeat until students are able to quickly label the numerator and denominator of a fraction.

Example

Compare. Write >, <, or =.

  $\frac{3}{6}$ are blue. $\frac{1}{6}$ is blue.

Step 1 Look at the denominators of the fractions. They are the same.

Step 2 Compare the numerators. 3 > 1

Step 3 Compare the fractions. $\frac{3}{6} > \frac{1}{6}$

Answer $\frac{3}{6}$ is greater than $\frac{1}{6}$.

Step-by-Step Practice

Compare. Write >, <, or =.

 $\frac{3}{9}$ are green. $\frac{7}{9}$ are green.

Step 1 Look at the denominators of the fractions. They are the same.

Step 2 Compare the numerators. __3__ ⊘ __7__

Step 3 Compare the fractions. $\frac{3}{9}$ ⊘ $\frac{7}{9}$

Answer $\frac{3}{9}$ is __less__ than $\frac{7}{9}$.

208 two hundred eight

Additional *Example*

Compare. Write >, <, or =

$\frac{4}{8}$ are red. $\frac{2}{8}$ are red.

Step 1 Look at the denominators of the fractions. They are the same.

Step 2 Compare the numerators. 4 > 2

Step 3 Compare the fractions. $\frac{4}{8} > \frac{2}{8}$

Answer $\frac{4}{8}$ is greater than $\frac{2}{8}$.

Math Coach Notes

Study Tip   Encourage visual learners to draw pictures of each fraction being compared. These students may also benefit from making fraction bars or fraction circles to use at home when studying or completing homework.

Intervention Strategy

Visual/ Kinesthetic Learners

Materials: fraction tiles, fraction cards

1. Have students work in pairs. Give each pair of students a set of fraction tiles. Hold up a fraction card and ask students to make a fraction with their fraction tiles that is greater than the fraction card you are holding. Remind students the fraction they make must have the same denominator as your fraction.

2. Check students' work and have several students share how they know their answer is correct.

3. Distribute fraction cards to each pair of students and have the students repeat the activity several times, recording the fraction on the card and the fraction they make.

3 Practice

Guided Practice

Direct students to complete Exercise 1 in Guided Practice.

Exercise 1 Remind students to compare the numerators.

Problem-Solving Practice

Guide students through the four-step problem-solving plan to complete Exercise 2.

- **What are the key words?** $\frac{7}{10}$ Texas quarters, $\frac{2}{10}$ Texas quarters, who has fewer Texas quarters

- **How many Texas quarters will you shade in each group?** 7 in the first group, 2 in the second group.

Ask students to check their work using the strategy suggested in the Check step. Students can compare the numerators in the fractions to solve the problem.

Using Manipulatives

Pattern Blocks Distribute pattern blocks to each student or to each student pair. Have the students use the pattern blocks to model this comparison $\frac{4}{7} < \frac{6}{7}$.

Students might show two groups one group of 4 triangles and 3 hexagons and another group of 6 triangles and 1 hexagon. Ask students to share with the class why their representation is correct. Repeat using different comparisons.

On-Hand Manipulatives In place of pattern blocks, students can use classroom objects such as, pencils, paper clips, or erasers.

Name _____

▶ Guided Practice

1 Compare. Write >, <, or =.

🎳🎳🎳🎳 $\frac{1}{4} \bigcirc \frac{3}{4}$ 🎳🎳🎳🎳

Problem-Solving Practice

2 Julia and Ann each have 10 state quarters. Julia's collection is $\frac{7}{10}$ Texas quarters. Ann's collection is $\frac{2}{10}$ Texas quarters. <u>Who has fewer Texas quarters?</u>

Understand   Underline key words.

Plan   Draw a model.

Solve   Shade ___7___ quarters in Julia's collection.

Shade ___2___ quarters in Ann's collection.

⬤⬤⬤⬤⬤ ⬤⬤◯◯◯
⬤⬤◯◯◯ ◯◯◯◯◯

Julia's Quarters   Ann's Quarters

___Ann___ has fewer Texas quarters.

Check   Compare the numerators.

GO on

Chapter 6   Lesson 5   two hundred nine **209**

Are They Getting It? ❓

Check students' understanding of common denominators by writing these comparisons on the board. Ask students to point out the correct and incorrect comparisons and explain their reasoning.

1. $\frac{6}{8} < \frac{5}{8}$ This is incorrect. The denominators are the same. The numerators are 6 and 5. 6 > 5 so $\frac{6}{8} > \frac{5}{8}$.

2. $\frac{4}{5} > \frac{3}{5}$ This is correct.

3. $\frac{4}{10} > \frac{3}{10}$ This is correct.

4. $\frac{5}{6} < \frac{2}{6}$ This is incorrect. The denominators are the same. The numerators are 5 and 2. 5 > 2 so $\frac{5}{6} > \frac{2}{6}$.

209 Chapter 6 Fraction Equivalence

▶ **Practice on Your Own**

Compare. Write >, <, or =.

3

$\frac{1}{3}$ is green. $\frac{2}{3}$ are green.

$\frac{1}{3}$ $<$ $\frac{2}{3}$

4 $\frac{8}{8} = \frac{8}{8}$

5 $\frac{2}{10} < \frac{9}{10}$

6 $\frac{4}{7} < \frac{6}{7}$

7 $\frac{6}{12} < \frac{11}{12}$

8 $\frac{6}{6} > \frac{4}{6}$

9 $\frac{3}{5} > \frac{1}{5}$

10 **WRITING IN ▶MATH** Paul ate $\frac{3}{6}$ of a pack of crackers. Kim ate $\frac{2}{6}$ of a pack of crackers. Who ate more crackers? Explain.

Paul ate more crackers. $\frac{3}{6} > \frac{2}{6}$

Vocabulary Check Complete.

11 In the fraction $\frac{3}{5}$, 3 is the __**numerator**__.

12 In the fraction $\frac{3}{5}$, 5 is the **denominator**.

STOP

210 two hundred ten

Math Challenge

Go Fishing for Fractions   Have student pairs make 20 fraction cards, each with a denominator no larger than 10.

Have Player 1 shuffle the cards, deal 7 cards to each player, and place the remaining cards in a pile.

Player 1 asks Player 2 for a fraction with a specific denominator. For example: "I'm fishing for a fraction with a denominator of 4."

If Player 2 has a card with 4 as the denominator, they hand it to Player 1. If not, Player 2 says "Go Fish," and Player 1 draws a card from the pile.

Students make pairs by stating a true comparison for two of their cards. For example: $\frac{3}{4} > \frac{1}{4}$. The students continue to play until one player has all of the cards.

Make fraction tiles or fraction circles available for students.

Practice on Your Own

Direct students to p. 210 in their student books. Have students complete Exercises 3–12 independently. You may need to review the directions of each section before students begin.

(4) Assess

See It, Do It, Say It, Write It

Step 1 Write $\frac{3}{5} > \frac{2}{5}$ on the board. Read the problem to the class and draw a model.

Step 2 Have the students write the comparison $\frac{7}{8}$ —— $\frac{5}{8}$ and draw a model to represent the problem.

Step 3 Have students present their answer and model to the class.

Step 4 Have students create a problem of their own. Have students draw a model to represent their answer.

Looking Ahead: Pre-teach

In the next lesson, students will learn how to compare fractions with common numerators.

Example

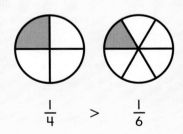

$\frac{1}{4}$ > $\frac{1}{6}$

Compare.

1. $\frac{1}{3} > \frac{1}{8}$ **2.** $\frac{1}{5} < \frac{1}{2}$ **3.** $\frac{1}{10} < \frac{1}{4}$

Lesson Notes

Lesson Planner

Math Objective Compare fractions with common numerators.

Vocabulary numerator, denominator, is greater than (>), is less than (<)

Materials/Manipulatives fraction circles, fraction tiles, number cubes

Chapter Resource Masters

- CRM Vocabulary and English Language Development (p. A154)
- CRM Skill Practice (p. A155)
- CRM Problem-Solving-Practice (p. A156)
- CRM Homework Practice (p. A157)

 **Introduce**

Vocabulary

Compare Vocabulary Make a poster titled "Parts of a Fraction." On the left write "numerator" and on the right write "denominator." Have students define each word. Using pictures as examples, help students see how numerators and denominators are alike and different. Repeat this process making a separate poster for "greater than" and "less than."

 **Teach**

Key Concept

Foundational Skills and Concepts After students have read through the Key Concept box, guide them through the following questions.

- **The circle on the left is divided into how many parts?** 3

- **The circle on the right is divided into how many parts?** 8

- **Which colored piece is larger?** red

- **Which fraction is greater?** $\frac{1}{3}$

Name _____

Common Numerators

Key Concept

Think about the size of the fraction parts to compare fractions.

$\frac{1}{3}$

This circle is divided into 3 parts.

$\frac{1}{8}$

This circle is divided into 8 parts.

The red piece is larger than the green piece.

$$\frac{1}{3} \bigcirc{>} \frac{1}{8}$$

Vocabulary

numerator the top number in a fraction

denominator the bottom number in a fraction

$\frac{3 \leftarrow \text{numerator}}{5 \leftarrow \text{denominator}}$

is greater than (>) $\frac{1}{3}$ is greater than $\frac{1}{8}$ $\frac{1}{3} > \frac{1}{8}$

is less than (<) $\frac{3}{6}$ is less than $\frac{5}{6}$ $\frac{3}{6} < \frac{5}{6}$

> One part of a whole that has only 3 parts is bigger than one part of a whole that has 8 parts.

When the numerators are the same, think about the size of the fraction parts.

Copyright © Macmillan/McGraw-Hill • Glencoe, a division of The McGraw-Hill Companies, Inc.

English Learner Strategy

The Meaning of *Common*

1. Write *common* on the board. Explain that the word refers to two or more objects sharing the same condition, such as color or size.

2. Locate two students in the classroom who are wearing the same color shirt. Call those two students to the front of the room.

- **What do these two students have in common?** Their shirts are the same color.

3. Write $\frac{1}{4}$ and $\frac{1}{2}$ on the board.

- **What do these two fractions have in common?** Their numerators are the same.

4. Explain that the fractions have common numerators. Ask students to write a pair of fractions that have common numerators.

Example

Shannon ran $\frac{1}{6}$ of a mile.

Robert ran $\frac{1}{2}$ of a mile.

Who ran farther?

$\frac{1}{6}$ $\frac{1}{2}$

Step 1   Shade each fraction.

Step 2   Compare the shaded areas.
The $\frac{1}{6}$ part is less than the $\frac{1}{2}$ part.

Step 3   Write the correct symbol. $\frac{1}{6} \;\textcircled{<}\; \frac{1}{2}$

Answer   Robert ran farther.

Step-by-Step Practice

Lucy painted for $\frac{1}{5}$ of an hour. Nick painted for $\frac{1}{10}$ of an hour. Who painted for less time?

Step 1   Shade each fraction.

Step 2   Compare the shaded areas.
The $\frac{1}{5}$ part is **greater** than the $\frac{1}{10}$ part.

$\frac{1}{5}$ $\frac{1}{10}$

Step 3   Write the correct symbol.

$\frac{1}{5} \;\textcircled{>}\; \frac{1}{10}$

Answer   __Nick__ painted for less time.

212   two hundred twelve

Bennett biked $\frac{1}{3}$ of a mile. Omar biked $\frac{1}{5}$ of a mile. Who biked farther?

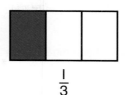 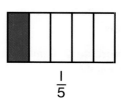

$\frac{1}{3}$ $\frac{1}{5}$

Step 1 Shade each fraction.

Step 2 Compare the shaded areas.
The $\frac{1}{3}$ part is greater than the $\frac{1}{5}$ part.

Step 3 Write the correct symbol. $\frac{1}{3} \;\textcircled{>}\; \frac{1}{5}$

Answer Bennett biked farther.

Math Coach Notes

Study Tips   Remind students that everyone learns and understands things differently. Help students explore many different strategies for comparing fractions including drawing pictures, using models, or using money.

Intervention Strategy

Linguistic/Intrapersonal Learners

Materials: fraction circles, fraction tiles, paper

1. Assign each student two fractions with the same numerator.
   For example $\frac{2}{4}$ and $\frac{2}{7}$.

2. Ask the students to write a short "I Would Rather . . . " story about a character who would rather have one fraction than the other and explain the character's choice.

   For example: The Big Bad Wolf would rather eat $\frac{2}{4}$ of the apples in the bin than $\frac{2}{7}$ because $\frac{2}{4}$ is greater than $\frac{2}{7}$ and the wolf is hungry!

   Have fraction circles and tiles available to students as a resource.

3. Have students share their stories. Discuss the fractions compared in each story.

3 Practice

Guided Practice

Direct students to complete Exercises 1 – 2 in Guided Practice.

Exercise 2 Remind students to shade the fractions before they compare.

Problem-Solving Practice

Guide students through the four-step problem-solving plan to complete Exercise 3.

- **What are the key words?** $\frac{1}{4}$ of a cup of flour, $\frac{1}{8}$ of a cup of sugar, more

- **How can fraction bars help compare the fractions?** They show how big $\frac{1}{4}$ is in comparison to $\frac{1}{8}$.

Ask students to check their work using the strategy suggested in the Check step. Students can look at the size of the parts in each fraction and compare to solve the problem.

Using Manipulatives

Fraction Circles Give student pairs a set of fraction circles. Ask students to model the comparison: $\frac{1}{3} \square \frac{1}{10}$. Check student work and have several students share how they know their answer is correct. Repeat using different fractions with the same numerator.

On-Hand Manipulatives Students can make their own fraction circles by folding paper circles into equal parts. Students can also draw pictorial models.

Name _____

▶ Guided Practice

Shade the figures and compare. Write >, <, or =.

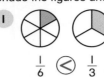

1 $\frac{1}{6}$ $\bigcirc<$ $\frac{1}{3}$

2 $\frac{1}{7}$ $\bigcirc=$ $\frac{1}{7}$

Problem-Solving Practice

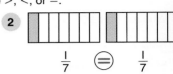

3 Lara needs $\frac{1}{4}$ of a cup of flour and $\frac{1}{8}$ of a cup of sugar.

Does Lara need <u>more</u> flour or sugar?

Understand Underline key words.

Plan Use fraction bars to compare.

Solve
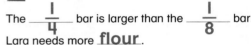

The _$\frac{1}{4}$_ bar is larger than the _$\frac{1}{8}$_ bar.
Lara needs more **flour**.

Check Are the parts bigger in a fraction divided into 4 parts or 8 parts?

GO on

Chapter 6 Lesson 6

two hundred thirteen **213**

Are They Getting It? ❓

Check students' understanding of comparing fractions with common numerators by writing these comparisons on the board. Ask students to point out the correct and incorrect comparisons and explain their reasoning.

1. $\frac{1}{8} < \frac{1}{4}$ This is correct.

2. $\frac{3}{5} < \frac{3}{9}$ This is incorrect. An object divided into 5 pieces will have larger pieces than an object divided into 9 pieces. So, $\frac{3}{5} > \frac{3}{9}$.

3. $\frac{4}{5} > \frac{4}{10}$ This is correct.

4. $\frac{2}{6} > \frac{2}{3}$ This is incorrect. An object divided into 6 pieces will have smaller pieces than an object divided into 3 pieces. So, $\frac{2}{6} < \frac{2}{3}$.

▶ Practice on Your Own

Compare. Write >, <, or =.

4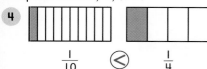

$\dfrac{1}{10}$ **<** $\dfrac{1}{4}$

5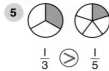

$\dfrac{1}{3}$ **>** $\dfrac{1}{5}$

Shade the figures. Compare. Write <, > or =.

6

$\dfrac{1}{9}$ **<** $\dfrac{1}{5}$

7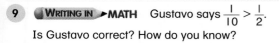

$\dfrac{1}{8}$ **<** $\dfrac{1}{2}$

8

$\dfrac{1}{3}$ **>** $\dfrac{1}{4}$

9 **WRITING IN ▶MATH** Gustavo says $\dfrac{1}{10} > \dfrac{1}{2}$.
Is Gustavo correct? How do you know?

No, Gustavo is not correct. One part of 10 parts is less than one part of 2 parts. So, $\dfrac{1}{10} < \dfrac{1}{2}$.

Vocabulary Check   Complete.

10 The **denominator** tells how many equal parts a whole is divided into.

STOP

214 two hundred fourteen

Copyright © Macmillan/McGraw-Hill • Glencoe, a division of The McGraw-Hill Companies, Inc.

Practice on Your Own

Direct students to p. 214 in their student books. Have students complete Exercises 4–10 independently. You may need to review the directions of each section before students begin.

(4) Assess

See It, Do It, Say It, Write It

Step 1 Write $\dfrac{2}{3} > \dfrac{2}{4}$ on the board. Read the problem to the class and draw a model.

Step 2 Write $\dfrac{3}{5} \square \dfrac{3}{8}$ on the board. Have students draw a model for the problem.

Step 3 Have students present their answer and strategy (which may include pictures, manipulatives, or knowledge of fractions).

Step 4 Have students write how they compared the fractions.

Math Challenge

Best of 11!

Have students work in pairs. Each student should have two number cubes. Student 1 tosses both number cubes and forms a fraction. Student 2 uses the same numerator as Student 1 and tosses one cube to determine their denominator.

The students compare their fractions. The student with the greater fraction wins a point.

Student 2 rolls both number cubes and the players repeat the process. Play is continued for 11 rolls. Whoever has the most points at the end of 11 rolls wins.

Make fraction tiles or fraction circles available for students.

Chapter 6 — Progress Check 3

Formative Assessment

Use the Progress Check to assess students' mastery of the previous lessons. Have students review the lesson indicated for the problems they answered incorrectly.

⚠ Common Error *Alert*

Students often confuse the greater than and less than symbols even if they can correctly compare numbers. Review the symbols before the students start the Progress Check.

Exercises 5–6 Remind students to read the directions carefully. They are asked to shade and then compare the fractions.

Name _____

Progress Check 3 (Lessons 6-5 and 6-6)

Compare. Write >, <, or =.

1

$\frac{2}{5}$ are blue.　　　　$\frac{4}{5}$ are blue.

$\frac{2}{5}$ $\bigcirc<$ $\frac{4}{5}$

2 $\frac{2}{3}$ $\bigcirc>$ $\frac{1}{3}$　　**3** $\frac{4}{6}$ $\bigcirc<$ $\frac{5}{6}$　　**4** $\frac{7}{8}$ $\bigcirc>$ $\frac{2}{8}$

Shade the figures and compare. Write >, <, or =.

5 $\frac{1}{3}$ $\bigcirc>$ $\frac{1}{8}$

6 $\frac{1}{6}$ $\bigcirc<$ $\frac{1}{4}$

7 $\frac{1}{4}$ $\bigcirc=$ $\frac{1}{4}$

---

8 Kiah wants to make cinnamon bread using her grandma's recipe. Does Kiah need more water or milk?

Kiah needs more __milk__.

Grandma's Cinnamon Bread	
$\frac{1}{3}$ cup sugar	2 cups flour
$\frac{1}{3}$ cup water	2 eggs
$\frac{1}{2}$ cup milk	3 Tbs. butter
	4 Tbs. cinnamon

Chapter 6　Progress Check　　　　two hundred fifteen **215**

Copyright © Macmillan/McGraw-Hill • Glencoe, a division of The McGraw-Hill Companies, Inc.

Data-Driven Decision Making

Students missing Exercises . . .	Have trouble with . . .	Should review and practice . . .
1–4	comparing fractions with common denominators.	SSG Lesson 6-5, p. 207 CRM Skills Practice, p. A151
5–7	comparing fractions with common numerators.	SSG Lesson 6-6, p. 211 CRM Skills Practice, p. A155
7	problem-solving that involves comparing fractions with common numerators.	SSG Lesson 6-6, p. 213 CRM Problem-Solving Practice, p. A156

Name _____

«« Replay

A-maze-ing Treasure

Begin at START.
Compare each pair of fractions.
Follow the direction of the correct symbol.
End at the TREASURE!

 START

$\frac{3}{6}$ ⊘ $\frac{4}{6}$ < >↓	$\frac{1}{2}$ ⊘ $\frac{1}{3}$ < >↓	$\frac{2}{5}$ ○ $\frac{3}{5}$ < → >↓	< $\frac{7}{10}$ ○ $\frac{3}{10}$ >↓
$\frac{1}{5}$ ○ $\frac{2}{5}$ → >↓	$\frac{1}{5}$ ⊘ $\frac{3}{5}$ < → >↓	$\frac{1}{10}$ ⊘ $\frac{1}{5}$ < → >↓	↑ $\frac{7}{8}$ ⊘ $\frac{3}{8}$ >↓
$\frac{1}{5}$ ○ $\frac{1}{8}$ < >↓	< $\frac{9}{10}$ ⊘ $\frac{6}{10}$ >↓	< $\frac{2}{4}$ ⊘ $\frac{3}{4}$ >↓	< $\frac{1}{6}$ ⊘ $\frac{1}{5}$ >↓
TREASURE!	>↑ < $\frac{1}{8}$ ⊘ $\frac{1}{6}$ →	<↑ $\frac{1}{6}$ ○ $\frac{1}{4}$ →	<↑ < $\frac{1}{8}$ ○ $\frac{1}{10}$

Use the Replay activity to review and reinforce the concepts and skills presented in Lessons 6-5 and 6-6.

Instructions

Have students read the directions at the top of the student page.

Remind students that they can use the fraction tiles in the top, right hand corner of the page.

Student Technology

Students can use the following technology resources to reinforce chapter content.

- StudentWorks™ Plus
- Math Online › macmillanmh.com
- eGlossary

Vocabulary

If students have difficulty answering Exercises 1–5, use the page references below to review the vocabulary words, or refer them to the glossary.

denominator (p. 207)
equivalent fractions (p. 197)
numerator (p. 207)
< (p. 191)
> (p. 191)

Vocabulary Review Strategies

Vocabulary Notes   Have students make a table with 3 columns. Write the chapter vocabulary words in the left column. In the center column, students should write the definition in their own words. In the right column, students should write what they associate with the word (i.e. greater than sign "eats" the bigger number, numerator is on top . . .).

Concepts

The exercises in this section are grouped to cover content from each lesson in the chapter. The first exercise of each set is partially completed for the student in order to show the method for solving the other exercise(s) in the set.

Exercises 6–10: Lesson 6-1 (p. 187)
Exercises 11–12: Lesson 6-2 (p. 191)
Exercises 13–14: Lesson 6-3 (p. 197)
Exercise 15: Lesson 6-4 (p. 201)
Exercise 16: Lesson 6-5 (p. 207)
Exercise 17: Lesson 6-6 (p. 211)

Find **Extra Practice** for these concepts in the Practice Worksheets, pp. A134–A157.

Name _____

Review

Vocabulary

Word Bank

denominator

equivalent fractions

numerator

<

>

Use the Word Bank to complete.

1. $\dfrac{3}{5}$ ◄········· <u>numerator</u>

2. $\dfrac{1}{3} = \dfrac{2}{6}$ <u>equivalent fractions</u>

3. $\dfrac{1}{4}$ $<$ $\dfrac{3}{4}$

4. $\dfrac{1}{2}$ $>$ $\dfrac{1}{3}$

5. $\dfrac{6}{8}$ ◄········· <u>denominator</u>

▶ Concepts

Name each fraction. Circle each fraction that equals 1.

6. $\dfrac{5}{5}$

7. $\dfrac{3}{4}$

8. $\dfrac{6}{6}$

Shade each model to show 1. Name each fraction.

9. $\dfrac{8}{8}$

10. $\dfrac{2}{2}$

GO on

Shade and compare the fractions. Write >, <, or =.

11

$$\frac{1}{6} \enspace \boxed{<} \enspace \frac{5}{6}$$

12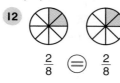

$$\frac{2}{8} \enspace \boxed{=} \enspace \frac{2}{8}$$

Write an equivalent fraction.

13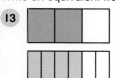

$$\frac{2}{3} = \frac{\boxed{4}}{6}$$

14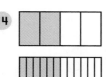

$$\frac{2}{4} = \frac{\boxed{6}}{\boxed{12}}$$

15 Measure to the nearest half-inch.

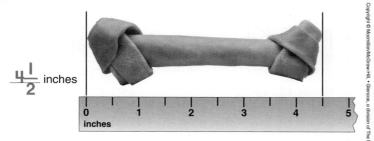

$$4\frac{1}{2} \enspace \text{inches}$$

Compare. Write >, <, or =.

16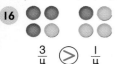

$$\frac{3}{4} \enspace \boxed{>} \enspace \frac{1}{4}$$

17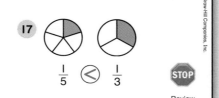

$$\frac{1}{5} \enspace \boxed{<} \enspace \frac{1}{3}$$

STOP

218 two hundred eighteen

Review

FOLDABLES® **Dinah Zike's**
Study Organizer **Foldables®**

Have students use the Foldable they created at the beginning of the chapter to review and reinforce the concepts and skills they learned during the chapter. (See Chapter Resource Masters p. A131 for instructions.)

Intervention Strategy

Use this Intervention Strategy activity at any point during the chapter to reinforce the concepts and skills presented in the chapter.

Cafeteria Count   Use the same recipe as you did in the real world applications section.

Step 1 Divide students into pairs. Give each pair a copy of the recipe and ask them to circle any fractions they find.

Step 2 Students should use blank sheets of paper to model fractions. For example, if the recipe calls for a $\frac{1}{2}$ cup of cereal, students should cut a piece of paper in half and label the paper as half a cup of cereal.

Step 3 Students should repeat the process for each ingredient in the recipe.

Step 4 The class can compare amounts of ingredients using the paper models as a visual aid.

• **What can you conclude from the models you have made?** Sample answer: The recipe requires more of one ingredient than another.

Chapter Resource Masters

Additional forms of the Chapter Test are available.

Test Format	Where to Find it
Chapter Test	**Math Online** ▶ macmillanmh.com
Blackline Masters	Assessment Masters, p. 74

ExamView®
Assessment Suite

Customize and create multiple versions of your chapter test and their answer keys. All of these questions from the chapter tests are available on ExamView® Assessment Suite.

Advance ᵀᴿᴬᶜᴷᴱᴿ

Online Assessment and Reporting
macmillanmh.com

This online assessment tool allows teachers to track student progress with easily accessible, comprehensive reports available for every student. Assess students using any internet-ready computer.

Alternative Assessment

Use Portfolios Ask students to summarize the strategies for completing the following:

- making fractional values equal to 1.
- comparing fractions.
- making equivalent fractions.
- measuring to the nearest half-inch.
- comparing fractions with common denominators.
- comparing fractions with common numerators.

The information should be organized and explained by the student.

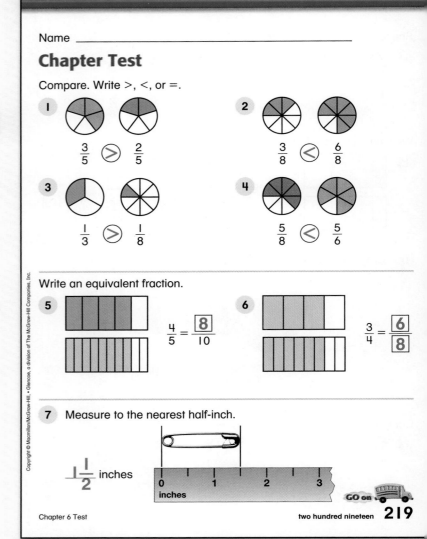

Name _____

Chapter Test

Compare. Write >, <, or =.

1. $\frac{3}{5}$ > $\frac{2}{5}$

2. $\frac{3}{8}$ < $\frac{6}{8}$

3. $\frac{1}{3}$ > $\frac{1}{8}$

4. $\frac{5}{8}$ < $\frac{5}{6}$

Write an equivalent fraction.

5. $\frac{4}{5} = \frac{8}{10}$

6. $\frac{3}{4} = \frac{6}{8}$

7. Measure to the nearest half-inch.

$1\frac{1}{2}$ inches

0   1   2   3
inches

GO on

Chapter 6 Test   two hundred nineteen **219**

8 **Who is Correct?**

Walter and Cindy find fractions greater than $\frac{1}{5}$.

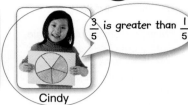

$\frac{1}{10}$ is greater than $\frac{1}{5}$.

Walter

$\frac{3}{5}$ is greater than $\frac{1}{5}$.

Cindy

Circle the correct answer. Explain.

Cindy is correct. The denominators of $\frac{3}{5}$ and $\frac{1}{5}$ are the same. 3 > 1, so $\frac{3}{5} > \frac{1}{5}$.

---

9 Sandra rode her bike for $\frac{4}{5}$ of an hour. Jon rode his bike for $\frac{2}{5}$ of an hour. Who rode for a longer time? **Sandra** rode for a longer time. $4 > 2$, so $\frac{4}{5} > \frac{2}{5}$.

10 Look at the window. What fraction represents the whole window? $\frac{8}{8}$

11 Jasmine walked $\frac{1}{4}$ of a mile. Henry walked $\frac{1}{6}$ of a mile. Who walked less distance? Explain.

Henry walked less distance; 1 part out of 6 < 1 part out of 4. $\frac{1}{6} < \frac{1}{4}$

STOP

Who Is Correct?

Diagnostic Teaching

- Walter says $\frac{1}{10}$ is greater than $\frac{2}{5}$. This is incorrect because a circle cut into 10 equal pieces will have smaller pieces than a circle cut into 5 equal pieces. The more parts there are, the smaller each part has to be.

- Cindy says $\frac{3}{5}$ is greater than $\frac{1}{5}$. This is correct. The denominators are the same and 3 parts of 5 is more than 1 part of 5.

Learning from Mistakes

Missed Questions   Review commonly missed questions as a small group or class. Ask students to share their methods of answering each question. Try to point out when any errors occur and take corrective measures.

Data-Driven Decision Making

Students missing Exercises . . .	Have trouble with . . .	Should review and practice . . .
1–2	comparing fractions with common denominators.	SSG Lesson 6-5, p. 207 CRM Skills Practice, p. A151
3–4	comparing fractions with common numerators.	SSG Lesson 6-6, p. 211 CRM Skills Practice, p. A155
5–6	writing equivalent fractions.	SSG Lesson 6-3, p. 197 CRM Skills Practice, p. A143
7	measuring length to the nearest half-inch.	SSG Lesson 6-4, p. 201 CRM Skills Practice, p. A147
8	comparing fractions.	SSG Lesson 6-2, p. 211 CRM Skills Practice, p. A139
9–11	problem-solving that involves comparing fractions with common denominators, naming fractions for one whole, and comparing fractions with common numerators.	SSG Lesson 6-5, p. 209 CRM Problem-Solving Practice, p. A152 SSG Lesson 6-1, p. 189 CRM Problem-Solving Practice, p. A136 SSG Lesson 6-6, p. 213 CRM Problem-Solving Practice, p. A156

Test Practice

Diagnose Student Errors

Survey student responses for each item. Class trends may indicate common errors and misconceptions.

1. $\frac{3}{1}$: chose a fraction that equals 3, not 1 whole

   $\frac{3}{3}$: correct

   $\frac{1}{3}$: chose fraction that represents 1 part of the apple

   $\frac{1}{2}$: does not understand the concept of 1 whole

2. $\frac{1}{2}$ inch: read the ruler incorrectly

   1 inch: read the ruler incorrectly

   $1\frac{1}{2}$ inches: read the ruler incorrectly

   2 inches: correct

3. $<$: correct
   $+$: does not understand the addition symbol
   $=$: does not understand the equals sign
   $>$: incorrectly compared the fractions

4. $\frac{6}{6}$: correct

   $\frac{6}{1}$: chose a fraction that equals 6, not 1 whole

   $\frac{1}{6}$: chose a fraction that represents 1 slice of the loaf

   6: does not understand concept of fractions

5. $\frac{1}{5} = \frac{1}{4}$: does not understand the equals sign

   $\frac{1}{4} > \frac{1}{5}$: correct

   $\frac{1}{4} < \frac{1}{5}$: did not compare the fractions correctly

   $\frac{1}{5} > \frac{1}{4}$: did not compare the fractions correctly

6. $\frac{1}{5}$: does not understand concept of fractions equal to 1

   $\frac{2}{5}$: does not understand concept of fractions equal to 1

   $\frac{4}{5}$: does not understand concept of fractions equal to 1

   $\frac{5}{5}$: correct

7. $\frac{2}{4} < \frac{1}{4}$: did not compare the fractions correctly

   $\frac{2}{4} = \frac{1}{4}$: does not understand the equals sign

---

Name _____

Test Practice

Choose the correct answer.

1 Molly's mother cut an apple into 3 equal pieces. Molly ate the whole apple. What fraction of the apple did Molly eat?

○ $\frac{3}{1}$ ● $\frac{3}{3}$ ○ $\frac{1}{3}$ ○ $\frac{1}{2}$

2 How long is the candle to the nearest half-inch?

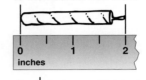

○ $\frac{1}{2}$ inch ○ I inch

○ $1\frac{1}{2}$ inches ● 2 inches

3 Complete.

$\frac{2}{6}$ ○ $\frac{2}{3}$

● $<$ ○ $+$ ○ $=$ ○ $>$

4 Paul baked banana bread. He sliced the bread into 6 pieces. What fraction represents the whole loaf of bread?

● $\frac{6}{6}$ ○ $\frac{6}{1}$ ○ $\frac{1}{6}$ ○ 6

5 Which number sentence is true?

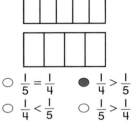

○ $\frac{1}{5} = \frac{1}{4}$ ● $\frac{1}{4} > \frac{1}{5}$

○ $\frac{1}{4} < \frac{1}{5}$ ○ $\frac{1}{5} > \frac{1}{4}$

6 Which fraction equals 1?

○ $\frac{1}{5}$ ○ $\frac{2}{5}$

○ $\frac{4}{5}$ ● $\frac{5}{5}$

GO ON

$\frac{1}{4} > \frac{2}{4}$: did not compare the fractions correctly

$\frac{2}{4} > \frac{1}{4}$: correct

8. $\frac{1}{2}$ inch: did not read the ruler correctly

   1 inch: did not read the ruler correctly

   $1\frac{1}{2}$ inches: correct

   2 inches: did not read the ruler correctly

9. $\frac{3}{10}$: does not understand equivalent fractions

   $\frac{4}{10}$: does not understand equivalent fractions

   $\frac{5}{10}$: does not understand equivalent fractions

   $\frac{6}{10}$: correct

7 Which number sentence is true?

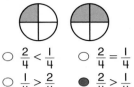

○ $\frac{2}{4} < \frac{1}{4}$ ○ $\frac{2}{4} = \frac{1}{4}$

○ $\frac{1}{4} > \frac{2}{4}$ ● $\frac{2}{4} > \frac{1}{4}$

8 How long is the key to the nearest half-inch?

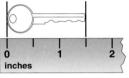

○ $\frac{1}{2}$ inch   ○ 1 inch

● $1\frac{1}{2}$ inches   ○ 2 inches

9 Carlos gave away $\frac{3}{5}$ of his model cars. Which fraction is equivalent to $\frac{3}{5}$?

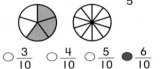

○ $\frac{3}{10}$ ○ $\frac{4}{10}$ ○ $\frac{5}{10}$ ● $\frac{6}{10}$

10 Which number sentence is true?

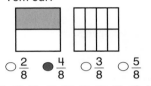

○ $\frac{5}{8} = \frac{3}{8}$ ○ $\frac{3}{8} > \frac{5}{8}$

● $\frac{3}{8} < \frac{5}{8}$ ○ $\frac{5}{8} < \frac{3}{8}$

11 Holly ate $\frac{1}{2}$ of her sandwich. Tom ate the same amount of his sandwich. His sandwich was cut into 8 pieces. What fraction of his sandwich did Tom eat?

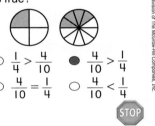

○ $\frac{2}{8}$ ● $\frac{4}{8}$ ○ $\frac{3}{8}$ ○ $\frac{5}{8}$

12 Which number sentence is true?

○ $\frac{1}{4} > \frac{4}{10}$ ● $\frac{4}{10} > \frac{1}{4}$

○ $\frac{4}{10} = \frac{1}{4}$ ○ $\frac{4}{10} < \frac{1}{4}$

STOP

222 two hundred twenty-two   Test Practice

Diagnosing Student Errors and Misconceptions

Fractions   For students who are struggling with comparing fractions, encourage them to make their own fraction cards or tiles and label each one. By creating these cards and reviewing them daily, students should be able to visualize what the fractions represent.

10. $\frac{5}{8} = \frac{3}{8}$: does not understand the equals sign

$\frac{3}{8} > \frac{5}{8}$: does not understand how to compare fractions with common denominators

$\frac{3}{8} < \frac{5}{8}$: correct

$\frac{5}{8} < \frac{3}{8}$: does not understand how to compare fractions with common denominators

11. $\frac{2}{8}$: does not understand equivalent fractions

$\frac{4}{8}$: correct

$\frac{3}{8}$: does not understand equivalent fractions

$\frac{5}{8}$: does not understand equivalent fractions

12. $\frac{1}{4} > \frac{4}{10}$: incorrectly compared the fractions

$\frac{4}{10} > \frac{1}{4}$: correct

$\frac{4}{10} = \frac{1}{4}$: does not understand the equals sign

$\frac{4}{10} < \frac{1}{4}$: incorrectly compared the fractions

Chapter 6 Test Practice **222**

Chapter Overview

Chapter 7

Chapter-at-a-Glance

Lesson	Math Objective	State/Local Standards
7-1 Three-Dimensional Figures (pp. 225–228)	Identify three-dimensional figures.	
7-2 Faces and Edges (pp. 229–232)	Identify faces and edges.	
Progress Check 1 (p. 233)		
7-3 Two-Dimensional Figures (pp. 235–238)	Identify two-dimensional figures.	
7-4 Sides and Vertices (pp. 239–242)	Count sides and vertices.	
7-5 Relate Two and Three-Dimensional Figures (pp. 243–246)	Relate two- and three-dimensional figures.	
Progress Check 2 (p. 247)		

Content-at-a-Glance
The diagram below summarizes and unpacks Chapter 7 content.

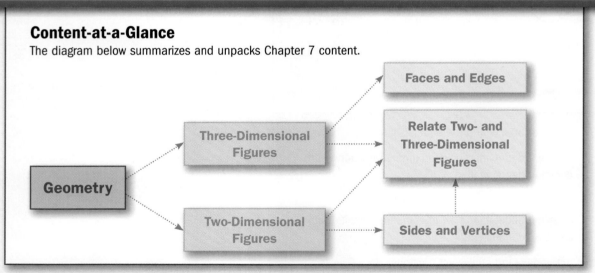

Chapter Assessment Manager

Diagnostic Diagnose students' readiness.

	Student Study Guide/ Teacher Editions	Assessment Masters	Technology
Course Placement Test		1	💿 ExamView® Assessment Suite
Book 3 Pretest		85	💿 ExamView® Assessment Suite
Chapter Pretest		88	💿 ExamView® Assessment Suite
Get Ready	SSG 224		Math Online ▸ macmillanmh.com StudentWorks™ Plus

Formative Identify students' misconceptions of content knowledge.

	Student Study Guide/ Teacher Editions	Assessment Masters	Technology
Progress Checks	SSG 233, 247		Math Online ▸ macmillanmh.com StudentWorks™ Plus
Vocabulary Review	SSG 228, 232, 238, 242, 246, 249		Math Online ▸ macmillanmh.com
Lesson Assessments			💿 ExamView® Assessment Suite
Are They Getting It?	TE 227, 231, 237, 241, 245		

Summative Determine student success in learning the concepts in the lesson, chapter, or book.

	Student Study Guide/ Teacher Editions	Assessment Masters	Technology
Chapter Test	SSG 251	91	💿 ExamView® Assessment Suite
Test Practice	SSG 253	94	💿 ExamView® Assessment Suite
Alternative Assessment	TE 251	97	
See It, Do It, Say It, Write It	TE 228, 232, 238, 242, 246		
Book 3 Test		124	💿 ExamView® Assessment Suite

Back-mapping and Vertical Alignment McGraw-Hill's *Math Triumphs* intervention program was conceived and developed with the final result in mind: student success in grade-level mathematics, including Algebra 1 and beyond. The authors, using the **NCTM Focal Points and Focal Connections** as their guide, developed this brand-new series by back-mapping from grade-level and Algebra 1 concepts, and vertically aligning the topics so that they build upon prior skills and concepts and serve as a foundation for future topics.

	Lesson 7-1	Lesson 7-2	Lesson 7-3	Lesson 7-4
Concept	Three-Dimensional Figures	Faces and Edges	Two-Dimensional Figures	Sides and Vertices
Objective	Identify three-dimensional figures.	Identify faces and edges.	Identify two-dimensional figures.	Count sides and vertices.
Math Vocabulary	cone cube cylinder sphere	edge face pyramid rectangular prism	circle rectangle square triangle	side two-dimensional figure vertex
Lesson Resources	**Materials** • paper • highlighter • index cards • a collection of objects that are spheres, cylinders, cones, or cubes **Manipulatives** • geometric solids **Other Resources** [CRM] Vocabulary and English Language Development [CRM] Skills Practice [CRM] Problem-Solving Practice [CRM] Homework Practice	**Materials** • overhead pens • stickers • chart paper • markers • paper • scissors • tape • small rectangular prism boxes **Manipulatives** • geometric solids • number cubes **Other Resources** [CRM] Vocabulary and English Language Development [CRM] Skills Practice [CRM] Problem-Solving Practice [CRM] Homework Practice	**Materials** • paper • scissors • glue • magazines • markers • index cards **Manipulatives** • pattern blocks • geometric solids **Other Resources** [CRM] Vocabulary and English Language Development [CRM] Skills Practice [CRM] Problem-Solving Practice [CRM] Homework Practice	**Materials** • paper • scissors • construction paper • markers • pencils **Manipulatives** • pattern blocks **Other Resources** [CRM] Vocabulary and English Language Development [CRM] Skills Practice [CRM] Problem-Solving Practice [CRM] Homework Practice
Technology	**Math Online** macmillanmh.com StudentWorks™ Plus ⊙ ExamView® Assessment Suite	**Math Online** macmillanmh.com StudentWorks™ Plus ⊙ ExamView® Assessment Suite	**Math Online** macmillanmh.com StudentWorks™ Plus ⊙ ExamView® Assessment Suite	**Math Online** macmillanmh.com StudentWorks™ Plus ⊙ ExamView® Assessment Suite

SSG Student Study Guide
CRM Chapter Resource Masters

TE Teacher Edition
DVD

Lesson 7-5	
Relate Two- and Three-Dimensional Figures	**Concept**
Relate two- and three-dimensional figures.	**Objective**
three-dimensional figure two-dimensional figure	**Math Vocabulary**
Materials • chart paper • markers • scissors • tape • geometric nets **Manipulatives** • geometric solids • pattern blocks **Other Resources** CRM Vocabulary and English Language Development CRM Skills Practice CRM Problem-Solving Practice CRM Homework Practice	**Lesson Resources**
Math Online macmillanmh.com StudentWorks™ Plus ExamView® Assessment Suite	**Technology**

Chapter Notes

Home Connection

Read the Home Connection letter with students and have them write their names in the space below.

Read and explain the activity under Help at Home. If time allows, complete a portion of the activity so students can introduce the activity to a parent or other caregiver.

Have students:

- find examples of different figures at home.

- find figures for which they do not know the name. Have students describe the figures.

Real-World Applications

Grocery Store Packaging Encourage students to walk through the grocery store and look at different packages.

- **Which shape is used most often?** rectangular prism

- **Why do you think that shape is used?** Sample answers: It does not roll. It stacks easily.

CHAPTER 7 Geometry

Home Connection

English   **Spanish**

Dear Family,
Today our class started **Chapter 7, Geometry**. In this chapter, I will learn about the names and properties of two- and three-dimensional figures.

Love, _____

Estimada familia:
Hoy en clase comenzamos el **Capítulo 7, Geometría.** En este capítulo aprenderé los nombres y propiedades de las figuras bidimensionales y tridimensionales.

Cariños, _____

Help at Home
You can help your child learn about two- and three-dimensional figures by asking him or her to name the shape of common household objects such as cubes of sugar, plates, or throw rugs. You can also help your child by describing the properties of these objects.

Ayude en casa
Usted puede ayudar a su hijo(a) a aprender acerca de las figuras bidimensionales y tridimensionales preguntándole el nombre de objetos de uso común en el hogar, como azúcar, platos o tapetes. También puede ayudar a su hijo(a) al describirle las propiedades de estos objetos.

Math Online Take the chapter Quick Check quiz at macmillanmh.com.

Copyright © Macmillan/McGraw-Hill • Glencoe, a division of The McGraw-Hill Companies, Inc.

Chapter 7   two hundred twenty-three **223**

Key Vocabulary

Find interactive definitions in 13 languages in the **eGlossary** at macmillanmh.com.

English   Español *Introduce the most important vocabulary terms from Chapter 7.*

cone   cono
a three-dimensional figure that narrows to a point from a circular base (p. 225)

cube   cubo
a three-dimensional figure with 6 square faces (p. 225)

cylinder   cilindro
a three-dimensional figure that looks like a can (p. 225)

sphere   esfera
a three-dimensional figure that has the shape of a round ball (p. 225)

rectangular prism
prisma rectangular
a three-dimensional figure with faces that are rectangles (p. 229)

face   cara
the flat part of a three-dimensional figure; a square is a face of a cube (p. 229)

edge   arista
the line where two sides or faces meet (p. 229)

pyramid   piramide
a three-dimensional figure with a

polygon as a base and triangular-shaped faces (p. 229)

side   lado
one of the line segments that make up a two-dimensional figure (p. 239)

vertex   vertice
a point where two or more sides meet; more than 1 vertex are called vertices (p. 239)

two-dimensional figure
figura bidimensional
a figure such as a triangle or square that is flat (p. 239)

Name _____

Get Ready

Draw an X on the figure that is different.

1

2

Count. Tell how many.

3 __3__

4 __6__

Name each shape.

5 YIELD
__triangle__

6 DETOUR →
__rectangle__

7 ROUTE 40
__circle__

STOP

Get Ready

Have students complete Get Ready to assess readiness for the chapter concepts and skills. Refer to the lessons below for additional support for prerequisite skills.

Grade 2, Lesson 1-1: Numbers 0 to 20 (p. 3)

You may also assess student readiness with the following resources:

 **Math Online** Online Readiness quiz at macmillanmh.com

Assessment Masters: Chapter Pretest (p. 88)

FOLDABLES® **Dinah Zike's**
Study Organizer **Foldables®**

Guide students through the directions on p. A158 in the Chapter Resource Masters to create their own Foldable graphic organizer for use with this chapter.

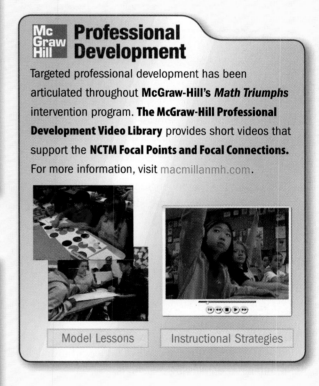

McGraw Hill **Professional Development**

Targeted professional development has been articulated throughout **McGraw-Hill's Math Triumphs** intervention program. **The McGraw-Hill Professional Development Video Library** provides short videos that support the **NCTM Focal Points and Focal Connections.** For more information, visit macmillanmh.com.

Model Lessons   Instructional Strategies

Vocabulary Preview

Model Vocabulary

• Write the chapter vocabulary on a poster. Tell students that most of the words relate to two- or three-dimensional figures.

• If students are familiar with the word, have them draw a picture or find and cut out a picture of the word.

• As students complete each lesson have them draw or find examples to describe or model the words.

• At the end of the chapter, the poster should be filled with examples of the two- and three-dimensional figures that were presented throughout the chapter.

Lesson Notes

Lesson Planner

Objective   Identify three-dimensional figures.

Vocabulary   cone, cube, cylinder, sphere

Materials/Manipulatives   geometric solids, paper, highlighter, index cards, a collection of objects that are spheres, cylinders, cones, or cubes

Chapter Resource Masters

- [CRM] Vocabulary and English Language Development (p. A162)
- [CRM] Skill Practice (p. A163)
- [CRM] Problem-Solving-Practice (p. A164)
- [CRM] Homework Practice (p. A165)

1 Introduce

Vocabulary

Explore Vocabulary   Provide a collection of objects that have the shape of cones, cubes, cylinders, and spheres for students to explore. For example: tennis ball, cone party hat, cylinder oatmeal container, or number cube. Have students group similar objects. Discuss the grouping and have students explain their reasoning.

2 Teach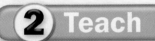

Key Concept

Foundational Skills and Concepts   After students have read through the Key Concept box, guide them through the following questions.

- **Which object is a cube?** puzzle
- **Which object is a sphere?** soccer ball
- **Which object is a cone?** orange cone
- **Which object is a cylinder?** soup can
- **Which figures can roll?** cone, cylinder, and sphere
- **Which figures can stack?** cube and cylinder

Name _____

Three-Dimensional Figures

Key Concept

Each object is a three-dimensional figure.

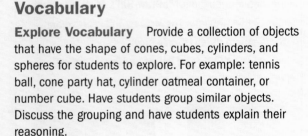

cone   **cube**

cylinder   **sphere**

Vocabulary

cone   a three-dimensional figure that narrows to a point from a circular base

cube   a three-dimensional figure with 6 square faces

cylinder   a three-dimensional figure that looks like a can

sphere   a three-dimensional figure that has the shape of a round ball

Cubes and cylinders are easy to stack. Spheres, cones, and cylinders can roll.

Chapter 7   Lesson 1   two hundred twenty-five **225**

English Learner Strategy

Say the Figure's Name

Allow students to hold and explore the three-dimensional figures.

1. Have students choose one figure. Name the figure.

2. Have students describe the figure.

   - **Is it easy to stack?** yes (for cubes and cylinders)

   - **Can it roll?** yes (for cylinders, spheres, and cones)

3. Repeat with other figures.

Example

Circle the object that is similar to the figure.

Step 1   The figure will stack and roll.

Step 2   The figure is a cylinder.

Step 3   The recycle bin will also stack and roll.

Answer   The recycle bin is similar to the cylinder.

Step-by-Step Practice

Circle the object that is similar to the figure.

Step 1   The figure will **stack**.

Step 2   The figure is a **cube**.

Step 3   The **dot cube** will also **stack**.

Answer   The **dot cube** is similar to the **cube**.

226   two hundred twenty-six

Intervention Strategy   Visual Learners

Materials: index cards with three-dimensional figures drawn on them, highlighter

Give each student a card with each of the four figures drawn on it. Have students trace the figures with a highlighter.

After tracing each figure, have students identify which figure it is.

Additional *Example*

Circle the object that is similar to the figure.

Step 1 The figure will roll.

Step 2 The figure is a sphere.

Step 3 The orange will also roll.

Answer The orange is similar to the sphere.

 Common Error *Alert*

Students often confuse the three-dimensional solids that can roll: sphere, cylinder, and cone. Have students hold each and describe how they are different. A sphere is completely round. A cone has a point. A cylinder has two flat ends.

Math Coach Notes

Strategies

1. Encourage students to use the new vocabulary to identify the figures. Praise students when they are correct, even when the pronunciation is incorrect.

2. As you walk through the school with your students, point out objects that have the shape of the figures discussed in the lesson.

3 Practice

Guided Practice

Direct students to complete Exercises 1–2 in Guided Practice.

Exercise 1 Students might not realize that the ice cream cone is similar to the cone since they are positioned differently. Remind them that orientation does not affect similarity of figures.

Problem-Solving Practice

Guide students through the four-step problem-solving plan to complete Exercise 3. Have students compare the present to models of all the figures.

- **Does the figure stack?** yes

- **Does the figure roll?** no

Ask students to check their work using the strategy suggested in the Check step. Have students think about the characteristics of each figure to solve the problem.

Using Manipulatives

Geometric Solids   Have students identify each of the solids. Divide students into four groups and assign each group one of the three-dimensional figures. Then have students go on a scavenger hunt to find classroom objects that have the shape of their figure.

Sample answers: A flat crayon, a trash can, and a coffee mug are all cylinders that could be found in the classroom.

On-Hand Manipulatives   Use common objects that have the shape of a cone, cylinder, cube, and sphere as models for the students.

Name _____

▶ Guided Practice

Circle the object that is similar to each figure.

1.

2.

Problem-Solving Practice

3. Liam brought a <u>wrapped present</u> to a party. What <u>three-dimensional figure</u> is the present?

Understand   Underline key words.

Plan   Use a model.

Solve   Look at models of three-dimensional figures.

The present is a __cube__.

Check   Will the present roll or stack like the figure?

GO on

Are They Getting It? ?

Check students' understanding of three-dimensional figures by writing the following statements on the board. Have students point out the correct and incorrect statements and explain their reasoning.

1. A figure with six square faces is a cylinder. This is incorrect. A figure with six square faces is a cube.

2. A solid figure that narrows to a point from a circular base is a cone. This is correct.

3. A solid figure that has the shape of a can is a sphere. This is incorrect. A solid figure that has the shape of a can is a cylinder.

Practice on Your Own

Name each three-dimensional figure.

4   sphere

5   cylinder

Circle the object that is similar to each figure.

6

7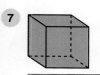

8 WRITING IN ▶MATH What three-dimensional figure is similar to the party hat? How do you know?

A cone is similar to the party hat. It will roll and has a pointed end like a cone.

Vocabulary Check Complete.

9 A three-dimensional figure that is similar to a soccer ball is called a ___sphere___.

STOP

228 two hundred twenty-eight

Math Challenge

What am I? Have students work in pairs. The first student should describe a three-dimensional object that they see in the classroom. Then the second student guesses the name of the object.

Have students clearly describe the object so that their partner guesses the figure in as few clues as possible. For example, a student may see a basketball in the room. The clues "I am orange and I roll," will help the other student identify the basketball.

Practice on Your Own

Direct students to p. 228 in their student books. Have students complete Exercises 4–9 independently. You may need to review the directions of each section before students begin.

 **4** **Assess**

See It, Do It, Say It, Write It

Step 1 Show geometric solids. Name a figure and show students the model.

Step 2 Name a three-dimensional figure. Have students choose the appropriate model from the set of geometric solids.

Step 3 Have students verbally identify the figure and its characteristics.

Step 4 Have students write the name of each three-dimensional figure and their characteristics.

Looking Ahead: Pre-teach

In the next lesson, students will learn how to identify faces and edges on figures.

Example

Count the number of faces.

There are faces on the top, bottom, front, back, left, and right. There are 6 faces.

Have students count the number of faces.

1. 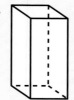 6

2.  5

3. 0

Lesson Planner

Objective   Identify faces and edges.

Vocabulary   rectangular prism, face, edge, pyramid

Materials/Manipulatives   geometric solids, small rectangular prism boxes, number cubes, overhead pens, stickers, paper, chart paper, markers, scissors, tape

Chapter Resource Masters

- CRM Vocabulary and English Language Development (p. A166)
- CRM Skill Practice (p. A167)
- CRM Problem-Solving-Practice (p. A168)
- CRM Homework Practice (p. A169)

Vocabulary

Vocabulary Interface   Ask students to tell what they know about rectangular prisms, edges, faces, and pyramids.

Give each student a box that is a rectangular prism. Have students use a marker to label the faces and edges of the box. Using math vocabulary, have students explain why the box is not a pyramid.

Key Concept

Foundational Skills and Concepts   After students have read through the Key Concept box, guide them through the following questions.

- **What do you call the flat part of a three-dimensional figure?** face

- **What do you call the line where two faces meet?** edge

- **Where do the faces of a pyramid meet?** at the points

Lesson 7-2

Name _____

Faces and Edges

Key Concept

Look at the **rectangular prism** below. There are 6 flat surfaces called **faces**.

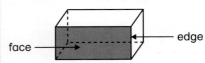

face ⟶   ⟵ edge

There are 12 lines where the faces touch. These are called **edges**.

Vocabulary

rectangular prism   a three-dimensional figure with faces that are rectangles

face   the flat part of a three-dimensional figure; a square is a face of a cube

edge   the line where two sides or faces meet

pyramid   a three-dimensional figure with a polygon as a base and triangular-shaped faces

This pyramid has five faces. Four faces are triangles. One face is a square.

Chapter 7   Lesson 2   two hundred twenty-nine   **229**

English Learner Strategy

Count the Faces and Edges

Materials: geometric solids (cube, rectangular solid, and pyramid), stickers, overhead pens, paper

Have students choose a geometric solid and write its name.

Have students place a sticker on each face of the solid and record the number of faces.

Have students trace each edge of the solid with an overhead pen and record the number of edges.

Example

Circle the figure that is similar to the blue face.

 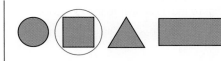

Step 1   The face has 4 edges.

Step 2   The second figure has the same shape.

Answer I circled the second figure.

Step-by-Step Practice

Circle the figure that is similar to the blue face.

 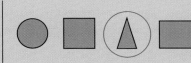

Step 1   The face has __3__ edges.

Step 2   The __third__ figure has the same shape.

Answer I circled the __third__ figure.

Additional *Example*

Circle the figure that is similar to the blue face.

Step 1 The face has 0 edges.

Step 2 The third figure has the same shape.

Answer I circled the third figure.

 Common Error *Alert*

Some students may confuse faces and edges. Remind students that faces are flat and edges are sharp.

Math Coach Notes

Strategies

1. Give students a number cube to use as a model to solve problem 6 on page 232.

2. As you walk through the school with your students, point out objects that are rectangular prisms or pyramids.

Intervention Strategy   Logical Learners

Materials: geometric solids

Have students work backward to identify figures.

Tell students the number of faces and edges a figures has.

Take turns giving clues. For example, "I am thinking of a figure with 6 faces and 12 edges."

Have students identify and name the figure that fits the description.

Guided Practice

Direct students to complete Exercises 1–2 in Guided Practice.

Exercises 1–2 Have students identify the characteristics of the shaded face before circling the similar figure.

Problem-Solving Practice

Guide students through the four-step problem-solving plan to complete Exercise 3. Have students compare the figure that is described to models of geometric solids.

- **What are the key words?** solid figure, 4 triangular faces that meet at a point

- **What is the figure?** pyramid

Ask students to check their work using the strategy suggested in the Check step. Students can count the triangular faces to solve the problem.

Using Manipulatives

Geometric Solids Create a chart listing each solid. Divide students into 6 groups and give them a geometric solid. Have each group determine how many faces and edges are on each solid. Record the number of faces and edges for each solid.

On-Hand Manipulatives Use common objects in the shape of a rectangular prism and pyramid as models for the students.

Name _____

▶ Guided Practice

Circle the figure that is similar to the blue face.

1

2

Problem-Solving Practice

3 I am a <u>solid figure with 4 triangular faces that meet at a point</u>. What figure am I?

Understand Underline key words.

Plan Use a model.

Solve Look at the three-dimensional figure models. Find the figure that matches the clues.

The figure is a __pyramid__.

Check Count the triangular faces.

A solid figure with 4 triangular faces that meet at a point?

GO on

Are They Getting It? ❓

Check students' understanding of faces and edges. Draw a rectangular prism and pyramid, and write the following statements on the board. Have students point out the correct and incorrect statements and explain their reasoning.

1. The rectangular prism has 6 faces. This is correct.

2. The pyramid has 6 edges. This is incorrect. The pyramid has 8 edges.

3. The rectangular prism has 8 edges. This is incorrect. The rectangular prism has 12 edges.

4. The pyramid has 5 faces. This is correct.

Practice on Your Own

Direct students to p. 232 in their student books. Have students complete Exercises 4–8 independently. You may need to review the directions of each section before students begin.

 Practice on Your Own

Circle the figure that is similar to the blue face.

4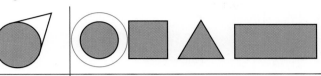

5

6 WRITING IN ►MATH   Look at the object. Hakeem says there are 4 faces. Is Hakeem correct? Explain.

No, Hakeem is not correct. The object is similar to a cube. A cube has 6 faces.

Vocabulary Check   Complete.

7 A __face__ is a flat surface of a three-dimensional figure.

8 An __edge__ is a line where two faces meet.

232   two hundred thirty-two

See It, Do It, Say It, Write It

Step 1   Find objects that have the shape of a pyramid or a rectangular prism. Identify the figures.

Step 2   Have students find other objects that have the shape of a pyramid or a rectangular prism.

Step 3   Have students explain how they identified the object.

Step 4   Have students write the names of the objects that have the shape of a pyramid or a rectangular prism.

Looking Ahead: Pre-teach

In the next lesson, students will learn how to identify two-dimensional figures.

Example   A rectangle has 4 sides.

Have students name each figure.

1.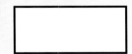
triangle

2.
square

3.
circle

Math Challenge

Parts that Make a Whole   Provide paper models of a cube, cylinder, and pyramid.

Have students cut the models apart so that each three-dimensional figure is now a collection of two-dimensional figures.

Then have students try to build the three-dimensional figure again by taping the pieces back together.

Students can show each other their pieces and try to predict which figure they will make.

Progress Check 1

Formative Assessment

Use the Progress Check to assess students' mastery of the previous lessons. Have students review the lesson indicated for the problems they answered incorrectly.

Common Error *Alert*

Three Dimensional Figures Some students will have trouble remembering the names of three dimensional figures. Use models to review three-dimensional figures. Name each figure and show what the figure looks like on paper.

Exercise 1 Have students use a paper towel roll to model the cylinder. Rotate it into different positions for comparison.

Exercise 5 Use a cereal box as a model of a rectangular prism.

Name _____

Progress Check 1 (Lessons 7-1 and 7-2)

1 Circle the object that is similar to the figure.

Name each three-dimensional figure.

2   3

_____ **sphere** _____   **rectangular prism**

4 Circle the figure that is similar to the blue face.

5 Draw a figure that looks similar to one face of a rectangular prism.

Sample answer:

Chapter 7   Progress Check

Data-Driven Decision Making

Students missing Exercises . . .	Have trouble with . . .	Should review and practice . . .
1–3	identifying three-dimensional figures.	SSG Lesson 7-1, p. 225 CRM Skills Practice, p. A163
4	identifying faces and edges.	SSG Lesson 7-2, p. 229 CRM Skills Practice, p. A167
5	problem-solving that involves identifying faces and edges.	SSG Lesson 7-2, p. 231 CRM Problem-Solving Practice, p. A168

Name _____

«« Replay 3-D Figure Match Up

Draw a line to match each three-dimensional figure to an object or description.

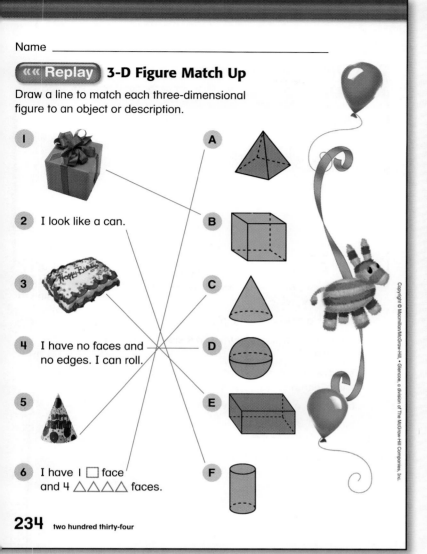

1.

2. I look like a can.

3.

4. I have no faces and no edges. I can roll.

5.

6. I have 1 ▢ face and 4 △△△△ faces.

A

B

C

D

E

F

234 two hundred thirty-four

Use the Replay activity to review and reinforce the concepts and skills presented in Lessons 7-1 and 7-2.

Instructions

Have students read the directions at the top of the student page.

Student Technology

Students can use the following technology resources to reinforce chapter content.

- 💿 StudentWorks™ Plus
- **Math Online** ⟩ macmillanmh.com
- eGlossary

Lesson Notes

Lesson Planner

Objective Identify two-dimensional figures.

Vocabulary circle, rectangle, square, triangle

Materials/Manipulatives paper, scissors, glue, magazines, geometric solids, pattern blocks, index cards, markers

Chapter Resource Masters

[CRM] Vocabulary and English Language Development (p. A170)

[CRM] Skill Practice (p. A171)

[CRM] Problem-Solving-Practice (p. A172)

[CRM] Homework Practice (p. A173)

1 Introduce

Vocabulary

Vocabulary Match Have students draw a circle, square, rectangle, and triangle on their papers. Then have students match each figure with its name.

2 Teach

Key Concept

Foundational Skills and Concepts After students have read through the Key Concept box, guide them through the following questions.

- **What is the name of the round figure?** circle

- **What are the names of the figures with 4 sides?** square and rectangle

- **What is the name of the figure with 3 sides?** triangle

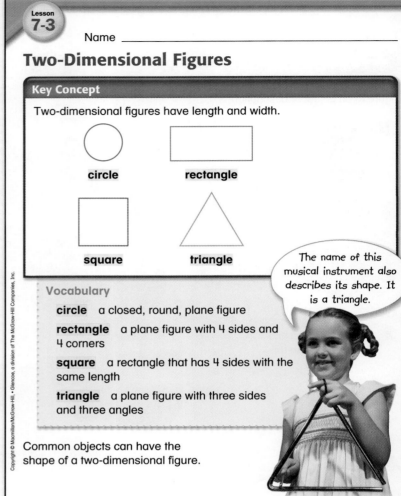

Two-Dimensional Figures

Key Concept

Two-dimensional figures have length and width.

circle   rectangle

square   triangle

The name of this musical instrument also describes its shape. It is a triangle.

Vocabulary

circle a closed, round, plane figure

rectangle a plane figure with 4 sides and 4 corners

square a rectangle that has 4 sides with the same length

triangle a plane figure with three sides and three angles

Common objects can have the shape of a two-dimensional figure.

Chapter 7   Lesson 3   two hundred thirty-five **235**

English Learner Strategy

Say the Name

Have students create flash cards with different figures on them. On the back of each card, have students write the name of each figure.

Use these flash cards to help students practice saying the name of each figure. Show the card and have students say the name. Use the cards to review figures throughout the chapter.

Example

Circle the similar figure.

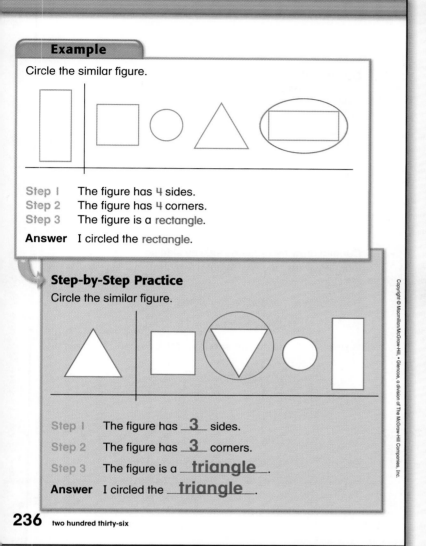

Step 1   The figure has 4 sides.
Step 2   The figure has 4 corners.
Step 3   The figure is a rectangle.

Answer   I circled the rectangle.

Step-by-Step Practice

Circle the similar figure.

Step 1   The figure has __3__ sides.

Step 2   The figure has __3__ corners.

Step 3   The figure is a __triangle__.

Answer   I circled the __triangle__.

236   two hundred thirty-six

Additional *Example*

Circle the similar figure.

Step 1 The figure has 0 sides.

Step 2 The figure has 0 corners.

Step 3 The figure is a circle.

Answer I circled the circle.

⚠ Common Error *Alert*

Students confuse squares and rectangles. Emphasize that a figure is a square only if all 4 sides have the same length.

Intervention Strategy   Visual Learners

Materials: index cards

- Have students work in pairs. Assign one student in each pair to pictures and the other student to words.

- Give each pair of students eight index cards. Have the "picture" student draw a circle, rectangle, square, and triangle on four of the cards. Have the "words" student write the respective names on the other four cards.

- Have students shuffle the cards and place them face down in an array.

- Students take turns trying to make a match by turning over two cards. If the picture of the figure matches the name of the figure, the student gets to keep the match and try again. If not, the cards are turned face down and play continues with the next student.

- When all cards are matched, the student with the most pairs wins.

③ Practice

Guided Practice

Direct students to complete Exercise 1 in Guided Practice.

Exercise 1 Remind students that a square always has four sides with the same length no matter how it is positioned.

Problem-Solving Practice

Guide students through the four-step problem-solving plan to complete Exercise 2. Have students draw a picture of what Carmen drew and name the new figure.

• **What did Carmen draw?** two squares side by side

• **What is the new figure?** rectangle

Ask students to check their work using the strategy suggested in the Check step. Students can outline the new figure to identify its name.

Using Manipulatives

Pattern Blocks Have students use pattern blocks to build triangles, squares, and rectangles.

Geometric Solids Students can trace the faces of geometric solids to create two-dimensional figures on paper. Have students name each figure.

On-Hand Manipulatives Use objects in your classroom to represent figures. When possible, cut out faces of objects to create figures. For example, cut out the side of an empty tissue box to model a rectangle.

Name _____

▶ Guided Practice

1. Circle the similar figure.

Copyright © Macmillan/McGraw-Hill, • Glencoe, a division of The McGraw-Hill Companies, Inc.

Problem-Solving Practice

2. Carmen drew <u>two squares</u> <u>side by side</u> so that they were <u>touching</u>. <u>What new figure</u> did Carmen draw?

Understand Underline key words.

Plan Draw a picture.

Solve Draw two squares side by side.

The new figure is a **rectangle**.

Check Outline the new figure you drew.

GO on

Are They Getting It?

Check students' understanding of identifying two-dimensional figures by writing the exercises on the board. Have students point out the correct and incorrect answers and explain their reasoning.

1. This figure is a square. This is incorrect. The figure is a triangle.

2. This figure is a rectangle. This is correct.

3. This figure is a circle. This is incorrect. The figure is a square.

▶ Practice on Your Own

Circle the similar figure.

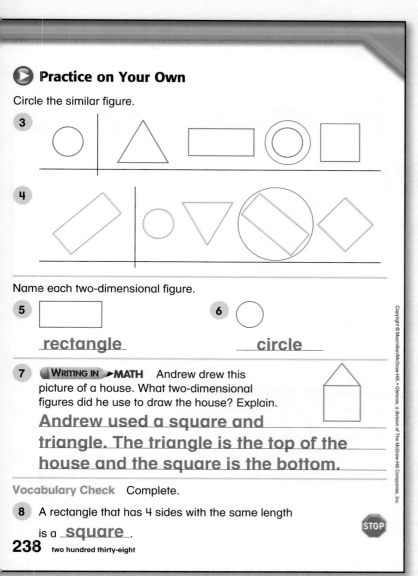

Name each two-dimensional figure.

5. rectangle

6. circle

7. **WRITING IN ▶MATH** Andrew drew this picture of a house. What two-dimensional figures did he use to draw the house? Explain.

Andrew used a square and triangle. The triangle is the top of the house and the square is the bottom.

Vocabulary Check Complete.

8. A rectangle that has 4 sides with the same length is a **square**.

238 two hundred thirty-eight

Math Challenge

Riddle Time Have students work in pairs. Have students write riddles about two-dimensional figures.

Students exchange papers and try to solve each other's riddle. For example, one student may write "I have 4 equal sides. What am I?" The other student should answer, "You are a square."

Practice on Your Own

Direct students to p. 238 in their student books. Have students complete Exercises 3–8 independently. You may need to review the directions of each section before students begin.

④ Assess

See It, Do It, Say It, Write It

Step 1 Locate two-dimensional figures in the classroom. Say the name of each figure located.

Step 2 Have students locate two-dimensional figures in the classroom and identify the name of each figure located.

Step 3 Have students explain how they named each figure using math vocabulary.

Step 4 Have students draw each two-dimensional figure and write its name.

Looking Ahead: Pre-teach

In the next lesson, students will learn how to count sides and vertices of figures.

Example Count how many sides.

4

Have students count how many sides.

1. 3

2. 0

3. 5

Lesson Notes

Copyright © Macmillan/McGraw-Hill, • Glencoe, a division of The McGraw-Hill Companies, Inc.

Lesson Planner

Math Objective   Count sides and vertices.

Vocabulary   side, vertex, two-dimensional figure

Materials/Manipulatives   markers, paper, construction paper, scissors, pattern blocks, pencils

Chapter Resource Masters

- [CRM] Vocabulary and English Language Development (p. A174)
- [CRM] Skill Practice (p. A175)
- [CRM] Problem-Solving-Practice (p. A176)

Introduce

Vocabulary

Vocabulary Interaction   Have students copy various two-dimensional figures from the board. Then trace the sides in one color and mark an X on each vertex.

Key Concept

Foundational Skills and Concepts   After students have read through the Key Concept box, guide them through the following questions.

- **What is the point called where two or more sides meet?** vertex

- **How many sides does the figure have?** 4

- **How many vertices does the figure have?** 4

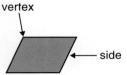

Name _____

Sides and Vertices

Key Concept

This figure has 4 **sides**.

vertex

side

There are 4 points on this figure where the sides meet. They are called **vertices**.

Vocabulary

side   one of the line segments that make up a two-dimensional figure

vertex   a point where two or more sides meet; more than 1 vertex are called vertices.

two-dimensional figure   a figure such as a triangle or square that is flat

The number of sides is equal to the number of vertices.

There are 8 vertices on a stop sign. So, there are 8 sides on a stop sign.

Chapter 7   Lesson 4

two hundred thirty-nine 239

English Learner Strategy

Vertex and Vertices

There are many irregular plurals in the English language, one of which is vertices.

Have students draw a picture of a rectangle and mark one vertex. Have students say, "one vertex," and write it on their papers.

Then have students draw a picture of a rectangle and mark all four vertices. Have students say, "four vertices," and write it on their papers.

Discuss how the words are similar because they both begin with *vert-*, but the ending changes depending on the number of vertices being considered.

Example

Aiden drew this two-dimensional figure.
How many sides and vertices did Aiden draw?

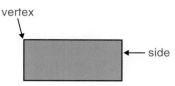

Step 1   Count the sides. There are 4 sides.

Step 2   Count the vertices. There are 4 vertices.

Answer   Aiden's figure has 4 sides and 4 vertices.

Step-by-Step Practice

Namid drew this two-dimensional figure.
How many sides and vertices did Namid draw?

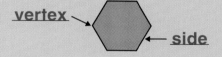

Step 1   Count the sides. There are __6__ sides.

Step 2   Count the vertices. There are __6__ vertices.

Answer   Namid's figure has __6__ sides
and __6__ vertices.

Additional *Example*

**Maria drew this two-dimensional figure.
How many sides and vertices did Maria draw?**

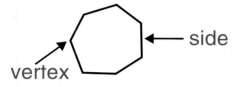

Step 1   Count the sides. There are 7 sides.

Step 2   Count the vertices. There are 7 vertices.

Answer   Maria's figure has 7 sides and 7 vertices.

⚠ **Common Error** *Alert*

When counting sides and vertices, students often omit or double count because they lose track of what has been counted. Have students highlight each side or vertex as it is counted.

Math Coach Notes

Strategy   Encourage students to count the sides or vertices in order around the figure.

Study Skills   Explain to students that sides are part of two-dimensional figures while edges are part of three-dimensional figures.

Intervention Strategy   Interpersonal Learners

Materials: paper

Have students work in pairs. Student 1 describes a figure by saying how many sides and vertices it has. Student 2 draws the figure. Student 1 checks the figure. If it is correct, students switch roles and repeat the activity. If it is incorrect, Student 2 continues to draw figures until drawing is correct.

Practice

Guided Practice

Direct students to complete Exercises 1–2 in Guided Practice.

Exercises 1–2 Have students first count the number of sides and then the number of vertices. Remind them that the number of sides and vertices should match.

Problem-Solving Practice

Guide students through the four-step problem-solving plan to complete Exercise 3.

- **What are the key words?** 10 sides, which piece
- **How many sides does the blue piece have?** 10
- **How many sides does the red piece have?** 6

Ask students to check their work using the strategy suggested in the Check step. Students can number the sides of each figure to solve the problem.

Using Manipulatives

Pattern Blocks Have students count the number of sides on each pattern block. Then group the blocks based on the number of sides.

On-Hand Manipulatives Cut various figures out of construction paper. Include figures with different numbers of sides. Have students count the sides and vertices on the figures.

Name _____

▶ **Guided Practice**

Count the sides and vertices of each figure.

1. **_3_** sides
    _3_ vertices

2. **_4_** sides
    _4_ vertices

Problem-Solving Practice

3. Jamal found these two puzzle pieces. The missing piece to his rocket puzzle has 10 sides. Which piece is missing from Jamal's rocket puzzle?

Understand Underline key words.

Plan Use the pictures.

Solve The blue puzzle piece has **_10_** sides.

The red puzzle piece has **_6_** sides.

The **_blue_** piece is missing from Jamal's rocket puzzle.

Check Number the sides of each figure.

GO on

Are They Getting It? ?

Check students' understanding of sides and vertices by drawing the following figures on the board. Have students point out the correct and incorrect statements and explain their reasoning.

1. The triangle has 3 sides and 3 vertices.
    This is correct.

2. The hexagon has 8 sides and 8 vertices.
    This is incorrect. The hexagon has 6 sides and 6 vertices.

3. The square has 4 sides and 4 vertices.
    This is correct.

Count the sides and vertices of each figure.

4

___3___ sides

___3___ vertices

5

___4___ sides

___4___ vertices

6

___4___ sides

___4___ vertices

7

___5___ sides

___5___ vertices

8 **WRITING IN** ▶**MATH** Laura says these figures have the same number of sides and vertices. Is Laura correct? How do you know?

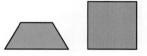

Yes, Laura is correct. I counted 4 sides and 4 vertices for each figure.

Vocabulary Check Complete.

9 A ___side___ is one of the line segments that make up a two-dimensional figure.

10 A ___vertex___ is a point where two or more sides meet. STOP

Practice on Your Own

Direct students to p. 242 in their student books. Have students complete Exercises 4–10 independently. You may need to review the directions of each section before students begin.

4 **Assess**

See It, Do It, Say It, Write It

Step 1 Draw figures with a specified number of sides. Count the number of vertices for each figure.

Step 2 Have students draw figures with a specified number of sides. Have students count the vertices for each.

Step 3 Have students point to each side and each vertex, saying "side" or "vertex," respectively.

Step 4 Have students write the words *side* and *vertex* on their paper. Then have them draw a figure and label the sides and vertices.

Looking Ahead: Pre-teach

In the next lesson, students learn how to relate two- and three-dimensional figures.

Example

A cube has 6 faces. What shape is the shaded face?

square

Have students name the shape of each shaded face.

1.

triangle

2.

circle

Math Challenge

Shape Search

Materials: paper, scissors, glue, magazines

• Have students number their papers from 1 to 10.

• Have them look through magazines to find a figure with the designated number of sides, from 1 to 10.

• When students find a figure, have them cut it out and glue it next to the corresponding number.

Lesson 7-4 Sides and Vertices **242**

Lesson Notes

Lesson Planner

Objective   Relate two- and three-dimensional figures.

Vocabulary   two-dimensional figure, three-dimensional figure

Materials/Manipulatives   chart paper, markers, pattern blocks, geometric solids, scissors, tape, geometric nets

Chapter Resource Masters

[CRM] Vocabulary and English Language Development (p. A178)

[CRM] Skill Practice (p. A179)

[CRM] Problem-Solving-Practice (p. A180)

[CRM] Homework Practice (p. A181)

① Introduce

Vocabulary

Nonexamples   Review two-dimensional figure. Introduce three-dimensional figure (have length, width, and height). Display a two-column chart, labeled two-dimensional and three-dimensional. Place an example of every figure from the chapter in each column. Have students cross off the nonexamples.

② Teach

Key Concept

Foundational Skills and Concepts   After students have read through the Key Concept box, guide them through the following questions.

- **What shape are the faces of a cube? pyramid? rectangular prism? cone?** squares; squares and triangle; rectangles; circle

- **How is a three-dimensional figure different from a two-dimensional figure?** Three-dimensional figures have length, width, and height and two-dimensional figures only have length and width.

243 Chapter 7 Geometry

Name _____

Relate Two- and Three-Dimensional Figures

Key Concept

Figure	Faces	Vertices
 cube	6 ☐	8
pyramid	1 ☐ and 4 △	5
rectangular prism	6 ▭	8
cone	1 ◯	1
sphere	no faces	0

A square is a two-dimensional figure. It has length and width.

A cube is a three-dimensional figure. It has length, width, and height.

The faces of a rectangular prism are rectangles.

Some three-dimensional figures have faces that are two-dimensional figures.

Chapter 7   Lesson 5

two hundred forty-three   243

English Learner Strategy

Representing Two- and Three-Dimensional Figures

Explain to students that they are going to learn the difference between two- and three-dimensional figures. Remind students that two-dimensional figures have length and width while three-dimensional figures have length, width, and height.

Show students a cube. Explain that the cube is a three-dimensional figure. Then show the students a picture of a square. Explain that the square is two-dimensional.

Present objects or drawings of figures one at a time to the students. Ask them to identify each figure as two-dimensional or three-dimensional.

Example

Name the figure.

Step 1	There are 5 faces in all.
Step 2	Look at the shapes of the faces. There are 4 triangles and 1 square.
Answer	The figure is a pyramid.

Step-by-Step Practice

Name the figure.

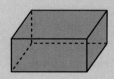 

Step 1	There are __6__ faces in all.
Step 2	Look at the shape of the faces. There are __6__ **rectangles**.
Answer	The figure is a **rectangular prism**.

Intervention Strategy   Logical Learners

Materials: chart paper, marker

Have students work in pairs to create a two-column chart.

In the first column have students list the two-dimensional figures they know: square, triangle, rectangle, and circle.

In the second column, have students list all the three-dimensional figures that have faces of that shape.

Two-Dimensional Figures	Three-Dimensional Figures
square	cube
circle	cone
	cylinder

Additional *Example*

Name the figure.

Step 1 The figure has 2 faces in all.

Step 2 Look at the shapes of the faces. There are 2 circles.

Answer The figure is a cylinder.

⚠ **Common Error** *Alert*

Students may say that curved areas are circular faces. Remind them that faces must be flat.

Math Coach Notes

Strategies

1. Help students understand that three-dimensional figures are made of two-dimensional figures. Give students a box (rectangular prism). Have them shade one face of the box. Ask students to identify the shape of the shaded area. Explain that a rectangle, a two-dimensional figure, is part of a rectangular prism, a three-dimensional figure.

2. Practice naming and counting faces on a variety of classroom objects.

③ Practice

Guided Practice

Direct students to complete Exercises 1–4 in Guided Practice.

Exercises 1–2 Remind students the a face is the flat part of a three-dimensional figure.

Problem-Solving Practice

Guide students through the four-step problem-solving plan to complete Exercise 5. Have students use a model to determine the shape of each face.

- **What are the key words?** pyramid, what two-dimensional figures

- **What figures are the faces of a pyramid?** square and triangles

Ask students to check their work using the strategy suggested in the Check step. Have students check that they counted all the faces on the pyramid.

Using Manipulatives

Pattern Blocks Have students tape pattern blocks together to see what three-dimensional figures they can build.

Geometric Solids Students can trace the faces of geometric solids to create figures on paper. Have students name each figure.

On-Hand Manipulatives Cut out various figures from file folders to create two-dimensional figures. Students can tape the figures together to create three-dimensional figures.

Name _____

▶ Guided Practice

Write the number of faces for each figure.

1 ____0____ faces

2 ____6____ faces

Name the shape of the faces for each figure.

3 __squares__

4 __rectangles__

Problem-Solving Practice

5 Olivia wants to make a <u>pyramid</u>. <u>What two-dimensional figures</u> will she need?

Understand Underline key words.

Plan Use a model.

Solve Look at the faces of a pyramid.

Olivia will need ___1___ **square** and ___4___ **triangles**.

Check Did you count all the faces on the pyramid?

GO on

Chapter 7 Lesson 5

two hundred forty-five **245**

Are They Getting It?

Check students' understanding of relating two- and three-dimensional figures by writing these statements on the board. Have students point out the correct and incorrect statements and explain their reasoning.

1. The faces of a cube are squares. This is correct.

2. The face of a cone is a triangle. This is incorrect. The face of a cone is a circle.

3. The faces of a rectangular prism are circles. This is incorrect. The faces of a rectangular prism are rectangles.

▶ Practice on Your Own

Write the number of faces for each figure.

6

___1___ face

7

___2___ faces

Name the shape(s) of the faces for each figure.

8

__square__
and __triangles__

9

__circle__

10

__circles__

11 **WRITING IN ▶MATH** Basir has one square and four triangles. What three-dimensional figure can Basir make? Explain.

__Basir can make a pyramid. He can use__
__the square as the bottom face and the__
__the triangles as the side faces.__

Vocabulary Check Complete.

12 Triangles and squares are flat figures called
__two__ - __dimensional__ figures.

STOP

246 two hundred forty-six

Practice on Your Own

Direct students to p. 246 in their student books. Have students complete Exercises 6–12 independently. You may need to review the directions of each section before students begin.

④ Assess

See It, Do It, Say It, Write It

Step 1 Make a three-dimensional figure from a net.

Step 2 Have students make a three-dimensional figure by taping the parts together.

Step 3 Have students explain how they made the three-dimensional figure.

Step 4 Have students write their explanation and include the formula for the three-dimensional figure. For example, pyramid = 1 square + 4 triangles.

 Common Error *Alert*

Students might have difficulty seeing that a pyramid is not made of only triangles. Have students shade the base to see that it is a square.

Math Challenge

Folding Shapes

Materials: geometric nets, scissors, tape

- Give each student a net of a geometric solid. Have students identify the two-dimensional figures in the net.

- Explain that each picture can be cut on the outside line and then folded on the other lines to form a three-dimensional figure. Have students predict which three-dimensional figure they will make.

- Have students check their prediction by cutting out the net and folding it into a figure.

Progress Check 2

Formative Assessment

Use the Progress Check to assess students' mastery of the previous lessons. Have students review the lesson indicated for the problems they answered incorrectly.

Common Error *Alert*

Three-Dimensional Figures Some students might not understand that three-dimensional figures are made from two-dimensional figures. Review the names of the faces on three-dimensional figures to reinforce this concept.

Exercises 1–3 Remind students that vertices are where two or more sides meet.

Exercises 7–9 Remind students that faces must be flat.

Exercise 10 Have students number the sides and vertices of the given triangle.

Name _____

Progress Check 2 (Lessons 7-3, 7-4, and 7-5)

Count the sides and vertices of each figure.

1 __4__ sides __4__ vertices

2 __3__ sides __3__ vertices

3 __4__ sides __4__ vertices

Name each figure.

4 circle

5 cube

6 cone

Write the number of faces for each figure.

7 __2__ faces

8 __0__ faces

9 __6__ faces

10 Tara wants to draw a triangle. How many sides and vertices does she need to draw?
__3__ sides and __3__ vertices

Chapter 7   Progress Check

two hundred forty-seven **247**

Data-Driven Decision Making

Students missing Exercises . . .	Have trouble with . . .	Should review and practice . . .
1–3	counting sides and vertices.	SSG Lesson 7-4, p. 239 CRM Skills Practice, p. A175
4	identifying two-dimensional figures.	SSG Lesson 7-3, p. 235 CRM Skills Practice, p. A171
5–6	identifying three-dimensional figures.	SSG Lesson 7-5, p. 243 CRM Skills Practice, p. 179
7–9	identifying faces.	SSG Lesson 7-5, p. 243 CRM Skills Practice, p. A179
10	problem-solving that involves counting sides and vertices.	SSG Lesson 7-4, p. 241 CRM Problem-Solving Practice, p. 176

Name _____

«« Replay Shade the Way "Four" Anna

Help Anna the Ant find her way to the ant hill!

Shade the boxes that show a two-dimensional figure
with 4 sides and 4 vertices.

Connect four in a row to show Anna the Ant which way to go.

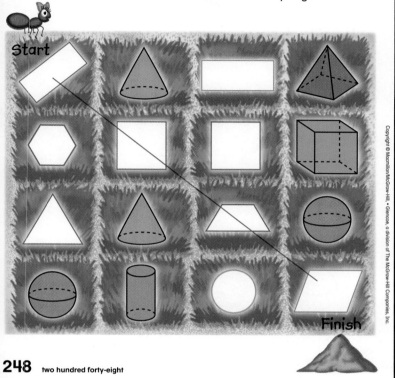

Copyright © Macmillan/McGraw-Hill • Glencoe, a division of The McGraw-Hill Companies, Inc.

248 two hundred forty-eight

Replay

Use the Replay activity to review and reinforce the concepts and skills presented in Lessons 7-3, 7-4, and 7-5.

Instructions

Have students read the directions at the top of the student page.

Student Technology

Students can use the following technology resources to reinforce chapter content.

- ⊙ StudentWorks™ Plus

- **Math Online** ⟩ macmillanmh.com

- eGlossary

Vocabulary

If students have difficulty answering Exercises 1–3, use the page references below to review the vocabulary words, or refer them to the glossary.

edge (p. 229)
face (p. 229)
side (p. 239)
vertex (p. 239)

Vocabulary Review Strategies

Vocabulary Collage   Give each student a large piece of paper. Have students create a collage to present the vocabulary from the chapter. Students can draw or cut and glue pictures to represent the chapter vocabulary on the poster. Have students label the pictures with chapter vocabulary terms.

Concepts

The exercises in this section are grouped to cover content from each lesson in the chapter.

Exercise 5: Lesson 7-1 (p. 225)
Exercise 6: Lesson 7-2 (p. 229)
Exercises 7–8: Lesson 7-3 (p. 235)
Exercises 9–10: Lesson 7-4 (p. 239)
Exercises 11–13: Lesson 7-5 (p. 243)

Find **Extra Practice** for these concepts in the Practice Worksheets, pp. A162–A181.

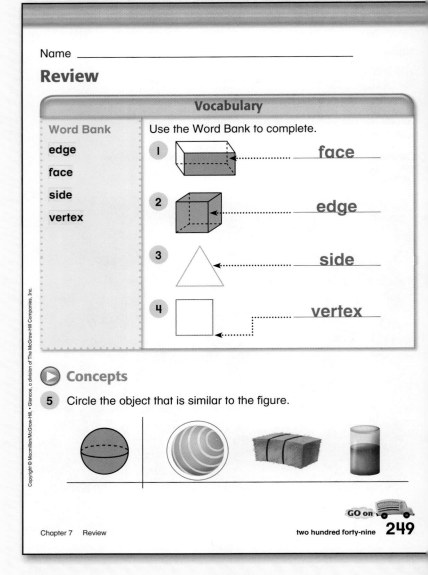

6 Circle the figure that is similar to the blue face.

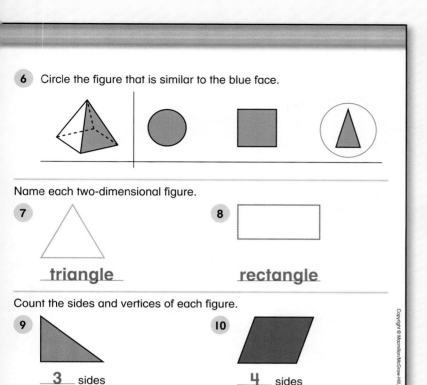

Name each two-dimensional figure.

7

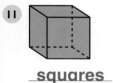

triangle

8

rectangle

Count the sides and vertices of each figure.

9

__3__ sides
__3__ vertices

10

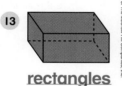

__4__ sides
__4__ vertices

Name the shape(s) of the faces for each figure.

11

squares

12

square
and triangles

13

rectangles

STOP

250 two hundred fifty

Review

Dinah Zike's Foldables®

Have students use the Foldable they created at the beginning of the chapter to review and reinforce the concepts and skills they learned during the chapter. (See Chapter Resource Masters p. A158 for instructions.)

Intervention Strategy

Use this Intervention Strategy activity at any point during the chapter to reinforce the concepts and skills presented in the chapter.

Store Packaging

Step 1 Have each student bring an empty packaged item from the store. They should identify and describe their package.

Step 2 Divide the class into pairs. Have each pair design a different package for their item. Encourage students to think about the figures they have learned in the chapter.

Step 3 Have students make the new package from classroom supplies. Have them identify the shape of the new package.

Step 4 Have students compare the two different packages. They should present their package options to the class.

• **Why do you think that the product is packaged the way it is?** Sample answer: It is easier to stack on the shelves.

Classroom Management

Jigsaw Group five students together and assign each a different lesson in this chapter. The students will then present the material from their lessons to the entire group as a review of what has been learned.

Chapter 7 Chapter Test

Chapter Resource Masters

Additional forms of the Chapter Test are available.

Test Format	Where to Find it
Chapter Test	**Math Online** macmillanmh.com
Blackline Masters	Assessment Masters, p. 91

ExamView®
Assessment Suite

Customize and create multiple versions of your chapter test and their answer keys. All of these questions from the chapter tests are available on ExamView® Assessment Suite.

Advance TRACKER

Online Assessment and Reporting
macmillanmh.com

This online assessment tool allows teachers to track student progress with easily accessible, comprehensive reports available for every student. Assess students using any internet-ready computer.

Alternative Assessment

Use Interviews Give students models of three-dimensional figures. Ask them to name the figure, count the edges and faces, and identify the shapes of the faces. Two-dimensional objects can also be assessed. Students should name the figure and count the number of sides and vertices.

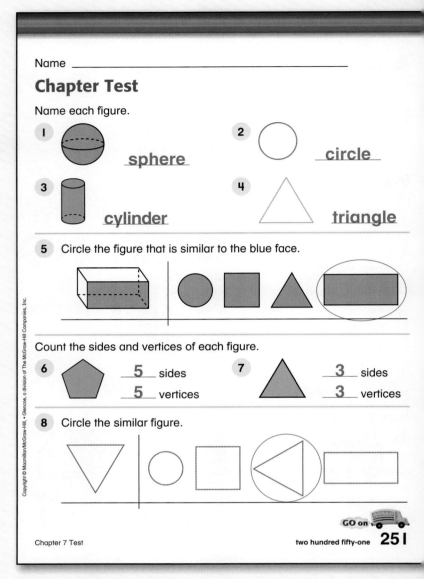

Name _____

Chapter Test

Name each figure.

1. sphere

2. circle

3. cylinder

4. triangle

5. Circle the figure that is similar to the blue face.

Count the sides and vertices of each figure.

6. _5_ sides
_5_ vertices

7. _3_ sides
_3_ vertices

8. Circle the similar figure.

GO on

Chapter 7 Test

two hundred fifty-one **251**

251 Chapter 7 Test

9 **Who is Correct?**

Mike and Benito describe a cube.

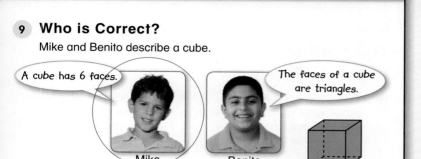

A cube has 6 faces.

The faces of a cube are triangles.

Mike   Benito

Circle the correct answer. Explain.

Mike is correct. A cube has 6 faces.
Benito is incorrect. The faces of a cube
are squares.

Write the number and shape(s) of the faces for each figure.

10   <u> I </u>   <u>circle</u> face

11   <u> I </u>   <u>square</u> face and
                                    <u> 4 </u>   <u>triangle</u> faces

12 Charlotte's mom packs a juice box with her lunch. What three-dimensional figure is similar to the juice box?

<u>rectangular prism</u>

252 two hundred fifty-two   Chapter 7 Test

Copyright © Macmillan/McGraw-Hill • Glencoe, a division of The McGraw-Hill Companies, Inc.

Who Is Correct?

Diagnostic Teaching

- Mike said a cube has 6 faces. This is correct.

- Benito said that the faces of a cube are triangles. This is incorrect. The faces of a cube are squares.

Learning from Mistakes

Missed Questions   Review commonly missed questions as a small group or class. Ask students to share their methods of answering each question. Try to point out when any errors occur and take corrective measures.

Data-Driven Decision Making

Students missing Exercises . . .	Have trouble with . . .	Should review and practice . . .
1, 3	identifying three-dimensional figures.	SSG Lesson 7-1, p. 225 CRM Skills Practice, p. A163
2, 4, 8	identifying two-dimensional figures.	SSG Lesson 7-3, p. 235 CRM Skills Practice, p. A171
5	identifying faces and edges.	SSG Lesson 7-2, p. 229 CRM Skills Practice, p. A167
6–7	counting sides and vertices.	SSG Lesson 7-4, p. 239 CRM Skills Practice, p. A175
9–11	relating two- and three-dimensional figures.	SSG Lesson 7-5, p. 243 CRM Skills Practice, p. A179
12	problem-solving that involves identifying three-dimensional figures	SSG Lesson 7-1, p. 227 CRM Problem-Solving Practice, p. A164

Chapter 7 Test **252**

Test Practice

Survey student responses for each item. Class trends may indicate common errors and misconceptions.

1. pyramid: correct
   rectangular prism: does not understand how to relate two- and three-dimensional figures
   triangle: does not understand how to relate two- and three-dimensional figures
   cylinder: does not understand how to relate two- and three-dimensional figures

2. sphere: does not understand vocabulary
   square: does not understand vocabulary
   triangle: does not understand vocabulary
   circle: correct

3. sphere: does not know the characteristics of a cone
   cone: correct
   cylinder: does not know the characteristics of a cone
   cube: does not know the characteristics of a cone

4. triangle and circle: incorrectly chose circle
   circle and rectangle: chose two incorrect figures
   square and triangle: correct
   square and rectangle: incorrectly chose a rectangle

5. square: did not name the face correctly
   cylinder: named a three-dimensional figure as a face
   circle: correct
   triangle: did not name the faces correctly

6. 4: counted the number of sides on a rectangle
   5: does not understand vocabulary
   6: correct
   12: counted the number of edges

7. 4: disregarded the edges of the square face
   5: counted the faces
   8: correct
   12: does not understand vocabulary

8. cube: chose a three-dimensional figure
   rectangular prism: chose a three-dimensional figure
   sphere: chose a three-dimensional figure
   rectangle: correct

9. △:   does not understand vocabulary
   ▭:   correct
   ⬠:   does not understand vocabulary
   ◯:   does not understand vocabulary

10. 0: correct
    1: does not understand vertices
    2: does not understand vertices
    4: does not understand vertices

Name _____

Test Practice

Choose the correct answer.

1 Kylie describes a three-dimensional figure. She says the figure has 1 square face and 4 triangle faces. What figure does Kylie describe?
- ● pyramid
- ○ rectangular prism
- ○ triangle
- ○ cylinder

2 Name the two-dimensional figure.

○ (circle shape)

- ○ sphere   ○ square
- ○ triangle   ● circle

3 A three-dimensional figure that narrows to a point from a circular base is a _____.
- ○ sphere   ● cone
- ○ cylinder   ○ cube

4 Jacob drew a house. What two-dimensional figures did Jacob draw?

(house drawing)

- ○ triangle and circle
- ○ circle and rectangle
- ● square and triangle
- ○ square and rectangle

5 Name the shape of the faces.

(cylinder drawing)

- ○ square   ○ cylinder
- ● circle   ○ triangle

6 There are _____ faces on a rectangular prism.

(rectangular prism drawing)

- ○ 4   ○ 5
- ● 6   ○ 12

Chapter 7   Test Practice

two hundred fifty-three **253**

➡ GO ON

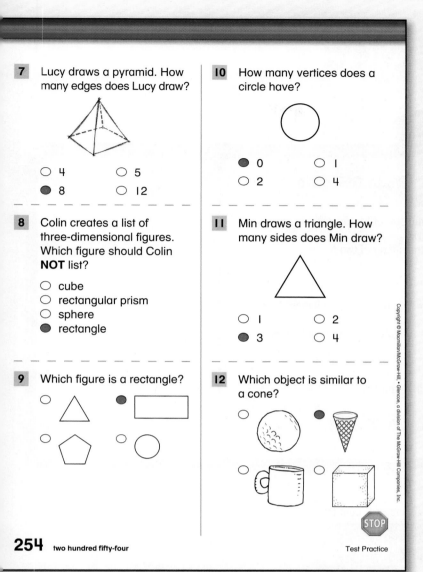

7 Lucy draws a pyramid. How many edges does Lucy draw?

○ 4   ○ 5
● 8   ○ 12

8 Colin creates a list of three-dimensional figures. Which figure should Colin **NOT** list?

○ cube
○ rectangular prism
○ sphere
● rectangle

9 Which figure is a rectangle?

○ ▲   ● ▭
○ ⬠   ○ ○

10 How many vertices does a circle have?

● 0   ○ l
○ 2   ○ 4

11 Min draws a triangle. How many sides does Min draw?

○ l   ○ 2
● 3   ○ 4

12 Which object is similar to a cone?

○ (golf ball)   ● (ice cream cone)
○ (mug)   ○ (box)

STOP

Test Practice

Diagnosing Student Errors and Misconceptions

Flash Cards   For students who are struggling with identifying figures, encourage them to analyze the characteristics of each figure. Create flash cards with questions that lead the students to identify distinguishing characteristics and thus the figure. Continue to use the flash cards until students can answer the questions and name the figures. Remove the questions from the flash cards so that students learn to ask themselves the questions and identify the figures independently.

11. 1: did not count sides correctly
2: did not count sides correctly
3: correct
4: did not count sides correctly

12. (golf ball): chose object similar to a sphere

(cone):   correct

(mug): chose object similar to cube

(box): chose object similar to a cylinder

Chapter-at-a-Glance

Lesson	Math Objective	Local/State Standards
8-1 Compare Size (pp. 257–260)	Compare the size of two figures.	
8-2 Compare Shape (pp. 261–264)	Compare the shape of two figures.	
Progress Check 1 (p. 265)		
8-3 Create Figures (pp. 267–270)	Create new figures by putting figures together.	
8-4 Take Apart Figures (pp. 271–274)	Take apart a figure to make new figures.	
Progress Check 2 (p. 275)		
8-5 Congruence (pp. 277–280)	Identify congruent figures.	
8-6 Symmetry (pp. 281–284)	Identify symmetry in figures.	
Progress Check 3 (p. 285)		

Content-at-a-Glance
The diagram below summarizes and unpacks Chapter 8 content.

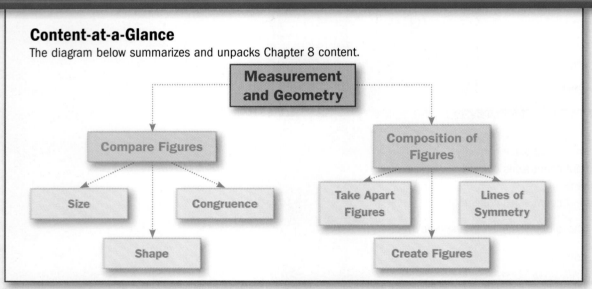

Chapter Assessment Manager

Diagnostic Diagnose students' readiness.

	Student Study Guide/ Teacher Editions	Assessment Masters	Technology
Course Placement Test		1	💿 ExamView® Assessment Suite
Book 3 Pretest		85	💿 ExamView® Assessment Suite
Chapter Pretest		100	💿 ExamView® Assessment Suite
Get Ready	SSG 256		Math Online ⟩ macmillanmh.com StudentWorks™ Plus

Formative Identify students' misconceptions of content knowledge.

	Student Study Guide/ Teacher Editions	Assessment Masters	Technology
Progress Checks	SSG 265, 275, 285		Math Online ⟩ macmillanmh.com StudentWorks™ Plus
Vocabulary Review	SSG 260, 264, 270, 274, 280, 284, 287		Math Online ⟩ macmillanmh.com
Lesson Assessments			💿 ExamView® Assessment Suite
Are They Getting It?	TE 259, 263, 269, 273, 279, 283		

Summative Determine students' success in learning the concepts in the lesson, chapter, or section.

	Student Study Guide/ Teacher Editions	Assessment Masters	Technology
Chapter Test	SSG 289	103	💿 ExamView® Assessment Suite
Test Practice	SSG 291	106	💿 ExamView® Assessment Suite
Alternative Assessment	TE 289	109	
See It, Do It, Say It, Write It	TE 260, 264, 270, 274, 280, 284		
Book 3 Test		124	💿 ExamView® Assessment Suite

Back-mapping and Vertical Alignment **McGraw-Hill's** *Math Triumphs* intervention program was conceived and developed with the final result in mind: student success in grade-level mathematics, including Algebra 1 and beyond. The authors, using the **NCTM Focal Points and Focal Connections** as their guide, developed this brand-new series by back-mapping from grade-level and Algebra 1 concepts, and vertically aligning the topics so that they build upon prior skills and concepts and serve as a foundation for future topics.

	Lesson 8-1	Lesson 8-2	Lesson 8-3	Lesson 8-4
Concept	Compare Size	Compare Shape	Create Figures	Take Apart Figures
Objective	Compare the size of two figures.	Compare the shape of two figures.	Create new figures by putting figures together.	Take apart a figure to make new figures.
Math Vocabulary	compare	compare side	create parallelogram trapezoid	parallelogram rectangle square trapezoid
Lesson Resources	**Materials** • index cards • graph paper **Manipulatives** • counters • flexible rulers • number cubes **Other Resources** [CRM] Vocabulary and English Language Development [CRM] Skills Practice [CRM] Problem-Solving Practice [CRM] Homework Practice	**Materials** • magazines • newspapers • index cards **Manipulatives** • counters • money • geoboards **Other Resources** [CRM] Vocabulary and English Language Development [CRM] Skills Practice [CRM] Problem-Solving Practice [CRM] Homework Practice	**Materials** • index cards • timer **Manipulatives** • connecting cubes • spinner • pattern blocks **Other Resources** [CRM] Vocabulary and English Language Development [CRM] Skills Practice [CRM] Problem-Solving Practice [CRM] Homework Practice	**Materials** • index cards **Manipulatives** • connecting cubes • pattern blocks **Other Resources** [CRM] Vocabulary and English Language Development [CRM] Skills Practice [CRM] Problem-Solving Practice [CRM] Homework Practice
Technology	**Math Online** ▷ macmillanmh.com StudentWorks™ Plus ◉ ExamView® Assessment Suite	**Math Online** ▷ macmillanmh.com StudentWorks™ Plus ◉ ExamView® Assessment Suite	**Math Online** ▷ macmillanmh.com StudentWorks™ Plus ◉ ExamView® Assessment Suite	**Math Online** ▷ macmillanmh.com StudentWorks™ Plus ◉ ExamView® Assessment Suite

Lesson 8-5	Lesson 8-6	
Congruence	Symmetry	**Concept**
Identify congruent figures.	Identify symmetry in figures.	**Objective**
compare congruent	line of symmetry symmetry	**Math Vocabulary**
Materials • index cards **Manipulatives** • pattern blocks • flexible ruler • geoboards **Other Resources** **CRM** Vocabulary and English Language Development **CRM** Skills Practice **CRM** Problem-Solving Practice **CRM** Homework Practice	**Materials** • construction paper • graph paper **Manipulatives** • pattern blocks • geoboards **Other Resources** **CRM** Vocabulary and English Language Development **CRM** Skills Practice **CRM** Problem-Solving Practice **CRM** Homework Practice	**Lesson Resources**
Math Online macmillanmh.com StudentWorks™ Plus ⊙ ExamView® Assessment Suite	**Math Online** macmillanmh.com StudentWorks™ Plus ⊙ ExamView® Assessment Suite	**Technology**

Chapter Notes

Home Connection

Read the Home Connection letter with students and have them write their names in the space below.

Read and explain the activity under Help at Home. If time allows, complete a portion of the activity so students can introduce the activity to a parent or other caregiver.

Have students:

- find examples of plane figures, such as squares and rectangles, at home.

- find examples of congruent figures, such as the stars and stripes on the American flag.

- bring examples to class.

Real-World Applications

Sports Have students list the balls used in various sports. Such items could include a soccer ball, tennis ball, baseball, golf ball, or basketball. Ask students to compare the size and shape of each. How are the balls alike and how are they different?

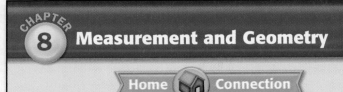

CHAPTER 8 Measurement and Geometry

Home Connection

English   **Spanish**

Dear Family,
Today our class started **Chapter 8, Measurement and Geometry.** In this chapter, I will compare the sizes and shapes of figures. I will also compose and decompose figures and determine symmetry and congruence.

Love, _____

Estimada familia:
Hoy en clase comenzamos el **Capítulo 8, Medición y Geometría.** En este capítulo compararé los tamaños y formas de las figuras. También formaré y separaré las partes de figuras, y determinaré su simetría y su congruencia.

Cariños, _____

Help at Home
You can help your child by asking him or her to compare the sizes and shapes of common household objects. You can also do paper folding activities to show symmetry.

Ayude en casa
Usted puede ayudar a su hijo(a) pidiéndole que compare las formas y el tamaño de objetos comunes del hogar. También puede hacer actividades en las que doble papel para demostrar la simetría de las figuras.

Math Online Take the chapter Get Ready quiz at macmillanmh.com.

Chapter 8   two hundred fifty-five **255**

Key Vocabulary

Find interactive definitions in 13 languages in the **eGlossary** at macmillanmh.com.

English   Español *Introduce the most important vocabulary terms from Chapter 8.*

compare   comparar
look at objects, shapes, or numbers and see how they are the same and different (p. 257)

side   lado
one of the line segments that make up a shape (p. 261)

create   crea
to make a new figure by joining together 2 or more figures (p. 267)

parallelogram   paralelogramo
a plane figure that has four sides; each pair of opposite sides is equal and parallel (p. 267)

trapezoid   trapecio
a four-sided plane figure with only two opposite sides that are the same length (p. 267)

rectangle   rectanfulo
a plane figure with four sides and four corners (p. 271)

square   cuadrado
a rectangle that has four equal sides (p. 271)

congruent   congruente
figures that are the same shape and size (p. 277)

symmetry   simetria
when a figure is folded on a line and the two parts are congruent (p. 281)

line of symmetry   línea simétrica
a line on a figure where you can fold the figure so that both halves match exactly (p. 281)

Name _____

Get Ready

Circle the greater number.

1 5 **(9)**　　**2** **(4)** 2

Count each number of sides.

3 __4__ sides　　**4** __6__ sides　　**5** __3__ sides

Name each shape.

6 __trapezoid__　　**7** __square__　　**8** __triangle__

9 __hexagon__　　**10** __rectangle__　　**11** __circle__

STOP

256 two hundred fifty-six

Vocabulary Preview

Write the key vocabulary words for the chapter on the board. Ask students to explain any of the words they already know. Discuss whether their understanding is correct.

Give students index cards. Tell them to write one vocabulary word on each card. On the other side, have them draw a picture to illustrate the word. They should skip any words they do not know.

As students learn new words in each lesson, have them add the definitions to their cards. They should draw pictures for new words as they learn them.

Get Ready

Have students complete Get Ready to assess readiness for the chapter concepts and skills. Refer to the lessons below for additional support for prerequisite skills.

7-3 Two-Dimensional Figures (p. 235)
7-4 Sides and Vertices (p. 239)

You may also assess student readiness with the following resources:

 Online Readiness quiz at macmillanmh.com

Assessment Masters: Chapter Pretest (p. 100)

FOLDABLES® Study Organizer **Dinah Zike's Foldables®**

Guide students through the directions on p. A182 in the Chapter Resource Masters to create their own Foldable graphic organizer for use with this chapter.

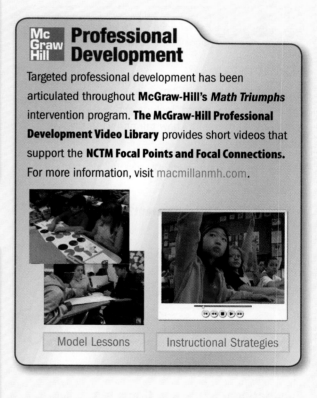

Professional Development

Targeted professional development has been articulated throughout **McGraw-Hill's** *Math Triumphs* intervention program. **The McGraw-Hill Professional Development Video Library** provides short videos that support the **NCTM Focal Points and Focal Connections.** For more information, visit macmillanmh.com.

Model Lessons　　Instructional Strategies

Lesson Planner

Objective Compare the size of two figures.

Vocabulary compare

Materials/Manipulatives index cards, graph paper, counters, flexible rulers, number cubes

Chapter Resource Masters

- CRM Vocabulary and English Language Development (p. A185)
- CRM Skill Practice (p. A186)
- CRM Problem-Solving-Practice (p. A187)
- CRM Homework Practice (p. A188)

1 Introduce

Vocabulary

Explore Vocabulary Draw two different sized rectangles on the board. Include grid lines and ask students to identify how tall and wide the rectangles are.

- **How are the figures alike?** They are the same shape.

- **How are the figures different?** They are different sizes.

Explain to students that they can compare figures by looking at size and shape.

2 Teach

Key Concept

Foundational Skills and Concepts After students have read through the Key Concept box, guide them through the following questions.

- **Is the size of the green and orange squares the same or different?** same

- **Is the size of the blue and red rectangles the same or different?** different

257 Chapter 8 Measurement and Geometry

Compare Size

Key Concept

You can **compare** the size of two figures.

These figures are the same size. 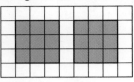   These figures are different sizes.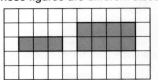

Vocabulary

compare look at objects, shapes, or numbers and see how they are the same and different

Count how many units tall and wide figures are to compare size.

The red square is 2 units tall and 2 units wide. The green square is 3 units tall and 3 units wide. The squares are different sizes.

Chapter 8 Lesson I   two hundred fifty-seven **257**

English Learner Strategy

Same and Different Use counters to help students understand the concept of comparing objects.

Place a group of counters on the desk. Hold up two counters which are the same color.

- **Are the counters the same or different? Explain.** Same; they are both green.

Hold up two counters which are different colors.

- **Are the counters the same or different? Explain.** Different; one is green and one is purple.

Ask students to point out two counters on the desk which are the same. Ask them to point out two counters which are different. Once students understand the idea of same and different, repeat the exercise with a different group of counters.

Example

Compare the size of the rectangles.

Celia's Rectangle	Amma's Rectangle

Step 1	Celia's rectangle is 3 units tall and 2 units wide.
Step 2	Amma's rectangle is 3 units tall and 4 units wide.
Step 3	Compare the lengths of the sides.
Answer	The rectangles are different sizes.

Step-by-Step Practice

Compare the size of the squares.

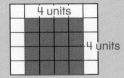

Celia's Square   **Amma's Square**

Step 1	Celia's square is __4__ units tall and __4__ units wide.
Step 2	Amma's square is __4__ units tall and __4__ units wide.
Step 3	Compare the lengths of the sides.
Answer	The squares are **the same size**.

258 two hundred fifty-eight

Additional *Example*

Compare the size of the rectangles.

Aaron's Rectangle   **Ali's Rectangle**

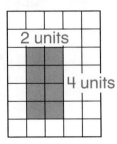
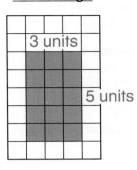

Step 1 Aaron's rectangle is 4 units tall and 2 units wide.

Step 2 Ali's rectangle is 5 units tall and 3 units wide.

Step 3 Compare the lengths of the sides.

Answer The rectangles are different sizes.

⚠ Common Error *Alert*

Students may confuse length and width. Make sure they do not transpose the number of units.

Intervention Strategy   Visual/Logical Learners

Materials: index cards, flexible rulers

Prepare a set of index cards by drawing or printing rectangles of different sizes on each card.

Give groups of 3 or 4 students a set of index cards and flexible rulers.

Have 2 students each select a card. Ask them to decide whether the figures are the same or different in size.

Have the students use rulers to measure the rectangles to see if they are correct. Tell them to keep track of whether their guesses were correct or incorrect.

Math Coach Notes

Study Tips

1. In this lesson, length refers to how tall the figure is.

2. When counting units, always start with length and end with width.

3. Be sure students understand figures that are the same size have the same length and width.

③ Practice

Guided Practice

Direct students to complete Exercise 1 in Guided Practice.

Exercise 1 Remind students that both length and width must have the same measure for two objects to be the same.

Problem-Solving Practice

Guide students through the four-step problem-solving plan to complete Exercise 2.

- **What are the key words?** square at the right, draw a square that is the same size

- **How does a grid help you solve the problem?** You can count the number of units for each side.

Ask students to check their work using the strategy suggested in the Check step. Students can compare the lengths of the sides on each square to check their work.

Using Manipulatives

Number Cubes Have students measure the length and width of rectangles using number cubes. They should line the cubes up along the sides and count the number of cubes to determine the measurement. Students can compare the sizes of figures based upon the number cube measurements.

Flexible Rulers Students can use rulers to determine the length and width of figures. They can compare the sizes of figures based upon the measurements.

On-Hand Manipulatives Use number cubes from a board game to determine the length and width of figures.

Name _____

▶ Guided Practice

Compare the size. Write "same" or "different."

1

4 units · 3 units · 3 units · 3 units

The triangles are __different__ sizes.

Problem-Solving Practice

2. Keith drew the <u>square at the right</u>. <u>Draw a square that is the same size</u> as Keith's square.

2 units · 2 units

Understand   Underline key words.

Plan   Draw a picture on a grid.

Solve   Keith's rectangle is

_2_ units tall and

_2_ units wide.

Check   Compare the lengths of the sides of your square and Keith's square. Are they the same?

GO on

Chapter 8   Lesson 1

Copyright © Macmillan/McGraw-Hill • Glencoe, a division of The McGraw-Hill Companies, Inc.

Are They Getting It? ?

Check students' understanding of comparing size by drawing the rectangles described on the board. Ask students to point out the correct and incorrect statements and explain their reasoning.

Draw two rectangles on the board. One should measure 4 units tall and 7 units wide. The other should measure 2 units tall and 7 units wide.

1. The rectangles have the same length. This is incorrect. One rectangle is 4 units long and the other is 2 units long.

2. The rectangles have the same width. This is correct.

3. The rectangles are the same size. This is incorrect. To be the same size, they must have the same length and width.

Practice on Your Own

3 Compare the size. Write "same" or "different."

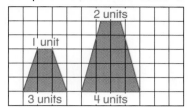

The trapezoids are

__different__ sizes.

4 Draw a square that is the same size as the one shown.

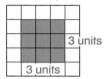

5 **WRITING IN** ▶**MATH** Are the figures the same size or different sizes? Explain.

The figures are the same size. They are in a different position. They are both 1 unit by 4 units.

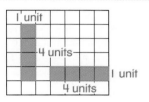

Vocabulary Check Complete.

6 When you __compare__ figures, you look to see how they are the same and different.

260 two hundred sixty

Math Challenge

Comparing Figures

Prepare a set of cards by drawing different sized squares on each card.

Have students shuffle the cards and place them face down in an array.

- Two students take turns flipping over one card each.
- The student who turned over the larger square takes both cards.
- When all the cards have been taken, the student with the most cards wins.

Practice on Your Own

Direct students to p. 260 in their student books. Have students complete Exercises 3–6 independently. You may need to review the directions of each section before students begin.

4 Assess

See It, Do It, Say It, Write It

Step 1 Draw two rectangles on the board that are both 7 units tall and 3 units wide. Point to each side and say the length or width. Have students determine if the rectangles are the same or different.

Step 2 Give each student a drawing of two rectangles that are either the same or different sizes. Ask students to determine if the rectangles are the same or different.

Step 3 Have students explain if their rectangles are the same or different. Students should use lesson vocabulary in their explanation.

Step 4 Ask students to draw two figures that are the same size and two figures that are different sizes. Have students write why each pair of figures are the same or different.

Looking Ahead: Pre-teach

In the next lesson, students will learn about comparing shape.

Example Compare the shape of the figures.

different shapes

Have students compare the shape of the figures.

1.

same shape

2.

different shapes

Lesson Notes

Lesson Planner

Objective   Compare the shape of two figures.

Vocabulary   compare, side

Materials/Manipulatives   magazines, newspapers, index cards, counters, money, geoboards

Chapter Resource Masters

CRM Vocabulary and English Language Development (p. A189)

CRM Skill Practice (p. A190)

CRM Problem-Solving-Practice (p. A191)

CRM Homework Practice (p. A192)

1 Introduce

Vocabulary

Review Vocabulary   Draw a square, triangle, and rectangle on the board. Have students join you in counting the number of sides of each figure.

- **Which figures have four sides?** the square and the rectangle

- **How many sides does the triangle have?** three

2 Teach

Key Concept

Foundational Skills and Concepts   After students have read through the Key Concept box, guide them through the following questions.

- **How many sides does Figure 1 have?** 3

- **How many sides does Figure 2 have?** 6

- **Are the shapes of the figures the same or different?** different

---

Name _____

Compare Shape

Key Concept

You can **compare** the shape of two figures.

Figure 1   Figure 2

3 sides   6 sides

The figures do not look the same.
Figure 1 and Figure 2 are different shapes.

Vocabulary

compare   look at objects, shapes, or numbers and see how they are alike and different

side   one of the line segments that make up a shape

Two figures can have the same number of sides and be different shapes.

4 sides   4 sides

A rectangle also has four sides. However, the sides can be two different lengths.

A square has four sides. All sides are the same length.

Copyright © Macmillan/McGraw-Hill. • Glencoe, a division of The McGraw-Hill Companies, Inc.

Chapter 8   Lesson 2   two hundred sixty-one **261**

English Learner Strategy

Size and Shape

English learners may not understand the difference between *size* and *shape.*

1. **In Lesson 1, we compared the size of figures.**
   Have student identify objects in the room that are the same and different sizes.

2. **In this lesson we will compare the shapes of figures.**
   Discuss that shape refers to the way the sides in a figure are arranged.

   Hold up a triangle. **What is the shape of this figure?** triangle

   Hold up a square. **What is the shape of this figure?** square

3. Emphasize that the number of sides on each figure is different which makes the shape of the figures different. Ask students to identify objects in the room that are the same and different shapes.

Example

Compare the shape of the figures.

Kendra's Figure   Simone's Figure

Step 1   Count the sides of each figure.
Kendra's figure has 4 sides.
Simone's figure has 4 sides.

Step 2   Do the figures look the same? yes

Answer   The figures are the same shape.

Step-by-Step Practice

Compare the shape of the figures.

Sonya's Figure   Peter's Figure

Step 1   Count the sides of each figure.

Sonya's figure has __4__ sides.

Peter's figure has __3__ sides.

Step 2   Do the figures look the same? **no**

Answer   The figures are **different shapes**.

262   two hundred sixty-two

Additional *Example*

Compare the shape of the figures.

Nia's Figure   Michelle's Figure

Step 1   Count the sides of each figure.
Nia's figure has 3 sides.
Michelle's figure has 3 sides.

Step 2   Do the figures look the same? yes

Answer   The figures are the same shape.

⚠ Common Error *Alert*

Remind students that when comparing the shape of figures, they should count the sides, but also check the length of each side as well.

Math Coach Notes

Strategy

Remind students that color does not determine if two figures are the same shape.

Intervention Strategy

Visual/Natural/Interpersonal Learners

Materials: magazines, newspapers

Divide students into groups. Assign each group a simple figure, such as a square, rectangle, or triangle. Give each group a blank piece of paper.

Have students look through magazines or newspapers to find examples of their shape. Students can work with a partner in their group.

Ask students to tape or glue all the figures that have the same shape to the appropriate poster.

Use the posters as a visual aid to reinforce the concept of same shape.

③ Practice

Guided Practice

Direct students to complete Exercise 1 in Guided Practice.

Exercise 1 Remind students that they should not be distracted by the colors of the figures.

Problem-Solving Practice

Guide students through the four-step problem-solving plan to complete Exercise 2.

- **What figures did Mrs. Perry draw?** 2 triangles and 1 square

- **How does counting the number of sides help solve the problem?** Figures with the same shape have the same number of sides.

Ask students to check their work using the strategy suggested in the Check step. Students can compare how the figures look to solve the problem.

Using Manipulatives

Geoboards Draw or print pictures of plane figures on index cards. Have students work in pairs. One student turns over a card with the name of a figure and says the name. The other student models the figure on a geoboard. The students then compare the figure on the card to the model on the geoboard to see if they match.

 On-Hand Manipulatives Have students use graph paper to draw figures.

Name _____

▶ **Guided Practice**

1. Compare the shape. Write "same" or "different."

   _____same_____

> **Problem-Solving Practice**
>
> 2. Mrs. Perry drew <u>three figures</u> on the board.
>
> Figure 1   Figure 2   Figure 3
>
>
>
> Which figure is a different shape?
>
> **Understand** Underline key words.
>
> **Plan** Compare the figures.
>
> **Solve** Count the sides of each figure.
>
>   Figures __1__ and __3__ have __3__ sides.
>
>   Figure __2__ has __4__ sides.
>
>   Figure __2__ is different.
>
> **Check** Does the figure you chose look different than the others?

Copyright © Macmillan/McGraw-Hill • Glencoe, a division of The McGraw-Hill Companies, Inc.

Are They Getting It? ❓

Check students' understanding of comparing shape by writing these statements on the board. Ask students to point out the correct and incorrect statements and explain their reasoning.

1. Figures that have the same shape have a different number of sides. This is incorrect. Figures that have the same shape have the same number of sides.

2. Figures that have the same number of sides always have the same shape. This is incorrect. Figures may have the same number of sides but be different shapes.

3. All squares have the same shape. This is correct. Every square has four equal sides.

▶ Practice on Your Own

Compare the shape. Write "same" or "different."

3  _different_

4  _same_ shape

5 Circle the figures with the same shape.

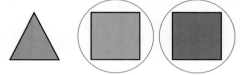

6 **WRITING IN ▶MATH** Ava said the figures have different shapes. Is Ava correct? Explain.

No, Ava is not correct. The figures have the same shape. They are in different positions.

Vocabulary Check Complete.

7 A __side__ is one of the line segments that make up a shape.

STOP

264 two hundred sixty-four

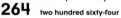

Math Challenge

Matching Sides

Prepare a set of cards by drawing or printing different geometric figures on each card. Prepare a second set of cards by writing the number of sides of each figure on the cards.

Have students work in pairs. Have students shuffle both sets of cards and place them face down in an array. Students take turns flipping over two cards. The goal is to match a figure with a card that lists the proper number of sides. Students keep the cards of any matches they make. The student with the most cards wins.

Practice on Your Own

Direct students to p. 264 in their student books. Have students complete Exercises 3–7 independently. You may need to review the directions of each section before students begin.

④ Assess

See It, Do It, Say It, Write It

Step 1 Use pattern blocks to demonstrate figures that have the same shape.

Step 2 Have students use pattern blocks to find figures that have the same shape.

Step 3 Have students explain why these figures have the same shape.

Step 4 Hold up two pattern blocks and have students draw the figures. Have students explain in writing if the figures are the same shape or different shapes.

Looking Ahead: Pre-teach

In the next lesson, students will learn about putting figures together to make a new figure.

Example

Two rectangles can be combined to make a square.

Have students identify the pattern block that completes the new figure.

1.

triangle

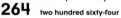

Copyright © Macmillan/McGraw-Hill • Glencoe, a division of The McGraw-Hill Companies, Inc.

Progress Check 1

Formative Assessment

Use the Progress Check to assess students' mastery of the previous lessons. Have students review the lesson indicated for the problems they answered incorrectly.

⚠ Common Error *Alert*

Comparing Size and Shape Make sure students understand the difference between size and shape. Remind them that figures do not need to be the same size to have the same shape.

Exercise 1 Remind students not to be distracted by color.

Exercise 5 Make sure students understand that more than two figures in the group could have the same size and shape.

Name _____

Progress Check 1 (Lessons 8-1 and 8-2)

Compare the size. Write "same" or "different."

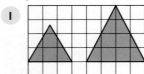

1 __**different**__ sizes

2 __**same**__ size

Compare the shape. Write "same" or "different."

3 __**different**__

4 __**same**__

5 Circle the figures that have the same size and shape.

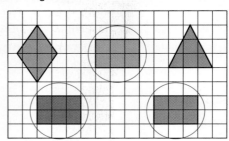

Copyright © Macmillan/McGraw-Hill, a Glencoe, a division of The McGraw-Hill Companies, Inc.

Data-Driven Decision Making

Students missing Exercises . . .	Have trouble with . . .	Should review and practice . . .
1–2	comparing size.	SSG Lesson 8-1, p. 257 CRM Skills Practice, p. A186
3–4	comparing shape.	SSG Lesson 8-2, p. 261 CRM Skills Practice, p. A190
5	comparing size and shape.	SSG Lesson 8-1, p. 257 CRM Skills Practice, p. A186 SSG Lesson 8-2, p. 261 CRM Skills Practice, p. A190

Name _____

«« Replay **Color by Figure**

Compare the figures shown in the picture size and shape.
Color the sections green for figures that are the same size and shape.
Color the sections orange for figures that are different sizes.
Color the sections purple for figures that are different shapes.

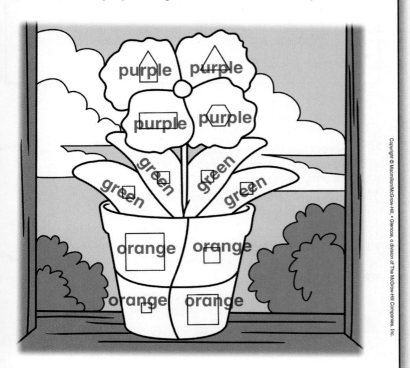

266 two hundred sixty-six

Replay

Use the Replay activity to review and reinforce the concepts and skills presented in Lessons 8-1 and 8-2.

Instructions

Have students read the directions at the top of the student page.

Remind students that figures that are the same have the same size and the same shape.

Student Technology

Students can use the following technology resources to reinforce chapter content.

- StudentWorks™ Plus
- **Math Online** macmillanmh.com
- eGlossary

Lesson Planner

Math Objective   Create new figures by putting figures together.

Vocabulary   create, parallelogram, trapezoid

Materials/Manipulatives   index cards, connecting cubes, spinner, pattern blocks, timer

Chapter Resource Masters

- CRM Vocabulary and English Language Development (p. A193)
- CRM Skills Practice (p. A194)
- CRM Problem-Solving Practice (p. A195)
- CRM Homework Practice (p. A196)

1 Introduce

Vocabulary

Connect Vocabulary   Explain to students that they will be creating new figures in this lesson. Tell them that create means to make something new. Say: "You can create a parallelogram from two triangles. You can create a rectangle from two squares."

Give students pattern blocks. When students identify a way to put two figures together to make a new figure, have them complete the sentence, "I can create a ____ from a ____ and a ____."

2 Teach

Key Concept

Foundational Skills and Concepts   After students have read through the Key Concept box, guide them through the following questions.

- **What figures combine to create the rectangle?** two squares

- **What figures combine to create the parallelogram?** two triangles

---

Name _____

Create Figures

Key Concept

You can put figures together to **create** a new figure.

 + =

Two squares put together create a rectangle.

Vocabulary

create   to make a new figure by joining together 2 or more figures

parallelogram   a plane figure that has four sides; each pair of opposite sides is equal and parallel

trapezoid   a four-sided plane figure with one pair of parallel sides

You can use pattern blocks to create new figures. Place two pattern blocks together to create a new figure.

Two triangles can make a parallelogram.

Chapter 8   Lesson 3

two hundred sixty-seven   **267**

English Learner Strategy

Combining Objects   Use connecting cubes to help students understand the concept of putting figures together.

1. Give students a set of connecting cubes.

2. Explain that in this lesson they will join objects together. Demonstrate joining the connecting cubes. Have students connect and disconnect the cubes.

3. Have students create an object that is three cubes long. Ask the students to compare the connected cubes with a single cube. Repeat with other numbers of cubes.

4. Compare connecting the cubes with the illustration at the top of page 267.

Example

Which pattern block completes the new figure?

Step 1	Identify the first pattern block. trapezoid
Step 2	Place the pattern block on the new figure.
Step 3	Which pattern block completes the new figure?

Answer completes the new figure.

Step-by-Step Practice

Which pattern block completes the new figure?

Step 1 Identify the first pattern blocks. **triangles**
Step 2 Place the pattern blocks on the new figure.
Step 3 Which pattern block completes the new figure?

Answer completes the new figure.

268 two hundred sixty-eight

Intervention Strategy

Visual/Kinesthetic/ Logical Learners

Materials: spinner, pattern blocks

Label a spinner with shapes that can be created from putting together pattern blocks.

- Divide students into groups. Give each group a spinner and a set of pattern blocks.

- Have one student spin the spinner.

- The student creates the figure indicated using pattern blocks.

- Students continue taking turns as time allows.

Additional *Example*

Which pattern block completes the new figure?

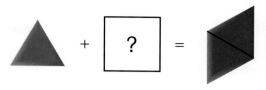

Step 1 Identify the first pattern block. triangle

Step 2 Place the pattern block on the new figure.

Step 3 Which pattern block completes the new figure?

Answer completes the figure.

⚠ **Common Error** *Alert*

Students might not think to change the orientation of a pattern block in order to create a new figure. Remind students that they can flip and turn pattern blocks.

Math Coach Notes

Study Skills Review the terms *triangle, square,* and *rectangle* with students. They will need to be familiar with these basic shapes and names in order to complete the lesson.

③ Practice

Guided Practice

Direct students to complete Exercise 1 in Guided Practice.

Exercise 1 Tell students to look at the space between the two parallelograms and visualize what figure would fit. Ask them to suggest a strategy they could use to solve the problem.

Problem-Solving Practice

Guide students through the four-step problem-solving plan to complete Exercise 2.

• **What are the key words?** two pattern blocks, make a house, what blocks can he use

• **How can you solve the problem?** place pattern blocks over the drawing

Ask students to check their work using the strategy suggested in the Check step. Students should check that they used exactly two pattern blocks to solve the problem.

Using Manipulatives

Pattern Blocks Students should use pattern blocks to complete the lesson. Allow students to place the pattern blocks over the outlined figures in the lesson. Also, students can create the figures on their desk to identify missing figures.

On-Hand Manipulatives Trace and cut out pattern blocks from construction paper. Use the cut outs to complete the lesson exercises.

Math Coach Note

Study Skills Introduce the word *compose*. Explain to students that another word for *create* is *compose*. Students can compose a square from two triangles.

Name _____

▶ Guided Practice

1 Circle the pattern block that completes the new figure.

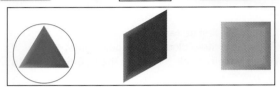

Copyright © Macmillan/McGraw-Hill • Glencoe, a division of The McGraw-Hill Companies, Inc.

Problem-Solving Practice

2 Matias wants to use <u>two pattern blocks</u> to <u>make a house</u>. <u>What blocks can he use</u>?

Understand   Underline key words.

Plan   Act it out.

Solve   Use pattern blocks to make a house.

Check students' work.

Matias can use a **rectangle** and a **triangle** to make a house.

Check   Did you use two pattern blocks to make a house?

GO on

Chapter 8   Lesson 3

two hundred sixty-nine **269**

Are They Getting It? ❓

Check students' understanding of creating figures by writing these statements on the board. Ask students to point out the correct and incorrect statements and explain their reasoning.

1. Creating figures means to take figures apart. This is incorrect. Creating figures means to put figures together.

2. Two triangles can create a hexagon. This is incorrect. Two triangles can create a figure with only four sides. A hexagon has six sides.

3. Two squares can create a triangle. This is incorrect. Two squares create a rectangle.

▶ Practice on Your Own

3 Circle the pattern block that completes the new figure.

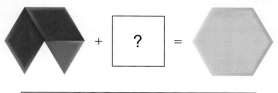

4 **WRITING IN ▶MATH** Lilly wants to make a parallelogram using two trapezoids. Can she do it? Explain.

Yes, Lilly can place one trapezoid right side up. Then place the other trapezoid beside it upside down.

Vocabulary Check Complete.

5 I can ___**create**___ a new figure by joining together 2 or more figures.

270 two hundred seventy

Math Challenge

Creating Figures

Materials: pattern blocks, timer

- Students work in pairs. Place pattern blocks in a bag.

- Student 1 pulls three pattern blocks from the bag.

- Student 2 times 30 seconds. During the 30 seconds, Student 1 creates as many figures as possible with the three chosen pattern blocks. The student must be able to name the shape of the figures created. After 30 seconds, Student 1 gets one point for each figure created. Place the three blocks back in the bag.

- Students switch roles and repeat.

- The first student to earn 20 points wins.

Practice on Your Own

Direct students to p. 270 in their student books. Have students complete Exercises 3–5 independently. You may need to review the directions of each section before students begin.

See It, Do It, Say It, Write It

Step 1 Use pattern blocks or a drawing on the board to combine two triangles into a rhombus.

Step 2 Have students create a rhombus using pattern blocks. Have students practice creating other figures with the pattern blocks.

Step 3 Have students name the shapes they combined and the figure they created.

Step 4 Have students draw the two triangles and the composed rhombus. Repeat for the other figures created.

Looking Ahead: Pre-teach

In the next lesson, students will learn about taking figures apart.

Example

A rectangle can be split into two squares.

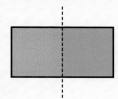

Have students draw a line to make the new given figures.

1. 2 trapezoids

line drawn horizontally in the middle splitting the hexagon into two trapezoids

2. 2 rectangles

line drawn horizontally in the middle splitting the square into two rectangles

Lesson 8-3 Create Figures **270**

Lesson 8-4 Lesson Notes

Lesson Planner

Math Objective Take apart a figure to make new figures.

Vocabulary rectangle, square, parallelogram, trapezoid

Materials/Manipulatives index cards, connecting cubes, pattern blocks

Chapter Resource Masters

- [CRM] Vocabulary and English Language Development (p. A197)
- [CRM] Skill Practice (p. A198)
- [CRM] Problem-Solving-Practice (p. A199)
- [CRM] Homework Practice (p. A200)

① Introduce

Vocabulary

Compare Vocabulary Draw a rectangle, square, parallelogram, and trapezoid on the board. Write the name underneath each figure. Ask students to describe similarities and differences between the figures.

② Teach

Key Concept

Foundational Skills and Concepts After students have read through the Key Concept box, guide them through the following questions.

- **What two figures are made when one line is drawn through the rectangle?** 2 squares

- **What three figures are made when two lines are drawn through the rectangle?** 3 smaller rectangles

---

Lesson 8-4

Name _____

Take Apart Figures

Key Concept

You can draw a line through a figure to make two new figures.

 =

This **rectangle** can be taken apart, or split, into two **squares**.

Vocabulary

rectangle a plane figure with four sides and four corners

square a rectangle that has four equal sides

parallelogram a plane figure that has four sides; each pair of opposite sides is equal and parallel

trapezoid a four-sided plane figure with only two opposite sides that are the same length

> I can take apart a hexagon into two trapezoids.

A rectangle can be taken apart into more than two figures.

 =

You can draw two lines to make three new rectangles.

Chapter 8 Lesson 4   two hundred seventy-one **271**

English Learner Strategy

Taking Apart Use connecting cubes to help students understand the concept of *take apart*.

1. Review the concept of creating figures from Lesson 3. Remind students that they learned to put figures together to make a new figure. Explain that in this lesson they will be doing the opposite, by taking figures apart.

   - **When we take apart figures, we make new, smaller figures.**

2. Give students a set of connecting cubes. Demonstrate putting cubes together. Now, pull one cube off the train. Explain that you are taking the cubes apart. Use words such as *separate, make new pieces,* and *take apart* to describe your actions. Have students use these words as they connect and disconnect the cubes.

Example

Draw one line to take apart the diamond into two triangles.

Step 1	Look at the figure.
Step 2	Identify a triangle in the figure.
Step 3	Draw a line through the figure to make two triangles.

Answer

Step-by-Step Practice

Draw one line to take apart the parallelogram into two trapezoids.

Step 1	Look at the figure.
Step 2	Identify a trapezoid in the figure.
Step 3	Draw a line through the figure to make two trapezoids.

Answer

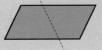

272 two hundred seventy-two

Copyright © Macmillan/McGraw-Hill • Glencoe, a division of The McGraw-Hill Companies, Inc.

Additional *Example*

Draw one line to take apart the square into two triangles.

Step 1 Look at the figure.

Step 2 Identify a triangle in the figure.

Step 3 Draw a line through the figure to make two triangles.

Answer

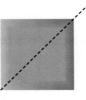

⚠ Common Error *Alert*

Students with poor spatial skills may not draw straight lines when taking figures apart. Offer students a ruler or other straight edge to help.

Math Coach Notes

Strategies

1. Provide students with construction paper cut outs of various shapes. Have student fold the cut outs to make new figures. Students can make more than two new figures with the cut out. For example, one large rectangle can make three smaller rectangles. Have students trace the fold(s) with a marker to show where the figures come apart.

2. Remind students that in Lesson 8-3 they *composed* figures. Review the term *compose*. Tell students that *decompose* is the opposite of *compose*.

   • **What does decompose mean?** to take apart

Intervention Strategy

Kinesthetic/Natural Learners

Ask students to find examples of figures that can be taken apart in the classroom. For example, a square window may consist of several rectangular panes of glass.

Have students keep a list of the items they find. Then have students gather in groups and compare the items they found.

Have each group present their items to the class. Keep a list on the board of the examples students found.

3 Practice

Guided Practice

Direct students to complete Exercises 1–2 in Guided Practice.

Exercise 2 Have students use trapezoid pattern blocks to model the hexagon.

Problem-Solving Practice

Guide students through the four-step problem-solving plan to complete Exercise 3.

- **What are the key words?** two lines, trapezoid, three new figures, rectangle, other two figures

- **How does drawing a picture of a trapezoid help solve the problem?** You can draw lines through the trapezoid.

Ask students to check their work using the strategy suggested in the Check step. Students should check that one of the figures they created is a rectangle.

Using Manipulatives

Pattern Blocks Students should use pattern blocks throughout the lesson. Students can also experiment with the blocks to determine what new figures are made when figures are decomposed.

On-Hand Manipulatives Use shapes cut from construction paper to perform the exercises.

Name _____

Guided Practice   Sample answers shown.

Draw one line to make the given figures.

1 2 triangles

2 2 trapezoids

Problem-Solving Practice

3 Alex drew <u>two lines</u> through a <u>trapezoid</u> to make <u>three new figures</u>. One of the figures is a <u>rectangle</u>. What are the <u>other two figures</u>?

Understand Underline key words.

Plan Draw a picture.

Solve Draw two lines to make one rectangle.

The other two figures are ___triangles___.

Check Is one of the figures you created a rectangle?

GO on

Chapter 8 Lesson 4   two hundred seventy-three **273**

Copyright © Macmillan/McGraw-Hill • Glencoe, a division of The McGraw-Hill Companies, Inc.

Are They Getting It? ?

Check students' understanding of taking figures apart by writing these statements on the board. Ask students to point out the correct and incorrect statements and explain their reasoning.

1. Figures can only be taken apart in one way. This is incorrect. For example, a rectangle can be taken apart into two squares or three smaller rectangles.

2. A triangle cannot be decomposed. This is incorrect. A triangle can be taken apart into four smaller triangles.

3. A square can be taken apart into two triangles. This is correct.

273 Chapter 8 Measurement and Geometry

Practice on Your Own Sample answers shown.

Draw one line to make the given figures.

4 I parallelogram and I triangle   **5** 2 triangles

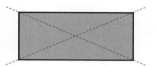

Draw two lines to make the given figures.

6 4 triangles   **7** I rectangle and 2 triangles.

8 **WRITING IN** ►**MATH**   Paul drew a line down the middle of a square. What two figures did he make? Explain.

Paul made two rectangles.
When a square is cut in half,
two rectangles are created.

Vocabulary Check   Complete.

9 A four-sided plane figure with one pair of parallel sides is a **trapezoid**.

STOP

274   two hundred seventy-four

Math Challenge

Figure Riddles

Students work in pairs to try and solve each riddle. Allow students to use pattern blocks to help them solve the riddles.

Write the following riddles on index cards:

I am a figure that can be taken apart into two rectangles. square

I am a figure that can be taken apart into two trapezoids. parallelogram

I am a figure that can be taken apart into two triangles and one rectangle. trapezoid

I am a figure that can be taken apart into one parallelogram and one triangle. trapezoid

Challenge students to write their own riddles.

Practice on Your Own

Direct students to p. 274 in their student books. Have students complete Exercises 4–9 independently. You may need to review the directions of each section before students begin.

4 **Assess**

See It, Do It, Say It, Write It

Step I Use pattern blocks or a drawing on the board to split a trapezoid into a parallelogram and a triangle.

Step 2 Have students use pattern blocks to split a trapezoid into a parallelogram and a triangle. Have students practice taking apart other figures.

Step 3 Have students name the original figures and the new figures they create.

Step 4 Have students draw the decomposed trapezoid, the parallelogram, and the triangle. Repeat for the other figures taken apart.

Looking Ahead: Pre-teach

In the next lesson, students will learn about congruent figures.

Example Congruent figures are the same size and shape. Are these two figures congruent? no

Have students identify if the figures are congruent.

1.
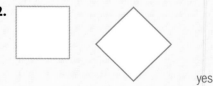
yes

2.
yes

Progress Check 2

Formative Assessment

Use the Progress Check to assess students' mastery of the previous lessons. Have students review the lesson indicated for the problems they answered incorrectly.

⚠ Common Error *Alert*

Visualizing Figures Some students may have difficulty visualizing figures. Suggest that they use a pencil to draw the missing figure or the figure which is being composed.

Exercise 4 Students may not recognize the triangles because they are different from those in the set of pattern blocks. Tell students to find the rectangle first.

Name _____

Progress Check 2 (Lessons 8-3 and 8-4)

1 Circle the pattern block that completes the new figure.

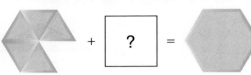

2 Draw the new figure.

3 Draw one line to make two squares.

4 Draw two lines to make two triangles and one rectangle.

Chapter 8   Progress Check

two hundred seventy-five **275**

Data-Driven Decision Making

Students missing Exercises . . .	Have trouble with . . .	Should review and practice . . .
1–2	creating figures.	SSG Lesson 8-3, p. 267 CRM Skills Practice, p. A194
3–4	taking figures apart.	SSG Lesson 8-4, p. 271 CRM Skills Practice, p. A198

Name _____

Help Rascal the Rabbit find his way through the maze.
Move from one square to the next by creating and taking apart figures.
You may not go through all of the squares.

Start

Finish

Replay

Use the Replay activity to review and reinforce the concepts and skills presented in Lessons 8-3 and 8-4.

Instructions

Have students read the directions at the top of the student page.

Student Technology

Students can use the following technology resources to reinforce chapter content.

- ● StudentWorks™ Plus
- **Math Online** ⟩ macmillanmh.com
- eGlossary

Lesson Planner

Math Objective   Identify congruent figures.

Vocabulary   compare, congruent

Materials/Manipulatives   index cards, pattern blocks, flexible ruler, geoboards

Chapter Resource Masters

- [CRM] Vocabulary and English Language Development (p. A201)
- [CRM] Skill Practice (p. A202)
- [CRM] Problem-Solving-Practice (p. A203)
- [CRM] Homework Practice (p. A204)

 **Introduce**

Vocabulary

Nonexamples   Congruent figures are figures that have the same size and the same shape. A square and a triangle are not congruent. Ask students to give other nonexamples of congruent figures. Sample answers: rhombus and trapezoid, large square and small square

 **Teach**

Key Concept

Foundational Skills and Concepts   After students have read through the Key Concept box, guide them through the following questions.

- **Are the figures the same size?** yes
- **Are the figures the same shape?** yes
- **What are figures called when they are the same size and the same shape?** congruent

---

Name _____

Congruence

> **Key Concept**
>
> You can **compare** the figures below.
>
>
>
> The figures are the same shape.
> The figures are the same size.
> The figures are **congruent**.

Vocabulary

compare   look at objects, shapes, or numbers and see how they are alike and different

congruent   figures that are the same shape and size

Figures in different positions are still congruent if they are the same shape and size.

The hearts are congruent.

Copyright © Macmillan/McGraw-Hill, • Glencoe, a division of The McGraw-Hill Companies, Inc.

Chapter 8   Lesson 5   two hundred seventy-seven   **277**

English Learner Strategy

Same and Different   Use this lesson to review the concepts of same and different. Connect the concept of same to congruent.

1. Place a set of pattern blocks on a desk. Use the four-sided figures for this exercise. Have students pick two figures that are the same. Have them explain why they are the same. Sample answer: They have the same number of sides and look alike.

2. Explain that figures with the same number of sides and of the same size are congruent. Hold up two figures that are congruent. Have students say "congruent" out loud.

3. Have students pick two figures that are different. Have them explain why they are different. Sample answer: They do not have the same number of sides and do not look alike.

4. Have students identify whether pairs of figures are the same or different.

Example

Compare. Are the figures congruent?

Figure 1   **Figure 2**

Step 1   Are the figures the same shape? yes

Step 2   Are the figures the same size? yes

Answer   The figures are congruent.

Step-by-Step Practice

Compare. Are the figures congruent?

Figure 1   **Figure 2**

Step 1   Are the figures the same shape? __yes__

Step 2   Are the figures the same size? __no__

Answer   The figures are __not congruent__.

278 two hundred seventy-eight

Compare. Are the figures congruent?

Figure 1   **Figure 2**

Step 1 Are the figures the same shape? yes

Step 2 Are the figures the same size? yes

Answer The figures are congruent.

⚠ Common Error *Alert*

Students might mistakenly think of congruent figures as either the same size or the same shape, but not both. Be sure students compare both size and shape when looking for congruency.

Students might mistakenly think figures are not congruent because of their position. Be sure students understand that orientation does not affect congruency.

Intervention Strategy

Natural/Linguistic/Kinesthetic Learners

Materials: flexible ruler

Ask students to bring examples of congruent objects from home.

Examples might include juice boxes, marbles, or a pair of earrings.

Ask students to share their items with the class and explain why the objects are congruent.

Students should then measure each other's objects to prove they are congruent.

Math Coach Notes

Study Tips

1. Use construction paper cut outs to help students visualize congruent figures. Ask students to find two figures that can be placed on top of each other and match exactly. Emphasize that the figures are congruent.

2. Encourage students to flip and turn congruent figures to reinforce that figures can be congruent even if they are in different positions.

3. Remind students to compare length and width when comparing size.

③ Practice

Guided Practice

Direct students to complete Exercises 1–4 in Guided Practice.

Exercises 1 and 4 Remind students not to be confused by the position of the figures when determining congruence.

Problem-Solving Practice

Guide students through the four-step problem-solving plan to complete Exercise 5.

- **What are the key words?** rectangle, 3 units tall, 2 units wide, draw a congruent rectangle

- **What is a congruent rectangle?** one that is the same size and shape as the given rectangle

- **How do the dots help you solve the problem?** The dots represent units.

Ask students to check their work using the strategy suggested in the Check step. Students should check that the rectangle they drew is the same size and shape as the given rectangle.

Using Manipulatives

Geoboards Divide students into groups. Each group has two geoboards. Have one student in the group name a plane figure. Tell two other students to model the figure on a geoboard. The students should then compare their figures. Ask them if the figures are congruent. If the figures are not congruent, have them explain why. Students should take turns naming and modeling figures.

On-Hand Manipulatives Use graph paper to draw the figures.

Name _____

▶ Guided Practice

Compare. Are the figures congruent? Write "yes" or "no."

1. <u>yes</u>

2. <u>no</u>

3. <u>no</u>

4. <u>yes</u>

Problem-Solving Practice

5. A <u>rectangle</u> is <u>3 units tall</u> and <u>2 units wide</u>. <u>Draw a congruent rectangle.</u>

Understand	Underline key words.
Plan	Use a grid.
Solve	Look at the blue figure. Draw a congruent figure. Make the figure 3 units tall and 2 unit wide.
Check	Are the figures the same shape and size?

GO on

Chapter 8   Lesson 5

two hundred seventy-nine **279**

Copyright © Macmillan/McGraw-Hill • Glencoe, a division of The McGraw-Hill Companies, Inc.

Are They Getting It? ?

Check students' understanding of congruent figures by writing these statements on the board. Ask students to point out the correct and incorrect statements and explain their reasoning.

I. All rectangles that have the same length are congruent. This is incorrect. Two rectangles must have the same length and width to be congruent.

2. Two squares that have the same length are congruent. This is correct. The width of a square is equal to its length.

3. One rectangle is 4 units long by 2 units wide. Another rectangle is 2 units long by 4 units wide. The rectangles are not congruent. This is incorrect. The rectangles are the same size and shape, just in different positions.

▶ Practice on Your Own

Compare. Are the figures congruent? Write "yes" or "no."

6

___no___

7

___yes___

Circle the congruent figures.

8

9 **WRITING IN ▶MATH** Bryan drew these two figures. Are the figures congruent? Explain.

__Yes, the figures are congruent.__
__The figures are in a different position,__
__but they are the same shape and size.__

Vocabulary Check Complete.

10 Figures that are the same shape and size are

___congruent___.

STOP

280 two hundred eighty

Math Challenge

Figure Match

Materials: pattern blocks

Remind students that figures are congruent if they have the same size and shape.

Have students work in pairs. Give each pair of students a set of pattern blocks.

Student 1 chooses three pattern blocks and arranges them to create a new figure. Then Student 1 gives two clues about the figure that was created. Example: I used 1 square and 2 triangles. The square is between the triangles.

Student 2 attempts to arrange pattern blocks to create a congruent figure.

Students compare figures switch roles, and repeat.

Practice on Your Own

Direct students to p. 280 in their student books. Have students complete Exercises 6–10 independently. You may need to review the directions of each section before students begin.

4 Assess

See It, Do It, Say It, Write It

Step 1 Draw and label a rectangle that measures 6 units by 3 units. Tell the students you will draw a congruent figure. Then draw another rectangle that measures 6 units by 3 units.

Step 2 Have students draw a rectangle that measures 6 units by 3 units on a piece of graph paper. Ask them to draw a congruent figure.

Step 3 Have students explain why the two figures are congruent.

Step 4 Have students draw two new congruent figures on the graph paper. Have students use lesson vocabulary to write why the figures are congruent.

Looking Ahead: Pre-teach

In the next lesson, students will learn about symmetry.

Example

A rectangle has symmetry because it can be folded on a line so the two parts are congruent.

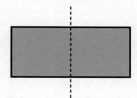

Have students identify if the figures have symmetry.

1.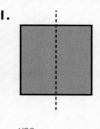

yes

2.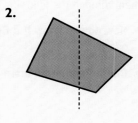

no

Lesson Notes

Lesson Planner

Math Objective Identify symmetry in figures.

Vocabulary symmetry, line of symmetry

Materials/Manipulatives construction paper, graph paper, pattern blocks, geoboards

Chapter Resource Masters

CRM Vocabulary and English Language Development (p. A205)

CRM Skill Practice (p. A206)

CRM Problem-Solving-Practice (p. A207)

CRM Homework Practice (p. A208)

 **1 Introduce**

Vocabulary

Relate Vocabulary Draw a trapezoid on a piece of paper, then cut it out. Fold the trapezoid along its line of symmetry. Use a marker to draw a line along the fold. Explain to students that the line creates two congruent figures. Relate this figure to the illustration in the Key Concept box.

 2 Teach

Key Concept

Foundational Skills and Concepts After students have read through the Key Concept box, guide them through the following questions.

• **How do you know if a figure has symmetry?** If it can be folded on a line to create two congruent parts.

• **Can a figure have more than one line of symmetry?** Yes, figures can be split into more than one pair of congruent parts by multiple lines of symmetry.

• **How many lines of symmetry does the trapezoid have? does the diamond have?** 1; 2

Name _____

Symmetry

Key Concept

A figure has **symmetry** if it can be folded on a line so the two parts are congruent.

I **line of symmetry**   2 lines of symmetry

Vocabulary

symmetry when a figure is folded on a line and the two parts are congruent

line of symmetry a line on a figure where you can fold the figure so that both halves match exactly

A figure that cannot be folded on a line to create two congruent parts does not have symmetry.

This figure has 0 lines of symmetry.

Chapter 8   Lesson 6   two hundred eighty-one **281**

English Learner Strategy

Relate Words

Students have been exposed to many new words in this chapter. Review the word *same* with students. Remind students that when figures are the same, they are like or congruent.

Write the word *symmetry* on the board. Write the word *same* underneath. Say the words out loud: symmetry, same. Emphasize the similarity in the beginning sound of the words.

Explain to students that figures have symmetry when they can be folded to create two figures that are the same.

Give students a square. Have them fold the square to make two congruent figures. Have students complete the sentence:

The square has symmetry because when I fold it, the two parts are the same.

Example

How many lines of symmetry does the heart have?

Step 1   Look at the heart.
          Can you make two congruent parts? yes

Step 2   Draw the line or lines.

Step 3   Count the line(s) of symmetry. 1

Answer   The heart has 1 line of symmetry.

Step-by-Step Practice

How many lines of symmetry does the rectangle have?

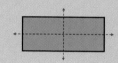

Step 1   Look at the rectangle.
          Can you make two congruent parts? **yes**

Step 2   Draw the line or lines.

Step 3   Count the line(s) of symmetry. __2__

Answer   The rectangle has __2__ lines of symmetry.

282   two hundred eighty-two

Additional *Example*

How many lines of symmetry does the triangle have?

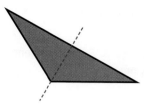

Step 1 Look at the triangle. Can you make two congruent parts? yes

Step 2 Draw the line or lines.

Step 3 Count the line(s) of symmetry. 1

Answer The triangle has 1 line of symmetry.

Math Coach Notes

Strategies

1. Use construction paper cut outs of various figures to help students find lines of symmetry. Note that if they can fold the figure into two congruent parts, then the figure has symmetry. Have students trace the line of symmetry with a marker.

2. Help students find shapes that have more than one line of symmetry. Point out that in these cases, each new pair of parts are congruent.

Intervention Strategy

Kinesthetic/Linguistic/ Interpersonal Learners

Materials: index cards

Remind students that figures can have more than one line of symmetry.

On index cards, draw symmetrical triangles, squares, and rectangles. Give each student a card.

Have students draw one line of symmetry on the figures. Ask the student to explain why it is a line of symmetry.

Students switch cards and draw another line of symmetry on the figure. Ask students to explain why it is a line of symmetry.

Continue passing the cards until all the lines of symmetry on each figure have been identified.

③ Practice

Guided Practice

Direct students to complete Exercises 1-2 in Guided Practice.

Exercises 1 and 2 Remind students that not all figures have symmetry.

Problem-Solving Practice

Guide students through the four-step problem-solving plan to complete Exercise 3.

- **How does a model help you solve the problem?**
  You can fold the model figure to find the lines of symmetry.

Ask students to check their work using the strategy suggested in the Check step. Students should check that each line of symmetry forms two congruent parts.

Using Manipulatives

Geoboards Divide students into groups. Provide each group with a geoboard. Have one student in the group model a plane figure on the geoboard. Have another student show one line of symmetry, using a different color band. Ask the students if the figure has any other lines of symmetry. Have the students work together to find all other lines of symmetry, and model them on the geoboard. Students should take turns modeling figures and lines of symmetry.

On-Hand Manipulatives Use graph paper to draw the figures.

Name _____

▶ **Guided Practice**

Count the lines of symmetry for each figure.

1.

    __1__ line of symmetry

2.

    __0__ lines of symmetry

Problem-Solving Practice

3. Luke drew this <u>figure</u> to show his age. <u>How many lines of symmetry</u> does this figure have?

   Understand   Underline key words

   Plan   Use a model.

   Solve   Trace the figure.

   Fold the figure to find the lines of symmetry. Draw each line of symmetry

   The figure has __2__ lines of symmetry.

   Check   Do the lines form congruent parts?

Copyright © Macmillan/McGraw-Hill, • Glencoe, a division of The McGraw-Hill Companies, Inc.

GO on

Are They Getting It?

Check students' understanding of symmetry by writing these statements on the board. Ask students to point out the correct and incorrect statements and explain their reasoning.

1. All figures have symmetry. This is incorrect. Some figures have 0 lines of symmetry.

2. A rectangle has one line of symmetry. This is incorrect. A rectangle has two lines of symmetry.

3. Lines of symmetry create congruent parts. This is correct.

▶ Practice on Your Own

Count the lines of symmetry for each figure.
Draw each line of symmetry.

4

└ line of symmetry

5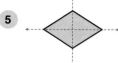

2 lines of symmetry

Circle each figure that has symmetry.

6

---

7 ◀WRITING IN ▶MATH Drew said the blue line is a line of symmetry. Is Drew correct? Explain.

No, Drew is not correct. If the rectangle were folded on the line, the parts would not match exactly.

Vocabulary Check   Complete.

8 A figure has **symmetry** if it can be folded on a line to create two congruent parts.

STOP

284 two hundred eighty-four

Copyright © Macmillan/McGraw-Hill • Glencoe, a division of The McGraw-Hill Companies, Inc.

Math Challenge

Symmetrical Letters

Write the capital letter A on the board. Show students the line of symmetry on the letter.

Have students go through the alphabet and determine which capital and lowercase letters have symmetry. Students can record their work in a two-column chart.

Letters with Symmetry	Letters without Symmetry

Challenge students to write symmetrical words.

Practice on Your Own

Direct students to p. 284 in their student books. Have students complete Exercises 4–8 independently. You may need to review the directions of each section before students begin.

④ Assess

See It, Do It, Say It, Write It

Step 1 Draw a rhombus on the board. Ask the students how many lines of symmetry a rhombus has. Draw the lines of symmetry on the rhombus.

Step 2 Have students cut a rhombus out of construction paper. Have them fold the rhombus along its lines of symmetry.

Step 3 Have students explain how a rhombus has two lines of symmetry and identify each pair of congruent parts.

Step 4 Ask students to draw a rectangle and identify the lines of symmetry. Have students explain in writing how they know the rectangle has symmetry.

⚠ Common Error Alert

Exercise 7 Students often mistake the number of lines of symmetry for rectangles. Using paper cut outs of figures aids students in visualizing and checking their assumptions.

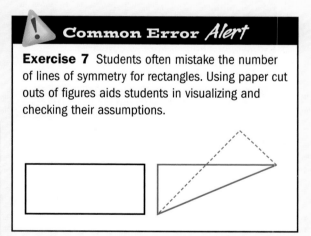

Chapter 8
Progress Check 3

Formative Assessment

Use the Progress Check to assess students' mastery of the previous lessons. Have students review the lesson indicated for the problems they answered incorrectly.

Common Error *Alert*

Students overlook that figures can be congruent even if they are in different positions. Encourage students to visualize the figures in different positions to determine if they are congruent.

Students often think that lines of symmetry must be vertical. Remind students that a line of symmetry can also be horizontal.

Name _____

Progress Check 3 (Lessons 8-5 and 8-6)

Compare. Are the figures congruent? Write "yes" or "no."

1 __no__

2 __yes__

Circle the congruent figures.

3

Count the lines of symmetry for each figure.
Draw each line of symmetry.

4 ___1___ line of symmetry

5 ___2___ lines of symmetry

6 Draw each line of symmetry.
The butterfly has ___1___ line(s) of symmetry.

Chapter 8   Progress Check

two hundred eighty-five **285**

Copyright © Macmillan/McGraw-Hill • Glencoe, a division of The McGraw-Hill Companies, Inc.

Data-Driven Decision Making

Students missing Exercises . . .	Have trouble with . . .	Should review and practice . . .
1–3	identifying congruent figures.	SSG Lesson 8-5, p. 277 CRM Skills Practice, p. A202
4–6	identifying lines of symmetry in figures.	SSG Lesson 8-6, p. 281 CRM Skills Practice, p. A206

285 Chapter 8 Measurement and Geometry

Name _____

Figure Match

Draw a line to match congruent figures.
Draw a line to match a figure's lines of symmetry.

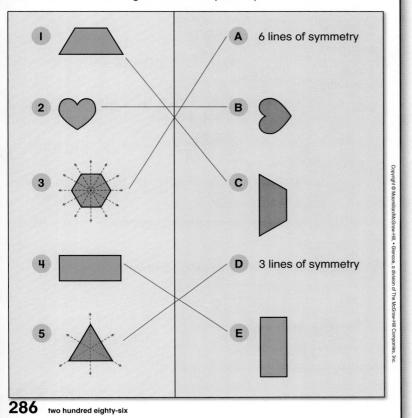

Replay

Use the Replay activity to review and reinforce the concepts and skills presented in Lessons 8-5 and 8-6.

Instructions

Have students read the directions at the top of the student page.

Student Technology

Students can use the following technology resources to reinforce chapter content.

- 💿 StudentWorks™ Plus

- Math Online ⟩ macmillanmh.com

- eGlossary

Review

Vocabulary

If students have difficulty answering Exercises 1–4, use the page references below to review the vocabulary words, or refer them to the glossary.

congruent (p. 277)
hexagon (p. 261)
line of symmetry (p. 281)
side (p. 261)

Vocabulary Review Strategies

Vocabulary Flashcards Have students use index cards to make flashcards. On the front side of each card, they should list a vocabulary word. On the back side of the card, they should write a definition of the word. They should also draw a picture to show an example of the word.

Concepts

The exercises in this section are grouped to cover content from each lesson in the chapter.

Exercise 5: Lesson 8-1 (p. 257)
Exercise 6: Lesson 8-2 (p. 261)
Exercise 7: Lesson 8-3 (p. 267)
Exercises 8–9: Lesson 8-4 (p. 271)
Exercises 10–11: Lesson 8-5 (p. 277)
Exercises 12–13: Lesson 8-6 (p. 281)

Find **Extra Practice** for these concepts in the Practice Worksheets, pp. A185–A208.

Name _____

Review

Vocabulary

Word Bank	Use the Word Bank to complete.
congruent	1. **line of symmetry**
hexagon	2. **congruent**
line of symmetry	3. **side**
side	4. **hexagon**

Concepts

5. Compare the size. Write "same" or "different."

2 units — 2 units
3 units   3 units

The triangles are the ___**same**___ size.

GO on

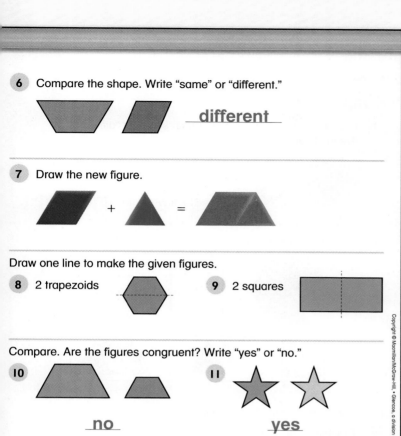

6 Compare the shape. Write "same" or "different."

different

7 Draw the new figure.

+ △ =

Draw one line to make the given figures.

8 2 trapezoids

9 2 squares

Compare. Are the figures congruent? Write "yes" or "no."

10

_no_

11

yes

Count the lines of symmetry for each figure.

12

___I___ line of symmetry

13 3

___I___ line of symmetry

288 two hundred eighty-eight

Copyright © Macmillan/McGraw-Hill • Glencoe, a division of The McGraw-Hill Companies, Inc.

Review

Intervention Strategy

Use this Intervention Strategy activity at any point during the chapter to reinforce the concepts and skills presented in the chapter.

Building Figures

Step 1 Divide students into groups. Have each group find examples of how figures fit together in the classroom or the school building. For example, they might consider how bricks or ceilings tiles combine to make a single figure.

Step 2 Have the students bring in magazines or illustrated books. Have the groups look at how articles, pictures, and captions fit together on a page.

Step 3 Have each group present its discoveries to the class. Lead a discussion on using space.

Step 4 Have the class work on a group project, such as designing a bulletin board or a scrapbook. Give each group the responsibility for designing one part of the project.

Classroom Management

Early Finishers

Some students will not require as much time to study and review. Be sure students have a solid understanding of the content and suggest that they come up with real-world examples of congruent figures and lines of symmetry. For example, students may explore symmetry in their faces (eyes, nose, mouth, ears, etc). They can present these examples to the class to help review the content.

Chapter 8 · Chapter Test

Chapter Resource Masters

Additional forms of the Chapter Test are available.

Test Format	Where to Find it
Chapter Test	**Math Online** macmillanmh.com
Blackline Masters	Assessment Masters, p. 103

ExamView® Assessment Suite

Customize and create multiple versions of your chapter test and their answer keys. All of these questions from the chapter tests are available on ExamView® Assessment Suite.

Advance Online Assessment and Reporting
macmillanmh.com

This online assessment tool allows teachers to track student progress with easily accessible, comprehensive reports available for every student. Assess students using any internet-ready computer.

Alternative Assessment

Use Portfolios Give students three different symmetrical figures to include in their portfolio. Ask them to draw and label each figure. They should take apart each figure into at least two new figures. Next, they should draw the lines of symmetry on each figure. Then for each figure, they should draw a congruent figure. The students should organize the figures in a way that best suits them such as a table, poster, or Foldable.

Name _____

Chapter Test

1 Compare the shape and size. Write "same" or "different." Are the figures congruent?

**same** shape

**same** size

The figures are _**congruent**_.

2 Circle the pattern block that completes the new figure.

+ [?] =

Draw two lines to make the given figures.

3 1 rectangle and 2 triangles

4 4 triangles

5 Who is Correct?

Kirstie and Sarita count how many lines of symmetry a rectangle has.

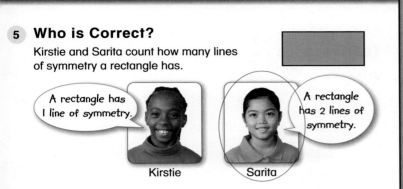

A rectangle has 1 line of symmetry.

Kirstie

A rectangle has 2 lines of symmetry.

Sarita

Circle the correct answer. Explain.

Sarita is correct. A rectangle has two lines of symmetry, one vertical (up and down) and one horizontal (side to side).

Count the lines of symmetry for each figure.
Draw each line of symmetry.

6

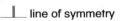

___1___ line of symmetry

7

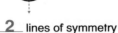

___2___ lines of symmetry

8 A rectangle is 3 units tall and 4 units wide.
Draw a congruent rectangle.

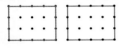

STOP

290 two hundred ninety

Chapter 8 Test

Who Is Correct?

Diagnostic Teaching

- Kirstie says a rectangle has 1 line of symmetry. This is not correct. Kirstie did not count both the vertical and horizontal lines of symmetry for the rectangle.

- Sarita says a rectangle has 2 lines of symmetry. Sarita remembered both the vertical and horizontal lines of symmetry. Sarita is correct.

Learning from Mistakes

Missed Questions Review commonly missed questions as a small group or class. Ask students to share their methods of answering each question. Try to point out when any errors occur and take corrective measures.

Data-Driven Decision Making

Students missing Exercises . . .	Have trouble with . . .	Should review and practice . . .	
1	comparing shape and size, and determining if figures are congruent.	[SSG] Lesson 8-1, p. 257 [SSG] Lesson 8-2, p. 261 [SSG] Lesson 8-5, p. 277	[CRM] Skills Practice, p. A186 [CRM] Skills Practice, p. A190 [CRM] Skills Practice, p. A202
2	creating new figures.	[SSG] Lesson 8-3, p. 267	[CRM] Skills Practice, p. A194
3–4	taking apart figures.	[SSG] Lesson 8-4, p. 271	[CRM] Skills Practice, p. A198
5–7	identifying lines of symmetry in figures.	[SSG] Lesson 8-6, p. 281	[CRM] Skills Practice, p. A206
8	drawing congruent figures.	[SSG] Lesson 8-5, p. 277 [CRM] Skills Practice, p. A202	

Chapter 8

Test Practice Notes

⚠ Diagnose Student Errors

Survey student responses for each item. Class trends may indicate common errors and misconceptions.

1. same size: does not understand concept of size
   congruent: does not understand concept of congruency
   different shape: does not understand concept of shape
   different size: correct

2. same size: does not understand concept of size
   congruent: does not understand concept of congruency
   same shape: correct
   different shape: does not understand concept of shape

3. 0: does not understand concept of symmetry
   1: student did not find all lines of symmetry
   2: correct
   4: does not understand concept of symmetry

4. ☐ : does not understand how to compose figures

   ⬡ : does not understand how to compose figures

   ◺ : correct

   ▱ : does not understand how to compose figures

5. square and triangle: correctly identifies only one figure
   2 squares: correct
   2 hexagons: does not understand how to decompose figures
   square and trapezoid: correctly identifies only one figure

6. ◺ : correct

   ☐ : does not understand concept of shape

   ◿ : does not understand that all triangles are not the same shape

   ☐ : does not understand concept of shape

Name _____

Test Practice

Choose the correct answer.

1 Bryan drew the figures below of the following. Describe the figures.

○ same size
○ congruent
○ different shape
● different size

2 Describe the figures.

○ same size
○ congruent
● same shape
○ different shape

3 Megan wants to draw all the lines of symmetry for the figure below. How many lines should she draw?

0   1   2   4
○   ○   ●   ○

4 Alberto is composing a new figure. Which figure is Alberto missing?

◺ + ? = ◼

○ ☐   ○ ▱
● ◺   ○ ▱

5 Which two figures make the rectangle?

○ square and triangle
● 2 squares
○ 2 hexagons
○ square and trapezoid

6 Which figure has the same shape as the triangle?

● ◺   ○ ☐
○ ◺   ○ ☐

GO ON ➡

Chapter 8   Test Practice

two hundred ninety-one 291

Copyright © Macmillan/McGraw-Hill, • Glencoe, a division of The McGraw-Hill Companies, Inc.

---

7. 1 square and 1 triangle: does not understand how to decompose figures
   2 triangles: does not understand how to decompose figures
   2 trapezoids: correct
   1 square and 1 triangle: does not understand how to decompose figures

8. same size: correct
   different size: does not understand concept of size
   not congruent: does not understand concept of congruency
   different shape: does not understand concept of shape

9. ☐ : does not understand how to compose figures

   ⬡ : correct

   ⬡ : does not understand how to compose figures

   △ : does not understand how to compose figures

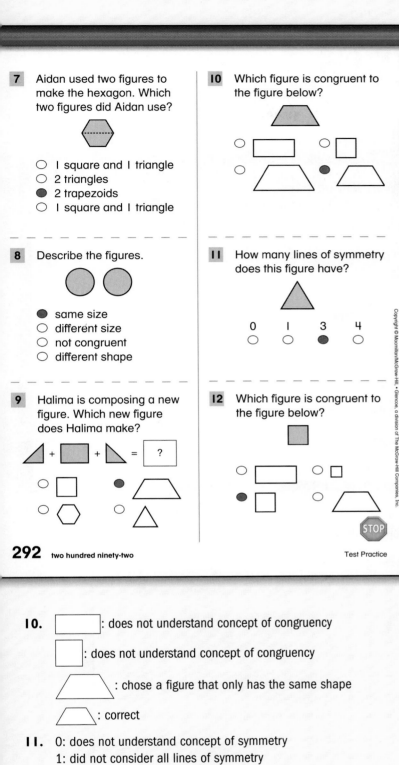

7 Aidan used two figures to make the hexagon. Which two figures did Aidan use?

- ○ I square and I triangle
- ○ 2 triangles
- ● 2 trapezoids
- ○ I square and I triangle

8 Describe the figures.

- ● same size
- ○ different size
- ○ not congruent
- ○ different shape

9 Halima is composing a new figure. Which new figure does Halima make?

10 Which figure is congruent to the figure below?

11 How many lines of symmetry does this figure have?

    0   I   3   4
    ○   ○   ●   ○

12 Which figure is congruent to the figure below?

STOP

Test Practice

Diagnosing Student Errors and Misconceptions

Figures and Symmetry Encourage students who are struggling with taking apart figures or lines of symmetry to practice using paper models. Students should create models of geometric figures and fold them to discover their lines of symmetry. This exercise will also reveal other figures which compose the original figure. Students can use scissors to cut figures such as trapezoids and hexagons into the figures which create them.

10. ▭ : does not understand concept of congruency

▢ : does not understand concept of congruency

⏢ : chose a figure that only has the same shape

⏢ : correct

11. 0: does not understand concept of symmetry
1: did not consider all lines of symmetry
3: correct
4: does not understand concept of symmetry

12. ▭ : does not understand concept of congruency

▢ : chose a figure with only the same shape

▢ : correct

⏢ : does not understand concept of congruency

Chapter Overview

Chapter-at-a-Glance

Lesson	Math Objective	State/Local Standards
9-1 Sort and Classify (pp. 295–298)	Sort and classify objects.	
9-2 Pictographs and Picture Graphs (pp. 299–302)	Display data in pictographs and picture graphs.	
Progress Check 1 (p. 303)		
9-3 Read Tables (pp. 305–308)	Read tables.	
9-4 Read Bar Graphs (pp. 309–312)	Read bar graphs.	
Progress Check 2 (p. 313)		
9-5 Make Bar Graphs (pp. 315–318)	Use data from tables to make bar graphs.	
9-6 Line Plots (pp. 319–322)	Read line plots.	
Progress Check 3 (p. 323)		

Content-at-a-Glance

The diagram below summarizes and unpacks Chapter 9 content.

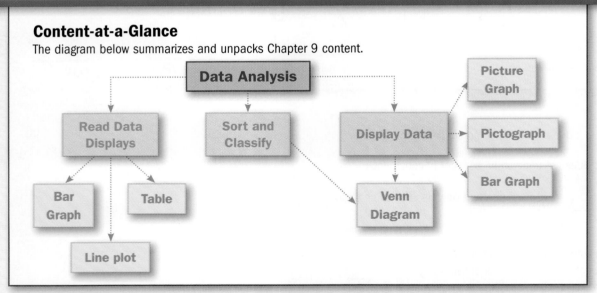

Chapter Assessment Manager

Diagnostic · Diagnose students' readiness.

	Student Study Guide/ Teacher Editions	Assessment Masters	Technology
Course Placement Test		1	💿 ExamView® Assessment Suite
Book 3 Pretest		85	💿 ExamView® Assessment Suite
Chapter Pretest		112	💿 ExamView® Assessment Suite
Get Ready	SSG 294		Math Online ▷ macmillanmh.com StudentWorks™ Plus

Formative · Identify students' misconceptions of content knowledge.

	Student Study Guide/ Teacher Editions	Assessment Masters	Technology
Progress Checks	SSG 303, 313, 323		Math Online ▷ macmillanmh.com StudentWorks™ Plus
Vocabulary Review	SSG 298, 302, 308, 312, 318, 322, 325		Math Online ▷ macmillanmh.com
Lesson Assessments			💿 ExamView® Assessment Suite
Are They Getting It?	TE 297, 301, 307, 311, 317, 321		

Summative · Determine student success in learning the concepts in the lesson, chapter, or book.

	Student Study Guide/ Teacher Editions	Assessment Masters	Technology
Chapter Test	SSG 327	115	💿 ExamView® Assessment Suite
Test Practice	SSG 329	118	💿 ExamView® Assessment Suite
Alternative Assessment	TE 327	121	
See It, Do It, Say It, Write It	TE 298, 302, 308, 312, 318, 322		
Book 3 Test		124	💿 ExamView® Assessment Suite

Back-Mapping and Vertical Alignment McGraw-Hill's *Math Triumphs* intervention program was conceived and developed with the final result in mind: student success in grade-level mathematics, including Algebra 1 and beyond. The authors, using the **NCTM Focal Points and Focal Connections** as their guide, developed this brand-new series by back-mapping from grade-level and Algebra 1 concepts, and vertically aligning the topics so that they build upon prior skills and concepts and serve as a foundation for future topics.

	Lesson 9-1	Lesson 9-2	Lesson 9-3	Lesson 9-4
Concept	Sort and classify	Pictographs and Picture Graphs	Read Tables	Read Bar Graphs
Objective	Sort and classify objects.	Display data in pictographs and picture graphs.	Read tables.	Read bar graphs.
Math Vocabulary	classify sort Venn diagram	pictograph picture graph	data table tally mark	bar graph data
Lesson Resources	**Materials** • string • leaves/rocks • beans • crayons **Manipulatives** • money • geometric solids **Other Resources** [CRM] Vocabulary and English Language Development [CRM] Skills Practice [CRM] Problem-Solving Practice [CRM] Homework Practice	**Materials** • paper • markers **Manipulatives** • fraction circles • counters • geometric solids **Other Resources** [CRM] Vocabulary and English Language Development [CRM] Skills Practice [CRM] Problem-Solving Practice [CRM] Homework Practice	**Materials** • tape • pencils • markers • paper **Manipulatives** • pattern blocks • rulers **Other Resources** [CRM] Vocabulary and English Language Development [CRM] Skills Practice [CRM] Problem-Solving Practice [CRM] Homework Practice	**Materials** • crayons • grid paper **Manipulatives** • connecting cubes • counters **Other Resources** [CRM] Vocabulary and English Language Development [CRM] Skills Practice [CRM] Problem-Solving Practice [CRM] Homework Practice
Technology	**Math Online** macmillanmh.com StudentWorks™ Plus ⊙ ExamView® Assessment Suite	**Math Online** macmillanmh.com StudentWorks™ Plus ⊙ ExamView® Assessment Suite	**Math Online** macmillanmh.com StudentWorks™ Plus ⊙ ExamView® Assessment Suite	**Math Online** macmillanmh.com StudentWorks™ Plus ⊙ ExamView® Assessment Suite

Lesson 9-5	Lesson 9-6	
Make Bar Graphs	Line Plots	**Concept**
Use data from tables to make bar graphs.	Read line plots.	**Objective**
bar graph data table	data line plot	**Math Vocabulary**
Materials • markers • paper • colored paper squares • grid paper **Manipulatives** • counters • color tiles • connecting cubes **Other Resources** CRM Vocabulary and English Language Development CRM Skills Practice CRM Problem-Solving Practice CRM Homework Practice	**Materials** • markers • paper • masking tape • beans • buttons **Manipulatives** • counters **Other Resources** CRM Vocabulary and English Language Development CRM Skills Practice CRM Problem-Solving Practice CRM Homework Practice	**Lesson Resources**
Math Online macmillanmh.com StudentWorks™ Plus ● ExamView® Assessment Suite	**Math Online** macmillanmh.com StudentWorks™ Plus ● ExamView® Assessment Suite	**Technology**

Chapter 9 Chapter Notes

Home Connection

Read the Home Connection letter with students and have them write their name in the space below.

Read and explain the activity under Help at Home. If time allows, complete a portion of the activity so students can introduce the activity to a parent or other caregiver.

Have students:

- find data displays in newspapers, magazines, or books. Display graphs students find.

- have students answer a question of the day each morning to collect data.

Real-World Applications

Pets   Have students list all of their pets. Count how many pets of each type for the class.

- **Which animal is most popular as a pet?**
  Answers will vary.

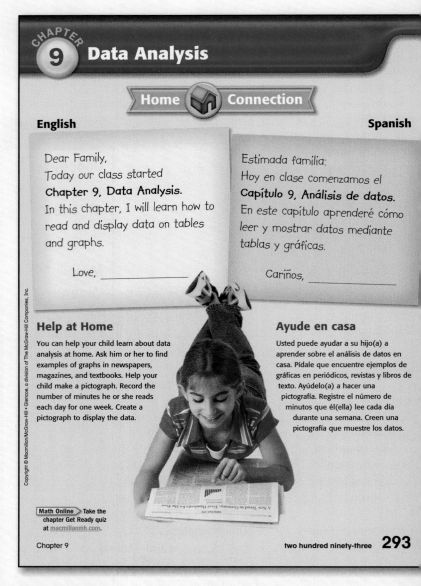

CHAPTER 9 Data Analysis

Home Connection

English

Dear Family,
Today our class started **Chapter 9, Data Analysis.** In this chapter, I will learn how to read and display data on tables and graphs.

Love, _____

Spanish

Estimada familia:
Hoy en clase comenzamos el **Capítulo 9, Análisis de datos.** En este capítulo aprenderé cómo leer y mostrar datos mediante tablas y gráficas.

Cariños, _____

Help at Home

You can help your child learn about data analysis at home. Ask him or her to find examples of graphs in newspapers, magazines, and textbooks. Help your child make a pictograph. Record the number of minutes he or she reads each day for one week. Create a pictograph to display the data.

Ayude en casa

Usted puede ayudar a su hijo(a) a aprender sobre el análisis de datos en casa. Pídale que encuentre ejemplos de gráficas en periódicos, revistas y libros de texto. Ayúdelo(a) a hacer una pictografía. Registre el número de minutos que él(ella) lee cada día durante una semana. Creen una pictografía que muestre los datos.

Copyright © Macmillan/McGraw-Hill · Glencoe, a division of The McGraw-Hill Companies, Inc.

Math Online Take the chapter Get Ready quiz at macmillanmh.com.

Chapter 9   two hundred ninety-three **293**

Key Vocabulary

Find interactive definitions in 13 languages in the **eGlossary** at macmillanmh.com.

English   Español *Introduce the most important vocabulary terms from Chapter 9.*

classify   clasificar
to label a group of items based on a common attribute (p. 295)

sort   organizar
to group together like items (p. 295)

Venn diagram   diagrama de Venn
a diagram that uses circles to organize and display data (p. 295)

picture graph   grafica de imagen
a graph that has different pictures to show the data (p. 299)

pictograph   pictografia
a graph that uses the same picture or symbol to show the data (p. 299)

table   tabla, gráfica
a way to organize data (p. 305)

data   datos
numbers or symbols that show information (p. 305)

tally mark   marca(s) de conteo
a mark used to record data collected in a survey (p. 305)

bar graph   gradfica de barras
a graph that uses bars to show data (p. 309)

line plot   diagrama de línea
a graph that uses columns of Xs above a number line to show frequency of data (p. 319)

Name _____

Get Ready

Circle the greatest number.

1. **3** (**9**) **5**   2. (**31**) **29** **15**

Circle the least number.

3. **7 8** (**4**)   4. **21 38** (**14**)

Find each sum or difference.

5. 6 − 4 = __2__   6. 5 + 3 = __8__

7. 2 + 7 = __9__   8. 8 − 1 = __7__

Find the missing numbers.

9.
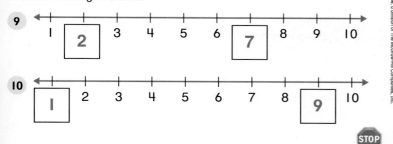
1 | 2 | 3 4 5 6 | 7 | 8 9 10

10.
| 1 | 2 3 4 5 6 7 8 | 9 | 10

294 two hundred ninety-four

Vocabulary Preview

Have students look through the chapter and find pictures of data displays.

As a class, create a chart that compares and contrasts the different displays based on students' observations.

Explain to students that data is displayed so it can be easily read and analyzed.

Get Ready

Get Ready

Have students complete Get Ready to assess readiness for the chapter concepts and skills. Refer to the lessons below for additional support for prerequisite skills.

1-1 Addition Facts 0 to 10 (p. 3)
1-3 Subtraction Facts 0 to 10 (p. 13)
4-1 Count to 100 (p. 121)

You may also assess student readiness with the following resources:

Math Online ⟩ Online Readiness quiz at macmillanmh.com

Assessment Masters: Chapter Pretest (p. 112)

 **Dinah Zike's Foldables®**

Guide students through the directions on p. A209 in the Chapter Resource Masters to create their own Foldable graphic organizer for use with this chapter.

Professional Development

Targeted professional development has been articulated throughout **McGraw-Hill's Math Triumphs** intervention program. **The McGraw-Hill Professional Development Video Library** provides short videos that support the **NCTM Focal Points and Focal Connections.**

For more information, visit macmillanmh.com.

Model Lessons   Instructional Strategies

Lesson Notes

Lesson Planner

Objective Sort and classify objects.

Vocabulary classify, sort, Venn diagram

Materials/Manipulatives money, string, leaves/rocks, geometric solids, beans, crayons

Chapter Resource Masters

- [CRM] Vocabulary and English Language Development (p. A213)
- [CRM] Skill Practice (p. A214)
- [CRM] Problem-Solving Practice (p. A215)
- [CRM] Homework Practice (p. A216)

 **Introduce**

Vocabulary

Vocabulary Interaction Use string to make a Venn diagram on the floor. Label one circle "Boys" and the other "Brown Hair."

Place students in the appropriate section of the Venn diagram. Explain the students' placements so they understand the classifying and sorting that occurs when creating a Venn diagram.

Repeat the activity with other categories.

 **Teach**

Key Concept

Foundational Skills and Concepts After students have read through the Key Concept box, guide them through the following questions.

- **How many figures are four-sided?** 2
- **How many figures are blue?** 2
- **How many figures are four-sided and blue?** 1
- **What type of display is used to classify and sort objects?** Venn diagram

295 Chapter 9 Data Analysis

Name _____

Sort and Classify

Key Concept

You can **classify** and **sort** objects using a **Venn diagram**. Figures can be classified by shape and color.

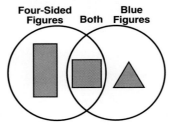

The figure on the left is a four-sided figure.
The figure on the right is a blue figure.
The figure in the middle is both a four-sided figure and a blue figure.

Vocabulary

classify to label a group of items based on a common attribute

sort to group together like items

Venn diagram a diagram that uses circles to organize and display data

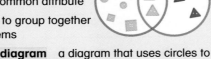

Chapter 9   Lesson 1   **two hundred ninety-five** **295**

English Learner Strategy

Sorting Money Use coins and dollar bills to practice sorting.

The term *sorting* may be new to students. Explain that when students put items in groups based on a shared characteristic they are *sorting*. Remind students of the vocabulary activity when they sorted students based on gender and hair color.

1. Have students sort the money into groups of like items. For example, coins and bills.

2. Have each student explain how the grouped items are alike. Ask students to use the sentence, "I sorted the items by _____."

3. Repeat. Encourage students to look for new ways to sort money.

Example

Classify and sort. Draw the
figures in the Venn diagram.

Step 1   Classify. There are triangles and red figures.

Step 2   Sort. The blue figure is a triangle.
The red circle is a red figure.
The red triangle is both.

Answer

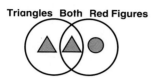

Triangles Both Red Figures

Step-by-Step Practice

Classify and sort. Draw the
figures in the Venn diagram.

Step 1   Classify. There are **circles**
and **yellow figures**.

Step 2   Sort. The blue figure is a **circle**.
The yellow square is a **yellow figure**.
The yellow circle is **both**.

Answer

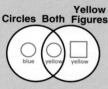

Circles Both Yellow Figures

blue yellow yellow

296 two hundred ninety-six

Copyright © Macmillan/McGraw-Hill • Glencoe, a division of The McGraw-Hill Companies, Inc.

Intervention Strategy   Naturalist Learners

Materials: leaves/rocks

Have students gather leaves or rocks from outside.

Discuss the characteristics of the leaves or rocks. Talk about color,
size, and shape.

Have students identify how the leaves or rocks could be classified.
Then have them sort the objects into groups.

Additional *Example*

**Classify and sort. Draw the figures in the Venn
diagram.**

Step 1   Classify. There are squares and green
figures.

Step 2   Sort. The orange figure is a square. The
green circle is a green figure. The green
square is both.

Answer

Squares   Both   Green
Figures

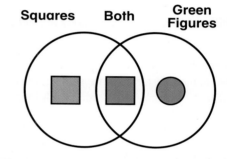

⚠ **Common Error** *Alert*

Students may not be able to distinguish the three
areas of the Venn diagram. Have them shade the
areas in different colors, leaving the shared
area white.

Math Coach Notes

Strategies

1. To practice identifying similarities in objects, have
students tell you how objects found in the
classroom are alike.

2. Have students collect groups of like objects.

Guided Practice

Direct students to complete Exercise 1 in Guided Practice.

Exercise 1 Remind students to look at the Venn diagram for the categories before they classify and sort.

Problem-Solving Practice

Guide students through the four-step problem-solving plan to complete Exercise 2.

- **What are the key words?** sorted, how many, stickers are stars

- **In which areas of the Venn diagram are the stars?** Star Stickers, Both

Ask students to check their work using the strategy suggested in the Check step. Have students circle and count each star in the Venn diagram to solve the problem.

Using Manipulatives

Geometric Solids Have students look at the geometric solids and determine a way to classify them. Then have students sort the solids and explain their reasoning.

On-Hand Manipulatives Use a variety of dried beans. Have students sort them by type, color, or size.

Name _____

▶ Guided Practice

1 Classify and sort. Draw the figures in the Venn diagram.

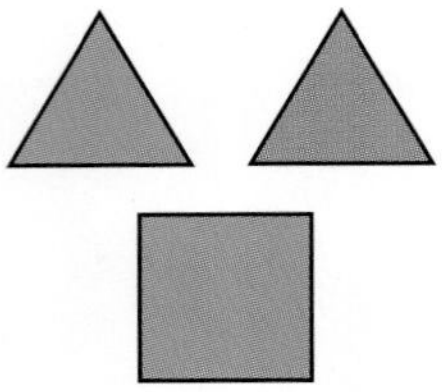

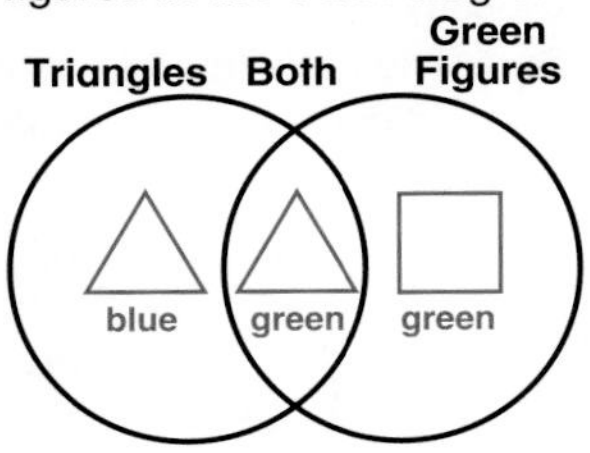

Triangles Both Green Figures

blue green green

Problem-Solving Practice

2 Pamela <u>sorted</u> her sticker collection. <u>How many</u> of her <u>stickers are stars</u>?

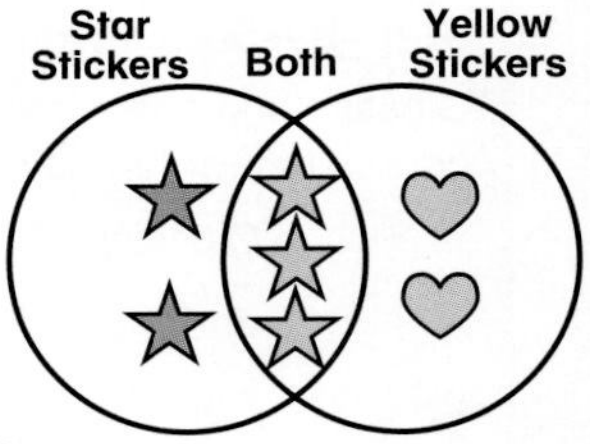

Star Stickers Both Yellow Stickers

Understand Underline key words.

Plan Use the diagram.

Solve Count the stickers in the **Star** section. __2__

Count the stickers in the **Both** section. __3__

Add. __2__ + __3__ = __5__

Pamela has __5__ star stickers.

Check Circle each star sticker in the Venn diagram. How many stars did you circle?

GO on

Are They Getting It? ?

Check students' understanding of Venn diagrams by drawing the following diagram on the board. Ask students to point out the correct and incorrect statements and explain their reasoning.

Circles Both Orange

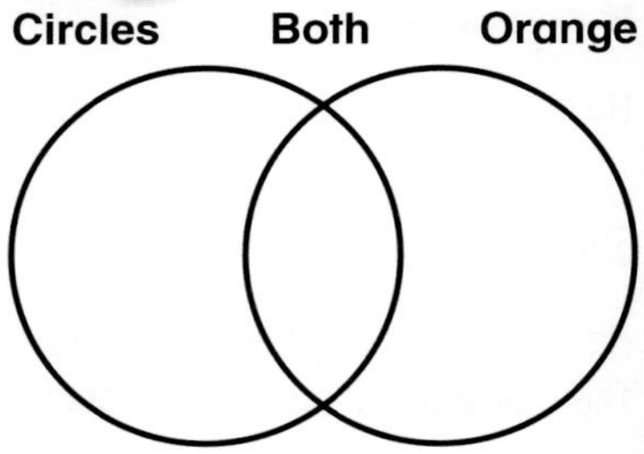

1. An orange triangle goes in the right section. This is correct.

2. A purple circle goes in the center section This is incorrect. A purple circle goes in the left section.

3. An orange circle goes in the center section. This is correct.

▶ Practice on Your Own

Classify and sort. Draw the figures in the Venn diagram.

3

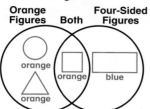

4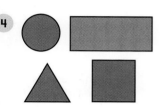

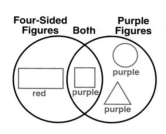

5 **WRITING IN ►MATH**   Look at Exercise 4. What is another figure that could be drawn in the section with the red rectangle? Explain.

Sample answer: A blue square is a four-sided figure that is not purple.

Vocabulary Check   Complete.

6   You can display objects that have been sorted in a

Venn diagram .

298   two hundred ninety-eight

Copyright © Macmillan/McGraw-Hill • Glencoe, a division of The McGraw-Hill Companies, Inc.

Math Challenge

Where Do I Belong?

Have students work in pairs.

Write categories on the board, such as Big, Small, Long, Short, Red, Blue, Yellow, Black, White.

The first student picks two categories from the list and draws a Venn diagram, labeling the three sections with the chosen categories.

The second student goes on a scavenger hunt through the room to find objects that belong in each section.

Have pairs reverse roles and repeat for other categories.

Practice on Your Own

Direct students to p. 298 in their student books. Have students complete Exercises 3–6 independently. You may need to review the directions of each section before students begin.

See It, Do It, Say It, Write It

Draw the following Venn diagram on the board.

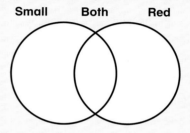

Step 1   Identify three objects in the room, one for each section of the Venn diagram. Write the name of each object in the appropriate section.

Step 2   Have students copy the Venn diagram and add one additional object from the room to each section of the diagram.

Step 3   Have students explain why they put the objects in each section.

Step 4   Have students write three sentences to explain the placement of the objects in the Venn diagram.

Looking Ahead: Pre-teach

In the next lesson, students will learn about picture graphs and pictographs.

Example   How many students chose red?   3

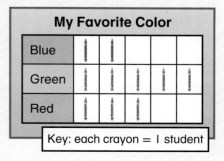

Have students answer the following question.

1.   How many students chose blue?   2

Lesson Notes

Lesson Planner

Objective   Display data in pictographs and picture graphs.

Vocabulary   picture graph, pictograph

Materials/Manipulatives   paper, markers, fraction circles, counters, geometric solids

Chapter Resource Masters

- [CRM] Vocabulary and English Language Development (p. A217)
- [CRM] Skill Practice (p. A218)
- [CRM] Problem-Solving-Practice (p. A219)
- [CRM] Homework Practice (p. A220)

1 Introduce

Vocabulary

Compare Vocabulary   Have students identify the differences and similarities between a pictograph and a picture graph.   Sample answers: They both use pictures. They both display information. A pictograph uses one picture to show information, but a picture graph uses different pictures.

2 Teach

Key Concept

Foundational Skills and Concepts   After students have read through the Key Concept box, guide them through the following questions.

- **How many students ride the bus to school?** 4

Remind students that each sticker in the pictograph equals 2 students.

- **How many students chose reading as their favorite subject?** 4

Name _____

Pictographs and Picture Graphs

Key Concept

Picture Graph

How I Get to School	
🚲 Bike	🚲 🚲 🚲
🚌 Bus	🚌 🚌 🚌 🚌
👟 Walk	👟 👟 👟

How many students walk to school?
3 👟 = 3 students
3 students walk to school.

Pictograph

Favorite Subject	
📕 Math	☺ ☺ ☺ ☺ ☺
📗 Reading	☺ ☺
📘 Science	☺ ☺ ☺

Key: ☺ = 2 students

How many students chose math as their favorite subject? Skip count five times by 2.
2, 4, 6, 8, 10
10 students chose math as their favorite subject.

Vocabulary

picture graph   a graph that has different pictures to show the data

pictograph   a graph that uses the same picture or symbol to show the data

Chapter 9   Lesson 2   **two hundred ninety-nine** **299**

English Learner Strategy

Graphs

English language learners may be unfamiliar with graphs.

1. Explain that a graph uses pictures to show information. Show students sample graphs. Identify the type of graph and then point out the information in the graph. Be sure students understand that the information in graphs usually represents numbers.

2. Have students predict what the pictures might represent.

   - **Cars**   Sample answer: number of cars sold
   - **Books**   Sample answer: number of books read
   - **Suns**   Sample answer: number of sunny days

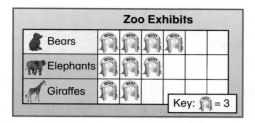

Zoo Exhibits

	Bears					
Bears						
Elephants						
Giraffes						

Key: = 3

Example

How many bears are on exhibit at the zoo?

Step 1   Count the number of after bears. 4

Step 2   Look at the key. = 3

Step 3   Skip count 4 times by 3.
3, 6, 9, 12

Answer   There are 12 bears on exhibit at the zoo.

Step-by-Step Practice

How many elephants are on exhibit at the zoo?

Step 1   Count the number of after elephants.

Step 2   Look at the key. = **3**

Step 3   Skip count **3** times by **3**.
3, **6**, **9**

Answer   There are **9** elephants on exhibit at the zoo.

300   three hundred

How many dogs are at the pet shop?

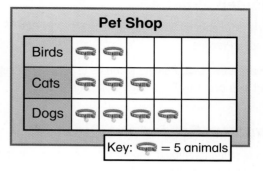

Pet Shop

Birds					
Cats					
Dogs					

Key: = 5 animals

Step 1   Count the number of after dogs. 4

Step 2   Look at the key. = 5

Step 3   Skip count 4 times by 5.
5, 10, 15, 20

Answer   There are 20 dogs at the pet shop.

⚠ Common Error *Alert*

Students might forget to look at the key to see how many each picture represents. Remind students to always look for a key when they are working with a pictograph or picture graph.

Math Coach Notes

Strategies

1. Have students look for data they could display in a picture graph. Have them identify what pictures could be used.

2. Encourage students to look for pictographs in places besides their textbook.

Intervention Strategy   Kinesthetic Learners

Materials: paper, fraction circles $\left(\frac{1}{2}, \frac{1}{3}, \frac{1}{4}\right)$, markers

• Have students take a handful of fraction circle pieces.

• On paper, have students write *Fraction Circles* as the title of a picture graph.

• Have them label the rows $\frac{1}{2}, \frac{1}{3}, \frac{1}{4}$.

• Have students make a picture graph by placing the fraction circle pieces in the appropriate rows.

Fraction Circles

$\frac{1}{2}$					
$\frac{1}{3}$					
$\frac{1}{4}$					

③ Practice

Guided Practice

Direct students to complete Exercises 1–2 in Guided Practice.

Exercises 1–2 Remind students to look at the key and skip count by 5s to get the answer.

Problem-Solving Practice

Guide students through the four-step problem-solving plan to complete Exercise 3.

- **How many votes does one whole pizza represent?** 10

- **What is half of 10?** 5

Ask students to check their work using the strategy suggested in the Check step. Students can divide 10 by 2 to solve the problem.

Using Manipulatives

Counters As students are reading pictographs and picture graphs, have them use counters to determine the amount shown by the symbols. For example, if one symbol equals 5 votes, have students make groups of 5 counters for each symbol. Students can find the total number of counters to interpret the graph.

 On-Hand Manipulatives Students can use beans or small pieces of paper as counters.

Name _____

▶ Guided Practice

Fruit Packed in Lunches on Friday

🍎 Apples	🍎 🍎 🍎 🍎				
🍌 Bananas	🍌 🍌 🍌				
🟠 Oranges	🟠 🟠				

Key: each item = 5 pieces

1 How many more bananas were packed in lunches than oranges? __5__

2 How many total pieces of fruit were packed in the students' lunches on Friday? __45__

Problem-Solving Practice

3 Lois made a <u>pictograph</u> with the key: 🍕 = 10 votes. What does represent? _____

Understand Underline key words.

Plan Use counters.

Solve Separate __10__ counters into __2__ equal groups.

⬤⬤⬤⬤⬤   ⬤⬤⬤⬤⬤

🍕 = __5__ votes

Check Divide 10 by 2.

Chapter 9   Lesson 2   three hundred one **301**

Copyright © Macmillan/McGraw-Hill • Glencoe, a division of The McGraw-Hill Companies, Inc.

Are They Getting It? ❓

Check students' understanding of picture graphs by drawing the following graph on the board. Ask students to point out the correct and incorrect statements and explain their reasoning.

My Favorite Sport

Baseball	🥎 🥎				
Basketball	🏀 🏀 🏀 🏀 🏀 🏀				
Football	🏈 🏈 🏈 🏈				

Key: each picture = 1 person

1. Two people chose baseball as their favorite sport. This is correct.

2. Ten people chose football as their favorite sport. This is incorrect. Four people chose football.

▶ Practice on Your Own

A second grade class chose their favorite musical instruments.

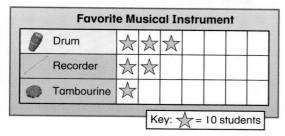

Favorite Musical Instrument

	Drum	☆	☆	☆			
	Recorder	☆	☆				
	Tambourine	☆					

Key: ☆ = 10 students

4 How many students does each ☆ represent?

__10__ students

5 Which instrument is the least favorite?

__tambourine__

6 How many students chose a recorder?

__20__ students

7 How many more students chose a drum than a recorder?

__10__ students

8 **WRITING IN ▶MATH** How many students are in the second grade? How do you know?

There are 60 students. Skip count 6 times by 10. 10, 20, 30, 40, 50, 60

Vocabulary Check Complete.

9 A __pictograph__ uses the same picture or symbol to show data.

STOP

302 three hundred two

Math Challenge

What is the Key?

Have students look at the pictograph.

Give students the following information:

- 12 people like green beans.
- 6 people like corn.
- 9 people like carrots.

Based on the information, have students draw the key.

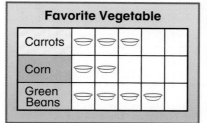

Favorite Vegetable

Carrots	⬭	⬭	⬭	
Corn	⬭	⬭		
Green Beans	⬭	⬭	⬭	⬭

⬭ = 3 votes

Practice on Your Own

Direct students to p. 302 in their student books. Have students complete Exercises 4–9 independently. You may need to review the directions of each section before students begin.

4 Assess

See It, Do It, Say It, Write It

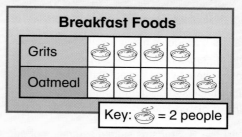

Breakfast Foods					
Grits	🥣	🥣	🥣	🥣	
Oatmeal	🥣	🥣	🥣	🥣	🥣

Key: 🥣 = 2 people

Step 1 Display the pictograph. Add a row to show that 4 people like cereal by adding 2 symbols.

Step 2 Have students copy the pictograph. Have students add another row to show that 6 people like eggs.

Step 3 Have students verbally explain how they filled in the additional row.

Step 4 Have students write how they can find the number of people all together who like cereal and eggs.

Looking Ahead: Pre-teach

In the next lesson, students will learn about reading tables.

Example How many pieces of chalk are there? 5

Art Supplies		
Supply	Tally	Total
Chalk	卌	5
Crayons	卌 卌 IIII	14
Paints	卌 III	8

Have students answer the following questions.

1. How many paints are there? 8

2. How many crayons are there? 14

Chapter 9 Progress Check 1

Formative Assessment

Use the Progress Check to assess students' mastery of the previous lessons. Have students review the lesson indicated for the problems they answered incorrectly.

Common Error *Alert*

Graphs Students might forget to read all the parts of graphs before answering questions. Remind them to find a graph's title, key, and labels to fully understand what information is being displayed.

Exercise 3 Students should subtract, not add, to find how many more.

Exercise 4 Students should skip count two times by 6.

Name _____

Progress Check 1 (Lessons 9-1 and 9-2)

1. Classify and sort. Draw the figures in the Venn diagram.

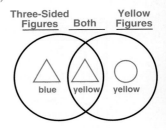

Use the graphs to answer each question.

2. How many students chose a fish as their favorite pet?

   __3__ students

3. How many more students chose a dog than cat?

   __2__ students

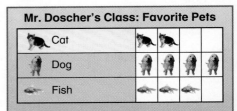

4. How many students play football?

   __12__ students

5. Which sport has the least players?

   __soccer__

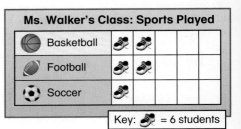

Copyright © Macmillan/McGraw-Hill • Glencoe, a division of The McGraw-Hill Companies, Inc.

Data-Driven Decision Making

Students missing Exercises . . .	Have trouble with . . .	Should review and practice . . .
1	classifying and sorting objects in a Venn diagram.	SSG Lesson 9-1, p. 295 CRM Skills Practice, p. A214
2–5	reading picture graphs and pictographs.	SSG Lesson 9-2, p. 299 CRM Skills Practice, p. A218

Name _____

«« Replay **SORT–O–RAMA**

Work with a partner to practice classifying and sorting objects.

Listen as your teacher instructs how to play.

Materials
pattern blocks
Venn diagram

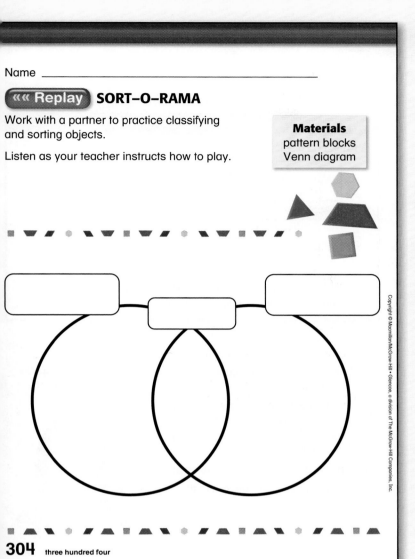

304 three hundred four

Use the Replay activity to review and reinforce the concepts and skills presented in Lessons 9-1 and 9-2.

Instructions

Write the following directions on the board. Have students listen as you read the directions out loud.

How to Play

1. Each partner takes two handfuls of pattern blocks.

2. Identify how to classify the group of pattern blocks.

3. Label each section of the Venn diagram.

4. Sort the pattern blocks into the Venn diagram.

5. How did you classify and sort? Share with the class.

Student Technology

Students can use the following technology resources to reinforce chapter content.

- StudentWorks™ Plus

- **Math Online** macmillanmh.com

- eGlossary

Lesson Planner

Math Objective   Read tables.

Vocabulary   table, data, tally mark

Materials/Manipulatives   pattern blocks, tape, rulers, pencils, markers, paper

Chapter Resource Masters

- CRM Vocabulary and English Language Development (p. A221)
- CRM Skill Practice (p. A222)
- CRM Problem-Solving-Practice (p. A223)
- CRM Homework Practice (p. A224)

 **Introduce**

Vocabulary

Review Vocabulary   Tell students that skip counting by 5s means you say every 5th number: 5, 10, 15, 20, . . .

Explain that tally marks are grouped in fives. To count them, you skip count by 5s.

|||| |||| |||| |||| |||| ||||
5   10   15   20   25   30

 **Teach**

Key Concept

Foundational Skills and Concepts   After students have read through the Key Concept box, guide them through the following questions

- **What is the title of the table?**
  Fruit at a Farm Stand

- **How many apples are there?**   12

- **How many more pears are there than peaches?**   2

Read Tables

Key Concept

A **table** can display **data**.

Fruit at a Farm Stand		
Fruit	Tally	Total
Apples	|||| |||| ||	12
Peaches	|||	3
Pears	||||	5

The title of the table is Fruit at a Farm Stand.
The columns show the type of Fruit and the Total number.
There are 12 apples, 3 peaches, and 5 pears.

Vocabulary

table   a way to organize data

data   numbers or symbols that show information

tally mark   a mark used to record data collected in a survey

|||| ||
tally marks

There are 17 apples and pears at the farm stand.

You can use a table to answer questions.
How many apples and pears are at the farm stand?

English Learner Strategy

Tables

Discuss with students the different meanings of the word *table*.

A table can be something that you sit at to work or eat.

In math, a table is a chart that organizes information. A table is made of rows and columns. A row goes across and a column goes up and down. The information across each row relates to each other. The column heading tells you what the data means.

Identify and explain the parts and data in the table in the key concept box.

Example

How many students ate eggs for breakfast?

Breakfast Food		
Food	Tally	Number of Students
Cereal	卌 卌 ||||	14
Eggs	卌 卌	10
Pancakes	卌 |||	8

Step 1 Find Eggs in the Food column.
Step 2 Look across the row to the Tally column.
There are 10 tallies.

Answer 10 students ate eggs for breakfast.

Step-by-Step Practice

How many students chose pizza for lunch?

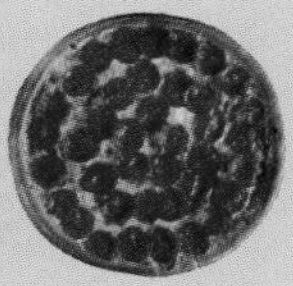

Lunch Count		
Food	Tally	Number of Students
Hamburger	卌 卌 ||||	14
Pizza	卌 卌 卌 卌	20
Turkey Sub	卌 卌 |||	13

Step 1 Find Pizza in the Food column.
Step 2 Look across the row to the Tally column.
There are 20 tallies.

Answer 20 students chose pizza for lunch.

Additional Example

How many students ate soup for lunch?

Lunch Food		
Food	Tally	Number of Students
Salad	||||	4
Sandwich	卌 卌 ||	12
Soup	卌 ||||	9

Step 1 Find Soup in the Food column.

Step 2 Look across the row to the Tally column. There are 9 tallies.

Answer 9 students ate soup for lunch.

Common Error *Alert*

Students might incorrectly read a table to solve a problem. In order to find the correct information, students might need to highlight the row they want in one color and the column they want in another color. The overlapped section is the answer.

Intervention Strategy — Interpersonal Learners

Materials: paper, markers

Have students interview each other to find out their favorite ice cream flavor: vanilla, chocolate, or other.

Have students create a table in which to record the responses. The table should be titled *Favorite Ice Cream Flavor* and have three columns: *Flavor*, *Tally*, and *Number of Students*. The rows are labeled: *Vanilla*, *Chocolate*, and *Other*.

Have students share their tables with the class.

Math Coach Notes

Strategies

1. Practice reading across rows and up and down columns to find answers. Encourage students to use their fingers to go across rows and up and down columns to find answers.
2. Encourage students to look for tables in newspapers, magazines, and other textbooks.

Guided Practice

Direct students to complete Exercises 1–3 in Guided Practice.

Exercise 3 First, have students find the number of students who chose red and green. Then, have them subtract to find the answer.

Problem-Solving Practice

Guide students through the four-step problem-solving plan to complete Exercise 4. Have students use the table to answer the questions.

- **How many people chose spring?** 12
- **How many people chose winter?** 7
- **What operation gives you a sum?** addition

Ask students to check their work using the strategy suggested in the Check step. Students can count the tally marks for spring and winter to solve the problem.

Using Manipulatives

Connecting Cubes Use connecting cubes as tally marks. Place one cube for each tally mark. When there are 5 cubes, connect the cubes to make a group of 5.

On-Hand Manipulatives Use tape to create a table on the floor. Students can use rulers or pencils to represent tally marks.

Name _____

▶ Guided Practice

1. How many people chose blue? __6__ people

2. How many people chose green? __4__ people

3. How many more people chose red than green?

   __9__ − __4__ = __5__ more people

Favorite Color		
Color	Tally	Number of People
Blue	HHT I	6
Green	IIII	4
Red	HHT IIII	9

Problem-Solving Practice

4. How many people chose <u>spring and winter</u> as their favorite season?

			Favorite Season		

Season	Tally	Number of People
Fall	HHT HHT	10
Spring	HHT HHT II	12
Summer	HHT HHT HHT	15
Winter	HHT III	7

Understand Underline key words.

Plan Write a number sentence.

Solve __12__ spring votes + __7__ winter votes

__19__ people chose spring and winter.

Check Count the tally marks for spring and winter.

GO on

Are They Getting It? ?

Check students' understanding of tables by drawing this table on the board. Ask students to point out the correct and incorrect statements and explain their reasoning.

Favorite Game		
Game	Tally	Number of Students
Chase	HHT III	8
Duck-Duck-Goose	II	2
Hide and Seek	HHT HHT	10

1. Two people like Hide and Seek. This is incorrect. Ten people like Hide and Seek.

2. Duck-Duck-Goose is the favorite game of 10 people. This is incorrect. It is the favorite game of 2 people.

3. Six more people like Chase than Duck-Duck-Goose. This is correct.

▶ Practice on Your Own

Playground Equipment at Shull Park		
Equipment	Tally	Total
Seesaws	IIII	4
Slides	ⱵⱵ I	6
Swings	ⱵⱵ III	8

5 How many swings are on the playground? __8__ swings

6 How many slides are on the playground? __6__ slides

7 How many more swings are on the playground than seesaws? __4__ more

8 How many swings, seesaws, and slides are on the playground in all? __18__ in all

9 WRITING IN ▶MATH   There are 20 students in Cameron's class. How many boys are in his class? Explain.

Students in Cameron's Class		
Gender	Tally	Total
Boys	?	?
Girls	ⱵⱵ ⱵⱵ I	11

There are 9 boys in Cameron's class.
20 − 11 = 9

Vocabulary Check   Complete.

10 A __table__ has a title and labels and is used to organize data.

STOP

308   three hundred eight

Math Challenge

Follow Directions

Have students develop a survey they could conduct. Example: number of siblings.

Have students collect the data by surveying their classmates.

Provide students with an outline of a table. Students should title the table and complete the row and column headings. Then students can add the data they collected.

Allow students to share their findings with the class.

Practice on Your Own

Direct students to p. 308 in their student books. Have students complete Exercises 5–10 independently. You may need to review the directions of each section before students begin.

④ Assess

See It, Do It, Say It, Write It

Bottles of Paint		
Color	Tally	Number of Bottles
Blue	ⱵⱵ II	
Red	ⱵⱵ	
Yellow	ⱵⱵ I	

Step 1   Copy the table. Fill in the tally column for each color. Leave the number column blank.

Step 2   Have students copy the table and fill in the number column for each color.

Step 3   Have students explain how they determined each number.

Step 4   Have students add another row labeled Green. Tell students to show 8 bottles of green paint. Ask students to write one sentence about each paint color.

Looking Ahead: Pre-teach

In the next lesson, students will learn about bar graphs.

Example   How many people like the two-step? 2

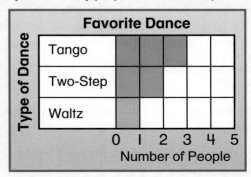

1. How many people like the waltz? 1

2. Which dance is most popular? Tango

Lesson Planner

Math Objective   Read bar graphs.

Vocabulary   data, bar graph

Materials/Manipulatives   connecting cubes, crayons, grid paper, counters

Chapter Resource Masters

- CRM Vocabulary and English Language Development (p. A225)
- CRM Skill Practice (p. A226)
- CRM Problem-Solving-Practice (p. A227)
- CRM Homework Practice (p. A228)

1 Introduce

Vocabulary

Vocabulary Relationships   There is a direct relationship between the length of the bars on a bar graph and the data. When comparing bars, the longer bars indicate greater amounts. Equal bars show equal amounts.

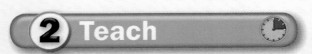

2 Teach

Key Concept

Foundational Skills and Concepts   After students have read through the Key Concept box, guide them through the following questions

- **How many students voted cheese as their favorite snack?** 4

- **How many more students voted for crackers than fruit?** 2

- **All together, how many students voted for their favorite snack?** 16

Name _____

Read Bar Graphs

Key Concept

You can read **data** from a **bar graph**.

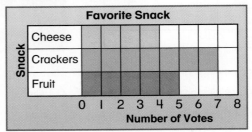

Each bar shows a different snack food. The length of the bar shows the number of students who voted for the snack.

Vocabulary

data   numbers or symbols that show information

bar graph   a graph that uses bars to show data

Bar graphs can be shown another way. The bars on this graph look different but show the same data.

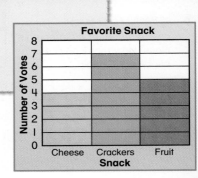

Chapter 9   Lesson 4

three hundred nine **309**

Copyright © Macmillan/McGraw-Hill • Glencoe, a division of The McGraw-Hill Companies, Inc.

English Learner Strategy

Understanding the Bars on a Graph

Students might have difficulty translating the bars on a graph into numbers. Have students use connecting cubes to represent the numbers in the graph from the Key Concept box.

Have students connect 4, 7, and 5 cubes to represent the bars from the Favorite Snack graph. Then, allow students to use the cubes to answer the questions from the Foundational Skills and Concepts section.

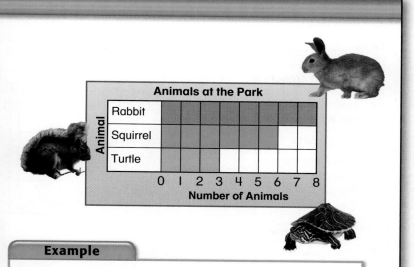

Animals at the Park

Animal	0	1	2	3	4	5	6	7	8
Rabbit									
Squirrel									
Turtle									

Number of Animals

Example

How many turtles are at the park?

Step 1   Find the bar for Turtle.
Step 2   Follow the bar to the right.
Step 3   Find the length of the bar. 3

Answer   There are 3 turtles at the park.

Step-by-Step Practice

How many squirrels are at the park?

Step 1   Find the bar for __**Squirrel**__.

Step 2   Follow the bar to the right.

Step 3   Find the length of the bar. __6__

Answer   There are __6__ squirrels at the park.

310   three hundred ten

How many oak trees are at the park?

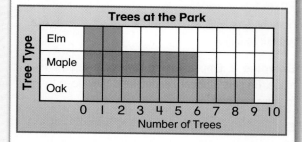

Trees at the Park

Tree Type	0	1	2	3	4	5	6	7	8	9	10
Elm											
Maple											
Oak											

Number of Trees

Step 1 Find the bar for Oak.

Step 2 Follow the bar to the right.

Step 3 Find the length of the bar. 9

Answer There are 9 oak trees at the park.

⚠ **Common Error** *Alert*

Students sometimes count the lines on bar graphs instead of looking at the scale. This leads to incorrect answers if they include the line marking zero or if the scale increments do not increase by one. Encourage students to use the scale provided on the graphs.

Intervention Strategy   **Kinesthetic Learners**

Materials: counters

Have students place 3 counters on the blue bar, 2 on the red, and 4 on the white. Then have students look at the counters to answer the following questions.

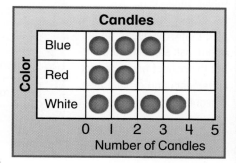

Candles

Color	0	1	2	3	4	5
Blue						
Red						
White						

Number of Candles

• **How many candles are white?** 4

• **How many more blue candles are there than red candles?** 1

• **How many blue and white candles are there all together?** 7

3 Practice

Guided Practice

Direct students to complete Exercises 1–3 in Guided Practice.

Exercise 2 Emphasize the key words *daisies and roses*. Be sure students understand they need to add to solve the problem.

Exercise 3 Emphasize the key words *how many more*. Be sure students understand they need to subtract to solve the problem.

Problem-Solving Practice

Guide students through the four-step problem-solving plan to complete Exercise 4. Have students use the bar graph to answer the question.

- **What does *twice as many* mean?** Add that number two times or multiply by 2.

- **How many roses did Maria plant?** 4

- **What is 4 + 4?** 8

Ask students to check their work using the strategy suggested in the Check step. Students can draw a picture to solve the problem.

Using Manipulatives

Connecting Cubes Students can use connecting cubes to create bars of different lengths, colors, and orientations.

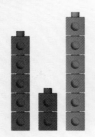 

On-Hand Manipulatives Have students use strips of graph paper to make the bars on a bar graph.

Name _____

▶ Guided Practice

1. How many daisies are in the garden?
   __7__ daisies

2. How many daisies and roses are in the garden?
   __7__ + __4__ = __11__ daisies and roses

3. How many more sunflowers are in the garden than roses? __5__ − __4__ = __1__ more sunflower

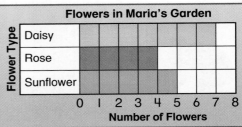

Flowers in Maria's Garden

Flower Type: Daisy, Rose, Sunflower — Number of Flowers (0 1 2 3 4 5 6 7 8)

Problem-Solving Practice

4. Maria wants to plant <u>twice as many daffodils</u> in her garden <u>as roses</u>. <u>How many daffodils will she plant?</u>

   Understand Underline key words.

   Plan Write a multiplication sentence.

   Solve There are __4__ roses in Maria's garden.
   __4__ roses × __2__ = __8__ daffodils
   Maria will plant __8__ daffodils.

   Check Draw a picture. Draw two groups of 4 flowers.

GO on

Chapter 9 Lesson 4

three hundred eleven **311**

Are They Getting It? ?

Check students' understanding of bar graphs by drawing this graph on the board. Ask students to point out the correct and incorrect statements and explain their reasoning.

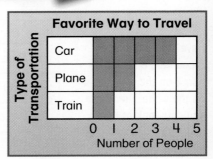

Favorite Way to Travel

Type of Transportation: Car, Plane, Train — Number of People (0 1 2 3 4 5)

1. One person likes traveling by train. This is correct.

2. All together, eight people chose their favorite way to travel. This is incorrect. Seven people chose their favorite way to travel.

3. The most people chose plane as favorite way to travel. This is incorrect. The most people chose car.

Mrs. Timon's Class: Birds Spotted

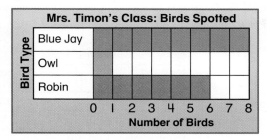

Bird Type									
Blue Jay									
Owl									
Robin									

0 1 2 3 4 5 6 7 8
Number of Birds

5 How many robins did the class spot? ___6___ robins

6 Which bird did the class spot only 1 time? **owl**

7 How many birds did the class spot in all? __15__ birds in all

8 How many more blue jays did the class spot than owls?

___7___ more blue jays than owls

9 ▶WRITING IN▶MATH Mrs. Timon's class spotted 3 more squirrels than owls. How many squirrels did Mrs. Timon's class spot? Explain.

Mrs. Timon's class spotted 4 squirrels. They saw 1 owl, and 1 + 3 = 4.

Vocabulary Check Complete.

10 A graph that uses bars to show data is called a

<u>bar graph</u>.

STOP

312 three hundred twelve

Math Challenge

Changing the Bars

Ask students to discuss the data shown in the bar graph.

Remind students that data can be shown in a variety of ways. Have students show the data in a vertical bar graph.

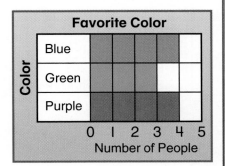

Favorite Color

Color						
Blue						
Green						
Purple						

0 1 2 3 4 5
Number of People

Challenge students to collect data and display it in a vertical and horizontal bar graph.

Practice on Your Own

Direct students to p. 312 in their student books. Have students complete Exercises 5–10 independently. You may need to review the directions of each section before students begin.

(4) Assess

See It, Do It, Say It, Write It

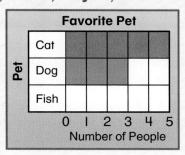

Favorite Pet

Pet						
Cat						
Dog						
Fish						

0 1 2 3 4 5
Number of People

Step 1 Display the bar graph. Explain how to read the data from the graph. Tell how many people like dogs.

Step 2 Tell students that 4 people like fish. Have them shade the graph to show this information.

Step 3 Ask students how many students like cats.

Step 4 Have students explain in writing how to find which type of pet was chosen by the most people.

Looking Ahead: Pre-teach

In the next lesson, students will learn about using data from a table to make bar graphs.

Example Use the data in the table to make a bar graph. What should the rows of the bar graph be labeled? Boating, Skiing, Swimming

Favorite Water Activity

Activity	Tally	Number of People
Boating	⊞∣	5
Skiing	∣∣∣	3
Swimming	⊞∣∣	7

Have students answer the following questions.

1. Which activity will have the longest bar? Swimming

2. Which activity will have the shortest bar? Skiing

Formative Assessment

Use the Progress Check to assess students' mastery of the previous lessons. Have students review the lesson indicated for the problems they answered incorrectly.

⚠ **Common Error** *Alert*

Reading a Table Students may incorrectly look across the rows in a table. Have them use a piece of paper to underline the row they are reading.

Exercise 3 Tell students when a problem includes the words *in all*, it gives the clue to add or find the sum.

Exercise 5 Be sure students understand that the question is giving the length of the bar. Students need to find which bar has a length of 6.

Name _____

Progress Check 2 (Lessons 9-3 and 9-4)

Use the table to answer each question.

1 How many water bottles were recycled?

  __17__ water bottles

2 What item had 9 recycled?

  __newspapers__

3 How many items were recycled in all? __38__ items in all

Recycled Items

Item	Tally	Number of Items
Cans	ⵑⵑⵑ ⵑⵑⵑ ‖	12
Newspapers	ⵑⵑⵑ ‖‖‖	9
Water Bottles	ⵑⵑⵑ ⵑⵑⵑ ⵑⵑⵑ ‖	17

Use the bar graph to answer each question.

Beach Hunt

(bar graph: Beach Item vs. Number Found, 0–8. Crab, Seashell, Starfish)

4 How many crabs were found? __4__ crabs

5 Which item was found 6 times? __seashell__

6 How many more seashells were found than starfish?

  __5__ more seashells than starfish.

Data-Driven Decision Making

Students missing Exercises . . .	Have trouble with . . .	Should review and practice . . .
1–3	reading tables.	SSG Lesson 9-3, p. 305 CRM Skills Practice, p. A222
4–6	reading bar graphs.	SSG Lesson 9-4, p. 309 CRM Skills Practice, p. A226

Name _____

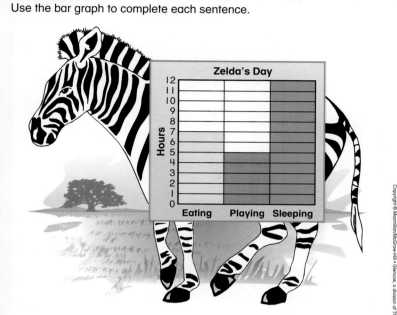

«« Replay **Read the ZE-BAR Graph!**

Use the bar graph to complete each sentence.

Zelda's Day

1. Zelda sleeps for _12_ hours each day.
2. Zelda spends the least time **playing**.
3. Zelda sleeps _7_ hours more than she plays.
4. Zelda spends _19_ hours eating and sleeping each day.
5. Zelda spends 2 more hours eating than **playing**.

314 three hundred fourteen

Replay

Use the Replay activity to review and reinforce the concepts and skills presented in Lessons 9-3 and 9-4.

Instructions

Have students read the directions at the top of the student page.

Note that the bar graph describes how Zelda the Zebra spends her day. There are 24 hours in a day. So the hours Zelda spends eating, sleeping, and playing total 24 hours.

Student Technology

Students can use the following technology resources to reinforce chapter content.

- 💿 StudentWorks™ Plus
- **Math Online** ⟩ macmillanmh.com
- eGlossary

Lesson Notes

Lesson Planner

Math Objective Use data from tables to make bar graphs.

Vocabulary data, table, bar graph

Materials/Manipulatives markers, paper, colored paper squares, color tiles, grid paper, counters, connecting cubes

Chapter Resource Masters

- CRM Vocabulary and English Language Development (p. A229)
- CRM Skill Practice (p. A230)
- CRM Problem-Solving-Practice (p. A231)
- CRM Homework Practice (p. A232)

1 Introduce

Vocabulary

Vocabulary Relationships

Draw the table and bar graph from the Key Concept box on the board. Explain that the bar graph and table present the same information. Draw a red circle around the tally marks for Movie. Then draw a red circle around the bar that shows Movie.

Have students color code the other tallies and bars.

2 Teach

Key Concept

Foundational Skills and Concepts After students have read through the Key Concept box, guide them through the following questions.

- **How many people like going to movies?** 9
- **Which is the least popular activity?** museum
- **All together, how many people picked their favorite weekend activity?** 19

Name _____

Make Bar Graphs

Key Concept

You can use **data** from a **table** to make a **bar graph**.

Weekend Activity

Activity	Tally	Number of People
Movie	$\cancel{||||}\ ||||$	9
Museum	$|||$	3
Park	$\cancel{||||}\ ||$	7

Weekend Activity

Activity									

Movie
Museum
Park

0 1 2 3 4 5 6 7 8 9
Number of People

The length of each bar matches the numbers in the table.

Vocabulary

data numbers or symbols that show information

table a way to organize data

bar graph a graph that uses bars to show data

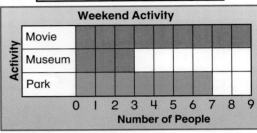

Chapter 9 Lesson 5

three hundred fifteen **315**

English Learner Strategy

Materials: connecting cubes, counters

Students may need assistance transferring tally marks into bars.

Draw a table on the board that presents the following data. Favorite Type of Exercise: Biking—7 people; Running—3 people; Swimming—9 people.

Have students make a three-column chart on a sheet of paper. Label the columns: Biking, Running, Swimming.

Have students place 7 counters in the Biking column. Then have students connect 7 connecting cubes and place them in the Biking column. Explain that the connecting cubes represent bars on a bar graph.

Repeat for each type of exercise.

Example

Use the table to complete the bar graph.

Dogs Washed		
Dog Type	Tally	Number of Dogs
Collie	IIII	4
Lab	HH	5
Poodle	II	2

Dogs Washed

Dog Type — Collie, Lab, Poodle

Number of Dogs: 0 1 2 3 4 5

Step 1   Shade the bar for Collie to show 4.
Step 2   Shade the bar for Lab to show 5.
Step 3   Shade the bar for Poodle to show 2.

Step-by-Step Practice

Use the table to complete the bar graph.

Animals Groomed		
Animal Type	Tally	Number of Animals
Cat	III	3
Dog	HH	5
Horse	I	1

Animals Groomed

Animal Type — Cat, Dog, Horse

Number of Animals: 0 1 2 3 4 5

Step 1   Shade the bar for Cat to show **3**.
Step 2   Shade the bar for Dog to show **5**.
Step 3   Shade the bar for Horse to show **1**.

316   three hundred sixteen

Additional *Example*

Use the table to complete the bar graph.

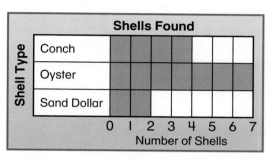

Shells Found		
Shell Type	Tally	Number of Shells
Conch	IIII	4
Oyster	HH II	7
Sand Dollar	II	2

Shells Found

Shell Type — Conch, Oyster, Sand Dollar

Number of Shells: 0 1 2 3 4 5 6 7

Step 1 Shade the bar for Conch to show 4.

Step 2 Shade the bar for Oyster to show 7.

Step 3 Shade the bar for Sand Dollar to show 2.

⚠ Common Error *Alert*

Students may incorrectly shade the bars on the graph. Have these students count the units in the bar they shaded and write it above or beside the bar. Students should be sure the number they wrote matches the number in the table.

Intervention Strategy   Kinesthetic Learners

Materials: grid paper, counters, markers

Have students create the horizontal bar graph shown below.

Siblings

	1	2	3	4	5	6	7	8	9	10
Brothers Only										
Sisters Only										
Brothers and Sisters										
None										

Number of Students

Ask each student to describe their siblings using one of the labels shown in the graph. As students answer, have them build a bar graph by placing a counter in each square. When the graph is complete, students can use markers to shade the bars around the counters.

3 Practice

Guided Practice

Direct students to complete Exercise 1 in
Guided Practice.

Exercise 1 Be sure the lengths of the bars equal the
number of people.

Problem-Solving Practice

Guide students through the four-step problem-solving
plan to complete Exercise 2. Have students use the
table from Exercise 1 to answer the questions.

- **What are the key words?** how many more, pears
  than bananas

- **How many people like pears?** 7

- **How many people like bananas?** 3

Ask students to check their work using the strategy
suggested in the Check step. Students can work
backward to solve the problem.

Using Manipulatives

Color Tiles Students can use colored tiles to show
the bars in a bar graph.

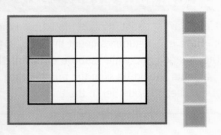

 On-Hand Manipulatives Students can use
squares of paper to show bars in a bar graph.
Be sure all of the squares are the same size before
comparing bar heights or lengths.

Name _____

▶ Guided Practice

1 Use the table to complete the bar graph.

Favorite Fruit		
Fruit	Tally	Number of People
Banana	|||	3
Orange	⫽⫽⫽		6
Pear	⫽⫽⫽ ||	7

Favorite Fruit

(bar graph: Number of People on vertical axis 0–8, Fruit on horizontal axis: Banana, Orange, Pear)

Problem-Solving Practice

2 How many more people chose
pears than bananas?

Understand Underline key words.

Plan Use the bar graph.

Solve How many people chose pears? __7__

How many people chose bananas? __3__

__7__ – __3__ = __4__ more people

Check Work backward. How many spaces taller
is "Pear" than "Banana"?

GO on

Are They Getting It? ❓

Check students' understanding of making bar graphs by drawing this
table on the board. Give students a blank bar graph and have them fill
in the data from the table. Ask students to point out the correct and
incorrect statements and explain their reasoning.

Coins		
Coin Type	Tally	Number of Coins
Penny	⫽⫽⫽ ⫽⫽⫽	10
Nickel	⫽⫽⫽ |||	8
Dime	⫽⫽⫽ ⫽⫽⫽ ||	12

1. The title of the graph is Coins. This is correct.

2. The length of the Penny bar is 12. This is incorrect. Based on the
table, the length is 10.

Use the tables to complete each bar graph.

3

Siblings		
Age	Tally	Number of Siblings
Older	|||	3
Twin			1
Younger	||||	4

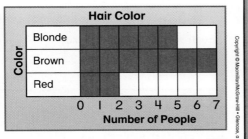

Siblings

4

Hair Color		
Color	Tally	Number of People
Blonde	⊮⊣⊩	5
Brown	⊮⊣⊩ ||	7
Red	||	2

Hair Color

5 **WRITING IN ▶MATH** Look at the data in Exercise 4. If 3 more people join the group with red hair, how many people would have red hair in all? Explain.

5 people would have red hair in all.

2 + 3 = 5

Vocabulary Check Complete.

6 You can display ___**data**___ from a table in a bar graph. STOP

318 three hundred eighteen

Copyright © Macmillan/McGraw-Hill Glencoe, a division of The McGraw-Hill Companies, Inc.

Math Challenge

Back to the Table

Have students create a table of the data displayed in the bar graph below.

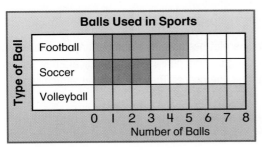

Balls Used in Sports

Practice on Your Own

Direct students to p. 318 in their student books. Have students complete Exercises 3–6 independently. You may need to review the directions of each section before students begin.

4 **Assess**

See It, Do It, Say It, Write It

Shirts		
Type of Shirt	Tally	Number of Shirts
Long Sleeve	||||	4
Short Sleeve	||	2
T-Shirt	⊮⊣⊩	5

Shirts	
Type of Shirt	
Long Sleeve	
Short Sleeve	
T-Shirt	

Number of Shirts

Step 1 Draw the table on the board. Then draw a blank bar graph. Shade the bar for Long Sleeve.

Step 2 Have students use the data in the table to shade the bars for Short Sleeve and T-Shirt.

Step 3 Have students verbally explain how they completed the bar graph.

Step 4 Have students write two sentences about the data.

Looking Ahead: Pre-teach

In the next lesson, students will learn about line plots.

Example How many times were 0 touchdowns made in a game? 1 time

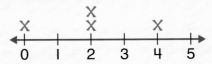

Touchdowns in a Game

Have students use the line plot to answer the question.

1. What was the most common number of touchdowns made in a game? 2 touchdowns

Lesson Notes

Lesson Planner

Math Objective   Read line plots.

Vocabulary   line plot, data

Materials/Manipulatives   markers, paper, masking tape, beans, buttons, counters

Chapter Resource Masters

- [CRM] Vocabulary and English Language Development (p. A233)
- [CRM] Skill Practice (p. A234)
- [CRM] Problem-Solving-Practice (p. A235)
- [CRM] Homework Practice (p. A236)

 1 Introduce

Vocabulary

Nonexamples   Display examples of bar graphs, line plots, and picture graphs. Tell the class that these are not line plots.

A line plot is a number line that shows the frequency of an event. Then Xs are used to show how many times that event occurred.

Draw the line plot shown below on the board.

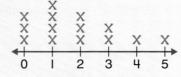

Number of Siblings

 2 Teach

Key Concept

Foundational Skills and Concepts   After students have read through the Key Concept box, guide them through the following questions.

- **How many kickball players kicked 2 homeruns?**
  3 kickball players

- **What was the most number of homeruns kicked by a kickball player?** 7 homeruns

319 Chapter 9 Data Analysis

Name _____

Line Plots

Key Concept

A **line plot** is another way to show **data**.

The line plot below shows the number of homeruns kicked by kickball players.

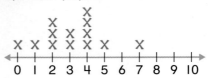

Homeruns Scored

Each X equals 1 kickball player.

There are 2 Xs above the 3.
So, 2 kickball players kicked 3 homeruns.

Vocabulary

line plot   a graph that uses columns of Xs above a number line to show frequency of data

data   numbers or symbols that show information

There are 0 Xs above the 6.
So, 0 kickball players kicked 6 homeruns.

Chapter 9   Lesson 6

three hundred nineteen **319**

English Learner Strategy

Lines

Discuss with students the different meanings of the word *line.*

A line can be something you stand in to wait your turn or something you draw on your paper.

In math, a line plot begins with a number line. A number line is a line with number labels. The plot uses Xs to indicate how often each value on the number line occurs. They are stacked vertically on top of the line.

Example

This line plot shows the number of points scored on a game show. How many people scored 3 points?

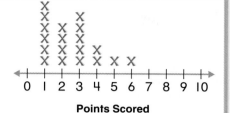

Points Scored

Step 1   Find 3 on the line plot.

Step 2   Count the number of Xs above the 3.
1, 2, 3, 4, 5

Answer   5 people scored 3 points.

Step-by-Step Practice

This line plot shows the number of hops frogs made in a jumping contest. How many frogs made 12 hops?

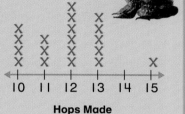

Hops Made

Step 1   Find __12__ on the line plot.

Step 2   Count the number of Xs above the __12__.
__1__ , __2__ , __3__ , __4__ , __5__ , __6__

Answer   __6__ frogs made 12 hops.

320   three hundred twenty

Additional *Example*

This line plot shows the number of questions students answered correctly on a math quiz. How many students answered 8 questions correctly?

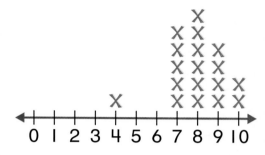

Correct Questions on a Quiz

Step 1 Find 8 on the line plot.

Step 2 Count the number of Xs above the 8.
1, 2, 3, 4, 5, 6

Answer 6 people correctly answered 8 questions.

⚠ **Common Error** *Alert*

Students might confuse the number line value with the number of Xs above it. Have students make a statement about what each X means as they place it on the line plot. For example: "One more student has 3 pets," when putting an X above 3 on a "Number of Pets" line plot.

Math Coach Notes

Strategy

Be sure students understand that the number lines on line plots do not always have to start with 0. Point out the line plot in the Step-by-Step Practice. Explain to students that this number line starts at 10 and ends at 15.

Intervention Strategy   Kinesthetic Learners

Materials: masking tape, marker

Use masking tape to create a number line on the floor. Write the tick marks on the line with a marker.

Have students make a human line plot by asking a question to which there is a numerical answer. For example, "How many pets do you have?"

Have students stand where they would put an X for their answer. For example, if a student has 3 pets, the student stands above the 3. If more than one student has 3 pets, they stand in a line above the 3.

Guided Practice

Direct students to complete Exercises 1–3 in Guided Practice.

Exercise 2 Students need to find the difference of two numbers to solve this problem. Be sure students count the number of players who scored 3 baskets and 5 baskets before subtracting.

Problem-Solving Practice

Guide students through the four-step problem-solving plan to complete Exercise 4. Have students use the line plot to answer the question.

- **What does *in all* mean in this exercise?** add the number of players that scored baskets

Ask students to check their work using the strategy suggested in the Check step. Students can count the total number of Xs on the line plot to solve the problem.

Using Manipulatives

Counters Students can put counters above a number line instead of Xs. This tactile approach will assist kinesthetic learners.

On-Hand Manipulatives Students can use beans or buttons as counters to place above the number line in a line plot.

Name _____

▶ Guided Practice

This line plot shows the number of baskets made by players during a game. Use the line plot to answer each question.

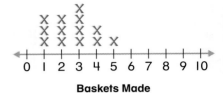

Baskets Made

1. How many players made 4 baskets? __2__ players

2. How many more players made 3 baskets than 5 baskets?

   __3__ more players

3. How many baskets did the greatest number of players make?

   __3__ baskets

Problem-Solving Practice

4. How many players made baskets in all?

Understand	Underline key words.
Plan	Write a number sentence.
Solve	Find the sum of the number of players that made 1, 2, 3, 4, and 5 baskets.

__3__ + __3__ + __4__ + __2__ + __1__ = __13__ players

Check Count the total number of Xs on the line plot.

 GO on

Chapter 9 Lesson 6   three hundred twenty-one **321**

Copyright © Macmillan/McGraw-Hill • Glencoe, a division of The McGraw-Hill Companies, Inc.

Are They Getting It?

Check students' understanding of line plots by drawing this line plot on the board. Ask students to point out the correct and incorrect statements and explain their reasoning.

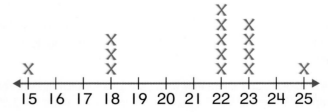

Number of Students in a Class

1. Four classes have 23 students. This is correct.

2. The largest class has 22 students. This is incorrect. The largest class has 25 students.

► Practice on Your Own

This line plot shows the number of goals made by hockey players over a season. Use the line plot to answer each question.

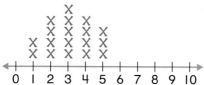

Goals Made

5 How many players made 5 goals? __3__ players

6 How many goals did 2 players make? __1__ goal

7 How many more players made 3 goals than 2 goals? __1__ more

8 🖊 WRITING IN ►MATH   Julie says that 15 players are shown in the line plot. Is Julie correct? Explain.

No, Julie is not correct. There are 18 Xs shown in the line plot. So, there are 18 players.

Vocabulary Check   Complete.

9 A graph that uses columns of Xs to display data is called a __line plot__.

STOP

322   three hundred twenty-two

Math Challenge

Line Up

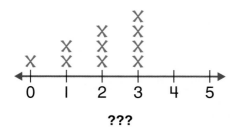

???

Have students write a story that this line plot could describe. Sample answer: In our class, there is one student that has 0 pencils, two students that have 1 pencil, three students that have 2 pencils, and four students that have 3 pencils.

Practice on Your Own

Direct students to p. 322 in their student books. Have students complete Exercises 5–9 independently. You may need to review the directions of each section before students begin.

4 Assess

See It, Do It, Say It, Write It

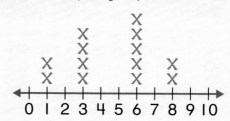

Hours Spent Doing Homework Each Week

Step 1 Identify each part of the line plot. Tell students that 4 students spend 3 hours doing homework each week.

Step 2 Have students circle the Xs that represent the students that do 1 hour of homework each week.

Step 3 Ask students to identify how many students do 6 hours of homework each week. Have students explain how they determined the answer.

Step 4 Have students write the number of students that do 8 hours of homework each week. Ask students to write three sentences about the line plot.

Chapter 9

Progress Check 3

Formative Assessment

Use the Progress Check to assess students' mastery of the previous lessons. Have students review the lesson indicated for the problems they answered incorrectly.

⚠ Common Error *Alert*

Line Plots Students may count more than one occurrence for each X. Remind them that one X represents one occurrence for the particular event.

Exercise 1 Students may not shade the bar lengths correctly. Be sure students make each bar length equal to the number of tally marks in the table.

Exercise 2 Students may misinterpret the question. Remind students that they are looking for the number of slices eaten by the most students, not the most slices eaten by a student.

Name _____

Progress Check 3 (Lessons 9-5 and 9-6)

1 Use the data in the table to complete the bar graph.

Favorite Pizza Topping		
Topping	Tally	Number of Votes
Cheese	₩₩ I	6
Pepperoni	III	3
Sausage	₩₩	5

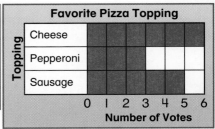

This line plot shows the number of pizza slices eaten by a third grade class for lunch one day. Use the line plot to answer each question.

2 How many slices of pizza did most students eat?

__2__ slices

3 How many students ate 3 slices of pizza?

__4__ students

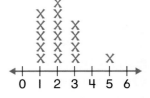

Slices of Pizza Eaten

4 There are no Xs over the 4. What does this mean?

__It means that no students ate 4 slices of pizza.__

Chapter 9   Progress Check   three hundred twenty-three **323**

Data-Driven Decision Making

Students missing Exercises . . .	Have trouble with . . .	Should review and practice . . .
1	using data from a table to make a bar graph.	[SSG] Lesson 9-5, p. 315 [CRM] Skills Practice, p. A230
2–3	reading line plots.	[SSG] Lesson 9-6, p. 319 [CRM] Skills Practice, p. A.234
4	problem-solving that involves reading line plots.	[SSG] Lesson 9-6, p. 321 [CRM] Problem-Solving Practice, p. A.235

323 Chapter 9 Data Analysis

Name _____

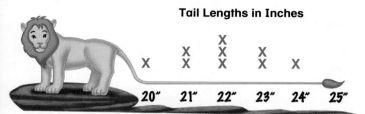

«« Replay   Make a Lion-Plot

Use the clues to place the X s on the line plot.
The line plot shows the lengths of 9 lion tails.

Tail Lengths in Inches

```
                    X
            X       X       X
    X       X       X       X
    X       X       X       X       X
   20"     21"     22"     23"     24"     25"
```

① Two lions have a 21-inch long tail.

② There is 1 lion with a tail 20 inches long.

③ Three lions have a 22-inch long tail.

④ No lion has a tail 25 inches long.

⑤ There is one lion with a tail 24 inches long.

⑥ Two lions have a 23-inch long tail.

324 three hundred twenty-four

Copyright © Macmillan/McGraw-Hill • Glencoe, a division of The McGraw-Hill Companies, Inc.

Use the Replay activity to review and reinforce the
concepts and skills presented in Lessons 9-5 and 9-6.

Instructions

Have students read the directions at the top of the
student page.

Make sure students follow the clues correctly to create
their line plot. Encourage students to revisit the clues
after completing the line plot. If they followed the clues
correctly, each statement will be true of the line plot.

Student Technology

Students can use the following technology resources to
reinforce chapter content.

- 💿 StudentWorks™ Plus

- **Math Online** ▷ macmillanmh.com

- eGlossary

Vocabulary

If students have difficulty answering Exercises 1–3, use the page references below to review the vocabulary words, or refer them to the glossary.

bar graph (p. 309)
line plot (p. 319)
picture graph (p. 299)

Vocabulary Review Strategies

Comparison Chart   As a class, create a chart that shows the similarities and differences among the different data displays learned in Chapter 9. Review what each display looks like and how it is read.

Concepts

The exercises in this section are grouped to cover content from each lesson in the chapter.

Exercise 4: Lesson 9-3 (p. 305)
Exercises 5–6: Lesson 9-2 (p. 299)
Exercise 7: Lesson 9-5 (p. 315)
Exercises 8–10: Lesson 9-4 (p. 309)

Find **Extra Practice** for these concepts in the Practice Worksheets, pp. A213–A236.

Name _____

Review

Vocabulary

Use the Word Bank to complete.

Word Bank

bar graph

line plot

picture graph

1   **Favorite Farm Animal**

Cow				
Horse				
Pig				

picture graph

2   **Favorite Color**

Color: Blue, Green, Orange
0 1 2 3 4 5
Number of Votes

bar graph

3
```
        X X X
        X X X   X
X X X X X X
5 6 7 8 9 10
```
line plot

Jumps with a Jump Rope

Concepts

4   How many veggie sandwiches were sold?
__17__

Number of Sandwiches Sold		
Sandwich	Tally	Number Sold
Ham	ЖЖ ЖЖ II	12
Tuna	ЖЖ IIII	9
Veggie	ЖЖ ЖЖ ЖЖ II	17

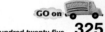
GO on

Copyright © Macmillan/McGraw-Hill • Glencoe, a division of The McGraw-Hill Companies, Inc.

---

5 Which dog biscuit flavor sold the greatest number? **milk**

6 How many peanut butter biscuits were sold? **15**

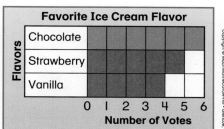

Number of Dog Biscuits Sold	
Milk	🦴 🦴 🦴 🦴
Mint	🦴 🦴
Peanut Butter	🦴 🦴 🦴

Key: 🦴 = 5 biscuits

7 Use the table to complete the bar graph and answer each question.

Favorite Ice Cream Flavor

Flavors	Tally	Number of Votes
Chocolate	⦀⦀ I	6
Strawberry	⦀⦀	5
Vanilla	⦀⦀⦀	4

Favorite Ice Cream Flavor

Flavors: Chocolate, Strawberry, Vanilla

Number of Votes: 0 1 2 3 4 5 6

8 How many people chose vanilla? **4** people

9 How many more people chose chocolate than strawberry?

1 more

10 How many people were surveyed in all?

15 people in all

STOP

326 three hundred twenty-six

FOLDABLES®
Study Organizer

Dinah Zike's Foldables®

Have students use the Foldable they created at the beginning of the chapter to review and reinforce the concepts and skills they learned during the chapter. (See Chapter Resource Masters p. A209 for instructions.)

Intervention Strategy

Use this Intervention Strategy activity at any point during the chapter to reinforce the concepts and skills presented in the chapter.

Displaying Data

1. In the beginning of the chapter, students collected data on types of pets. As you progress through the chapter, have students practice displaying data in the various data displays. Use the pet data to create a:

- Venn diagram.
- pictograph.
- picture graph.
- table.
- bar graph.
- line plot.

Students can pose questions to one another about their data displays.

Allow students to create graphs using paper and pencil or manipulatives.

Classroom Management

Roundtable Have students work in groups of four. Assign each group a type of graph.

The first student writes the name of the graph at the top of the page and something they know about the graph.

Pass the paper to the next student who will write another fact about the graph.

Continue passing until all students in the group have added their thoughts.

Have groups review their list to be sure it is correct before presenting it to the class.

Chapter Resource Masters

Additional forms of the Chapter Test are available.

Test Format	Where to Find it
Chapter Test	 Math Online macmillanmh.com
Blackline Masters	Assessment Masters, p. 115

ExamView®
Assessment Suite

Customize and create multiple versions of your chapter test and their answer keys. All of these questions from the chapter tests are available on ExamView® Assessment Suite.

Advance TRACKER

Online Assessment and Reporting
macmillanmh.com

This online assessment tool allows teachers to track student progress with easily accessible comprehensive reports available for every student. Assess students using any internet-ready computer.

Alternative Assessment

Use Projects Have students survey a group of people by asking the following question.

• What is your favorite type of movie?

Give the following choices: drama, action, comedy.

Have students display the data in a pictograph, table, bar graph, and line plot. Ask students to share their findings with the class.

Name _____

Chapter Test

1 Classify and sort. Draw the figures in the Venn Diagram.

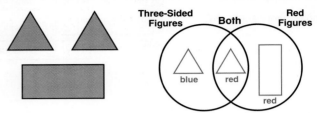

Use the bar graph to answer each question.

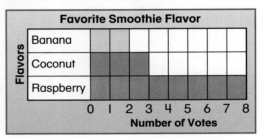

2 How many people chose banana? __2__

3 How many more people chose raspberry than banana? __6__

4 How many people chose coconut and banana? __5__

5 How many people voted in all? __13__

GO on

6 ## Who is Correct?

Ethan and Matt say how many goldfish are in the tank.

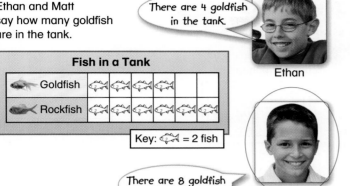

There are 4 goldfish in the tank.

Ethan

There are 8 goldfish in a tank.

Matt

Fish in a Tank

🐟 Goldfish	🐟	🐟	🐟	🐟		
🐟 Rockfish	🐟	🐟	🐟	🐟	🐟	

Key: 🐟 = 2 fish

Circle the correct answer. Explain.

<u>**Matt is correct. He used the key to tell how many goldfish are in the tank. Each symbol equals 2 fish. 4 × 2 = 8**</u>

This line plot shows the number of fish caught by local fishers. Use the line plot to answer each question.

7 How many fish did the greatest number of fishers catch?

<u>20</u> fish

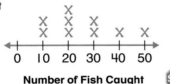

8 How many fishers caught 30 fish? <u>2</u> fishers

STOP

Number of Fish Caught

Who Is Correct?

Diagnostic Teaching

- Ethan said there are 4 goldfish in the tank. This is incorrect because according to the key, each symbol equals 2 fish.

- Matt said there are 8 goldfish in the tank. This is correct. He understood that each symbol represents 2 fish.

Learning from Mistakes

Missed Questions   Review commonly missed questions as a small group or class. Ask students to share their methods of answering each question. Try to point out when any errors occur and take corrective measures.

Data-Driven Decision Making

Students missing Exercises . . .	Have trouble with . . .	Should review and practice . . .
1	classifying and sorting objects in a Venn diagram.	SSG Lesson 9-1, p. 295 CRM Skills Practice, p. A214
2–5	reading bar graphs.	SSG Lesson 9-4, p. 309 CRM Skills Practice, p. A226
6	reading pictographs.	SSG Lesson 9-2, p. 299 CRM Skills Practice, p. A218
7–8	reading line plots.	SSG Lesson 9-6, p. 319 CRM Skills Practice, p. A234

!▲ **Diagnose Student Errors**

Survey student responses for each item. Class trends may indicate common errors and misconceptions.

1. 2: correct
3: chose number of elephants
4: chose number of giraffes
5: does not understand how to read a picture graph

2. 1: correct
2: found how many more giraffes than lions
3: does not understand how to read a picture graph
4: does not understand how to read a picture graph

3. 1: chose how many people own 9 DVDs
3: chose how many people own 7 DVDs
4: correct
5: chose how many people own 6 DVDs

4. 3: does not understand how to read a table
6: chose the number of juice bottles
8: correct
10: chose the number of soda bottles

5. 6: chose only the number of juice bottles
10: chose only the number of soda bottles
14: found how many juice and water bottles
16: correct

6. 2: correct
3: found how many more chose camping than picnics
5: found how many more chose camping than hiking
10: found how many chose hiking and picnics

7. Picnics: does not understand how to read a table
Camping: correct
Hiking: does not understand how to read a table
Fishing: does not understand how to read a table

8. 2: does not understand how to read a bar graph
3: chose the number of bears
4: correct
6: chose the number of bobcats

9. 3: chose only the number of bears
6: chose only the number of bobcats
9: correct
10: chose the number of foxes and bobcats

Name _____

Test Practice

Choose the correct answer.

1 How many lion cookie cutters are there?

Animal Cookie Cutters	
Elephant	🐘🐘🐘🐘
Giraffe	🦒🦒🦒🦒🦒
Lion	🦁🦁🦁

  2   3   4   5
  ●   ○   ○   ○

2 Look at the picture graph in Question 1. How many more giraffe than elephant cookie cutters are there?

  1   2   3   4
  ●   ○   ○   ○

3 How many people own 5 DVDs?

```
        X
   X    X        X
   X    X   X    X
   X    X   X    X
   X    X   X    X   X
  ---+---+---+---+---+---
   5   6   7   8   9
```
Number of DVDs Owned

  1   3   4   5
  ○   ○   ●   ○

4 How many water bottles were recycled?

Bottles Recycled		
Bottle	Tally	Total
Juice	卌 I	6
Soda	卌 卌	10
Water	卌 III	8

  3   6   8   10
  ○   ○   ●   ○

5 Look at the table in Question 4. How many juice and soda bottles were recycled?

  6   10   14   16
  ○   ○   ○   ●

6 How many more people chose picnics than hiking?

Favorite Activity		
Activity	Tally	Total
Camping	卌 IIII	9
Hiking	IIII	4
Picnics	卌 I	6

  2   3   5   10
  ●   ○   ○   ○

→ GO ON

Chapter 9   Test Practice

three hundred twenty-nine 329

---

10. 1: correct
2: found how many more bobcats than foxes
5: does not understand how to read a bar graph
7: found how many foxes and bears

11. ⬤ : chose a figure that is not four-sided

▬ : correct

▢ : chose a figure that is not shaded

◯ : chose a figure that is not four-sided or shaded

12. ◯ : correct

▬ : chose a figure that belongs in both sections

▢ : chose a figure that belongs in the four-sided figures section

▲ : chose a figure that belongs in the shaded figures section

7 Look at the table in Question 6. Which activity had the greatest number of votes?

○ Picnics   ● Camping
○ Hiking   ○ Fishing

8 How many foxes are in the forest?

Animals in a Forest

2   3   4   6
○   ○   ●   ○

9 Look at the bar graph in Question 8. How many bobcats and bears are in the forest?

3   6   9   10
○   ○   ●   ○

10 Look at the bar graph in Question 8. How many more foxes are in the forest than bears?

1   2   5   7
●   ○   ○   ○

11 Which figure goes in the **Both** section?

12 Look at the Venn diagram in Question 11. Which figure does not belong in the diagram?

STOP

Copyright © Macmillan/McGraw-Hill · Glencoe, a division of The McGraw-Hill Companies, Inc.

330 three hundred thirty

Test Practice

Diagnosing Student Errors and Misconceptions

Polls   When working on the Test Practice problems, have students write explanations of how they arrived at their answers on a separate sheet of paper. After the class has completed the Test Practice, solicit answers to each question. If you find a significant number of students missed a specific question, review the students' explanations and correct any misconceptions. You may also want to reteach the type of data display associated with any particular error.

Chapter 9 Test Practice **330**

268, 272, 278, 282, 296, 300, 306, 310, 316, 320

Intrapersonal Learners. *See* Learning Styles

Key Concept, 5, 7, 13, 17, 23, 29, 45, 49, 55, 59, 65, 69, 83, 87, 93, 97, 103, 107, 121, 125, 131, 135, 149, 153, 159, 163, 169, 173, 187, 192, 197, 201, 207, 211, 225, 229, 235, 239, 243, 257, 261, 267, 271, 277, 281, 295, 299, 305, 309, 315, 319

Key Vocabulary, 1, 43, 81, 119, 147, 185, 223, 255, 293

Kinesthetic Learners. *See* Learning Styles

Learning from Mistakes, 40, 78, 116, 144, 182, 220, 252, 290, 328

Learning Objectives, 1A, 43A, 81BA, 119A, 147A, 185A, 223A, 255A, 293A

Learning Styles
Auditory Learners, 18, 50, 104, 108, 122, 188
Interpersonal Learners, 24, 60, 84, 104, 108, 160, 164, 170, 239, 262, 282, 306,
Intrapersonal Learners, 150, 212
Kinesthetic Learners, 4, 14, 18, 24, 25, 31, 56, 66, 84, 98, 126, 136, 164, 188, 192, 198, 202, 208, 268, 272, 278, 282, 300, 310, 320
Linguistic Learners, 8, 30, 126, 212, 278, 282
Logical Learners, 98, 164, 230, 244, 258, 268
Naturalist Learners, 24, 30, 46, 150, 170, 174, 202, 262, 272, 278, 296
Visual/Spatial Learners, 14, 56, 66, 88, 132, 136, 154,

164, 192, 198, 202, 208, 225, 236, 258, 262, 268
Tactile, 132

Lesson Planner, 5, 7, 13, 17, 23, 29, 45, 49, 55, 59, 65, 69, 83, 87, 93, 97, 103, 107, 121, 125, 131, 135, 149, 153, 159, 163, 169, 173, 187, 192, 197, 201, 207, 211, 225, 229, 235, 239, 243, 257, 261, 267, 271, 277, 281, 295, 299, 305, 309, 315, 319

Lesson Review. *See* Progress Check

line of symmetry, 281

Line Plots, 319–322

Linguistic Learners. *See* Learning Styles

Logical Learners. *See* Learning Styles

Looking Ahead: Pre-teach, 6, 10, 16, 20, 27, 48, 52, 58, 62, 68, 86, 90, 96, 100, 106, 124, 128, 134, 152, 156, 162, 166, 172, 191, 195, 200, 204, 210, 228, 232, 238, 242, 260, 264, 270, 274, 280, 298, 303, 308, 312, 318

Manipulatives
base-ten blocks, 26, 47, 51, 57, 61, 66, 67, 71, 94, 99, 105, 109, 123, 127, 137
CD player, 122
centimeter graph paper, 100
chart paper, 244
coins, 9
color tiles, 317
colored pencils, 98
connecting cubes, 5, 14, 61, 70, 85, 94, 99, 105, 109, 122, 127, 133, 161, 165, 171, 307, 311, 315
counters, 4, 47, 84, 85, 88, 89, 94, 96, 104, 108, 164, 165, 301, 310, 315, 316, 321
dimes, 25, 32, 123
egg cartons, 4

flexible rulers, 175, 258, 259, 278
fraction cards, 208
fraction circles (strips), 155, 161, 193, 198, 199, 212, 300
fraction tiles, 151, 155, 161, 189, 193, 199, 208, 212, 213
geoboards, 94, 105, 109, 151, 263, 279, 283
geometic solids, 226, 230, 231, 237, 245, 297
glue, 242
graph paper, 98
grid paper, 66, 316
hundreds chart, 32
index cards, 10, 132, 156, 172, 176, 236, 258, 282
leaves or rocks, 296
magazines, 126, 242, 262
marbles, 132,
markers, 244, 306, 316, 320
masking tape, 320
newspapers, 126, 262
nickels, 70
number cubes, 8, 138, 259
number lines, 19, 70, 89, 105, 109, 133
paper, 8, 46, 212, 239, 242, 300, 306
paper models of cube, 232
paper money, 19
pattern blocks, 85, 99, 123, 151, 165, 171, 209, 237, 240, 245, 268, 269, 273
pennies, 25, 32, 123
pencil, 242, 239
photos, 46, 150
poster paper, 18, 96
recording sheet, 14
ruler, 202, 203
scissors, 242
small bell, 50
spinner, 268
two-color counters, 15, 51, 56, 57, 67, 71, 199

Math Challenge
Apple Coloring, 166
Back to the Table, 318
Best of 11!, 214
Build a Number, 124
Changing the Bars, 312
Coin Toss, 68

trapezoid, 267

triangle, 235

Two-Digit Numbers
round, 131–134

Universal Access. *See also*
Learning Styles; Differentiated
Instruction

Venn diagram, 295

vertex, 239

Vertical Alignment, 1B, 43B,
81B, 119B, 147B, 185B, 223B,
255B, 293B

Visual/Spatial Learners. *See*
Learning Styles

Vocabulary, 5, 7, 13, 17, 23, 29,
45, 49, 55, 59, 65, 69, 83, 87,
93, 97, 103, 107, 121, 125, 131,
135, 149, 153, 159, 163, 169,
173, 187, 192, 197, 201, 207,
211, 225, 229, 235, 239, 243,
257, 261, 267, 271, 277, 281,
295, 299, 305, 309, 315, 319

Vocabulary
Compare, 13, 49, 121, 148,
201, 211, 271, 299
Connect, 267

Examples, 23
Explore, 45, 187, 225, 257
Extend, 29,
Key, 1, 43, 81, 119, 147, 185,
223, 255, 293
Interaction, 7, 97, 131, 173,
239, 295
Interface, 159, 229
Match, 125, 197, 235
Model, 107, 223
Nonexamples, 3, 65, 135,
191, 243, 277, 319
Preview, 2, 44, 59, 82, 93,
120, 147, 186, 256, 294
Reenact, 69, 169, 207
Relate, 281
Relationships, 55, 83, 153,
309, 315
Review, 37, 75, 87, 103, 113,
141, 163, 179, 217, 249,
261, 287, 305, 325
Subtraction Action, 17

Vocabulary Check, 6, 10, 16, 20,
27, 34, 48, 52, 58, 62, 68, 72,
86, 90, 96, 100, 106, 110, 124,
128, 134, 138, 152, 156, 162,
166, 172, 176, 191, 195, 200,
204, 210, 214, 228, 232, 238,
242, 248, 260, 264, 270, 274,
280, 284, 298, 303, 308, 312,
318, 322

Vocabulary Review, 6, 10, 16,
20, 28, 34, 37, 48, 52, 58, 62,
68, 72, 75, 86, 87, 90, 96, 100,
103, 106, 110, 113, 124, 128,
134, 138, 141, 152, 156, 162,
163, 166, 172, 176, 179, 190,
194, 200, 204, 210, 214, 217,
228, 232, 238, 242, 246, 249,
260, 261, 264, 270, 274, 280,
284, 287, 298, 302, 305, 308,
312, 318, 322, 325

Vocabulary Review Strategies
Connections, 75
Game Time, 141
Remember Vocabulary, 114
Vocabulary Collage, 249
Vocabulary Flashcards, 37,
179, 287
Vocabulary Notes, 217

Who is Correct?, 40, 78, 116,
144, 182, 220, 252, 290, 328

Whole, parts of, 159–162

Whole Numbers
less than 10,000, 135–138

word form, 125

Writing in Math, 6, 10, 16, 20,
27, 34, 48, 52, 58, 62, 68, 72,
86, 90, 96, 100, 106, 110, 124,
128, 134, 138, 152, 156, 162,
166, 172, 176, 191, 195, 200,
204, 210, 214, 228, 232, 238,
242, 248, 260, 264, 270, 274,
280, 284, 298, 303, 308, 312,
318, 322

Image Credits

Chapter Resource Masters

Chapter Resource Masters

Name _____

Foldables Study Organizer

Dinah Zike's Foldables

Help students with the steps below to create their Foldables.

1 Begin with four sheets of $8\frac{1}{2}$" × 11" paper. Stack four sheets of paper. Place each sheet $\frac{3}{4}$ inch apart.

2 Roll up the edges, so all tabs are the same size.

3 Crease and staple along the fold.

4 Label the tabs with the lesson tittles from the chapter.

TAKING NOTES

As students read through the chapter, have them use their Foldable to explain and write an example from each lesson. Have them write the answers under each tab.

USING YOUR FOLDABLE

As students review, ask them to solve the problems that they wrote on their Foldable without looking at the answer. If they have any difficulties, then go over that concept again.

USING YOUR FOLDABLE

In pairs, have students quiz each other by stating the addition or subtraction facts written on their Foldable. Be sure students give their partner the correct answer if he or she gets it wrong.

Games and Puzzles
Addition Spin

GET READY

Give each student a sharpened pencil, a large paper clip, a copy of the spinner sheet, and a copy of the score sheet.

DIRECTIONS:

- Students take turns. The first student places the point of the pencil inside the paper clip and positions it on the first spinner. The student spins the paper clip and writes the number where the paper clip stops in the tens column of the first place value chart. The student spins the paper clip again and writes the number in the ones column of the chart.

- The student repeats the process to fill in the second two-digit number on the same chart using the second spinner.

- The student adds the two 2-digit numbers.

- The second student repeats the process described above.

- Both students compare the sum of their numbers. The student with the higher sum scores 1 point.

- The student that scores the point writes it on the scorecard as 1. The student that does not score a point writes it on the scorecard as 0.

- Students play three rounds. At the end of all rounds, both students add their points. The student with the greatest number of points wins the game.

What You Need
- Addition Spin score sheet
- Addition Spin spinner sheet
- pencil
- paper clip

Number of Players
2

Spinner Sheet
Addition Spin

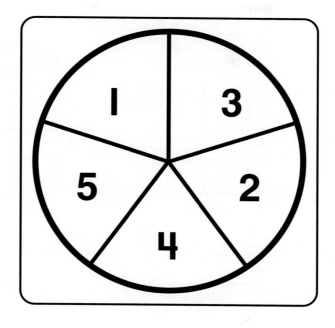

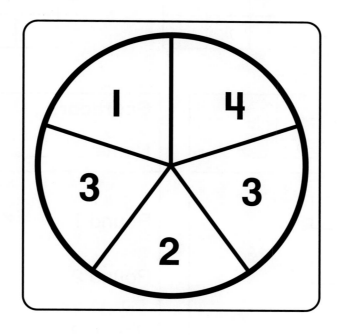

Math Triumphs

Score Sheet
Addition Spin

Student 1 Name _____

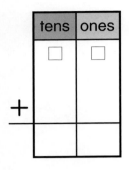

Student 2 Name _____

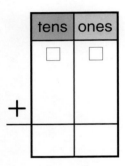 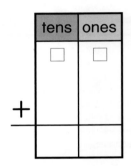 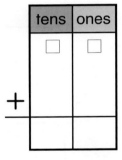

Scorecard
Name _____
Round 1 ☐
Round 2 ☐
Round 3 + ☐
☐

Scorecard
Name _____
Round 1 ☐
Round 2 ☐
Round 3 + ☐
☐

Math Triumphs

Name _____

Vocabulary and English Language Development

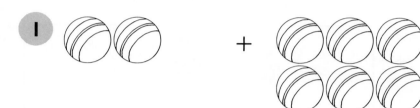

Add $3 + 4$.

$3 + 4 = 7$

⤷ **sum**

Add. Write the sum.

1 $2 + 6 = $ _____

2 $5 + 1 = $ _____

3 $4 + 5 = $ _____

4 $3 + 4 = $ _____

ACTIVITY Explain that **addition** means to find how many in all. The answer in addition is the **sum.** Show students 3 red cubes and 2 blue cubes by lining them up next to each other. Say: "3 plus 2 is 5." Point out that 5 is the sum. Then ask students to model $4 + 2$ using cubes.

WORKSHEET DIRECTIONS Have students use red and blue connecting cubes to model each addition sentence above. Then, have them write the sum.

Name _____

Skills Practice

Write an addition sentence. Find the sum.

1  +

_____ + _____ = _____

2  +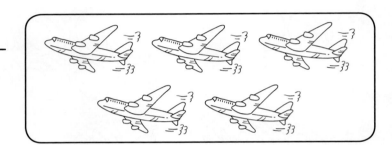

_____ + _____ = _____

3 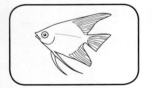 +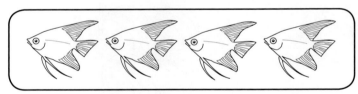

_____ + _____ = _____

Find each sum. Use the number line.

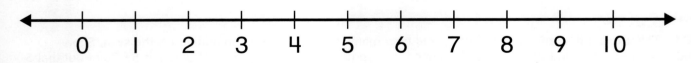

4 $2 + 7 =$ _____   5 $5 + 5 =$ _____   6 $8 + 1 =$ _____

Math Triumphs

Lesson 1-1

Name _____

Problem-Solving Practice

Draw a picture. Solve.

1 Kenny has 3 flowers. He picks 6 more. How many flowers does Kenny have in all?

┌─────────────────────┐   ┌─────────────────────┐
│   │   +   │   │
└─────────────────────┘   └─────────────────────┘

Kenny has _____ flowers in all.

2 Sharon has 4 books. Her brother has 3 books. How many books do they have in all?

┌─────────────────────┐   ┌─────────────────────┐
│   │   +   │   │
└─────────────────────┘   └─────────────────────┘

They have _____ books in all.

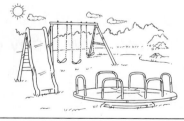

3 There are 2 girls on the playground. There are 4 boys on the playground. How many children are there in all?

┌─────────────────────┐   ┌─────────────────────┐
│   │   +   │   │
└─────────────────────┘   └─────────────────────┘

There are _____ children in all.

Math Triumphs

Name _____

Homework Practice

Write an addition sentence. Find the sum.

1  +

____ + ____ = ____

2

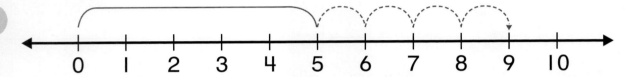

____ + ____ = ____

Find each sum.

3 1 + 7 = ____   **4** 7 + 3 = ____   **5** 4 + 3 = ____

Draw a picture. Solve.

6 There are 5 boys in the library. There are 2 girls in the library. How many children are in the library in all?

 +

There are _____ children in the library in all.

Math Triumphs

Name _____

Vocabulary and English Language Development

addition sentence

$$7 + 5 = 12$$

↑
sum

Draw. Then add.

1 3 + 8 = _____

+

2 9 + 4 = _____

+

3 6 + 7 = _____

+

4 6 + 8 = _____

+

ACTIVITY Write the word **_addition_** on the board. Underline the word **_add_** in addition. Explain to students that when you add, you find a total. The total is called the **sum**. Write 5 + 6 = ____ on the board. Draw five circles underneath the number 5. Then have a student draw six more circles underneath the number 6. Count all the circles with the students. Write the sum and label it "sum."

WORKSHEET DIRECTIONS Have students look at each addition sentence above. Ask them to use the space provided to draw circles to show each addition. Then, have students write the sum.

Lesson 1-2

Name ______________________________

Skills Practice

Write an addition sentence. Find each sum.

1 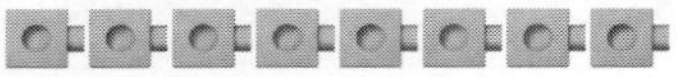

\+ 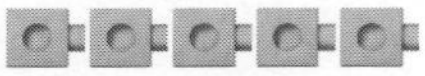

$$\begin{array}{r} \square \\ + \square \\ \hline \square \end{array}$$

2 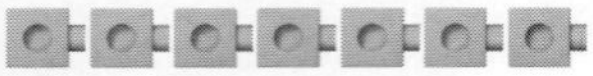 + 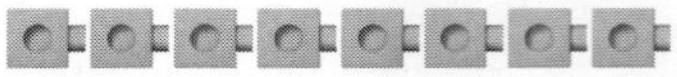

________ + ________ = ____________

3 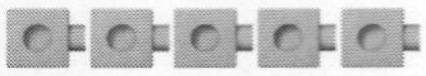 + 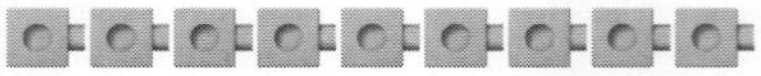

________ + ________ = ____________

Add.

4 $\begin{array}{r} 9 \\ +8 \\ \hline \square \end{array}$ **5** $\begin{array}{r} 7 \\ +7 \\ \hline \square \end{array}$ **6** $\begin{array}{r} 6 \\ +9 \\ \hline \square \end{array}$ **7** $\begin{array}{r} 3 \\ +8 \\ \hline \square \end{array}$ **8** $\begin{array}{r} 7 \\ +6 \\ \hline \square \end{array}$

9 $\begin{array}{r} 9 \\ +9 \\ \hline \square \end{array}$ **10** $\begin{array}{r} 7 \\ +4 \\ \hline \square \end{array}$ **11** $\begin{array}{r} 7 \\ +9 \\ \hline \square \end{array}$ **12** $\begin{array}{r} 8 \\ +6 \\ \hline \square \end{array}$ **13** $\begin{array}{r} 9 \\ +3 \\ \hline \square \end{array}$

Name _____

Problem-Solving Practice

Draw a picture. Solve.

1 Alice has 8 goldfish. She gets 3 more goldfish. How many goldfish does Alice have in all?

 +

Alice has _____ goldfish in all.

2 Jacob has 7 red marbles. He has 8 green marbles. How many marbles does Jacob have in all?

 +

Jacob has _____ marbles in all.

3 There are 3 green toy trucks. There are 9 yellow toy trucks. How many toy trucks are there in all?

 +

There are _____ toy trucks in all.

Lesson 1-2

Name ______________________________

Homework Practice

Write an addition sentence. Find each sum.

1 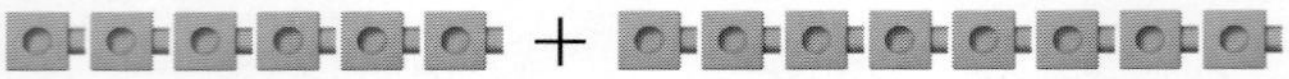

_______ + _______ = __________

2 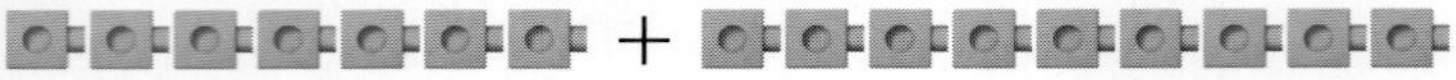

_______ + _______ = __________

Add.

3
$$\begin{array}{r} 7 \\ +\,5 \\ \hline \square \end{array}$$

4
$$\begin{array}{r} 8 \\ +\,8 \\ \hline \square \end{array}$$

5
$$\begin{array}{r} 6 \\ +\,5 \\ \hline \square \end{array}$$

6
$$\begin{array}{r} 7 \\ +\,8 \\ \hline \square \end{array}$$

7
$$\begin{array}{r} 9 \\ +\,4 \\ \hline \square \end{array}$$

Draw a picture. Solve.

8 Misha has 6 toy cars. He gets 7 more toy cars. How many toy cars does Misha have in all?

[ ] + [ ]

Misha has _______ toy cars in all.

Name _____

Vocabulary and English Language Development

Subtract 7 − 3.

7 − 3 = 4

↑

difference

Subtract. Write the difference.

1 ▢▢▢⊠⊠⊠⊠⊠   8 − 5 = _____

2 ▢⊠⊠⊠⊠⊠⊠   7 − 6 = _____

3 ▢▢▢⊠⊠⊠   6 − 3 = _____

4 ▢▢▢▢▢▢▢⊠⊠   9 − 2 = _____

ACTIVITY Write the word *subtraction* on the board. Underline the word *subtract* in subtraction. Explain to students that when you subtract, you find the **difference**, or the number left over. Write 9 − 5 = ____ on the board. Show students a train of 9 connecting cubes. Then have a student take away 5 of the connecting cubes. Help students count the connecting cubes left over. Write the difference and label it "difference."

WORKSHEET DIRECTIONS Have students look at Exercises 1–4. Ask them to use the train of connecting cubes shown for each exercise to find the difference for each subtraction sentence above.

Name _____

Skills Practice

Write a subtraction sentence. Find each difference.

1

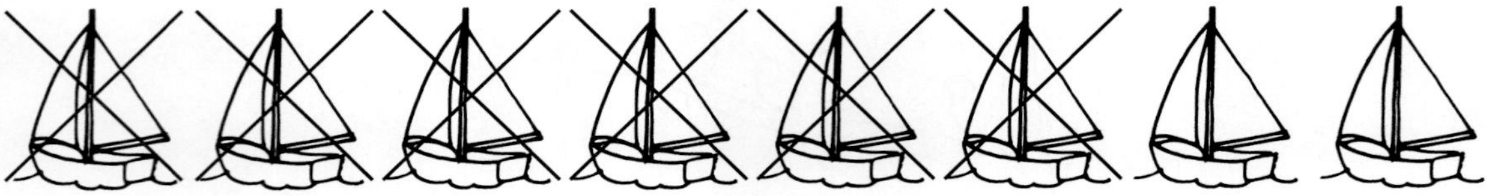

_____ – _____ = _____

2

_____ – _____ = _____

3

_____ – _____ = _____

Find each difference. Use the number line.

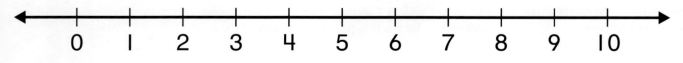

4 9 – 3 = _____   **5** 10 – 7 = _____   **6** 6 – 4 = _____

Math Triumphs

Name _____

Problem-Solving Practice

Use a number line. Count back. Solve.

1 Felicia has 8 crayons. She gives 4 crayons to her sister. How many crayons does Felicia have left?

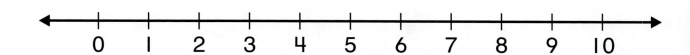

Felicia has _____ crayons left.

2 There are 10 students on the bus. Then 3 students get off the bus. How many students are left on the bus?

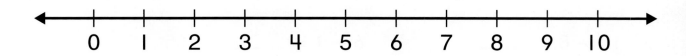

There are _____ students left.

3 Luis has 9 pennies. He puts 3 pennies in a bank. How many pennies does Luis have left?

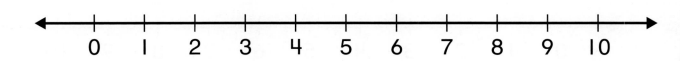

Luis has _____ pennies left.

Name _____

Homework Practice

Write a subtraction sentence. Find each difference.

1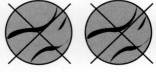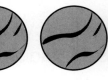

_____ − _____ = _____

2

_____ − _____ = _____

Find each difference. Use the number line.

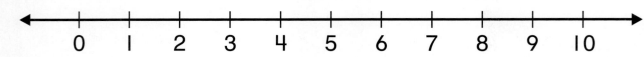

3 $10 - 8 =$ _____ **4** $6 - 1 =$ _____ **5** $9 - 7 =$ _____

Use the number line. Count back. Solve.

6 Keisha has 10 apples. She gives 5 apples to her friends. How many apples does Keisha have left?

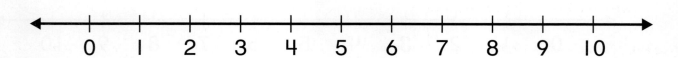

Keisha has _____ apples left.

Math Triumphs

Name _____

Vocabulary and English Language Development

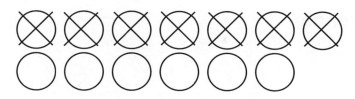

subtraction sentence

$13 - 7 = 6$

↑

difference

Draw. Then subtract.

1 $14 - 9 = $ _____

2 $17 - 8 = $ _____

3 $11 - 6 = $ _____

4 $12 - 6 = $ _____

ACTIVITY Write the word ***subtraction*** on the board. Underline the word ***subtract*** in subtraction. Remind students that to subtract is to find the **difference**, or the number left over. Write $13 - 9 = $ _____ on the board. Show students a train of 13 connecting cubes. Then have a student take away 9 of the connecting cubes. Help students count the connecting cubes left over. Write the difference and label it "difference."

WORKSHEET DIRECTIONS Have students look at Exercises 1–4. Encourage students to use connecting cubes to model each subtraction sentence to help them draw and write the difference.

Name _____

Skills Practice

Find each difference.

1
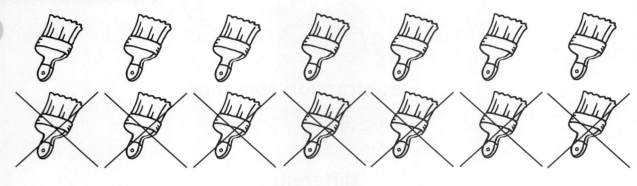

___ – ___ = ___

2
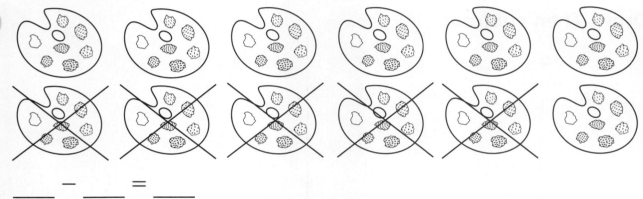

___ – ___ = ___

Find each difference. Use the number line.

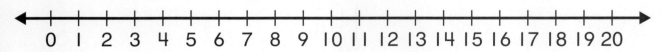

0 1 2 3 4 5 6 7 8 9 10 11 12 13 14 15 16 17 18 19 20

3 $15 - 6 =$ ___   **4** $18 - 9 =$ ___   **5** $15 - 9 =$ ___

Subtract.

6
$$\begin{array}{r} 14 \\ -\ 8 \\ \hline \end{array}$$

7
$$\begin{array}{r} 13 \\ -\ 4 \\ \hline \end{array}$$

8
$$\begin{array}{r} 11 \\ -\ 8 \\ \hline \end{array}$$

9
$$\begin{array}{r} 16 \\ -\ 7 \\ \hline \end{array}$$

10
$$\begin{array}{r} 12 \\ -\ 8 \\ \hline \end{array}$$

Math Triumphs

Name _____

Problem-Solving Practice

Use a number line. Count back. Solve.

1 Amanda has 15 baskets of fruit. She sells 7 baskets. How many baskets of fruit does Amanda have left?

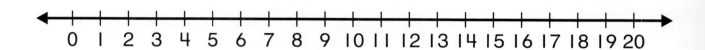

Amanda has _____ baskets of fruit left.

2 Corey has 13 apples. He has 6 bananas. How many more apples than bananas does Corey have?

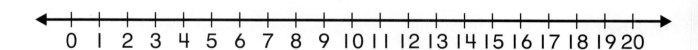

Corey has _____ more apples than bananas.

3 Manuel has 11 quarters. He has 6 dimes. How many more quarters than dimes does Manuel have?

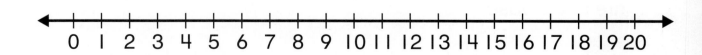

Manuel has _____ more quarters than dimes.

Name _____

Homework Practice

Find each difference.

1

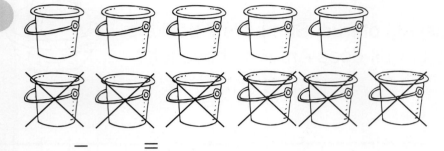

___ − ___ = ___

2

___ − ___ = ___

Subtract.

3
$$\begin{array}{r} 11 \\ -\ 2 \\ \hline \end{array}$$

4
$$\begin{array}{r} 17 \\ -\ 9 \\ \hline \end{array}$$

5
$$\begin{array}{r} 12 \\ -\ 9 \\ \hline \end{array}$$

6
$$\begin{array}{r} 14 \\ -\ 7 \\ \hline \end{array}$$

7
$$\begin{array}{r} 13 \\ -\ 5 \\ \hline \end{array}$$

Use a number line. Count back. Solve.

8 There are 14 daisies in a vase. There are 6 roses in the same vase. How many more daisies than roses are in the vase?

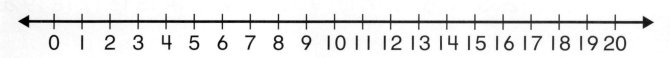

There are ____ more daisies than roses in the vase.

Math Triumphs

Name _____

Vocabulary and English Language Development

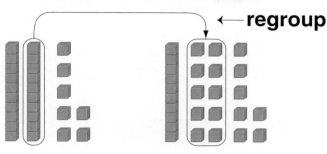

← regroup

2 tens and 7 ones   1 ten and 17 ones

Regroup.

1 38

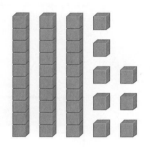

____ tens ____ ones

38

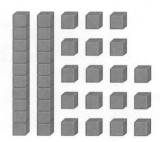

____ tens ____ ones

2 42

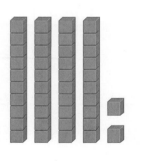

____ tens ____ ones

42

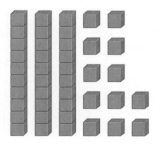

____ tens ____ ones

Activity Write 27 on the board. Tell students that the 2 represents the number of tens in that number. Then, explain that the 7 represents the number of ones in that number. Say: "27 has 2 tens and 7 ones." Explain to students that to **regroup** a number is to take it apart and write it a new way. Point out that one way to regroup 27 is to write it as 1 **ten** and 17 **ones**. Show students 2 ten rods and 7 unit cubes. Replace 1 ten rod with 10 unit cubes. Help students count the number of tens and the number of ones. Point out that 2 tens and 7 ones has been regrouped as 1 ten and 17 ones.

WORKSHEET DIRECTIONS Tell students to look at each number above. Encourage them to use base-ten blocks to model each number to help them write the number of tens and ones.

Math Triumphs

Name _____

Skills Practice

Find each sum.

1 35 + 13

tens	ones
3	5
+ 1	3

2 27 + 10

tens	ones
2	7
+	

3 42 + 23

tens	ones
+	

4 48 + 19

tens	ones
☐	
4	8
+ 1	9

5 47 + 25

tens	ones
☐	
4	7
+	

6 53 + 38

tens	ones
☐	
+	

Add.

7

```
  ☐
  3│6
+ 4│9
─────
```

8

```
  2│3
+ 3│5
─────
```

9

```
  1│4
+ 6│0
─────
```

Copyright © Macmillan/McGraw-Hill, • Glencoe, a division of The McGraw-Hill Companies, Inc.

Math Triumphs

Name _____

Problem-Solving Practice

Solve each problem.

1 Betina makes 24 muffins.
Her mother makes 32 muffins. How
many muffins do they make in all?

They make _____ muffins in all.

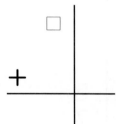

2 Marty has 37 baseball cards.
He buys 25 more cards. How
many baseball cards does
Marty have?

Marty has _____ cards.

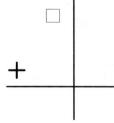

3 Zach has 55 pennies. He gets
18 more pennies. How many
pennies does Zach have?

Zach has _____ pennies.

Math Triumphs

Name _____

Homework Practice

Find each sum.

1 54 + 27

tens	ones
☐	
5	4
+ 2	7

2 45 + 13

tens	ones
4	5
+	

3 39 + 36

tens	ones
☐	
+	

4
```
  ☐
  4 | 3
+ 1 | 7
```

5
```
  3 | 5
+ 5 | 2
```

6
```
  ☐
  2 | 6
+ 2 | 9
```

7
```
  ☐
  3 | 8
+ 1 | 4
```

8
```
  ☐
  4 | 9
+ 2 | 8
```

9
```
  2 | 1
+ 7 | 3
```

Solve.

10 Lauren scored 29 points. Then she scored 57 more points. How many points did she score in all?

```
  ☐
+
```

Lauren scored _____ points in all.

Math Triumphs

Name _____

Vocabulary and English Language Development

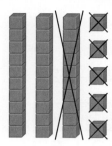

3 tens 5 ones – 1 ten 5 ones = 2 tens
35 – 15 = 20

Subtract.

1

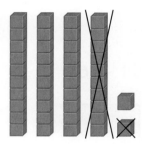

42 – 11 = _____

2

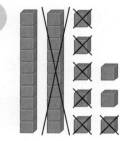

28 – 16 = _____

3

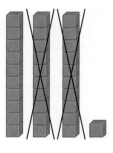

31 – 20 = _____

4

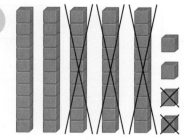

54 – 32 = _____

ACTIVITY Write the subtraction sentence 35 – 15 = _____ on the board. Model the number 35 for students using base-ten blocks. Take away 1 tens rod and 5 unit cubes. Have students count the base-ten blocks left over. Tell students that the number left over is the difference.

WORKSHEET DIRECTIONS Have students look at each exercise above. Encourage them to use base-ten blocks to model each exercise to help them find the difference.

Name _____

Skills Practice

Find each difference.

1 78 − 25

tens	ones
7	8
− 2	5

2 85 − 42

tens	ones
8	5
−	

2 54 − 34

tens	ones
−	

Regroup. Then subtract.

4 63 − 29

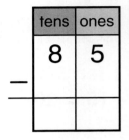

tens	ones
☐	☐
6	3
− 2	9

5 76 − 47

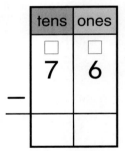

tens	ones
☐	☐
7	6
−	

6 91 − 65

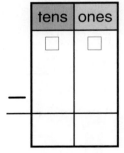

tens	ones
☐	☐
−	

Subtract.

7

$$\begin{array}{r} 4\,|\,8 \\ -\ 1\,|\,1 \\ \hline \end{array}$$

8

$$\begin{array}{r} \square\ \square \\ 8\,|\,4 \\ -\ 2\,|\,8 \\ \hline \end{array}$$

9

$$\begin{array}{r} \square\ \square \\ 7\,|\,3 \\ -\ 4\,|\,9 \\ \hline \end{array}$$

Math Triumphs

Name _____

Problem-Solving Practice

Use a model. Solve each problem.

1 Josh has 63 baseball cards.
He gives 25 cards to his little sister. How many cards does Josh have left?

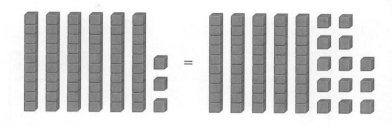

Josh has _____ cards left.

2 Ronnie picks 36 apples. He gives 18 apples to his mother. How many apples does Ronnie have left?

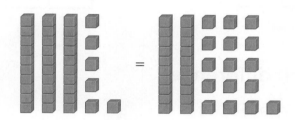

Ronnie has _____ apples left.

Solve

3 Yasmin makes 42 necklaces with beads. She sells 26 of them. How many necklaces does Yasmin have left?

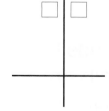

Yasmin has _____ necklaces left.

Name _____

Homework Practice

Regroup when needed. Then subtract.

1 85 − 28

tens	ones
☐	☐
8	5
− 2	8

2 62 − 35

tens	ones
☐	☐
6	2
−	

3 76 − 31

tens	ones
−	

Find each difference.

4

$$\begin{array}{r} \square\ \square \\ 6\ 0 \\ -\ 2\ 2 \\ \hline \end{array}$$

5

$$\begin{array}{r} \square\ \square \\ 5\ 2 \\ -\ 3\ 7 \\ \hline \end{array}$$

6

$$\begin{array}{r} 7\ 6 \\ -\ 4\ 5 \\ \hline \end{array}$$

Solve.

7 Claude has 52 shells. Some of the shells are large and 28 shells are small. How many large shells does Claude have?

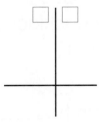

Claude has _____ large shells.

Math Triumphs

Name _____

Foldables Study Organizer

FOLDABLES®
Study Organizer

Dinah Zike's Foldables

Help students with the steps below to create their Foldables.

1. Begin with four sheets of $8\frac{1}{2}'' \times 11''$ paper. Fold one piece of paper in half.

2. Fold one side up five inches as shown to make a pocket. Glue the outer edges.

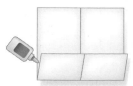

3. Label with the lesson titles. Record what you learn.

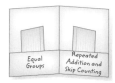

   Equal Groups   Repeated Addition and Skip Counting

4. Repeat steps 1-3 with two more pieces of paper.

TAKING NOTES
As students read through the chapter, have them use their Foldable to explain and write an example of each of the following:
- Equal Groups
- Repeated Addition and Skip Counting
- Arrays
- Area Models
- Multiply by 0 and 1
- Multiply by 2 and 5

USING YOUR FOLDABLE
As the students review, have them check their understanding by writing additional examples.

USING YOUR FOLDABLE
Have the students trade their Foldables with a partner to check each other's work. Did their partner write an example correctly under each tab? If not, have the student provide the correct answer.

Math Triumphs

Games and Puzzles

What's the Factor?

GET READY

- Give each pair of students a game sheet, counters, and a number cube.

- Explain to students that they are going to identify the missing factors to make complete multiplication facts.

DIRECTIONS:

- Point out that each game card on the game sheet has rows and columns. Tell students that each row and column makes up a multiplication fact, and they must put factors in the empty boxes to make each multiplication fact true.

- Point out the set of numbers at the bottom right corner on each game card. Explain that these numbers are the missing factors which they will use to complete the multiplication facts. HINT: Each number will be used once.

- Tell students that they will play **What's the Factor?** with a partner. Partners can roll the number cube to determine the first player.

- Explain that the first player should find the missing factors for the first game card. Then his or her partner should check the answers.

- Each player will get one counter for each correct multiplication fact. So, if a player fills in all the missing factors correctly, he or she will collect four counters each turn.

- Partners should take turns until all the game cards have been filled in. The player with more counters wins.

VARIATION

Partners cover the numbers that are at the bottom right corner on each game card and determine which factors to use.

Game Sheet

What's the Factor?

Play with a partner. Find the missing factors.

Game Card 1		
		16
		10
4	**40**	2 2 / 5 8

Game Card 2		
		45
		0
25	**0**	0 5 / 5 9

Game Card 3		
		20
		0
0	**30**	0 4 / 5 6

Game Card 4		
		14
		5
35	**2**	1 2 / 5 7

Game Card 5		
		7
		18
14	**9**	1 2 / 7 9

Game Card 6		
		8
		15
20	**6**	2 3 / 4 5

Name _____

Vocabulary and English Language Development

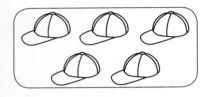 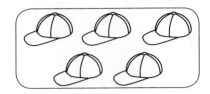 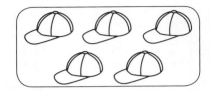

3 equal groups

Circle the equal groups.

1

2

3

4

ACTIVITY Ask six students to come to the front of the class. Have them stand in two groups with three students in each group. Help students count the number of students in each group. Point out that each group has the same number of students. Say: "These students are in **equal groups**." Ask a volunteer to tell another way to make equal groups with these six students (three groups of two). Repeat using eight students.

WORKSHEET DIRECTIONS Tell students to look at each group of things in Exercises 1–4 and identify the ones that show equal groups. Tell them to circle the equal groups in each exercise.

Math Triumphs

Name _____

Skills Practice

Write how many in all.

1

3   3

_____ groups of _____ flowers   _____ flowers in all

2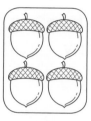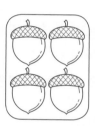

4   4   4

_____ groups of _____ acorns   _____ acorns in all

3

5   5   5

_____ groups of _____ books   _____ books in all

4

4   4

_____ groups of _____ ants   _____ ants in all

Name _____

Problem-Solving Practice

Draw a picture. Write how many in all.

1 Victor has a fish tank with 2 types of fish. He has 4 of each type of fish. How many fish does he have in all?

Victor has _____ fish in all.

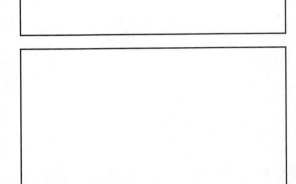

2 Pat has 5 types of shells. She has 3 shells of each type. How many shells does she have in all?

Pat has _____ shells in all.

Solve.

3 Elliot has 8 oranges. Can Elliot place the oranges in equal groups? Explain.

_____

_____

4 Tia has 10 bones for her dog. Can Tia place the dog bones in equal groups? Explain.

_____

_____

Math Triumphs

Name _____

Homework Practice

Write how many in all.

_____ groups of _____ baseballs   _____ baseballs in all

 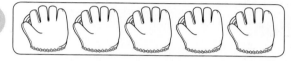 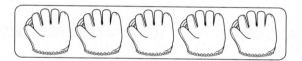

_____ groups of _____ mitts   _____ mitts in all

Draw a picture. Write how many in all.

3 Asha buys 2 bunches of flowers for her mom. There are 6 flowers in each bunch. How many flowers does Asha buy for her mom?

Asha buys _____ flowers for her mom.

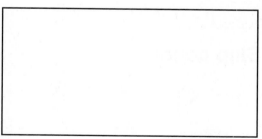

Solve.

4 Ellen has 6 baseball cards. Can Ellen place the cards in equal groups? Explain.

_____

_____

Chapter 2

Name _____

Vocabulary and English Language Development

repeated addition

$$2 + 2 + 2 + 2 = 8$$

skip count

2,   4,   6,   8

Draw cubes to show repeated addition.

1 $5 + 5 + 5 + 5 + 5 =$ _____

2 $2 + 2 + 2 =$ _____

Skip count.

3

4

____ ____ ____ ____   ____ ____ ____ ____

ACTIVITY Ask eight students to come to the front of the class. Have them make four groups with two students in each group. As you point to each group, say: "2 + 2 + 2 + 2 = 8. I used **repeated addition** to find the total." Point to each group again and say: "2, 4, 6, 8. I used **skip counting** to find the total." Repeat using ten students with five groups of two. Have a volunteer say the repeated addition and skip counting aloud.

WORKSHEET DIRECTIONS Have students look at each repeated addition for Exercises 1–2 and draw cubes to find the total. Then, have them use the cubes on Exercises 3–4 to skip count and find the total as they write the numbers on the lines provided.

Name _____

Skills Practice

Use repeated addition and skip counting to find each sum.

1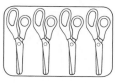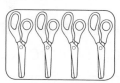

_____ + _____ + _____ = _____

4 , _____ , _____

There are _____ scissors in all.

2

_____ + _____ + _____ + _____ + _____ = _____

3 , _____ , _____ , _____ , _____

There are _____ pencils in all.

3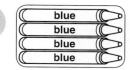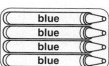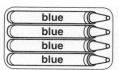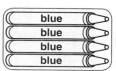

_____ + _____ + _____ + _____ = _____

4 , _____ , _____ , _____

There are _____ crayons in all.

4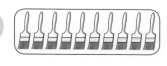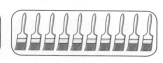

_____ + _____ + _____ = _____

10 , _____ , _____

There are _____ paintbrushes in all.

Name _____

Problem-Solving Practice

Solve.

1 Andy has 4 bunches of bananas.
Each bunch has 6 bananas.
How many bananas does Andy have in all?

_____ + _____ + _____ + _____ = _____

Andy has _____ bananas in all.

2 Brooke has 3 plates of muffins.
There are 5 muffins on each plate.
How many muffins does Brooke have in all?

_____ + _____ + _____ = _____

Brooke has _____ muffins in all.

3 Nestor put 5 pictures on each page of his album.
There are 10 pages. How many pictures did he put
on the pages in all? Explain.

_____

_____

4 Brett put 10 shells in each jar. There are 4 jars.
How many shells did Brett put in the jars in all? Explain.

_____

_____

Math Triumphs

Name _____

Homework Practice

Use repeated addition and skip counting to find each sum.

1

_____ + _____ + _____ + _____ = _____
_5_,   _____,   _____,   _____

There are _____ seashells in all.

2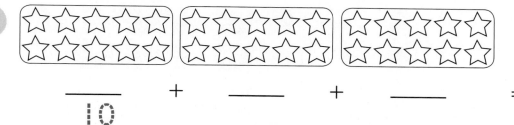

_____ + _____ + _____ = _____
_10_,   _____,   _____

There are _____ stars in all.

Solve.

3 Jordan has 2 bags of oranges. There are 7 oranges in each bag. How many oranges does Jordan have in all?

_____ + _____ = _____

Jordan has _____ oranges in all.

4 Sam put 10 cans in each box. There are 4 boxes. How many cans did Sam put in the boxes in all? Explain.

_____

_____

Name _____

Vocabulary and English Language Development

array

multiplication sentence

$4 \times 5 = 20$ ← product

↑ number of rows ↑ number in each row

Write a multiplication sentence. Find each product.

1

_____ × _____ = _____

2

_____ × _____ = _____

3

_____ × _____ = _____

4

_____ × _____ = _____

ACTIVITY Write the word **array** on the board. Then draw four rows of circles with two circles in each row. Say: "There are 4 rows with 2 circles in each row." Under the array, write 4 x 2 = 8. Point to the 4 and say: "This is the number of rows." Then point to the 2 and say: "This is the number in each row." Point to the multiplication sign. Say: "This is a multiplication sign. It is found in a **multiplication sentence**." Point to the product. Say: "This is the **product**, or answer." Have students use cubes to show arrays for other multiplication sentences.

WORKSHEET DIRECTIONS Tell students to look at each array and write the multiplication sentence and product for each one.

Math Triumphs

Name _____

Skills Practice

Write a multiplication sentence. Find each product.

1

_____ × _____ = _____

2

_____ × _____ = _____

3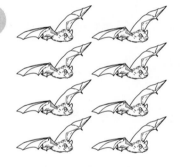

_____ × _____ = _____

4

_____ × _____ = _____

5

_____ × _____ = _____

6

_____ × _____ = _____

Name _____

Problem-Solving Practice

Write a multiplication sentence. Find each product.

1 There are 3 pails. There are 6 shells in each pail. How many shells are there in all?

_____ × _____ = _____

There are _____ shells in all.

2 There are 2 cars. There are 6 people in each car. How many people are there in all?

_____ × _____ = _____

There are _____ people in all.

Solve.

3 Mrs. Peters has a garden with 4 rows. There are 5 plants in each row. Nora says there are 9 plants in all. Is Nora correct? Explain.

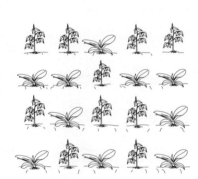

_____

_____

4 There are 5 rows on a game card. There are 5 squares in each row. Martin says there are 10 squares on the game card in all. Is Martin correct? Explain.

B	I	N	G	O
12	2	75	18	5
17	37	67	42	10
3	9	★	57	69
10	24	6	61	16
74	33	44	54	53

_____

_____

Homework Practice

Write a multiplication sentence. Find each product.

1

_____ × _____ = _____

2

_____ × _____ = _____

3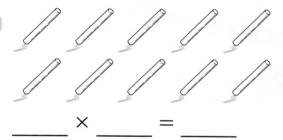

_____ × _____ = _____

4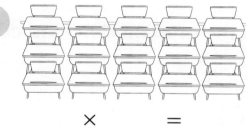

_____ × _____ = _____

Solve.

5 There are 5 rows on a calendar page. There are 7 squares in each row. Judy says there are 12 squares on the calendar page in all. Is she correct? Explain.

July

Sunday	Monday	Tuesday	Wednesday	Thursday	Friday	Saturday
		1	2	3	4	5
6	7	8	9	10	11	12
13	14	15	16	17	18	19
20	21	22	23	24	25	26
27	28	29	30	31		

_____

_____

Name _____

Vocabulary and English Language Development

area model
↓

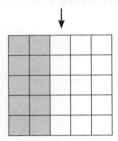

$5 \times 2 = \boxed{10}$ ← **product**
↑   ↑
factors

5 shaded rows
2 shaded squares in each row
10 shaded squares in all

Shade the area model. Find each product.

1 $3 \times 3 = $ _____

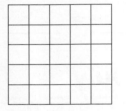

2 $5 \times 5 = $ _____

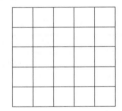

3 $2 \times 4 = $ _____

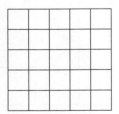

4 $4 \times 3 = $ _____

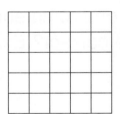

ACTIVITY Tell students that an **area model** is another way to show multiplication. Write 4 x 5 = 20 on the board. Say: "In this multiplication sentence, 4 and 5 are the **factors**. The **product** is 20." Hold up a five-by-five grid. Demonstrate how to fill it in correctly to show 4 x 5. Demonstrate for other multiplication sentences.

WORKSHEET DIRECTIONS Tell students to look at each factor and shade the area model to show the correct multiplication sentence. Then have students use the area model to find the product.

Name _____

Skills Practice

Shade the area model. Find each product.

1 _____ rows of _____

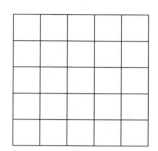

$4 \times 2 =$ _____

2 _____ rows of _____

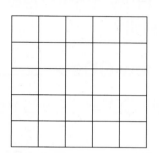

$3 \times 5 =$ _____

3 _____ rows of _____

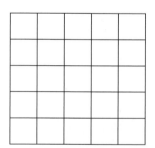

$3 \times 3 =$ _____

4 _____ rows of _____

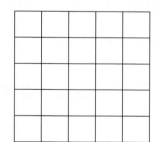

$4 \times 5 =$ _____

5 _____ rows of _____

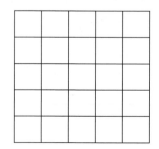

$3 \times 2 =$ _____

6 _____ rows of _____

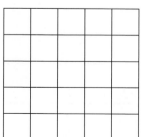

$5 \times 5 =$ _____

Name _____

Problem-Solving Practice

Shade the area model. Find each product.

1 Jose has 4 new CDs. Each new CD has 5 songs. How many new songs does Jose have in all?

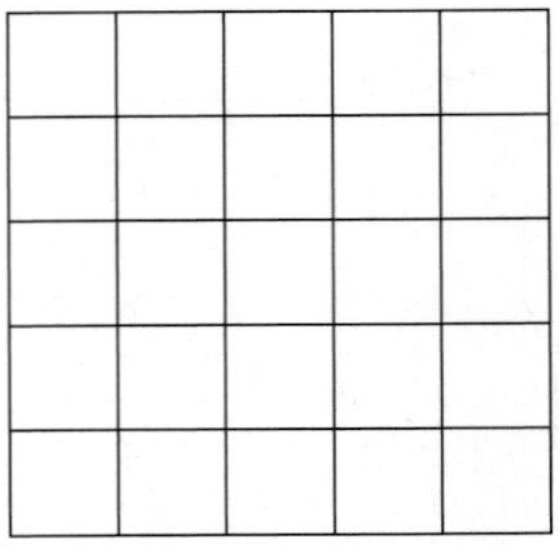

_____ new CDs × _____ songs

on each CD = _____ new songs

Jose has _____ new songs.

2 Juanita has 5 cats. Each cat has 5 kittens. How many kittens does Juanita have in all?

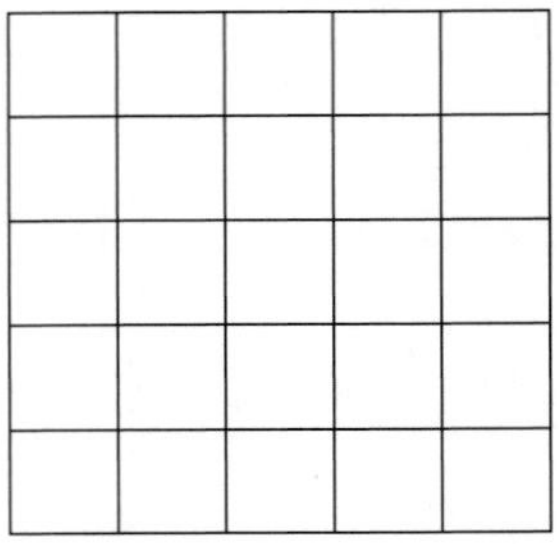

_____ cats × _____ kittens

from each cat = _____ kittens

Juanita has _____ kittens.

Solve.

3 Look at the area model.
Write a multiplication sentence. Explain.

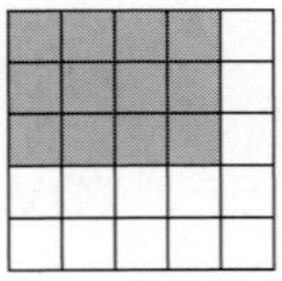

_____

_____

_____

Math Triumphs

Name _____

Homework Practice

Shade the area model. Find the each product.

1 _____ rows of _____

4 × 3 = _____

2 _____ rows of _____

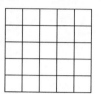

5 × 2 = _____

3 _____ rows of _____

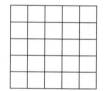

4 × 4 = _____

4 _____ rows of _____

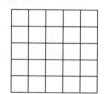

4 × 5 = _____

Solve.

5 There are 5 children in a family. Each child has 2 pets. How many pets does the family have in all?

_____ Children × _____ pets for each child = _____ pets.

The family has _____ pets.

6 Look at the area model.
Write a multiplication sentence. Explain.

_____

_____

_____

Name _____

Vocabulary and English Language Development

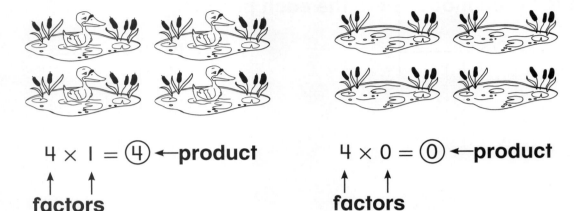

$4 \times 1 = ④$ ←**product**

↑   ↑

factors

$4 \times 0 = ⓪$ ←**product**

↑   ↑

factors

Multiply the factors. Write the product.

1

$3 \times 1 =$ _____

2

$5 \times 0 =$ _____.

ACTIVITY Explain that when you **multiply factors**, you are combining equal groups. On the board, draw eight circles with one triangle in each circle. Write *8 × 1* under the group of circled triangles. Point to the 8. Say: "The first factor tells how many groups: 8." Point to the 1. Say: "The second factor tells how many in each group: 1." Explain to students that 1 triangle in each of 8 groups equals a total of 8 triangles. Multiply 8 × 1 = 8. Ask students to use counters to model 8 × 1.

WORKSHEET DIRECTIONS For Exercise 1 tell students to identify the number of logs and the number of frogs on each log. Have them multiply to find the product. For Exercise 2 tell students to identify the number of nests and the number of birds on each nest. Have them multiply to find the product. Encourage them to use counters to model each multiplication.

Math Triumphs

Name _____

Skills Practice

Find each product.

1

$$5 \times 1 = \underline{\hspace{1cm}}$$
number of groups   number in each group   product

2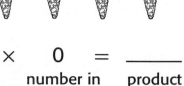

$$5 \times 0 = \underline{\hspace{1cm}}$$
number of groups   number in each group   product

3 $3 \times 1 = \underline{\hspace{1cm}}$

4 $0 \times 5 = \underline{\hspace{1cm}}$

5 $7 \times 1 = \underline{\hspace{1cm}}$

6 $0 \times 10 = \underline{\hspace{1cm}}$

7 $10 \times 1 = \underline{\hspace{1cm}}$

8 $1 \times 4 = \underline{\hspace{1cm}}$

9 $1 \times 6 = \underline{\hspace{1cm}}$

10 $4 \times 0 = \underline{\hspace{1cm}}$

11 $9 \times 1 = \underline{\hspace{1cm}}$

12 $1 \times 5 = \underline{\hspace{1cm}}$

13 $0 \times 3 = \underline{\hspace{1cm}}$

14 $1 \times 0 = \underline{\hspace{1cm}}$

Chapter 2

Name _____

Problem-Solving Practice

Find each product.

1 Randi sends cards to 4 cousins. She sends 1 card to each cousin. How many cards does Randi send?

_____ × _____ = _____

Randi sends _____ cards.

2 Kayla takes 3 friends on a bike ride. She has 1 bike for each friend to use. How many bikes does Kayla have?

_____ × _____ = _____

Kayla has _____ bikes.

Solve.

3 Look at the eggs. Write a multiplication sentence that models the eggs in the nests. Explain.

_____

4 Look at the baking cups. Write a multiplication sentence that models the muffins in the baking cups. Explain.

_____

_____

Math Triumphs

Name _____

Homework Practice

Find each product.

1 $2 \times 1 =$ _____

2 $0 \times 5 =$ _____

3 $10 \times 1 =$ _____

4 $4 \times 1 =$ _____

5 $9 \times 1 =$ _____

6 $0 \times 8 =$ _____

7 $1 \times 7 =$ _____

8 $5 \times 1 =$ _____

9 $3 \times 1 =$ _____

10 $1 \times 10 =$ _____

11 $1 \times 4 =$ _____

12 $1 \times 3 =$ _____

13 $1 \times 2 =$ _____

14 $10 \times 0 =$ _____

15 $1 \times 9 =$ _____

16 $1 \times 1 =$ _____

17 $8 \times 1 =$ _____

18 $2 \times 0 =$ _____

Solve.

19 Kelly makes lunch for 6 friends. She makes 1 hotdog for each friend. How many hotdogs does Kelly make?

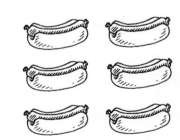

_____ × _____ = _____

Kelly makes _____ hotdogs.

20 Look at the melons. Write a multiplication sentence that models the melons in the baskets. Explain.

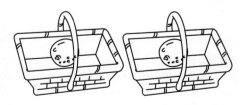

_____

_____

Name _____

Vocabulary and English Language Development

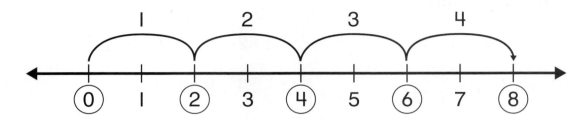

4 jumps of 2

$2 \times 4 = ⑧$ ←**product**

Use the number line to skip count. Find each product.

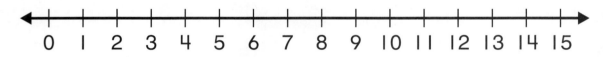

1 $2 \times 6 = 12$ 2, _____ , _____ , _____ , _____ , _____

2 $2 \times 3 =$ _____   2, _____ , _____

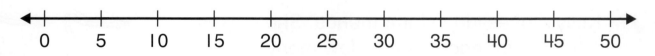

3 $5 \times 4 =$ _____   5, _____ , _____ , _____

4 $5 \times 6 =$ _____   5, _____ , _____ , _____ , _____ , _____

ACTIVITY Display a 0–20 number line. On the board, write *2 × 5*. Say: "Let's use the number line and skip count to find the **product**. Two is a factor. Skip count by 2s." As students skip count, point to each skip on the number line. Then reverse the problem to 5 × 2. Say: "Five is a factor. Skip count by 5s." Once again, as the students skip count, point to each skip on the number line. Then have students use number lines to find the product for other multiplications where they have to skip count by 2s and by 5s.

WORKSHEET DIRECTIONS Tell students to use the number lines and skip count to find the product.

Name _____

Skills Practice

Skip count to find each product.

1 $5 \times 5 =$ _____   _____ , _____ , _____ , _____ , _____

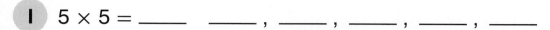

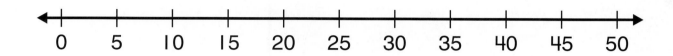

2 $2 \times 7 =$ _____   _____ , _____ , _____ , _____ , _____ , _____ , _____

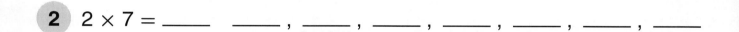

3 $2 \times 8 =$ _____

_____ , _____ , _____ , _____ , _____ , _____ , _____ , _____

4 $5 \times 8 =$ _____

_____ , _____ , _____ , _____ , _____ , _____ , _____ , _____

5 $2 \times 9 =$ _____

_____ , _____ , _____ , _____ , _____ , _____ , _____ , _____ , _____

6 $5 \times 7 =$ _____

_____ , _____ , _____ , _____ , _____ , _____ , _____

Name _____

Problem-Solving Practice

Skip count to find each product.

1 Brenda has 6 pairs of gloves. How many gloves does she have in all?

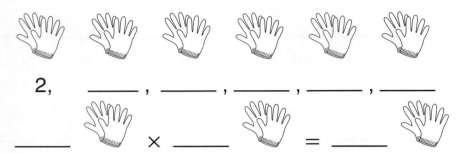

2, _____ , _____ , _____ , _____ , _____

_____ × _____ = _____

2 Bertha has 8 pairs of boots. How many shoes does she have in all?

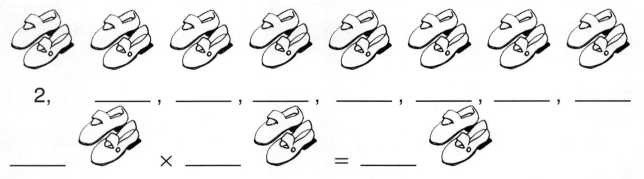

2, _____ , _____ , _____ , _____ , _____ , _____ , _____

_____ × _____ = _____

Solve.

3 Tim has 7 jars of buttons. There are 5 buttons in each jar. How many buttons does Tim have in all? Explain.

_____

_____

_____

_____

Math Triumphs

Name _____

Homework Practice

Skip count to find each product.

1 2 × 2 = _____

_____ , _____

2 5 × 3 = _____

_____ , _____ , _____

3 5 × 4 = _____

_____ , _____ , _____ , _____

4 5 × 2 = _____

_____ , _____

5 5 × 5 = _____

_____ , _____ , _____ , _____ , _____

6 2 × 7 = _____

_____ , _____ , _____ , _____ , _____ , _____ , _____

7 5 × 9 = _____

_____ , _____ , _____ , _____ , _____ , _____ , _____ , _____ , _____

Solve.

8 Jim sees 10 ladybugs. Each ladybug has 5 spots.
How many spots do the ladybugs have in all?
Explain.

_____

_____

_____

Name _____

Foldables Study Organizer

FOLDABLES®
Study Organizer

Dinah Zike's Foldables

Help students with the steps below to create their Foldables.

1 Begin with four sheets of $8\frac{1}{2}'' \times 11''$ paper. Fold one piece of paper in half.

2 Fold one side up five inches as shown to make a pocket. Glue the outer edges.

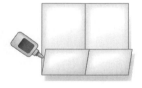

3 Label with the lesson titles. Record what you learn.

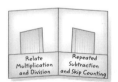

4 Repeat steps 1-3 with two more pieces of paper.

TAKING NOTES

As students read through the chapter, have them use their Foldable to explain and write an example of each of the following:

- Relate Multiplication and Division
- Repeated Subtraction and Skip Counting
- Use Arrays to Model Division
- Use Area Models to Show Division
- Divide by 0 and 1
- Divide by 2 and 5

USING YOUR FOLDABLE

As students review, have them check their understanding by writing additional examples.

USING YOUR FOLDABLE

Have the students trade their Foldables with a partner to check each other's work. Did their partner write an example correctly under each tab? If not, have the student provide the correct answer.

Games and Puzzles
Division Drop

GET READY
Give pairs of students a copy of the game sheet, a copy of the score sheet, and a penny or counter.

DIRECTIONS:

- Students take turns. The first student takes the counter and with his or her eyes closed, drops it on the first game board.

- The student writes the number where the counter landed in the first box on his or her scorecard.

- The same student then closes his or her eyes again and drops the counter on the second game board.

- He or she writes the number where the counter landed in the second box. If the counter lands between two numbers have the student choose the number which the counter mostly covers.

- Students write a division sentence using the two numbers they landed on, and try to solve it.

- Students score one point for each correct answer (quotient) to their division sentence. The game ends when one student scores five points.

VARIATION
Students can score points by adding the quotients for each division sentence they solve. At the end of five rounds, students add to find the total number. The student with the highest total wins.

What You Need
- Division Drop game sheet
- Division Drop score sheet
- counter or penny

Number of Players
2

Chapter 3

Game Board 2

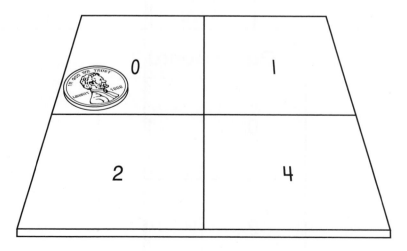

Math Triumphs

Game Sheet
Division Drop

Game Board 1

4	0	16	28	12
24	36	72	20	32
44	56	LOSE A TURN	40	64
2	68	80	48	52
60	76	8	1	36

Game Board 2

0	1
2	4

Math Triumphs

Score Sheet
Division Drop

Scorecard
Name _____

____ ÷ ____ = ____

____ ÷ ____ = ____

____ ÷ ____ = ____

____ ÷ ____ = ____

____ ÷ ____ = ____

Scorecard
Name _____

____ ÷ ____ = ____

____ ÷ ____ = ____

____ ÷ ____ = ____

____ ÷ ____ = ____

____ ÷ ____ = ____

Math Triumphs

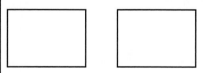
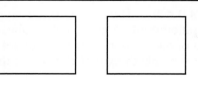

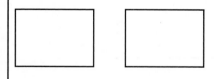
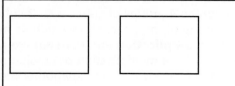

Name _____

Vocabulary and English Language Development

Multiply and divide are opposites.

$$4 \times 2 = 8$$
$$8 \div 4 = 2$$

Complete.

$4 \times$ _____ = _____

$12 \div$ _____ = _____

$3 \times$ _____ = _____

$6 \div$ _____ = _____

_____ × _____ = _____

_____ ÷ _____ = _____

_____ × _____ = _____

_____ ÷ _____ = _____

ACTIVITY Model making 4 trains of 2 cubes each. Point to the multiplication sentence at the top of the page and show students how the 4 groups of cubes with 2 cubes each, have a total of 8 cubes. Then point to the division sentence at the top of the page. Show students how the 8 cubes are separated into 4 groups of 2 cubes each. Tell students that **multiplication** and **division** are related, or the opposite of each other. They can use the same three numbers to solve a multiplication or division problem. Point out that the only thing that changes is the order in which the numbers are written. Make another model as needed.

WORKSHEET DIRECTIONS Have students look at Exercises 1–4. Ask them to use cubes to model the multiplication and division sentences to help them complete the exercises.

Math Triumphs

Name _____

Skills Practice

Write related multiplication and division sentences.

1

_____ × _____ = _____

_____ ÷ _____ = _____

2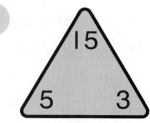

_____ × _____ = _____

_____ ÷ _____ = _____

3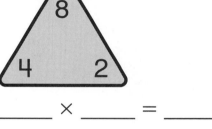

_____ × _____ = _____

_____ ÷ _____ = _____

4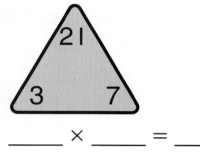

_____ × _____ = _____

_____ ÷ _____ = _____

5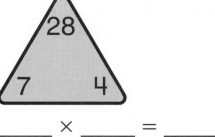

_____ × _____ = _____

_____ ÷ _____ = _____

6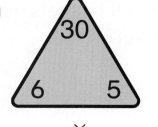

_____ × _____ = _____

_____ ÷ _____ = _____

Chapter 3

Name _____

Problem-Solving Practice

Draw a picture. Solve.

1 Marta has 15 dolls. She puts the dolls in groups of 3. How many dolls are in each group?

There are _____ dolls in each group.

2 Miss Cody has 20 flowers. She puts equal groups of flowers into 5 vases. How many flowers are in each vase?

There are _____ flowers in each vase.

3 Ben has 12 apples. He puts the same number of apples into 4 baskets. How many apples are in each basket?

There are _____ apples in each basket.

Math Triumphs

Homework Practice

Write related multiplication and division sentences.

1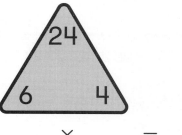

_____ × _____ = _____

_____ ÷ _____ = _____

2

_____ × _____ = _____

_____ ÷ _____ = _____

3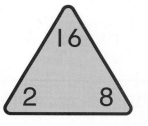

_____ × _____ = _____

_____ ÷ _____ = _____

4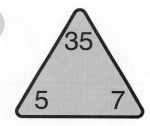

_____ × _____ = _____

_____ ÷ _____ = _____

Draw a picture. Solve.

5 Jamal has 30 stamps. He puts 6 stamps on each page of a stamp album. How many pages does Jamal use for his stamps?

Jamal uses _____ pages for his stamps.

Name _____

Vocabulary and English Language Development

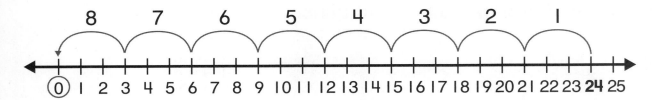

You can subtract to help divide.

$$24 - \underset{1}{3} - \underset{2}{3} - \underset{3}{3} - \underset{4}{3} - \underset{5}{3} - \underset{6}{3} - \underset{7}{3} - \underset{8}{3} = 0$$

$$24 \div 3 = 8$$

Subtract to divide.

1

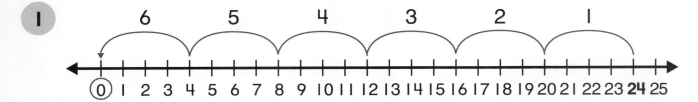

$$24 - 4 - 4 - 4 - 4 - 4 - 4 = 0$$

$$24 \div 4 = \underline{\hspace{1cm}}$$

2

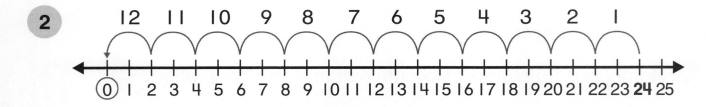

$$24 - 2 - 2 - 2 - 2 - 2 - 2 - 2 - 2 - 2 - 2 - 2 - 2 = 0$$

$$24 \div 2 = \underline{\hspace{1cm}}$$

ACTIVITY Before beginning, review **skip counting** with students. Show 10 cube trains of 2 and help students skip count aloud to 20. Next, draw a number line on the board and repeat the skip counting. Then, show how to skip count backward by 2s from 20. Skip count aloud as you draw jumps on the number line. Then write the **repeated subtraction**: $20 - 2 - 2 - 2 - 2 - 2 - 2 - 2 - 2 - 2 - 2 = 0$. Count the number of 2s aloud and write the answer (10). Relate this to the division sentence $20 \div 2 = 10$. Repeat for counting by 4s and 5s.

WORKSHEET DIRECTIONS Have students skip count along the number lines and use the number of skips to find the quotient.

Name _____

Skills Practice

Divide. Use the number line.

1 16 ÷ 2 = _____

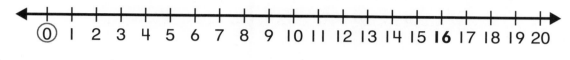

2 20 ÷ 5 = _____

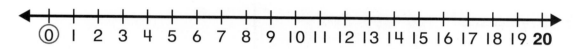

3 18 ÷ 3 = _____

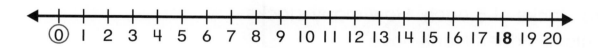

Write a division sentence. Use the number line

4

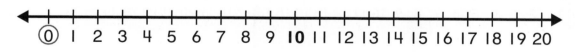

_____ ÷ _____ = _____

5

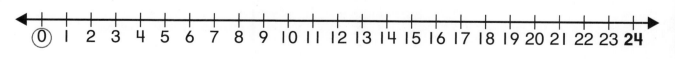

_____ ÷ _____ = _____

Name _____

Problem-Solving Practice

Use a number line to solve.

1 Sara has 28 pennies. She puts 4 pennies
on each page of a coin album.
How many pages does she use?

$28 \div 4 =$ _____

Sara uses _____ pages.

2 Hank has 30 nickels. He puts the nickels
into stacks of 5 each. How many stacks
of nickels does Hank have?

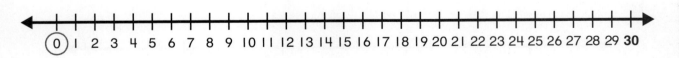

$30 \div 5 =$ _____

Hank has _____ stacks of nickels.

Math Triumphs

Name _____

Homework Practice

1 Divide. Use the number line.

$20 \div 4 =$ _____

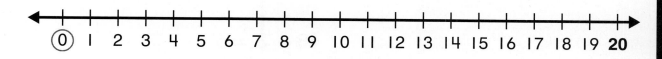

2 Write a division sentence. Use the number line.

_____ $\div$ _____ = _____

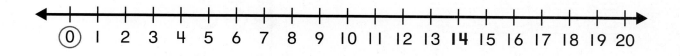

Use a number line to solve.

3 Kim buys 16 treats for her party's goody bags.
She puts 4 treats in each goody bag.
How many goody bags does Kim make?

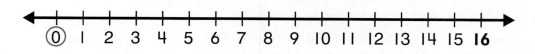

$16 \div 4 =$ _____

Kim makes _____ goody bags.

Name _____

Vocabulary and English Language Development

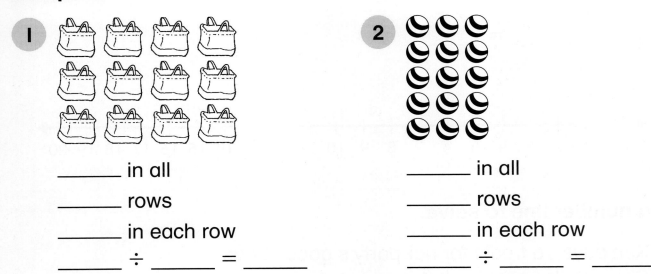

array

1. 18 in all
2. 3 rows
3. 6 in each row

$$18 \div 3 = 6$$

Complete.

1

_____ in all

_____ rows

_____ in each row

_____ ÷ _____ = _____

2

_____ in all

_____ rows

_____ in each row

_____ ÷ _____ = _____

ACTIVITY

- Give students 18 counters. Have them arrange the counters in 3 rows of 6. Ask: "How many counters are there in all?" (18)

- Next, help students count the rows. Ask: "How many rows?" (3) Then, help students identify the number of counters in each row. Ask: "How many in each row?" (6)

- Point to the division sentence 18 ÷ 3 = 6 at the top of the page and tell students they can use **arrays** to solve division sentences. Tell students that 18 is the total number of counters. It is divided by the number of rows, 3. Make sure students notice that the answer, 6, is equal to the number of counters in each row. Point out that the same is true for all the examples on this page.

WORKSHEET DIRECTIONS Have students use the arrays to write each division sentence.

Name _____

Skills Practice

Write a division sentence for each array.

1

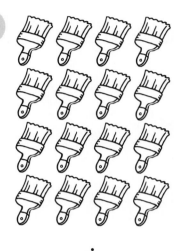

_____ ÷ _____ = _____

2

_____ ÷ _____ = _____

3

_____ ÷ _____ = _____

4

_____ ÷ _____ = _____

5 Draw an array that shows 9 ÷ 3 = 3.

Math Triumphs

Name _____

Problem-Solving Practice

Draw an array picture to solve.

1   Mr. Mooney has 35 oranges. He puts
    equal groups of oranges in 5 baskets.
    How many oranges are in each basket?

    There are _____ oranges in each basket.

2   Miss Wang has 24 crayons. She gives
    6 students an equal number of crayons.
    How many crayons does each student
    get?

    Each student gets _____ crayons.

3   There are 15 cars in a parking lot. The
    cars are parked in equal rows of 3. How
    many cars are in each row?

    There are _____ cars in each row.

4   Charlie has 12 shoes. He puts them in
    pairs of 2. How many pairs of shoes does
    Charlie have?

    Charlie has _____ pairs of shoes.

Math Triumphs

Name _____

Homework Practice

Write a division sentence for each array.

1

_____ ÷ _____ = _____

2

_____ ÷ _____ = _____

3

_____ ÷ _____ = _____

4 Draw an array that shows $14 \div 2 = 7$.

Draw an array picture to solve.

5 Lila has 18 pencils. She puts equal groups of pencils in 3 pencil holders. How many pencils are in each pencil holder?

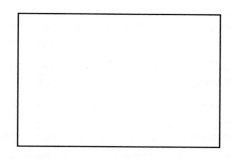

There are _____ pencils in each pencil holder.

Chapter 3

Name _____

Vocabulary and English Language Development

area model

28 squares in all

4 rows

7 squares in each row

$28 \div 4 = 7$

Complete.

1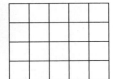

_____ squares in all

_____ rows

_____ squares in each row

_____ ÷ _____ = _____

2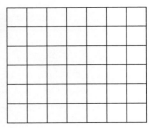

_____ squares in all

_____ rows

_____ squares in each row

_____ ÷ _____ = _____

ACTIVITY

- Have students cover the front of their math books with one-inch squares. Ask students to count and tell the total number of squares it takes to cover the front of their books.

- Run your fingers over one row and have students repeat the word *row*. Help them count the number of rows it takes to cover the front of their book.

- Then, ask students to count the number of squares in each row. Count aloud with students as you write on the board the total number of squares, number of rows, and number of squares in each row. Write the corresponding division sentence on the board. Say the sentence aloud with students.

WORKSHEET DIRECTIONS Have students count the total number of squares, the number of rows, and the number of squares in each row, to write the corresponding division sentence.

Math Triumphs

Name _____

Skills Practice

Write a division sentence.

1

_____ squares in all

_____ rows and _____ columns

_____ ÷ _____ = _____

2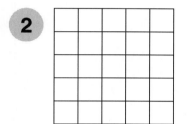

_____ squares in all

_____ rows and _____ columns

_____ ÷ _____ = _____

3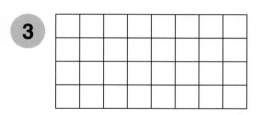

_____ squares in all

_____ rows and _____ columns

_____ ÷ _____ = _____

4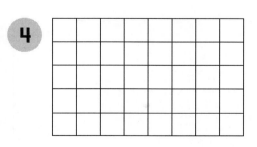

_____ squares in all

_____ rows and _____ columns

_____ ÷ _____ = _____

Name _____

Problem-Solving Practice

Draw an area model to solve.

1 Sasha covers a rectangle with 36 square tiles. She places 9 tiles in each row. How many rows of tiles does Sasha make?

Sasha makes _____ rows of tiles.

2 Brett covers the top of a box with 28 square tiles. He places 4 tiles in each row. How many rows of tiles does Brett make?

Brett makes _____ rows of tiles.

3 Ming covers the top of a desk with 50 square tiles. He places 10 tiles in each row. How many rows of tiles does Ming make?

Ming makes _____ rows of tiles.

4 Jorge covers a place mat with 49 square tiles. He places 7 tiles in each row. How many rows of tiles does Jorge make?

Jorge makes _____ rows of tiles.

Math Triumphs

Name _____

Homework Practice

Write a division sentence.

1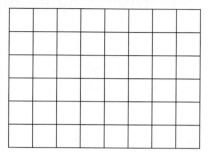

_____ squares in all

_____ rows and _____ columns

_____ ÷ _____ = _____

2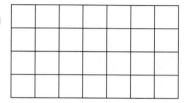

_____ squares in all

_____ rows and _____ columns

_____ ÷ _____ = _____

Draw an area model to solve.

3 Megan covers the top of a rectangle with 48 square tiles. She places 8 tiles in each row. How many rows of tiles does Megan make?

Megan makes _____ rows of tiles.

Solve.

4 Harley places 54 square tiles in equal rows of 9. How many tiles are in each column? How do you know?

_____

_____

_____

Name _____

Vocabulary and English Language Development

Divide with 0.	**Divide by 1.**	**Divide by itself.**
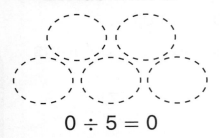	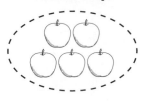	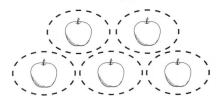
$0 \div 5 = 0$	$5 \div 1 = 5$	$5 \div 5 = 1$

Divide.

1
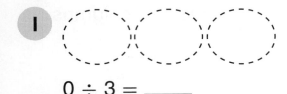

$0 \div 3 = $ _____

2

$4 \div 4 = $ _____

3

$3 \div 1 = $ _____

4

$0 \div 2 = $ _____

ACTIVITY

- Draw 5 empty circles on the board. Ask students to tell the number of apples they see inside the circles you drew (0). Write $0 \div 5 = 0$. Explain to students that when 0 is divided by any number, except 0, the answer is 0.

- Draw 5 apples and enclose them in a single dashed circle. Have students count the number of apples you drew inside the circle (5). Write $5 \div 1 = 5$. There is one group of 5. Explain to students that any number divided by 1 is that number.

- Draw 5 individual dashed circles with an apple inside each circle. Have a volunteer tell you the number of apples you drew inside each circle (1). Write $5 \div 5 = 1$. There are 5 groups of 1. Tell students that any number, except 0, divided by itself is 1.

WORKSHEET DIRECTIONS Have students use the pictures from each exercise above to help them find the answer to each division sentence.

Name _____

Skills Practice

Write a division sentence.

1 0 muffins in 6 baking cups

_____ ÷ _____ = _____

2 12 eggs in 1 carton

_____ ÷ _____ = _____

3 11 apples in 1 basket

_____ ÷ _____ = _____

4 7 ice cubes in 7 cups

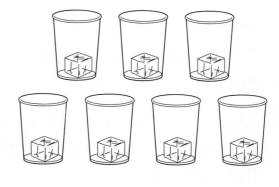

_____ ÷ _____ = _____

Divide.

5 24 ÷ 1 = _____

6 0 ÷ 14 = _____

7 0 ÷ 1 = _____

8 42 ÷ 42 = _____

9 39 ÷ 39 = _____

10 54 ÷ 1 = _____

Chapter 3

Name _____

Problem-Solving Practice

Write a division sentence.
Draw a picture to check your answer.

1 Nathan has 6 flowers. If he has only one vase, how many flowers are in the vase?

_____ ÷ _____ = _____

There are _____ flowers in the vase.

2 Annie has 0 pencils. She has 7 pencil holders. How many pencils are in the pencil holders?

_____ ÷ _____ = _____

There are _____ pencils in the pencil holders.

3 Manny has 4 apples. If he has only one basket, how many apples are in the basket?

_____ ÷ _____ = _____

There are _____ apples in the basket.

4 Mei has 22 marbles. If she divides them equally among her 22 friends, how many marbles does each friend get?

_____ ÷ _____ = _____

Each friend will get _____ marble.

Name _____

Homework Practice

Write a division sentence.

1 6 scoops on one cone

_____ ÷ _____ = _____

2 0 oranges in 9 bags

_____ ÷ _____ = _____

Divide.

3 $0 \div 47 =$ _____

4 $100 \div 1 =$ _____

5 $37 \div 37 =$ _____

6 $13 \div 1 =$ _____

Write a division sentence. Draw a picture.

7 There are 30 students. If there is only one bus, how many students are on the bus?

_____ ÷ _____ = _____

Solve.

8 Carson has 18 party favors. He divides them equally among 18 children. How many party favors does each child get? How do you know?

_____

_____

Name _____

Vocabulary and English Language Development

Skip count backward.

by 2s:

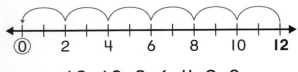

12, 10, 8, 6, 4, 2, 0

by 5s:

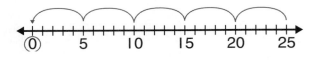

25, 20, 15, 10, 5, 0

Skip count. Divide.

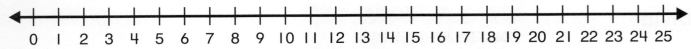

0 1 2 3 4 5 6 7 8 9 10 11 12 13 14 15 16 17 18 19 20 21 22 23 24 25

1 $16 \div 2 =$ _____

_____, _____, _____, _____, _____, _____, _____, _____, _____

2 $14 \div 2 =$ _____

_____, _____, _____, _____, _____, _____, _____, _____

3 $25 \div 5 =$ _____

_____, _____, _____, _____, _____, _____

4 $20 \div 5 =$ _____

_____, _____, _____, _____, _____

ACTIVITY Display or draw a number line. Starting with the number 12, skip count backward to 0 aloud. Help students count along with you. Write $12 \div 2 = ?$ on the board. Skip count backward again, making a checkmark above each number you count. Next, count the number of checkmarks aloud as students count with you. Write $12 \div 2 = 6$. Tell students that the number of skips is the answer to the **division** sentence. Say the division sentence aloud as students repeat after you. Repeat for $25 \div 5 = 5$.

WORKSHEET DIRECTIONS Have students use the number line to skip count and divide.

Math Triumphs

Name _____

Skills Practice

Write each division sentence.

0 1 2 3 4 5 6 7 8 9 10 11 12 13 14 15 16 17 18 19 20 21 22 23 24 25 26 27 28 29 30

1 Mr. Potter has 30 tomato plants. He wants to plant a garden with 5 plants in each row. How many rows will Mr. Potter have in his garden?

_____ ÷ _____ = _____

Mr. Potter will have _____ rows in his garden.

2 Nicholas divides 16 pencils into 2 equal groups. How many pencils does Nicholas put in each group?

_____ ÷ _____ = _____

Nicholas puts _____ pencils in each group.

Skip count backward to divide.

3 $18 \div 2 =$ _____

18, _____, _____, _____, _____, _____, _____, _____, _____, _____

4 $40 \div 5 =$ _____

40, _____, _____, _____, _____, _____, _____, _____, _____

Chapter 3

Name _____

Problem-Solving Practice

Use a number line. Skip count backward to solve.

1 Elliot puts 25 baseball cards in equal
groups of 5. How many groups of
baseball cards does Elliot have?

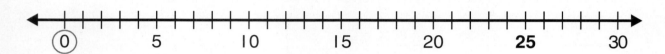

Elliot has _____ groups of baseball cards.

2 Latisha displays 20 dolls in sets of 2. How many
sets of dolls does Latisha have?

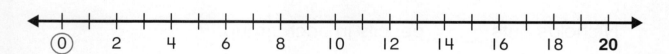

Latisha has _____ sets of dolls.

3 Miss Peters makes 55 muffins. She puts
5 muffins on each plate. How many
plates does Miss Peters use?

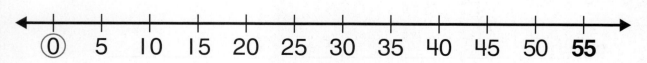

Miss Peters uses _____ plates.

Math Triumphs

Name _____

Homework Practice

Use a number line. Skip count backward to solve.

1 Nagi puts 25 flowers in equal bunches of 5.
How many flowers are in each bunch?

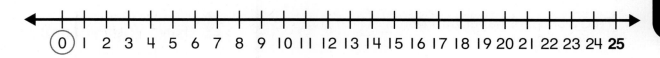

_____ ÷ _____ = _____

There are _____ flowers in each bunch.

2 Rory lines up 16 action figures in rows of 2.
How many rows of action figures does he have?

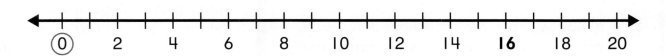

Rory has _____ rows of action figures.

Skip count backward to divide.

3 $35 \div 5 =$ _____

_____, _____, _____, _____, _____, _____, _____, _____

4 $14 \div 2 =$ _____

_____, _____, _____, _____, _____, _____, _____, _____

Chapter 3

Name _____

Foldables Study Organizer

Dinah Zike's Foldables

Help students with the steps below to create their Foldables.

1. Fold a sheet of paper into thirds from top to bottom.

2. Then fold the paper into thirds from side to side. (Fold the paper in half, and then fold it in half again.)

3. Unfold the paper and draw lines down each crease to create a chart of three columns and four rows. At the top of each column write 100, 10, and 1.

   Row 2: Write a number in standard form. (Example: 257)

   Row 3: Write the number in expanded form. (Example: 200 + 50 + 7)

   Row 4: Write a number in word form. (Example: two hundred fifty-seven)

TAKING NOTES

As students read through the chapter, have them use their Foldable to write the standard, expanded and word form of numbers.

USING YOUR FOLDABLE

As students review, have them check their understanding by creating additional Foldables and writing additional examples.

USING YOUR FOLDABLE

Have the students work in groups of three, and take turns choosing a number. One student will give both members of their group the same number. One member will write the expanded word form and the other member will write the word form of the number.

Games and Puzzles
The Big Number Spin

GET READY
Give each pair of students a sharpened pencil, a paper clip, a copy of the spinner, and a copy of the score sheet.

DIRECTIONS:
- Students take turns. The first student places the point of the pencil inside the paper clip and positions it on the spinner. The student spins and writes the number in the first row of the scorecard for the first round. The student spins three more times to write three more numbers in the same row.

- The student uses the four numbers to write the greatest number possible in the place-value chart. The student then writes that number in the *big number* space below.

- The second student repeats these steps during his or her turn.

- Students then compare thousands. The student whose number has the greater digit in the thousands place scores a point. If the thousands digits are the same, it is a tie and both players score a point. Students alternate who starts for each round.

- Students continue to spin and write numbers for three rounds of play. The first student that reaches three points wins the game.

VARIATION
Students spin and make a number with the least amount of thousands possible.

What You Need
- The Big Number Spin spinner
- The Big Number Spin score sheet
- paper clip
- pencil

Number of Players
2

Spinner
The Big Number Spin

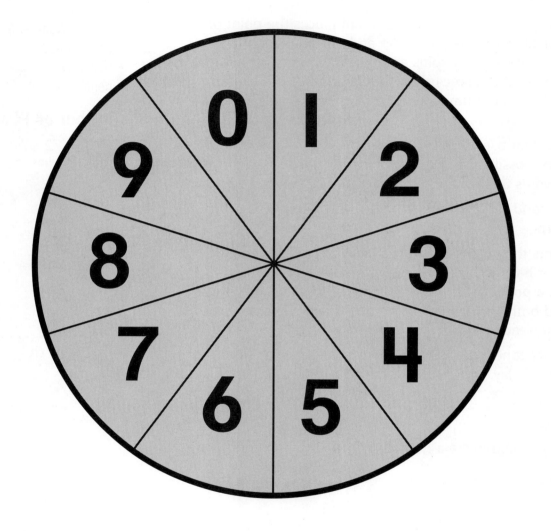

Score Sheet
The Big Number Spin

Round 1

| Player 1 _____ | Player 2 _____ |

Numbers spun

_____ _____ _____ _____

thousands	hundreds	tens	ones

The big number _____

Numbers spun

_____ _____ _____ _____

thousands	hundreds	tens	ones

The big number _____

Round 2

| Player 1 _____ | Player 2 _____ |

Numbers spun

_____ _____ _____ _____

thousands	hundreds	tens	ones

The big number _____

Numbers spun

_____ _____ _____ _____

thousands	hundreds	tens	ones

The big number _____

Round 3

| Player 1 _____ | Player 2 _____ |

Numbers spun

_____ _____ _____ _____

thousands	hundreds	tens	ones

The big number _____

Numbers spun

_____ _____ _____ _____

thousands	hundreds	tens	ones

The big number _____

Name _____

Vocabulary and English Language Development

3 tens   4 ones = 34
                    └── **standard form**

Write the number.

1

_____ tens   _____ ones

2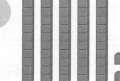

_____ tens   _____ ones

3

_____ tens   _____ one

4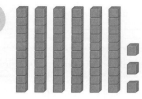

_____ tens   _____ ones

5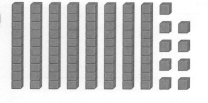

_____ tens   _____ ones

6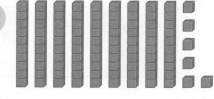

_____ tens   _____ ones

ACTIVITY Display 5 tens rods and 6 ones. Count the number of **tens** aloud and write *5 tens* on the board. Count the number of **ones** aloud and write *6 ones*. Then write *56*. Tell students that 56 is written in **standard form**. Give students tens and ones rods. Write *3 tens* and *4 ones* on the board. Have students model the number and write it in standard form. Say the number aloud and have students repeat after you.

WORKSHEET DIRECTIONS Students count the number of tens and ones, then write the number in standard form.

Math Triumphs

Name _____

Skills Practice

Write each missing number.

1
61	62	63		65	66	67	68	69	70

2 16, 17, 18, _____, 20

3 24, 25, _____, 27, 28

4 _____, 80, 81, 82, 83

5 37, _____, 39, 40, 41

6 88, 89, _____, 91, 92

7 40, 41, 42, _____, 44

8 Match each number with the correct place values.

| 52 | 47 | 95 | 77 |

9 tens 5 ones	5 tens 2 ones	4 tens 7 ones	7 tens 7 ones

Complete each place value.

9 18 = _____ ten _____ ones

10 67 = _____ tens _____ ones

11 30 = _____ tens _____ one

12 85 = _____ tens _____ ones

13 49 = _____ tens _____ ones

14 12 = _____ ten _____ ones

15 95 = _____ tens _____ ones

16 71 = _____ tens _____ one

Name _____

Problem-Solving Practice

Solve. Find the mystery number.

1 The mystery number comes just after 45 and just before 47. What is the mystery number?

41	42	43	44	45		47	48	49	50

Count on: 41, _____, _____, _____, _____, _____, _____

The mystery number is _____.

2 The mystery number comes just after 73 and just before 75. What is the mystery number?

71	72	73		75	76	77	78	79	80

Count on: 71, _____, _____, _____, _____

The mystery number is _____.

3 The mystery number comes just after 26 and just before 28. What is the mystery number?

21	22	23	24	25	26		28	29	30

Count on: 21, _____, _____, _____, _____, _____, _____, _____

The mystery number is _____.

Name _____

Homework Practice

Write each missing number.

1

41	42	43	44	45	46	47		49	50

2 52, _____, 54, 55, 56

3 _____, 20, 21, 22, 23

4 28, 29, _____, 31, 32

5 92, 93, 94, _____, 96

Complete each place value.

6 45 = _____ tens _____ ones

7 19 = _____ ten _____ ones

8 38 = _____ tens _____ ones

9 71 = _____ tens _____ one

10 67 = _____ tens _____ ones

11 80 = _____ tens _____ one

Solve.

12 The mystery number comes just after 64 and just before 66. What is the mystery number?

61	62	63	64		66	67	68	69	70

Count on: ___61___, _____, _____, _____, _____, _____

The mystery number is _____.

Name _____

Vocabulary and English Language Development

standard form	23
expanded form	20 + 3
word form	twenty-three

Complete each table.

1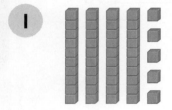

standard form	
expanded form	
word form	forty-five

2

standard form	
expanded form	
word form	thirty-six

3

standard form	
expanded form	
word form	nineteen

ACTIVITY Display 3 tens rods and 5 ones. Count the number of tens aloud and write *30* on the board. Explain that 3 tens rods are equal to 3 tens, or 30. Count the number of ones aloud and write *5*. Explain that 5 ones are equal to 5. Then write *30 + 5 = 35*. Tell students that *30 + 5* is written in **expanded form** and *35* is written in **standard form**. Give students tens and ones rods. Write *42* on the board. Have students model the number and write it in standard form and expanded form. Say the number aloud and have students repeat after you.

WORKSHEET DIRECTIONS Students count the number of tens and ones, then write the number in standard form and expanded form.

Math Triumphs

Name _____

Skills Practice

Write each number in expanded form.

1 28 = _____ + _____

2 76 = _____ + _____

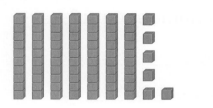

3 43 = _____ + _____

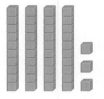

4 35 = _____ + _____

Complete each table.

5

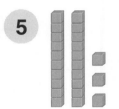

standard form	23
expanded form	
word form	

6

standard form	89
expanded form	
word form	

7

standard form	
expanded form	
word form	fifty-seven

Lesson 4-2

Name ____________________

Problem-Solving Practice

Work backward to solve.

1 I am greater than 30, but less than 40.
I have 3 tens and 8 ones.
What number am I?

3 tens = ______

8 ones = ______

______ + ______ = ______

The number is ______.

2 I am less than 70, but greater than 60.
I have 6 tens and 4 ones.
What number am I?

6 tens = ______

4 ones = ______

______ + ______ = ______

The number is ______.

3 I am greater than 90, but less than 100.
I have 9 tens and 2 ones.
What number am I?

9 tens = ______

2 ones = ______

______ + ______ = ______

The number is ______.

Name _____

Homework Practice

Write each number in expanded form.

1 42 = _____ + _____

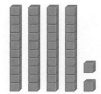

2 33 = _____ + _____

Complete each table.

3

standard form	63
expanded form	
word form	

4

standard form	
expanded form	
word form	eighty-five

Work backward to solve.

5 I am greater than 40, but less than 50.
I have 4 tens and 9 ones.
What number am I?

4 tens = _____

9 ones = _____

_____ + _____ = _____

The number is _____.

Name _____

Vocabulary and English Language Development

number line

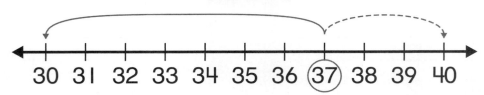

37 rounds to 40.

Draw jumps. Round to the nearest ten.

1

50 51 52 53 54 55 56 57 58 59 60

52 rounds to _____.

2

20 21 22 23 24 25 26 27 28 29 30

27 rounds to _____.

3

70 71 72 73 74 75 76 77 78 79 80

74 rounds to _____.

ACTIVITY Create a **number line** on the floor using masking tape and index cards. Label the numbers 40 to 50. Have a student stand on 47. Ask the student to jump to 50. Count the number of jumps aloud as the student jumps. Repeat the procedure for jumping from 47 to 40. Tell students that there are fewer jumps from 47 to 50, so 47 **rounds** to 50. Write *47 rounds* to *50* on the board. Then repeat with other numbers, including 45. Students may be confused about why 45 rounds up and not down; explain that any number with a 5 or higher in the ones place will round up.

WORKSHEET DIRECTIONS Students draw jumps for each number line and count aloud. Then they complete each exercise.

Name _____

Skills Practice

Use the number line to round each number.

1 46 rounds to _____.

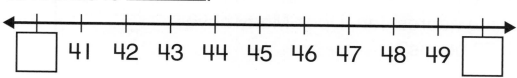

41 42 43 44 45 46 47 48 49

2 83 rounds to _____.

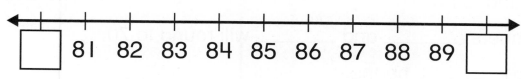

81 82 83 84 85 86 87 88 89

Fill in the blanks.

3 37 is between

_____ and _____.

37 rounds to _____.

4 62 is between

_____ and _____.

62 rounds to _____.

5 43 is between

_____ and _____.

43 rounds to _____.

6 18 is between

_____ and _____.

18 rounds to _____.

Write the tens and ones. Then round to the nearest ten.

7

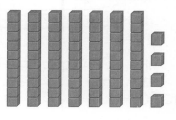

_____ tens _____ ones rounds to _____.

Math Triumphs

Name _____

Problem-Solving Practice

Round to solve.

1 Marty has about 80 beans in a jar when he rounds to the nearest ten. Does Marty have 71, 74, or 79 beans?

The number _____ is closest to 80.

It will round to 80.

The numbers _____ and _____ will round to 70.

Marty has _____ beans.

2 Denzel has about 40 marbles when he rounds to the nearest ten. Does Denzel have 42, 47, or 49 marbles?

The number _____ is closest to 40.

It will round to 40.

The numbers _____ and _____ will round to 50.

Denzel has _____ marbles.

3 Zach has about 30 apples when he rounds to the nearest ten. Does Zach have 33, 36, or 38 apples?

The number _____ is closest to 30.

It will round to 30.

The numbers _____ and _____ will round to 40.

Zach has _____ apples.

Math Triumphs

Name _____

Homework Practice

Use the number line to round the number.

1 67 rounds to _____.

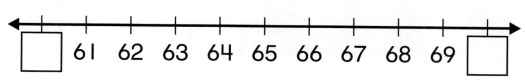

Fill in the blanks.

2 41 is between

_____ and _____.

41 rounds to _____.

3 86 is between

_____ and _____.

86 rounds to _____.

Write the tens and ones. Then round to the nearest ten.

4

_____ tens _____ ones rounds to _____.

Solve.

5 Tyler has about 60 pennies when he rounds to the nearest ten. Does Tyler have 53, 54, or 58 pennies?

The number _____ is closest to 60.

It will round to 60.

The numbers _____ and _____ will round to 50.

Tyler has _____ pennies.

Name _____

Vocabulary and English Language Development

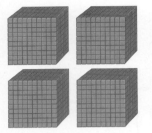

4 thousands

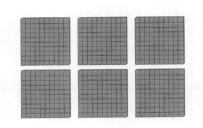

6 hundreds

3 tens   2 ones

place-value chart ⟶

thousands	hundreds	tens	ones
4	6	3	2

Write the number.

1

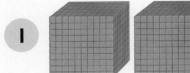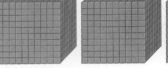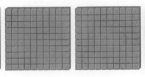

_____ thousands _____ hundreds _____ tens _____ ones

_____

2

thousands	hundreds	tens	ones
5	9	2	6

_____ thousands _____ hundreds _____ tens _____ ones

_____

ACTIVITY Draw a **place-value chart** on the board and write the number *3,627*. Model the number using place-value blocks, then write *3 **thousands**, 6 hundreds, 2 tens, and 7 ones*. Say the numbers aloud and have students repeat after you. Then write *3,627* and say the number aloud. Students should again repeat after you. Repeat, having students model the number 2,849.

WORKSHEET DIRECTIONS Students can use place-value blocks to model the numbers in each exercise. Work with students as they model the numbers saying each number aloud.

Name _____

Skills Practice

Complete each place-value chart.

1 A number has 7 thousands, 3 hundreds, 6 tens, and 1 one. What is the number?

thousands	hundreds	tens	ones

2 A number has 3 thousands, 7 hundreds, 0 tens, and 9 ones. What is the number?

thousands	hundreds	tens	ones

Write each number.

3 _____

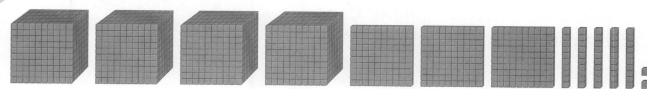

4 A number has 8 thousands, 2 hundreds, and 5 ones. What is the number?

_____

5 A number has 2 thousands, 4 hundreds, and 9 tens. What is the number?

_____

6 How many hundreds are in the number 4,693?

_____

Name _____

Problem-Solving Practice

Solve. Use a place-value chart.

1 Jessie's house has a number. The house number has 4 thousands, 8 tens, and 3 ones. What is Jessie's house number?

The number is _____.

2 Liz punches a number into a calculator. The number has 2 thousands, 9 hundreds, 4 tens, and 5 ones. What number does Liz punch into the calculator?

The number is _____.

3 Mr. Green drives a car. The car has a license plate with a number. The number has 6 thousands, 4 hundreds, and 8 ones. What is Mr. Green's license plate number?

The number is _____.

Name _____

Homework Practice

Complete the place-value chart.

1 A number has 3 thousands, 2 hundreds, 8 tens, and 7 ones. What is the number?

thousands	hundreds	tens	ones

Write each number.

2 _____

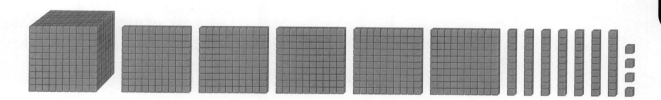

3 A number has 5 thousands, 8 hundreds, and 9 ones. What is the number?

_____

Solve. Use a place-value chart.

4 Mark's concert ticket has a number. The number has 3 thousands, 8 hundreds, 6 tens, and 5 ones? What is the number on Mark's concert ticket?

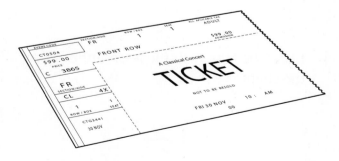

The number is _____.

Foldables Study Organizer

Dinah Zike's Foldables

Help students with the steps below to create their Foldables.

1. Begin with four sheets of $8\frac{1}{2}'' \times 11''$ paper. Stack four sheets of paper. Place each sheet $\frac{3}{4}$ inch apart.

2. Roll up the edges, so all tabs are the same size.

3. Crease and staple along the fold.

4. Label the tabs with the lesson titles from the chapter.

TAKING NOTES

As students read through the chapter, have them write one example from each lesson.

USING YOUR FOLDABLE

Have students check their understanding by creating different examples.

USING YOUR FOLDABLE

In pairs, choose a lesson and have students take turns drawing a model of a fraction from that lesson.

Chapter 5
Games and Puzzles
Tossing Fractions

DIRECTIONS:

- Explain to students that they are going to make fractions from numbers on the number cubes and match them to the fractions on each step of the game board.

- Tell students that they will play **Tossing Fractions** with a partner. Partners will toss the number cubes to determine the first player. The player who rolls a greater number goes first.

- Each player places his or her game piece at the bottom of the board. To begin, the first player tosses both number cubes. The lesser number is the numerator, and the greater number is the denominator.

- If the fraction matches a number on the first step, the player names the fraction, and then moves his or her game piece to that step.

- If there is no match, allow the player to toss one or both number cubes a second time. If after a second toss, there is still no match, his or her turn is over.

- Have players take turns tossing the number cubes and making fractions. The goal of each turn is to match a fraction on the next step and move there.

- The first player to make a match on the top step wins.

VARIATION

Players can switch sides or toss number cubes only one time per turn.

What You Need

- 2 number cubes (1–6)
- 2 game pieces
- Tossing Fractions game board

Number of Players

2

Game Board

Tossing Fractions

Play with a partner. Match the fractions.

$\frac{3}{5}$ $\frac{1}{4}$	$\frac{2}{6}$ $\frac{1}{5}$

$\frac{1}{6}$ $\frac{2}{5}$ $\frac{3}{4}$	$\frac{1}{4}$ $\frac{2}{6}$ $\frac{3}{5}$

$\frac{1}{1}$ $\frac{2}{4}$ $\frac{3}{5}$ $\frac{5}{6}$	$\frac{1}{5}$ $\frac{2}{3}$ $\frac{3}{4}$ $\frac{5}{6}$

$\frac{1}{2}$ $\frac{2}{5}$ $\frac{3}{6}$ $\frac{4}{4}$ $\frac{5}{6}$	$\frac{1}{4}$ $\frac{2}{3}$ $\frac{3}{6}$ $\frac{4}{5}$ $\frac{5}{5}$

$\frac{1}{3}$ $\frac{2}{2}$ $\frac{3}{5}$ $\frac{4}{6}$ $\frac{5}{5}$ $\frac{1}{4}$	$\frac{1}{1}$ $\frac{2}{6}$ $\frac{3}{5}$ $\frac{4}{6}$ $\frac{1}{3}$ $\frac{2}{4}$

$\frac{1}{6}$ $\frac{2}{5}$ $\frac{3}{4}$ $\frac{4}{4}$ $\frac{1}{2}$ $\frac{2}{3}$ $\frac{5}{6}$	$\frac{1}{5}$ $\frac{2}{4}$ $\frac{3}{3}$ $\frac{4}{5}$ $\frac{1}{6}$ $\frac{2}{3}$ $\frac{6}{6}$

START Player 1	START Player 2

Math Triumphs

Name _____

Vocabulary and English Language Development

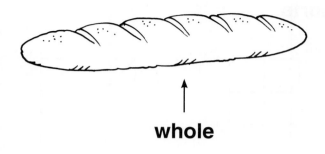

whole

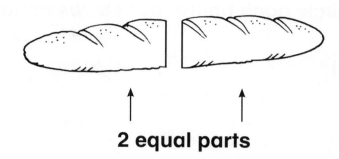

2 equal parts

Write how many equal parts.

1

_____ equal parts

2

_____ equal parts

3

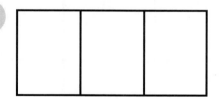

_____ equal parts

4

_____ equal parts

ACTIVITY Hold up a sheet of paper, and have students do the same. Say: "This is a **whole** sheet of paper. Fold it in half and then unfold it." Ask: "How many **equal parts** are there?" (2). Count the parts aloud with the students. Then tell students to refold the paper in half and then fold it in half again. Have them unfold the paper. Ask: "How many equal parts are there now?" (4). Count the parts aloud with students as you point to each one. Repeat two more times.

WORKSHEET DIRECTIONS Tell students to look at each shape and identify the number of equal parts. Tell them to write the number of equal parts.

Name _____

Skills Practice

Circle each figure that shows equal parts.

1

2

How many equal parts are there?

3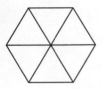

_____ equal parts

4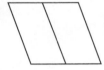

_____ equal parts

5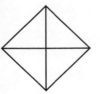

_____ equal parts

6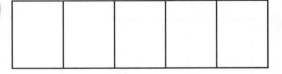

_____ equal parts

7

_____ equal parts

8

_____ equal parts

Math Triumphs

Name _____

Problem-Solving Practice

Solve.

1 Mrs. Cole wants to cut the pie into 6 equal parts. Show how the pie will look after she cuts it.

2 Terry wants to cut a yogurt bar into 3 equal parts. Show how the bar will look after he cuts it.

3 Rosa wants to cut a paper heart into 2 equal parts. Show how the heart will look after she cuts it.

4 Justin wants to cut the shape into 8 equal parts. Show how his shape will look after he cuts it.

5 Shirley has a string that she wants to cut into 3 equal parts. Show how her string will look after she cuts it.

Chapter 5

Name _____

Homework Practice

Circle each figure that shows equal parts.

1   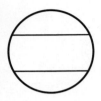   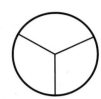   2

How many equal parts are there?

3

_____ equal parts

4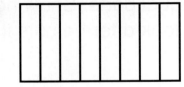

_____ equal parts

Solve.

5   Shep wants to cut a stick of gum into 3 equal
     pieces. Show how the stick of gum will look
     after he cuts it.

6   Alfonzo cuts a square into 8 equal parts.
     How can you show this?

_____

_____

Math Triumphs

Name _____

Vocabulary and English Language Development

fractions

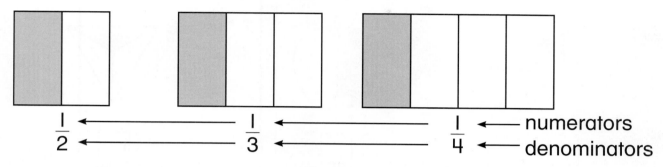

numerators
denominators

Color one part. Write the numerator.

Chapter 5

1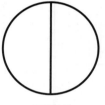

$\dfrac{\square}{2}$

2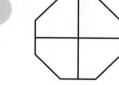

$\dfrac{\square}{4}$

3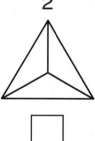

$\dfrac{\square}{3}$

4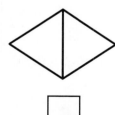

$\dfrac{\square}{2}$

ACTIVITY On the board, draw a circle, a square, and a rectangle. Have a volunteer divide the circle into two equal parts and color one part. Explain to students that the part that was colored is $\frac{1}{2}$. Write $\frac{1}{2}$ under the figure. Tell them that $\frac{1}{2}$ is called a **_fraction_**. Point to the 1 and tell them that the 1 is called the **_numerator_**. Then, point to the 2 and tell them that the 2 is called the **_denominator_**. Explain to students that the numerator tells the number of shaded parts and the denominator tells the number of equal parts. Repeat for $\frac{1}{4}$ and $\frac{1}{3}$ using the square and the rectangle.

WORKSHEET DIRECTIONS Have students color one part of each figure. Then have them write the numerator in the box.

Math Triumphs   **Lesson 5-2   A111**

Name _____

Skills Practice

Write the fraction that names each shaded part.

1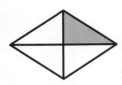

☐
—
☐

2

☐
—
☐

3

☐
—
☐

4

☐
—
☐

5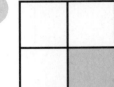

☐
—
☐

6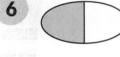

☐
—
☐

7

☐
—
☐

8

☐
—
☐

9

☐
—
☐

Math Triumphs

Name _____

Problem-Solving Practice

Solve.

1 Marcos is drawing a poster. He wants to color $\frac{1}{4}$ of the poster. Show what the poster will look like. Explain.

_____

_____

2 Lori cut out a paper snowflake. She colors $\frac{1}{2}$ of the snowflake. Show what the snowflake will look like. Explain.

_____

_____

3 Kevin made a spinner and colored $\frac{1}{3}$ of it. Show what the spinner will look like. Explain.

_____

_____

4 Mr. Lopez made a pizza. He put pepperoni on $\frac{1}{4}$ of the pizza. Show what the pizza will look like. Explain.

_____

_____

Math Triumphs

Name _____

Homework Practice

Write the fraction that names each shaded part.

1 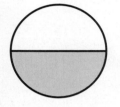 ☐/☐

2 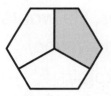 ☐/☐

3 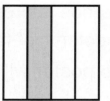 ☐/☐

4 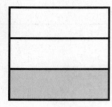 ☐/☐

5 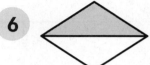   ☐/☐

6   ☐/☐

Solve.

7 Tyler folds a sheet of paper and colors $\frac{1}{4}$ of the paper. Show what the paper will look like. Explain.

_____

_____

8 Mrs. James is knitting a scarf. She wants to make $\frac{1}{2}$ of the scarf blue. How can you show this?

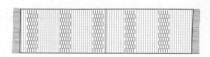

_____

_____

Math Triumphs

Name _____

Vocabulary and English Language Development

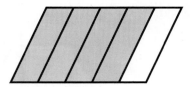

$\dfrac{4}{5}$ ← numerator
← denominator

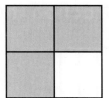

$\dfrac{3}{4}$ ← numerator
← denominator

Color to show the fraction.

1
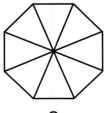
$\dfrac{3}{8}$

2

$\dfrac{5}{6}$

3
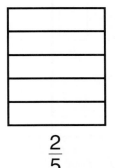
$\dfrac{2}{5}$

4
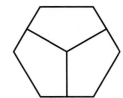
$\dfrac{3}{3}$

Chapter 5

ACTIVITY On the board, draw a rectangle. Divide it into three equal parts. Say: "Three equal parts make up the whole." Color in two parts. Write the fraction $\frac{2}{3}$ under the rectangle. Point to the 2. Say: "This part of the fraction tells the number of parts that are colored." Then, point to the 3. Say: "This part of the fraction tells how many equal parts there are in all." Have students fold a sheet of paper into six equal parts, color two parts, and name the fraction $\left(\frac{2}{6}\right)$. Have them color three more parts and name the fraction $\left(\frac{5}{6}\right)$. Be sure students read fractions from top to bottom, such as two thirds for $\frac{2}{3}$.

WORKSHEET DIRECTIONS Tell students to read each fraction and determine how many parts should be colored. Remind students that the number of colored parts is the **numerator** and the total number of equal parts is the **denominator**.

Math Triumphs

Name _____

Skills Practice

Write each fraction that names each shaded part.

1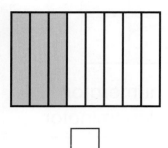

$$\frac{\square}{8}$$

2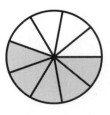

$$\frac{\square}{9}$$

3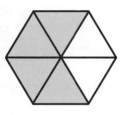

$$\frac{\square}{6}$$

4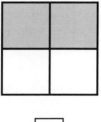

$$\frac{\square}{4}$$

5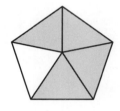

$$\frac{\square}{5}$$

6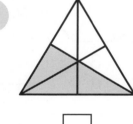

$$\frac{\square}{6}$$

7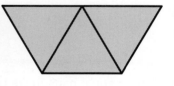

$$\frac{\square}{3}$$

8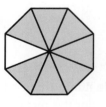

$$\frac{\square}{8}$$

9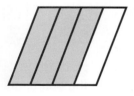

$$\frac{\square}{4}$$

Math Triumphs

Problem-Solving Practice

Solve. Circle your answer.

1 Todd wants to cut a sandwich so that he and three of his friends each get an equal part. Which sandwich shows the way Todd should cut the sandwich? Explain.

_____

_____

2 Maria has seven friends at her party. Which cake can she share so that they each get one equal slice? Explain.

_____

_____

3 Will and four friends want to share an apple pie. Which pie can they share so that each child gets one slice? Explain.

_____

_____

Name _____

Homework Practice

Write each fraction that names each shaded part.

1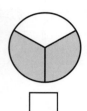

$\dfrac{\square}{3}$

2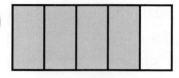

$\dfrac{\square}{5}$

3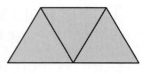

$\dfrac{\square}{3}$

4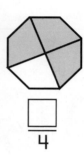

$\dfrac{\square}{4}$

5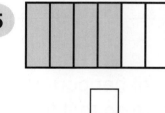

$\dfrac{\square}{6}$

6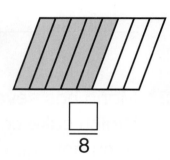

$\dfrac{\square}{8}$

Solve. Circle your answer.

7 Ashley folds a paper rectangle. She wants to use four colored pencils to color each equal part of the rectangle. Which rectangle did Ashley fold? Explain.

          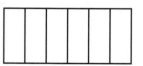

_____

_____

_____

Name _____

Vocabulary and English Language Development

numerator ——————→ $\dfrac{1}{5}$ footballs in all $\dfrac{4}{5}$ _____

denominator ——————→ footballs in all

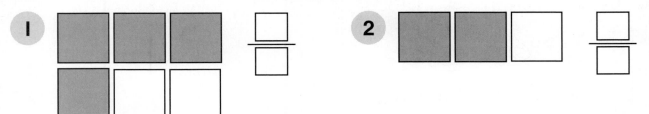

Write the fraction for the shaded parts.

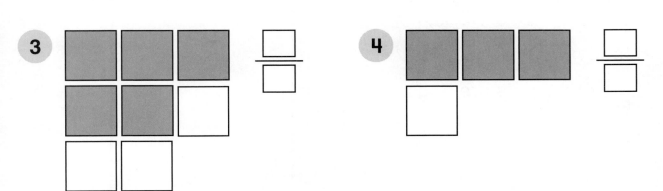

1

2

3

4

ACTIVITY Write *4 out of 5* on the board. Then draw five circles and shade in four of them. Say: "There are five circles and four of the circles are shaded. The fraction for the shaded part is $\frac{4}{5}$." Repeat for $\frac{2}{3}$. Then have students use color counters to model other parts of a set such as, $\frac{3}{4}$, $\frac{3}{5}$, $\frac{5}{8}$, and so on. Ask students to tell the **numerator** and **denominator** of each fraction.

WORKSHEET DIRECTIONS Tell students to count the total number of objects for the denominator. Tell them that the numerator should match the number of objects that are shaded. Have students write the fraction for the shaded parts.

Chapter 5

Name _____

Skills Practice

Name each fraction.

1.

    $\dfrac{\square}{5}$ of the insects are ladybugs.

2.

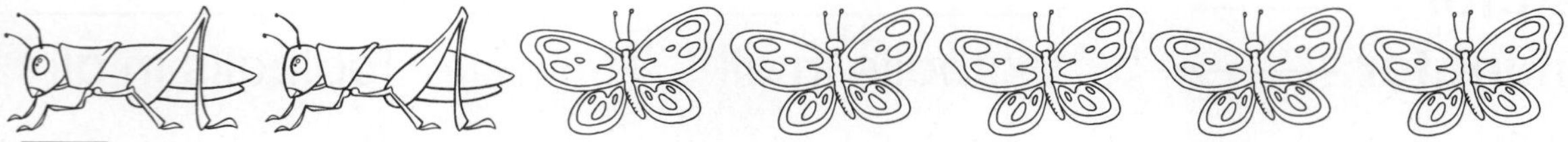

    $\dfrac{\square}{7}$ of the insects are butterflies.

3.

    $\dfrac{\square}{4}$ of the animals are frogs.

4.

    $\dfrac{\square}{5}$ of the pets are dogs.

5.

    $\dfrac{\square}{7}$ of the animals are ducks.

6.

    $\dfrac{\square}{6}$ of the wild animals are lions.

Name _____

Problem-Solving Practice

Solve.

1 Carmen draws 7 squares. She colors 3 of the squares blue. Color the part of the squares that is blue. Name the fraction.

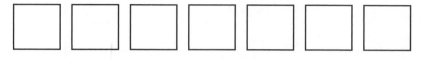

$\dfrac{\square}{\square}$ of the squares are blue.

2 Jack lines up 5 animal cookies. Two of the cookies are lion-shaped. Color the cookies that are lion-shaped. Name the fraction.

$\dfrac{\square}{\square}$ of the cookies are lion-shaped.

3 Sam picks 6 apples. Of the apples, 4 are green. What fraction of the apples are green? How can you show this? Explain.

_____

_____

Chapter 5

Name _____

Homework Practice

Name each fraction.

1

$\dfrac{\square}{7}$ of the fruit are apples.

2

$\dfrac{\square}{9}$ of the fruit are cherries.

3
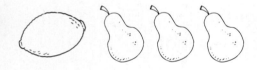

$\dfrac{\square}{4}$ of the fruit are lemons.

4

$\dfrac{\square}{5}$ of the fruit are pineapples.

Solve.

5 Kenya buys 6 balloons. Of the balloons,
two are red. What fraction of the balloons
are red? How can you show this? Explain.

_____

_____

Name _____

Vocabulary and English Language Development

fraction models

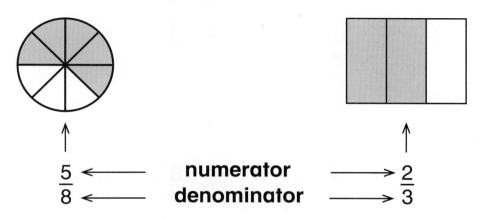

$$\frac{5}{8} \xleftarrow{\hspace{1cm}} \begin{array}{c}\text{numerator} \\ \text{denominator}\end{array} \xrightarrow{\hspace{1cm}} \frac{2}{3}$$

Draw a picture to model the fraction.

1 $\frac{3}{5}$ of the rectangle is shaded.

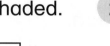

2 $\frac{1}{3}$ of the square is shaded.

3 $\frac{5}{6}$ of the hexagon is shaded.

4 $\frac{2}{4}$ of the square is shaded.

ACTIVITY On the board, draw two rectangles, one above the other. Divide one into three equal parts and one into five equal parts. Ask: "Which rectangle has the larger parts?" (the one divided into 3 parts) "Which rectangle has the larger **denominator**?" (the one divided into 5 parts) Guide students to understand that when the denominator increases, the size of the parts decreases. Have students draw two circles and divide one into two parts and one into six parts. Ask them to compare the parts and the denominators.

WORKSHEET DIRECTIONS Tell them to look at the fraction and first decide how many parts the model should have. Then tell them to decide how many parts should be shaded.

Math Triumphs

Name _____

Skills Practice

Draw a picture to model each fraction.

1 $\frac{1}{2}$

2 $\frac{3}{5}$

3 $\frac{2}{6}$

4 $\frac{3}{4}$

Draw circles to model each fraction.

5 $\frac{4}{5}$

6 $\frac{2}{6}$

7 $\frac{1}{3}$

8 $\frac{3}{7}$

9 $\frac{2}{2}$

10 $\frac{4}{8}$

Name _____

Problem-Solving Practice

Draw a picture to model each fraction.

1 Marsha has 8 hair clips. Of the hair clips, $\frac{3}{8}$ have flowers. Model the fraction using red and yellow counters.

2 Alex collected 12 trading cards. The same superhero is shown on $\frac{4}{12}$ of the cards. Model the fraction using red and yellow counters.

Solve.

3 Mr. Jackson has 5 trees in his garden. Of the trees, $\frac{2}{5}$ are fruit trees. How can you model this fraction using counters?

_____

_____

_____

Name _____

Homework Practice

Draw a picture to model each fraction.

1 $\frac{4}{9}$

2 $\frac{5}{6}$

Draw circles to model each fraction.

3 $\frac{3}{8}$

4 $\frac{1}{4}$

5 $\frac{4}{9}$

6 $\frac{3}{3}$

Solve.

7 Ben collected 12 marbles. Of the marbles, $\frac{4}{12}$ are large. How can you model this fraction using counters?

_____

_____

_____

Math Triumphs

Name _____

Vocabulary and English Language Development

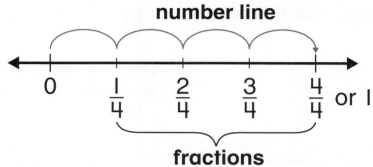

number line

fractions

Write each numerator. Circle the fraction.

1 $\frac{2}{3}$

0   □/3   □/3   □/3 or I

2 $\frac{3}{6}$

0   □/6   □/6   □/6   □/6   □/6   □/6 or I

3 $\frac{6}{7}$

0   □/7   □/7   □/7   □/7   □/7   □/7   □/7 or I

ACTIVITY On the board, draw a **number line** with six tick marks $\frac{1}{5}$ equally spaced $\frac{5}{5}$. Write a zero (0) at the first tick mark. Point to the remaining tick marks and explain to students that every tick mark represents a **fraction**. Remind students that a fraction is part of a whole. Label the first fraction tick mark $\frac{1}{5}$. Tell students that this tick mark is the first part of the whole. Point to the second fraction tick mark. Say: "This is the second part of the whole." Label it $\frac{2}{5}$. Help students label the remaining fraction tick marks.

WORKSHEET DIRECTIONS Have students fill in each missing numerator by counting on the number line. Then ask them to circle it the given fraction.

Math Triumphs

Chapter 5

Name _____

Skills Practice

Write each numerator on the number line.
Circle the fraction.

1 $\frac{1}{5}$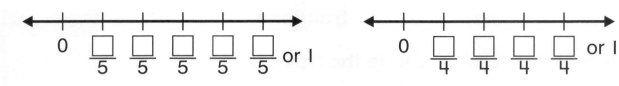

2 $\frac{3}{4}$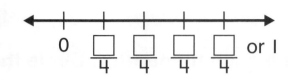

3 $\frac{4}{7}$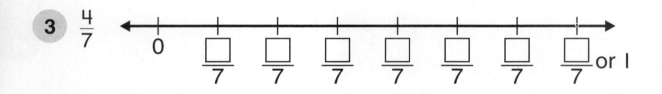

4 $\frac{4}{6}$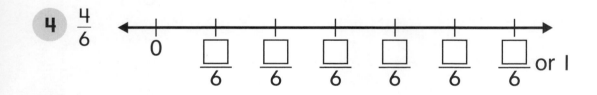

5 $\frac{2}{8}$

Math Triumphs

Name _____

Problem-Solving Practice

Write each numerator on the number line.
Circle the fraction.

1 Tony has 5 sweaters. Of the sweaters, 2 are blue.
What fraction of Tony's sweaters are blue?

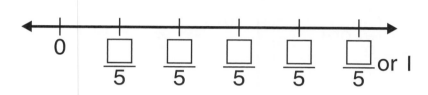

$\dfrac{\square}{5}$ $\dfrac{\square}{5}$ $\dfrac{\square}{5}$ $\dfrac{\square}{5}$ $\dfrac{\square}{5}$ or 1

Solve.

2 Louise sees 8 kittens. Of the kittens, 6 are sleeping.
What fraction of the kittens are sleeping? How can
you use a number line to show your answer? Explain.

_____

_____

_____

3 Tina sees 4 ducks. Of the ducks, 1 is swimming.
What fraction of the ducks are swimming? How can
you use a number line to show your answer? Explain.

_____

_____

_____

Chapter 5

Name _____

Homework Practice

Write each numerator on the number line.
Circle the fraction.

1 $\frac{1}{6}$

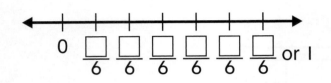

$\frac{\square}{6}$ $\frac{\square}{6}$ $\frac{\square}{6}$ $\frac{\square}{6}$ $\frac{\square}{6}$ $\frac{\square}{6}$ or 1

2 $\frac{2}{3}$

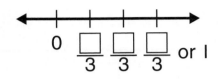

$\frac{\square}{3}$ $\frac{\square}{3}$ $\frac{\square}{3}$ or 1

3 $\frac{6}{8}$

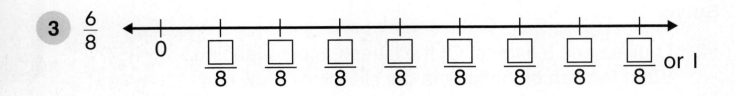

$\frac{\square}{8}$ $\frac{\square}{8}$ $\frac{\square}{8}$ $\frac{\square}{8}$ $\frac{\square}{8}$ $\frac{\square}{8}$ $\frac{\square}{8}$ $\frac{\square}{8}$ or 1

4 $\frac{5}{9}$

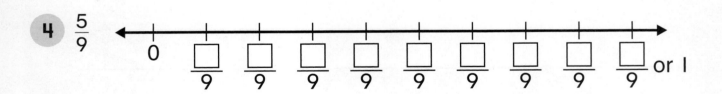

$\frac{\square}{9}$ $\frac{\square}{9}$ $\frac{\square}{9}$ $\frac{\square}{9}$ $\frac{\square}{9}$ $\frac{\square}{9}$ $\frac{\square}{9}$ $\frac{\square}{9}$ $\frac{\square}{9}$ or 1

Solve.

5 Indira sees 12 flowers. Of the flowers, 7 are yellow. What fraction of the flowers are yellow? How can you use a number line to show your answer? Explain.

_____

_____

_____

Math Triumphs

Name _____

Foldables Study Organizer

Dinah Zike's Foldables

Help students with the steps below to create their Foldables.

1 Stack seven sheets of paper, one on top of the other. On the top sheet of paper, trace a large circle.

2 With the paper still stacked, cut out all six circles at the same time.

3 Staple the paper circles together at one point around the edge.

Fraction Equivalence

4 Label the top of the circles with the lesson titles from the chapter.

TAKING NOTES

As students read through the chapter, have them use their Foldable to explain and write an example of each of the following:
- Fractions Equal to 1
- Compare Fractions
- Equivalent Fractions
- Fractions and Measurement
- Common Denominators
- Common Numerators

USING YOUR FOLDABLE

As students review, have them check their understanding by writing additional examples of each type of fraction.

**USING YOUR FOLDABLE**

In pairs, have students take turns naming a type of fraction and writing an example of that type of fraction.

Chapter 6

Games and Puzzles
You're My Equal!

GET READY

- Tell students that they will play **You're My Equal!** with a partner to practice naming equivalent fractions.

- Give each pair of students a **You're My Equal!** game sheet, a number cube, two playing pieces, fraction strips, pencils, and counters.

DIRECTIONS:

- Partners roll the number cube to determine the first player. Playing pieces should be placed at START.

- The first player rolls the number cube and moves his or her playing piece that many spaces forward.

- Students use fraction strips to help find the fraction that is equivalent to the fraction in the space they landed on. The player should write his or her answer in the space.

- The other player should check that the answer is the correct equivalent fraction. Remind students that there can be more than one correct answer.

- Each time the fraction is correct, the player who identified the equivalent fraction takes a counter. If the player is incorrect, he or she does not take a counter. Play continues with the other player taking a turn.

- If a player lands on a space that already shows an equivalent fraction, he or she identifies another equivalent fraction.

- Once both players reach FINISH, the player with the greatest number of counters wins.

VARIATION

Players can roll the number cube two times and form a fraction from the numbers. Players can determine if the fraction they formed is $>$, $<$ or $=$ to the fraction on the space they have landed.

Sample Answers for Game Sheet (start to finish): $\frac{2}{4}$, $\frac{8}{10}$, $\frac{4}{8}$, $\frac{6}{9}$, $\frac{1}{3}$, $\frac{2}{16}$, $\frac{4}{10}$, $\frac{2}{6}$, $\frac{6}{8}$, $\frac{10}{10}$, $\frac{2}{14}$, $\frac{2}{3}$, $\frac{4}{4}$ and $\frac{3}{12}$.

What You Need

- You're My Equal! game sheet
- 1 number cube (1–6)
- 2 playing pieces
- fraction strips
- pencils
- counters

Number of Players

2

Game Sheet

You're My Equal!

Play with a partner. Find equivalent fractions.

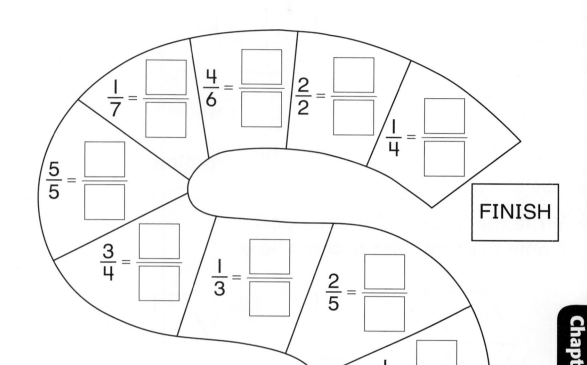

FINISH

START

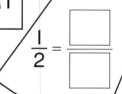
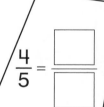
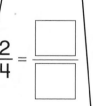
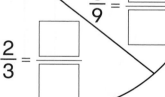

Name _____

Vocabulary and English Language Development

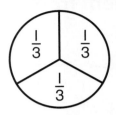

$$\frac{3}{3} = 1 \text{ whole}$$

↑ fraction

Write the fraction for each part.
Name the fraction for one whole.

1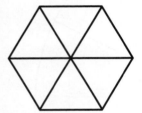

2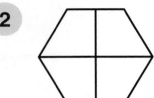

3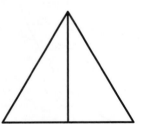

4

ACTIVITY Talk with students about equally sharing foods that are whole. For example, a pizza, a pie, and bread. Ask: "How do you equally share foods that are whole?" (Accept all reasonable responses.) Next, draw a rectangle on the board. Divide it into eight equal parts. Shade in one part at a time, and help students name the **fraction** for each shaded part. Write the fraction in each part. Then together, count the parts. Ask: "What fraction equals the whole rectangle?" ($\frac{8}{8}$) Have students work with partners to draw squares and divide them into equal parts. Tell them to repeat the activity and name different fractions that equal one whole.

WORKSHEET DIRECTIONS Have students count the number of equal parts and write the fraction for each part. Then have them write the fraction that equals one whole.

Math Triumphs

Name _____

Skills Practice

Name each fraction. Circle each fraction that equals 1.

1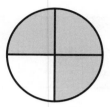

2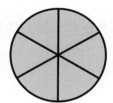

3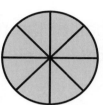

$\dfrac{\square}{\square}$ $\dfrac{\square}{\square}$ $\dfrac{\square}{\square}$

Circle each fraction that equals 1.

4 $\dfrac{5}{5}$ $\dfrac{5}{6}$ $\dfrac{6}{7}$

5 $\dfrac{4}{4}$ $\dfrac{4}{5}$ $\dfrac{5}{6}$

6 $\dfrac{8}{9}$ $\dfrac{9}{9}$ $\dfrac{9}{10}$

Shade each model to show 1. Name each fraction.

7

8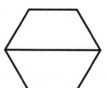

9

$\dfrac{\square}{\square}$ $\dfrac{\square}{\square}$ $\dfrac{\square}{\square}$

Math Triumphs

Name _____

Problem-Solving Practice

Solve.

1 Look at the model. Name the fraction in two ways. Explain.

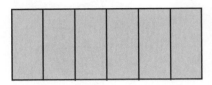

_____

_____

2 Ashley cuts an apple pie into 8 equal pieces. What fraction shows the whole pie? Explain.

_____

_____

3 Marley's quilt is made up of 9 equal parts. What fraction shows the whole quilt? Explain.

_____

_____

Math Triumphs

Name _____

Homework Practice

Name each fraction. Circle each fraction that equals 1.

1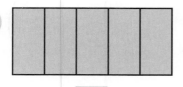

□/□

2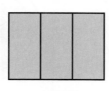

□/□

3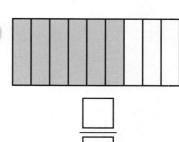

□/□

Circle each fraction that equals 1.

4 $\dfrac{2}{3}$ $\dfrac{3}{4}$ $\dfrac{3}{3}$

5 $\dfrac{5}{7}$ $\dfrac{5}{5}$ $\dfrac{5}{6}$

6 $\dfrac{7}{7}$ $\dfrac{7}{8}$ $\dfrac{8}{9}$

Shade each model to show 1. Name each fraction.

7

□/□

8

□/□

9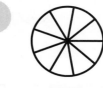

□/□

Solve.

10 Look at the model. Name the fraction in two ways. Explain.

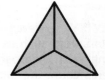

_____

_____

Chapter 6

Name _____

Vocabulary and English Language Development

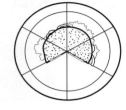
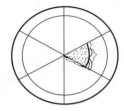

$\frac{1}{4}$ < $\frac{3}{4}$ $\frac{4}{6}$ > $\frac{1}{6}$

is less than   is greater than

Shade and compare. Write > or <.

1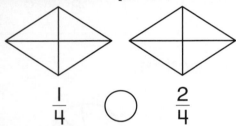

$\frac{1}{4}$ ◯ $\frac{2}{4}$

2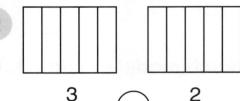

$\frac{3}{5}$ ◯ $\frac{2}{5}$

3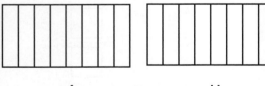

$\frac{6}{8}$ ◯ $\frac{4}{8}$

4

$\frac{4}{9}$ ◯ $\frac{7}{9}$

ACTIVITY Review the meaning of **less than** (<) and **greater than** (>) by having students describe things in the classroom such as the number of boys is less than or greater than the number of girls. Next, draw two rectangles on the board with one rectangle below the other. Divide both rectangles into four equal parts. Have students count the total number of parts and ask: "What fraction tells about the whole?" ($\frac{4}{4}$) Shade two parts in the first rectangle. Ask: "What fraction tells about the shaded parts?" ($\frac{2}{4}$) Next, shade one part in the second rectangle, and ask: "What fraction tells about the shaded part?" ($\frac{1}{4}$) Have students compare the number of shaded parts of each rectangle. Then, ask them to write > or < to compare the fractions. (>)

WORKSHEET DIRECTIONS Have students look at the top number (numerator) of each fraction and shade in that number of parts. Then tell them to compare the fractions using > or <.

Math Triumphs

Name _____

Skills Practice

Compare the fractions. Write >, <, or =.

1 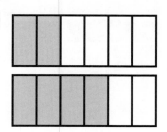 $\frac{2}{6}$ ◯ $\frac{4}{6}$

2 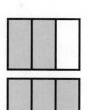 $\frac{2}{3}$ ◯ $\frac{3}{3}$

3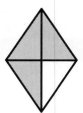

$\frac{3}{4}$ ◯ $\frac{1}{4}$

4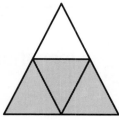

$\frac{3}{4}$ ◯ $\frac{3}{4}$

Chapter 6

Shade and compare the fractions. Write >, <, or =.

5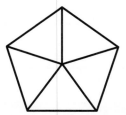

$\frac{3}{5}$ ◯ $\frac{4}{5}$

6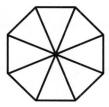

$\frac{5}{8}$ ◯ $\frac{2}{8}$

Math Triumphs

Name _____

Problem-Solving Practice

Solve.

1 Alberto eats $\frac{1}{4}$ of a sandwich. Marcos eats $\frac{1}{2}$ of a same size sandwich. Who eats the larger piece? Explain.

_____

_____

2 Lisa says that $\frac{1}{3}$ is less than $\frac{1}{5}$. Is she correct? Explain.

_____

_____

3 Dan swims $\frac{1}{4}$ of a mile. Emily swims $\frac{1}{6}$ of a mile. Who swims farther? Explain.

_____

_____

4 Ben says that $\frac{1}{2}$ is greater than $\frac{1}{10}$. Is he correct? Explain.

_____

_____

Math Triumphs

Name _____

Homework Practice

Compare the fractions. Write >, <, or =.

1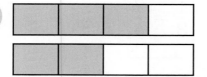

$$\frac{3}{4} \bigcirc \frac{2}{4}$$

2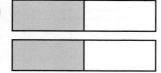

$$\frac{1}{2} \bigcirc \frac{1}{2}$$

Shade and compare the fractions. Write >, <, or =.

3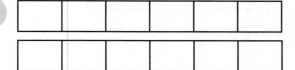

$$\frac{4}{6} \bigcirc \frac{6}{6}$$

4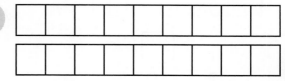

$$\frac{3}{9} \bigcirc \frac{5}{9}$$

Solve.

5 Serena says $\frac{1}{4}$ is less than $\frac{1}{3}$.
Is she correct? Explain.

_____

_____

Name _____

Vocabulary and English Language Development

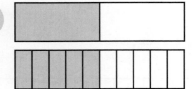

$\dfrac{1}{3}$

$\dfrac{2}{6}$

$$\dfrac{1}{3} = \dfrac{2}{6}$$

equivalent fractions

Write an equivalent fraction.

1

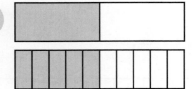

$\dfrac{1}{2} = \dfrac{\square}{10}$

2

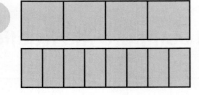

$\dfrac{4}{4} = \dfrac{\square}{8}$

3

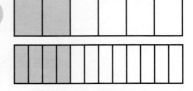

$\dfrac{2}{6} = \dfrac{\square}{12}$

4

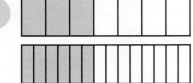

$\dfrac{3}{7} = \dfrac{\square}{14}$

ACTIVITY Tell students that **equivalent fractions** are fractions that show the same amount. Provide students with fraction strips. Guide them to fold two strips into 4 equal parts and then to fold one strip into 8 equal parts. Say: "Color 3 parts of the 4-part strip." Ask: "What fraction does this show?" ($\frac{3}{4}$) Say: "Color 6 parts of the 8-part strip." Ask: "What fraction does this show?" ($\frac{6}{8}$) Have them place one fraction strip below the other lining up the ends. Ask: "What do you notice about them?" (Both strips and both parts colored are the same length.) Say: "That shows that the fractions are equivalent fractions." On the board, complete more examples as needed.

WORKSHEET DIRECTIONS Tell students to compare the fraction strips and have them write a fraction for the second strip that is equivalent to the first fraction strip.

Math Triumphs

Name _____

Skills Practice

Write an equivalent fraction.

1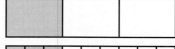

$$\frac{1}{3} = \frac{\boxed{}}{9}$$

2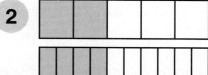

$$\frac{2}{5} = \frac{\boxed{}}{10}$$

3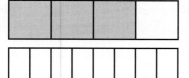

$$\frac{3}{4} = \frac{\boxed{}}{8}$$

4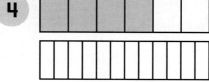

$$\frac{4}{6} = \frac{\boxed{}}{12}$$

5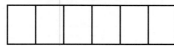

$$\frac{2}{3} = \frac{\boxed{}}{6}$$

6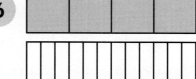

$$\frac{4}{4} = \frac{\boxed{}}{12}$$

7

$$\frac{1}{2} = \frac{\boxed{}}{12}$$

8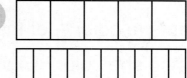

$$\frac{4}{5} = \frac{\boxed{}}{10}$$

Math Triumphs

Name _____

Problem-Solving Practice

Use the fraction bars to solve.

1 Justin ate $\frac{1}{3}$ of a cornbread. Amanda ate $\frac{2}{6}$ of the same size cornbread. Who ate more cornbread? Explain.

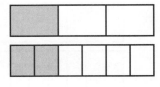

_____

_____

2 Chen rode his bike $\frac{3}{4}$ of a mile. Kim rode her bike $\frac{9}{12}$ of a mile. Kim says she rode further. Is she correct? Explain.

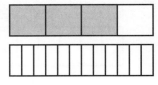

_____

_____

3 Leroy's orange is cut into 8 slices. He eats $\frac{1}{2}$ of the orange. How many slices of orange did he eat? Explain.

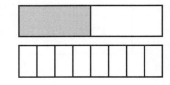

_____

_____

4 Maria wants to color $\frac{1}{4}$ of the poster. How many parts should she color? Explain.

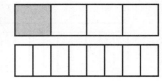

_____

_____

Math Triumphs

Name _____

Homework Practice

Write an equivalent fraction.

1

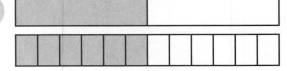

$$\frac{1}{2} = \frac{\boxed{}}{12}$$

2

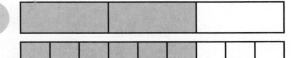

$$\frac{2}{3} = \frac{\boxed{}}{9}$$

3

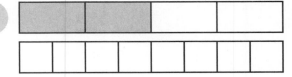

$$\frac{2}{4} = \frac{\boxed{}}{8}$$

4

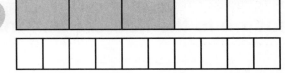

$$\frac{3}{5} = \frac{\boxed{}}{10}$$

5

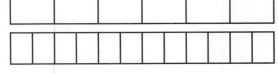

$$\frac{6}{6} = \frac{\boxed{}}{12}$$

6

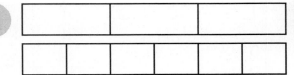

$$\frac{1}{3} = \frac{\boxed{}}{6}$$

Solve.

7 A screen is divided into 10 equal parts. Maribel
wants to paint $\frac{4}{5}$ of the screen blue. How many
parts should Maribel paint? Explain.

_____

_____

Chapter 6

Math Triumphs

Name _____

Vocabulary and English Language Development

start at 0   ends halfway between 3 and 4

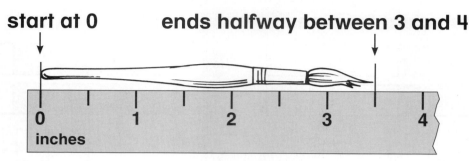

The paintbrush is $3\frac{1}{2}$ inches long.

Measure to the nearest half-inch.

1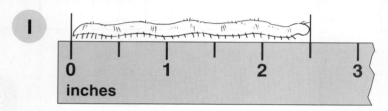

The centipede is

_____ inches long.

2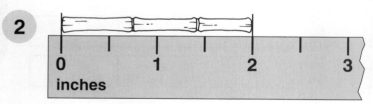

The bamboo stick is

_____ inches long.

3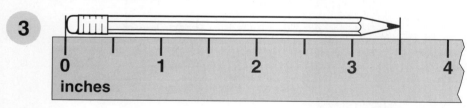

The pencil is

_____ inches long.

ACTIVITY Show students a piece of wood about $5\frac{1}{2}$ inches long. Tell students that carpenters use wood to make things. Encourage students to name some things that can be made with wood (birdhouses, chairs, tables). Explain to students that carpenters use rulers to **measure** the **lengths** of the wood they work with. Demonstrate how to measure the piece of wood with an inch ruler. Say: "Place the left end of the piece of wood at the left end of the ruler (0). Then read the measurement at the right end of the piece of wood." Distribute inch rulers to students and have them look at the markings. Point out where the inch and half-inch marks are found. Provide them with small objects to measure to the nearest half-inch.

WORKSHEET DIRECTIONS Tell students to find the half-inch or whole inch marking that is closest to the end of the object.

Math Triumphs

Name _____

Skills Practice

Measure to the nearest half-inch.

1

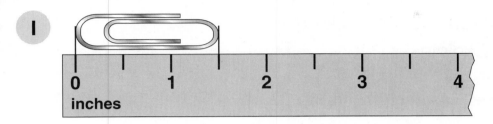

The paper clip is _____ inches long.

2

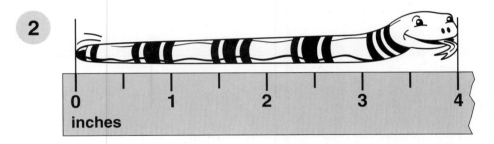

The snake is _____ inches long.

3

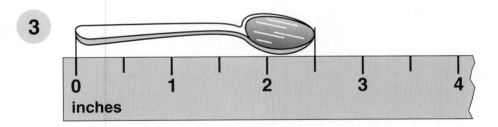

The spoon is _____ inches long.

4

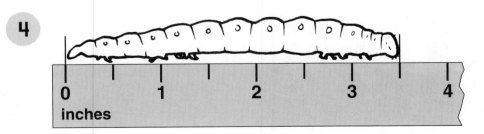

The caterpillar is _____ inches long.

Name _____

Problem-Solving Practice

Solve.

1 Greg says the crayon is 2 inches long.
Is Greg correct? Explain.

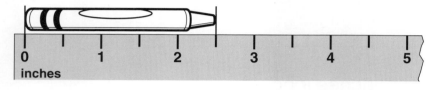

_____

_____

2 Tamika wants to measure the length of the fork.
What is the length of the fork to the nearest half-inch?

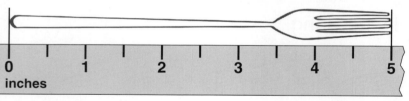

The fork is _____ inches long.

3 Lee says the leaf is 5 inches long. Is Lee correct? Explain.

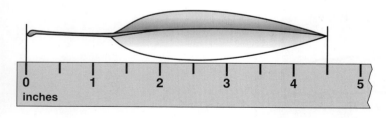

_____

_____

Math Triumphs

Name _____

Homework Practice

Measure to the nearest half-inch.

1

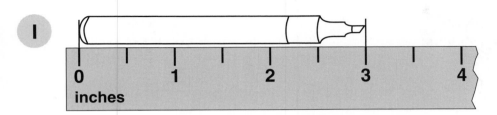

The marker is _____ inches long.

2

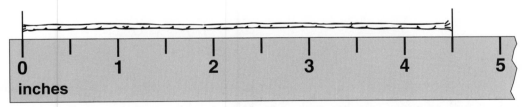

The token is _____ inch long.

Solve.

3 Cindy says the string is 5 inches long. Is Cindy correct? Explain.

_____

_____

Chapter 6

Name _____

Vocabulary and English Language Development

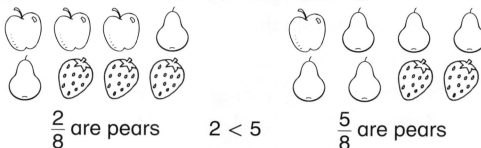

$\frac{2}{8}$ are pears $2 < 5$ $\frac{5}{8}$ are pears

So, $\frac{2}{8} < \frac{5}{8}$.

Write >, <, or =.

1 Compare the soccer balls.

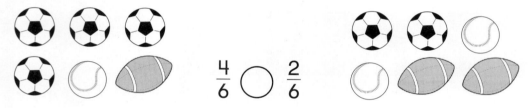

$\frac{4}{6} \bigcirc \frac{2}{6}$

2 Compare the top hats.

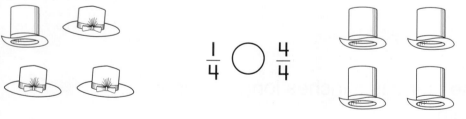

$\frac{1}{4} \bigcirc \frac{4}{4}$

3 $\frac{1}{5} \bigcirc \frac{3}{5}$

4 $\frac{4}{7} \bigcirc \frac{6}{7}$

ACTIVITY Provide students with counters. Together, make a model to solve this problem: Jamie and Nikki each receive the same allowance. Jamie uses $\frac{3}{5}$ of her allowance to buy a CD. Nikki uses $\frac{2}{5}$ of her allowance to buy a book. Ask: "Who spends less money? (Nikki) How do you know?" ($\frac{2}{5} < \frac{3}{5}$) Remind students that when the denominators are the same, the fraction with the larger numerator is the larger fraction. Have students create other problems for partners to solve.

WORKSHEET DIRECTIONS Tell students to compare the fractions using >, <, or =.

Math Triumphs

Name _____

Skills Practice

Compare. Write >, <, or =.

1 $\frac{3}{4}$ ◯ $\frac{2}{4}$

2
   $\frac{1}{5}$ ◯ $\frac{3}{5}$

3
   $\frac{2}{6}$ ◯ $\frac{4}{6}$

4 $\frac{1}{6}$ ◯ $\frac{3}{6}$ **5** $\frac{3}{3}$ ◯ $\frac{3}{3}$ **6** $\frac{2}{4}$ ◯ $\frac{1}{4}$

7 $\frac{4}{5}$ ◯ $\frac{2}{5}$ **8** $\frac{5}{10}$ ◯ $\frac{8}{10}$ **9** $\frac{2}{3}$ ◯ $\frac{1}{3}$

10 $\frac{1}{8}$ ◯ $\frac{1}{8}$ **11** $\frac{3}{12}$ ◯ $\frac{1}{12}$ **12** $\frac{5}{7}$ ◯ $\frac{7}{7}$

13 $\frac{6}{9}$ ◯ $\frac{8}{9}$ **14** $\frac{4}{4}$ ◯ $\frac{3}{4}$ **15** $\frac{3}{5}$ ◯ $\frac{3}{5}$

Chapter 6

Math Triumphs

Name _____

Problem-Solving Practice

Solve.

1 Sarah's family ate $\frac{2}{5}$ of a pizza pie. Ruth's family ate $\frac{3}{5}$ of a same size pizza pie. Who ate more pizza? Explain.

_____

2 Trevor and Ellen each have 8 stickers. Trevor's collection is $\frac{6}{8}$ animal stickers. Ellen's collection is $\frac{4}{8}$ animal stickers. Who has fewer animal stickers? Explain.

_____

3 Ling ate $\frac{4}{10}$ of a case of apples in a week. Amy ate $\frac{6}{10}$ of a case of apples in a week. Who ate more apples in a week? Explain.

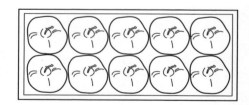

_____

4 Elise and Maria each brought carrot sticks for a snack. Elise ate $\frac{9}{12}$ of the carrot sticks. Maria ate $\frac{6}{12}$ of her carrot sticks. Who ate fewer carrot sticks? Explain.

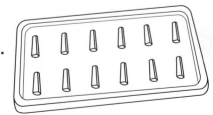

_____

Name _____

Homework Practice

Compare. Write >, <, or =.

1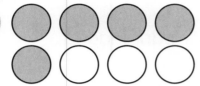

$\frac{5}{8}$ are shaded $\frac{7}{8}$ are shaded

$\frac{5}{8}$ ◯ $\frac{7}{8}$

2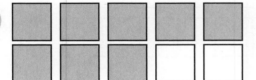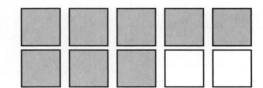

$\frac{8}{10}$ are shaded $\frac{8}{10}$ are shaded

$\frac{8}{10}$ ◯ $\frac{8}{10}$

3 $\frac{6}{12}$ ◯ $\frac{4}{12}$ **4** $\frac{2}{4}$ ◯ $\frac{2}{4}$ **5** $\frac{3}{7}$ ◯ $\frac{7}{7}$

6 $\frac{2}{2}$ ◯ $\frac{2}{2}$ **7** $\frac{5}{9}$ ◯ $\frac{3}{9}$ **8** $\frac{7}{10}$ ◯ $\frac{9}{10}$

Solve.

9 Paul jogged $\frac{3}{7}$ of a mile. Janice jogged $\frac{5}{7}$ of a mile.
Who jogged the shorter distance? Explain.

_____

Chapter 6

Name _____

Vocabulary and English Language Development

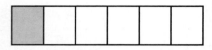 6 total parts, 1 part shaded

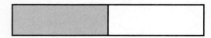 2 total parts, 1 part shaded

$$\frac{1}{6} < \frac{1}{2}$$

Shade and compare. Write >, <, or =.

1

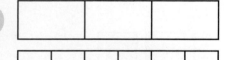

$$\frac{1}{3} \bigcirc \frac{1}{6}$$

2

$$\frac{1}{4} \bigcirc \frac{1}{10}$$

3

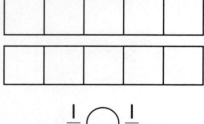

$$\frac{1}{5} \bigcirc \frac{1}{5}$$

4

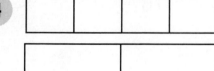

$$\frac{1}{4} \bigcirc \frac{1}{2}$$

ACTIVITY To help students understand that the greater the **denominator,** the more parts there are in the whole use quarters and dimes. Write the following on the board: 1 quarter $= \frac{1}{4}$ of a dollar; 1 dime $= \frac{1}{10}$ of a dollar. Ask: "Which is greater?" ($\frac{1}{4}$ of a dollar, 1 quarter) Write $\frac{1}{4} > \frac{1}{10}$ on the board. Ask: "Suppose you have 3 quarter and 3 dimes. Which is greater?" (quarters) "Why?" ($\frac{3}{4} > \frac{3}{10}$) Repeat with nickels and pennies.

WORKSHEET DIRECTIONS Have students compare the fractions. Ask students to shade the part of the model indicated by the fraction. Encourage them to use the models to identify which fraction is >, <, or =.

Name _____

Skills Practice

Compare. Write >, <, or =.

1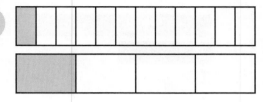

$$\frac{1}{12} \bigcirc \frac{1}{4}$$

2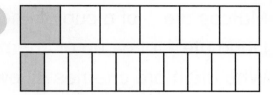

$$\frac{1}{6} \bigcirc \frac{1}{10}$$

Shade the figures and compare. Write >, <, or =.

3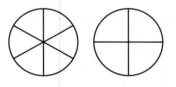

$$\frac{1}{6} \bigcirc \frac{1}{4}$$

4

$$\frac{1}{8} \bigcirc \frac{1}{3}$$

5

$$\frac{1}{2} \bigcirc \frac{1}{9}$$

6

$$\frac{1}{5} \bigcirc \frac{1}{3}$$

7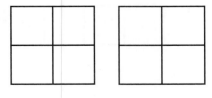

$$\frac{1}{4} \bigcirc \frac{1}{4}$$

8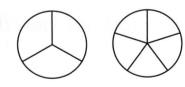

$$\frac{1}{3} \bigcirc \frac{1}{5}$$

Math Triumphs

Chapter 6

Name _____

Problem-Solving Practice

Use fraction bars to solve.

1 Marcos ate $\frac{1}{2}$ of a cup of cherries.
Dana ate $\frac{1}{4}$ of a cup of cherries.
Who ate more cherries? How do
you know?

_____

Shade the figures to solve.

2 Grettel says that $\frac{1}{6} > \frac{1}{12}$.
Is Grettel correct?
How do you know?

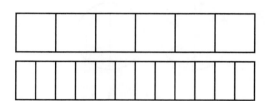

_____

_____

3 John used $\frac{1}{3}$ cup of nuts and $\frac{1}{5}$ cup of
raisins to make muffins. Did John use
more nuts or raisins? How do you know?

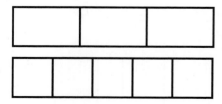

_____

Math Triumphs

Name _____

Homework Practice

Compare. Write >, <, or =.

1
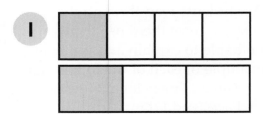

$\dfrac{1}{4}$ ◯ $\dfrac{1}{3}$

Shade the figures and compare. Write >, <, or =.

2

$\dfrac{1}{9}$ ◯ $\dfrac{1}{3}$

3

$\dfrac{1}{8}$ ◯ $\dfrac{1}{8}$

4

$\dfrac{1}{2}$ ◯ $\dfrac{1}{4}$

5

$\dfrac{1}{3}$ ◯ $\dfrac{1}{12}$

Solve.

6 Matt says that $\dfrac{1}{8} > \dfrac{1}{3}$. Is Matt correct?
How do you know?

_____

_____

_____

Chapter 6

Foldables Study Organizer

Dinah Zike's Foldables

Help students with the steps below to create their Foldables.

1   Begin with one sheet of notebook paper. Fold the sheet of paper in half as shown.

2   Cut every sixth line on one side. The result is five tabs.

3   Label each tab as shown.

TAKING NOTES

As students read through the chapter, have them use their Foldable to explain and write an example of each of the following:
- Three-Dimensional Figures
- Faces and Edges
- Sides and Vertices
- Two-Dimensional Figures
- Relate Two- and Three-Dimensional Figures

USING YOUR FOLDABLE

As students review, have them check their understanding by drawing additional examples of each term.

USING YOUR FOLDABLE

Have students work in pairs. One student should name a term. The other student should name and draw a real-world example of the term.

Games and Puzzles
Figure Match

GET READY
- Cut apart the **Figure Match** game cards. You will need one set of game cards for each pair of students.

DIRECTIONS:
- Students mix up the game cards and place them face down in rows of five. Students take turns turning over two cards at a time. If students can make a match, they pick up the cards and keep the pair. Play continues until the student cannot make a match.

- If the student cannot make a match, the cards are turned face down again and the student's turn is over.

- Students can match cards in the following ways:

  - a two-dimensional figure with the face of a three-dimensional figure

  - a two-dimensional figure with a two-dimensional figure

  - a three-dimensional figure with a three-dimensional figure

- The game is over when all the cards have been matched. The student with the most pairs wins.

VARIATION
Students can use the cards to play a game of "Go Fish."

What You Need
- Figure Match game cards
- scissors

Number of Players
2

Chapter 7

Game Cards 1
Figure Match

You may match figures three ways.

A two-dimensional figure with the face of a three-dimensional figure.

A two-dimensional figure with another two-dimensional figure.

A three-dimensional figure with another three-dimensional figure.

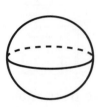
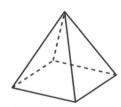

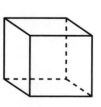
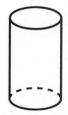
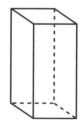

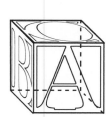

Soup

Chapter 7

Name _____

Vocabulary and English Language Development

cone

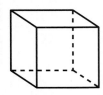

cube

cylinder

sphere

Write the name of each figure.

1

_____

2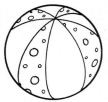

_____

3

_____

4

_____

ACTIVITY Display geometric solids for **cone, cube, cylinder,** and **sphere**. Say the name of each solid figure and have students repeat after you. Then have students find an object in the classroom that has the same shape as a specific solid. Say the name of the object aloud. Then say: "This ____ is shaped like a ____."

WORKSHEET DIRECTIONS Have students write the name of each figure and say the name aloud.

Math Triumphs

Name _____

Skills Practice

Name each three-dimensional figure.

1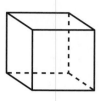

_____

2

_____

3

_____

4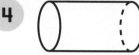

_____

Circle the object that is similar to each figure.

5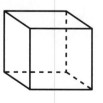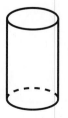

6

Chapter 7

Name _____

Problem-Solving Practice

Solve.

1 William put some toys inside a box. What three-dimensional figure is the box?

The box is a _____.

2 Mandy made a clay figure that is shaped like a soup can. What three-dimensional figure is the clay figure?

The clay figure is a _____.

3 Cole has a blue and white beach ball. What three-dimensional figure is the beach ball?

The beach ball is a _____.

4 Lynda made an art project that is shaped like a teepee. What three-dimensional figure is the teepee?

The teepee is a _____.

Name _____

Homework Practice

Name each three-dimensional figure.

1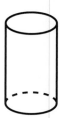

_____

2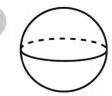

_____

Circle the object that is similar to each figure.

3 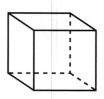 |

4 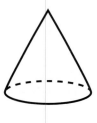 |   (Crackers)

Solve.

5 Jared has a TV set. What three-dimensional figure is similar to the TV set?

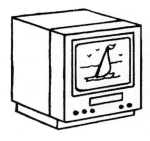

The TV set is similar to a _____.

Math Triumphs

Chapter 7

Name _____

Vocabulary and English Language Development

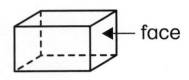

rectangular prism
6 faces

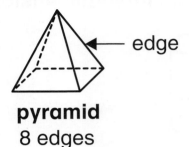

pyramid
8 edges

Color the same face.

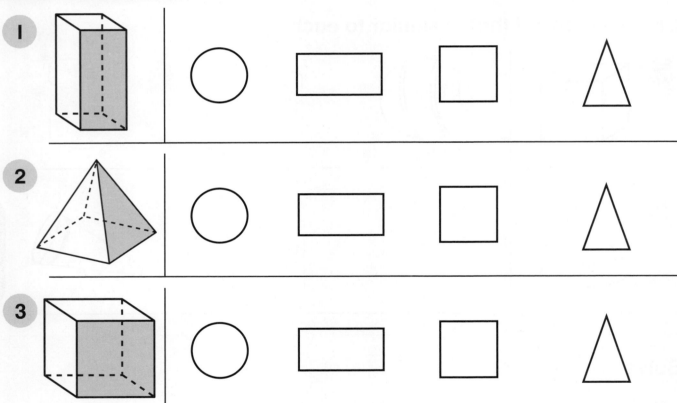

ACTIVITY Display geometric solids for **rectangular prism** and **pyramid**. Say the name of each solid figure and have students repeat after you. Point to and count the number of **faces** on the prism. Say: "A rectangular prism has 6 faces." Repeat with the pyramid. Then point to and count the number of **edges** on the rectangular prism. Say: "A rectangular prism has 12 edges." Repeat with the pyramid.

WORKSHEET DIRECTIONS Have students color the two-dimensional figure that has the same shape as the shaded face of the solid figure.

Name _____

Skills Practice

Circle the figure that is similar to the shaded face.

1 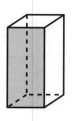

2 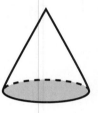

3 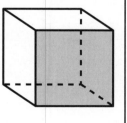

4 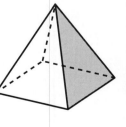

Chapter 7

Name _____

Problem-Solving Practice

Look at the solid figures.
Find the figure that matches the clues.

cone

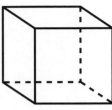
cube

cylinder

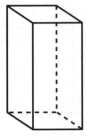
rectangular prism

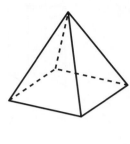
pyramid

1 I am a solid figure with 2 circular faces.
I can roll. What figure am I?

The figure is a _____.

2 I am a solid figure with 6 square faces.
I can slide. What figure am I?

The figure is a _____.

3 I am a solid figure with 1 circular face.
I can roll and slide. What figure am I?

The figure is a _____.

4 I am a solid figure with 4 rectangular faces.
I have 2 square faces. What figure am I?

The figure is a _____.

Math Triumphs

Name _____

Homework Practice

Circle the figure that is similar to the shaded face.

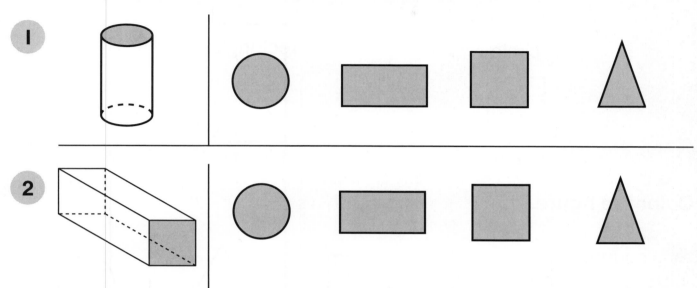

1

2

Look at the solid figures.
Find the figure that matches the clues.

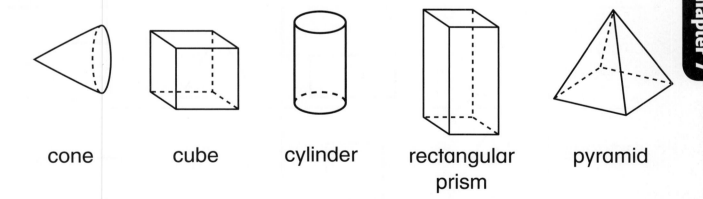

cone   cube   cylinder   rectangular prism   pyramid

3 I am a solid figure with 4 triangular faces that come to a point. I have 1 square face. What figure am I?

The figure is a _____.

Name _____

Vocabulary and English Language Development

circle

rectangle

square

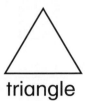

triangle

Color the figure.

1 square

2 triangle

  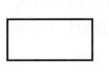

3 circle

   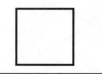

4 rectangle

ACTIVITY Provide students with cutouts of a **circle, square, rectangle,** and **triangle.** Help students write the names of the figures on the cutouts. Next, have students place the figures in front of them. Call out the name of a figure. Have students hold up the correct figure. Then have students check the name and say it aloud.

WORKSHEET DIRECTIONS Have students color the correct figure in each row.

Math Triumphs

Name _____

Skills Practice

Circle the similar figure.

1  |

_____

2 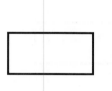 |

_____

3 |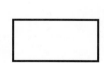

_____

Name each two-dimensional figure.

4

_____

5

_____

6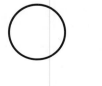

_____

7

_____

Chapter 7

Name _____

Problem-Solving Practice

Use the pictures to solve.

1 Dylan wants to draw a triangle. How many sides and angles does he need to draw?

_____ sides and _____ angles

2 Elliot drew two rectangles on top of each other so that they were touching. What new figure did Elliot draw?

The new figure is a _____ .

3 Sasha drew this picture. What two-dimensional figures did Sasha use to draw this picture? Explain.

_____

_____

_____

4 Amy drew this picture. What two-dimensional figures did Amy use to draw this picture? Explain.

_____

_____

_____

Math Triumphs

Name _____

Homework Practice

Circle the similar figure.

1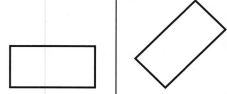

2

Name each two-dimensional figure.

3

_____

4

_____

Use the picture to solve.

5 Midori drew this picture. What
two-dimensional figures did Midori
use to draw this picture? Explain.

_____

_____

_____

Chapter 7

Name _____

Vocabulary and English Language Development

vertex

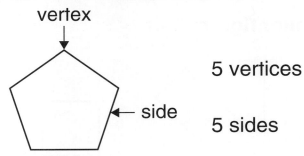

5 vertices

side

5 sides

Mark an X on each side. Write the number.

1

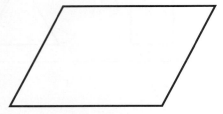

_____ sides

2

_____ sides

Circle the vertices. Write the number.

3

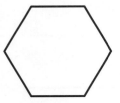

_____ vertices

4

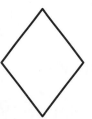

_____ vertices

ACTIVITY Display pattern blocks. Hold up the trapezoid block and point to and count the number of **sides** aloud. Ask: "How many sides does this figure have?" (4 sides) Repeat with other pattern blocks. Then hold up the trapezoid and count the **vertices.** (4 vertices) Draw and write the number of sides and vertices for each figure on the board.

WORKSHEET DIRECTIONS For Exercises 1–2, have students mark each side with an X, counting aloud. Then write the number of sides. For Exercises 3–4, have students circle the number of vertices, counting aloud. Then write the number of vertices.

Name _____

Skills Practice

Count the sides and vertices of each figure.

1

_____ sides

_____ vertices

2

_____ sides

_____ vertices

3

_____ sides

_____ vertices

4

_____ sides

_____ vertices

5

_____ sides

_____ vertices

6

_____ sides

_____ vertices

Chapter 7

Math Triumphs

Name _____

Problem-Solving Practice

Use the pictures to solve.

1   Joaquin found these two puzzle pieces.
    The missing piece to his puzzle has 6
    sides. Which piece is missing from
    Joaquin's puzzle?

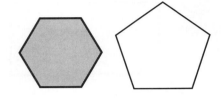

The gray piece has _____ sides.

The white piece has _____ sides.

The _____ pieces is missing from Joaquin's puzzle.

2   Carly makes a pattern with tiles.
    A missing tile has 8 sides. Which tile
    fits into Carly's tile pattern?

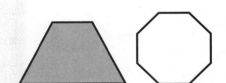

The gray tile has _____ sides.

The white tile has _____ sides.

The _____ tile fits into Carly's tile pattern.

3   Paul says these figures have the same
    number of sides and vertices. Is Paul
    correct? How do you know?

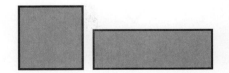

_____

_____

Math Triumphs

Name _____

Homework Practice

Count the sides and vertices of each figure.

1

_____ sides

_____ vertices

2

_____ sides

_____ vertices

3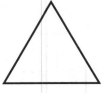

_____ sides

_____ vertices

4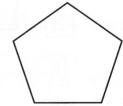

_____ sides

_____ vertices

Use the pictures to solve.

5 Sam makes a pattern with tiles. A missing tile has 6 sides. Which tile fits into Sam's tile pattern?

The gray tile has _____ sides.

The white tile has _____ sides.

The _____ tile fits into Sam's tile pattern.

Chapter 7

Name _____

Vocabulary and English Language Development

The faces of a cube are squares.

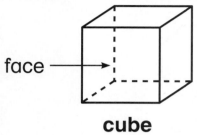

face →

cube

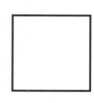

square

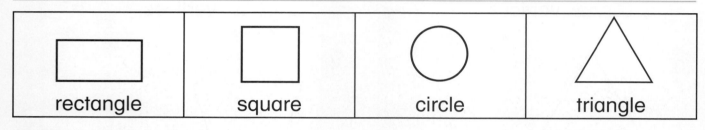

| rectangle | square | circle | triangle |

Write the shape of the face.

1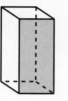

_____

2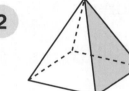

_____

3

_____

4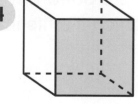

_____

ACTIVITY Provide students with cutout shapes of a circle, square, rectangle, and triangle. Help students write the names of the shapes on the cutouts. Have students place the shapes face up in front of them. Hold up a **three-dimensional figure.** Say the name of the figure and point to a face. Say: "Name the face." Students select and hold up the correct shape. Then ask them to say aloud the name of the shape. Repeat for other figures.

WORKSHEET DIRECTIONS Have students write the name of the shaded face on each figure. You may provide students with three-dimensional figures to use when completing the worksheet.

Math Triumphs

Name _____

Skills Practice

Write the number of faces for each figure.

1

_____ faces

2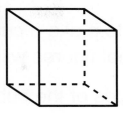

_____ faces

3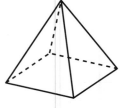

_____ faces

4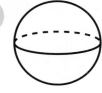

_____ faces

Name the shape(s) of the faces for each figure.

5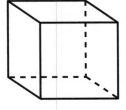

_____

6

_____

7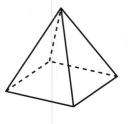

_____ and

_____

8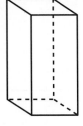

_____ and

_____

Name _____

Problem-Solving Practice

Use a model to solve.

1 Kaylee wants to make a cube. What two-dimensional figures will she need?

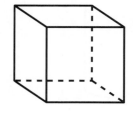

Look at the faces of the cube. What figures do you see?

_____

Kaylee will need

_____ _____.

2 Hideki wants to make a rectangular prism. What two-dimensional figures will he need?

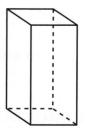

Look at the faces of the rectangular prism. What figures do you see?

_____ and _____

Hideki will need

_____ _____ and _____ _____.

3 Michel has one square and three triangles. Can she make a pyramid? Explain.

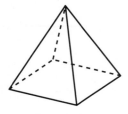

_____

_____

Math Triumphs

Name _____

Homework Practice

Write the number of faces for each figure.

1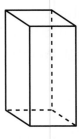

_____ faces

2

_____ face

Name the shape(s) of the faces for each figure.

3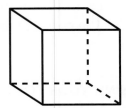

_____

4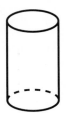

_____

Use a model to solve.

5 Devon wants to make a pyramid. What two-dimensional figures will he need?

Look at the faces of a pyramid.
What figures do you see?

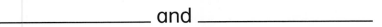 and _____

Devon will need

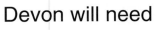 and _____.

Math Triumphs

Foldables Study Organizer

Dinah Zike's Foldables

Help students with the steps below to create their Foldables.

1 Begin with one sheet of 11" × 17" paper. Fold the paper so that both ends meet in the center.

2 Fold twice in the opposite direction as shown.

3 Open the paper and cut to make six flaps.

4 Label as shown. Have the students record what they have learned in the chapter.

TAKING NOTES

As students read through the chapter, have them use their Foldable to write an example for each topic.

USING YOUR FOLDABLE

As students review, have them check their understanding by writing an additional example for each topic without lifting the tabs. Then, have them lift the tab to check themselves and copy the example under the correct tab.

USING YOUR FOLDABLE

In pairs, have students take turns explaining their examples to one another. Have them alternate until they have both discussed each topic in their Foldables.

Games and Puzzles
Same or Symmetrical

GET READY

Give each pair of students a copy of the game board, a number cube, two playing pieces, and 40 counters.

DIRECTIONS:

- Explain to students that they are going to practice identifying congruent figures and figures with lines of symmetry.

- Tell students that they will play **Same or Symmetrical** with a partner. Partners can roll the number cube to determine the first player. Playing pieces should be placed at START on the game board.

- The first player rolls the number cube and moves forward his or her playing piece that many spaces. Players take turns.

- Some spaces will show figures that may or may not be congruent. Other spaces will show figures that may or may not have symmetry. Students must decide if the figures in the space they land on are congruent, symmetrical, or neither.

- The opposite player should check that the answer is correct.

- Players take one counter for each correct answer.

- When both players reach FINISH, have them count the counters each has. The player with the greatest number of counters wins.

VARIATIONS

- When figures are not congruent, or do not have symmetry, players can draw congruent figures or a symmetrical figure and receive two counters.

- If player draws figures that are congruent or symmetrical, he or she takes another turn.

What You Need

- Same or Symmetrical game board
- 1 number cube (1–6)
- 2 playing pieces
- 40 counters

Number of Players

2

Chapter 8

Game Board

Same or Symmetrical

Math Triumphs

Name _____

Vocabulary and English Language Development

same size

different size

Compare.

1

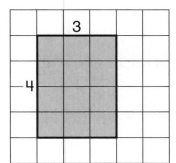

_____ size

2

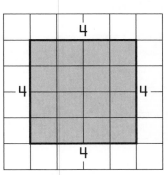

_____ size

ACTIVITY Discuss with students times it might be useful to know when things are the same or different sizes. Say: "When you look at objects to find if they are the same or different sizes, you **compare** the objects." Show students two objects that are the same size, such as two books. Place both books flat on a desk. Use cubes to fill the cover of the books. Have students count the number of cubes used to fill each cover. Then, have students count the number of cubes each book is wide and the number of cubes each book is long. Help students determine if the books are the same size or different sizes. Then have partners find other objects of all sizes and use cubes to compare them.

WORKSHEET DIRECTIONS Have students count the total number of units to compare the figures. Then, have them write if the figures are the same or different.

Chapter 8

Math Triumphs

Name _____

Skills Practice

Compare the size. Write "same" or "different."

1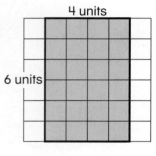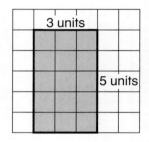

The rectangles are the

_____ size.

2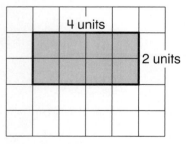

The rectangles are

_____ sizes.

Draw a figure that is the same size as the one shown.

3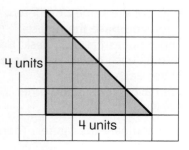

4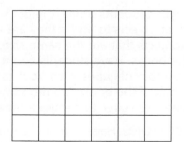

Name _____

Problem-Solving Practice

Solve.

1 Ruth and Amin drew triangles. Compare the size of the triangles.

The triangles are

_____ sizes.

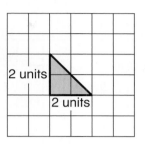
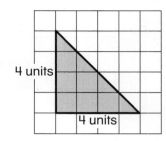

2 Steven drew the square at the right. Draw a square that is the same size as Steven's square.

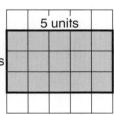
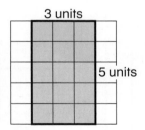

3 Are the rectangles the same size or different sizes? Explain.

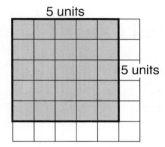
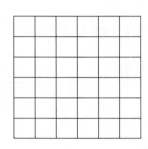

_____

_____

4 Are the trapezoids the same size or different sizes? Explain.

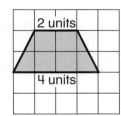
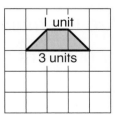

_____

_____

Chapter 8

Name _____

Homework Practice

Compare the size. Write "same" or "different."

1

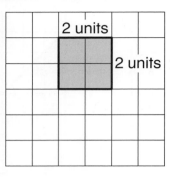

The rectangles are

_____ sizes

Draw a figure that is the same size as the one shown.

2

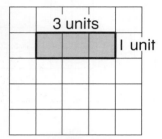

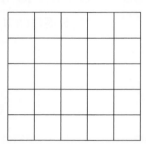

3

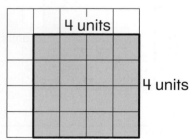

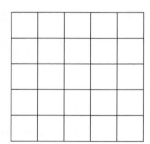

Solve.

4 Are the triangles the same size or different sizes? Explain.

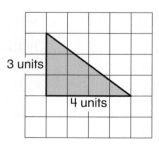

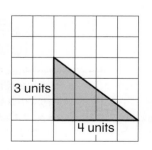

_____

_____

Math Triumphs

Name _____

Vocabulary and English Language Development

same shape

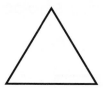

different shape

Circle the same shapes.

1

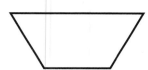  

2

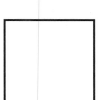  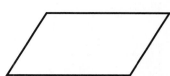

Chapter 8

ACTIVITY Show students two different plane figures, such as a square and a triangle. Ask: "How many **sides** do these figures have?" Count aloud with them. (4 and 3) "Are these figures the same shape?" (No.) Explain to students that figures with different numbers of sides do not have the same shapes. Be sure students understand that having the same number of sides does not mean that the shapes are the same. Then, take two plane figures that are the same shape. Count the sides and compare the figures. Tell students that those figures have the same shapes. Explain to students that figures that have the same shape are not always the same size.

WORKSHEET DIRECTIONS Have students compare the plane figures in each exercise and circle the two with the same shape.

Name _____

Skills Practice

Compare the shapes. Write "same" or "different."

1 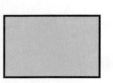 _____

2 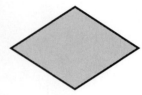 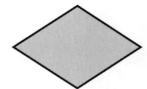 _____

Circle the figures that are the same shape.

3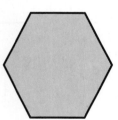

4

5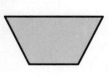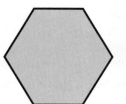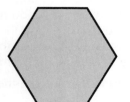

Math Triumphs

Name _____

Problem-Solving Practice

Solve.

1 Sam drew three figures in his notebook. Which figure is a different shape?

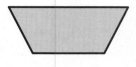

Figure 1

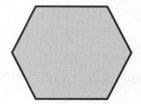

Figure 2

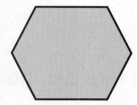

Figure 3

Figure _____ is a different shape.

2 Mr. Liu drew three figures on the board. Which figures have the same shape?

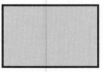

Figure 1

Figure 2

Figure 3

Figures _____ and _____ have the same shape.

3 Jason said these figures have the same shape. Is Jason correct? Explain.

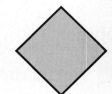

_____

_____

_____

Chapter 8

Homework Practice

Compare the shapes. Write "same" or "different."

1 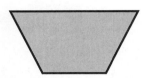 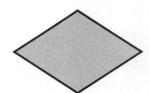 _____

Circle the figures that are the same size and shape.

2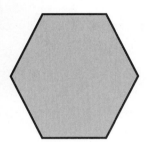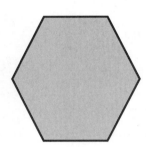

3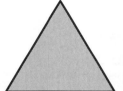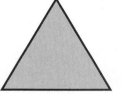

Solve.

4 Paula drew three figures in her book. Which figure is a different shape?

Figure 1   Figure 2   Figure 3

Figure _____ is a different shape.

Math Triumphs

Name _____

Vocabulary and English Language Development

 +  =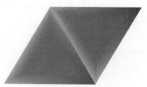

triangle   **triangle**   **parallelogram**

Join.

  +  =

2 + +  =

Chapter 8

ACTIVITY Draw a triangle on the board. Provide students with pattern blocks or construction-paper triangles. Say: "We can put triangles together to **create** other shapes." Model how to create a square with four triangles and a hexagon with six triangles. Have partners do the same. Encourage students to see how many shapes they can make using two or more pattern blocks. Have them draw the new shapes they make.

WORKSHEET DIRECTIONS Have students join a triangle and a parallelogram to make a trapezoid. Then, ask students to join three triangles to make another trapezoid.

Name _____

Skills Practice

1 Circle the pattern block that completes the new figure.

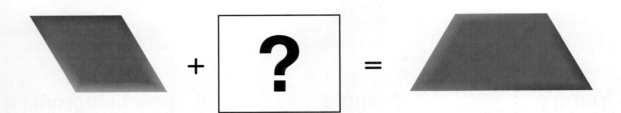

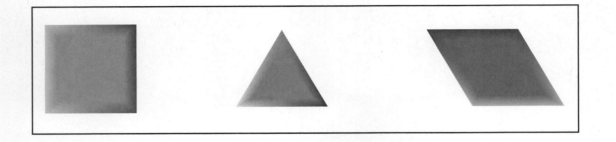

2 Draw the new figure.

 **+**  **=**

Math Triumphs

Problem-Solving Practice

Solve.

1 Calvin wants to use three of the same pattern blocks to make a trapezoid. What block can he use?

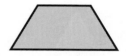

Calvin can use three _____ to make a trapezoid.

2 Jen wants to use three different pattern blocks to make a hexagon. What blocks can she use?

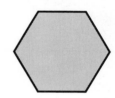

Jen can use a _____, a _____,

and a _____ to make a hexagon.

3 Hiro wants to make a rhombus using two triangles. Can he do it? Explain.

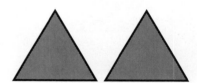

_____

_____

_____

4 Katie wants to make a pentagon using a square and a triangle. Can she do it? Explain.

_____

_____

_____

Chapter 8

Math Triumphs

Name _____

Homework Practice

1 Circle the pattern block that completes the new figure.

 **+** **=**

2 Draw the new figure.

 **+**  **=**

Solve.

3 Seth wants to use two of the same pattern blocks to make a parallelogram. What block can he use?

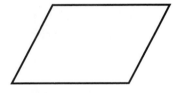

Seth can use two _____
to make a parallelogram.

Math Triumphs

Name _____

Vocabulary and English Language Development

trapezoid

=

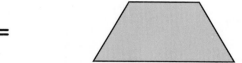

I triangle + I rhombus

Draw lines.

1 6 triangles

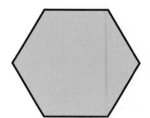

2 3 triangles

Chapter 8

ACTIVITY Draw a **parallelogram** on the board. Say: "Drawing one line through this parallelogram takes it apart and makes two triangles." Provide students with pattern blocks. Have them model how to *take apart* shapes by creating a new shape with pattern blocks. Then, place the pattern blocks on top of one pattern block that shows the new shape.

WORKSHEET DIRECTIONS Tell students to take apart each shape by drawing the correct number of lines to make the given number of figures.

Name _____

Skills Practice

Draw one line to make the given figures.

1 2 squares

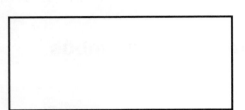

2 2 triangles

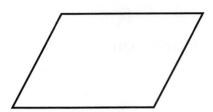

Draw two lines to make the given figures.

3 2 triangles and
2 rhombuses

4 3 triangles

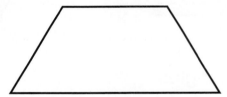

5 4 triangles

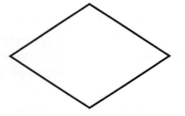

6 4 squares

Math Triumphs

Name _____

Problem-Solving Practice

Draw one line to solve.

1 Roberto drew a line through a trapezoid to make two figures. One of the figures is a triangle. What is the other figure?

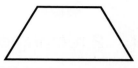

The other figure is a _____.

2 Lisa drew a line across the center of a hexagon, from left to right. What two figures did she make? Explain.

_____

_____

_____

3 Kevin drew a line down the center of a parallelogram, from top to right. What two figures did he make? Explain.

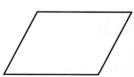

_____

_____

_____

Chapter 8

Math Triumphs

Name _____

Homework Practice

Draw one line to make the given figures.

1   2 rectangles

2   2 triangles

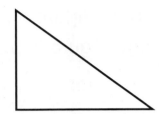

Draw two lines to make the given figures.

3   1 triangle, 1 rhombus, and
       1 trapezoid

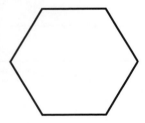

4   3 triangles

Draw three lines to solve.

5   Mr. Gordan drew three lines through a hexagon
       connecting opposite corners to make six new
       figures. What six figures did he make? Explain.

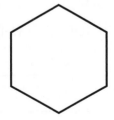

_____

_____

_____

Math Triumphs

Name _____

Vocabulary and English Language Development

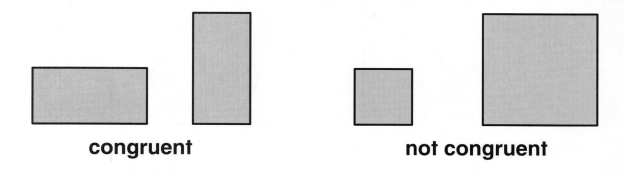

congruent   **not congruent**

Compare. Then circle.

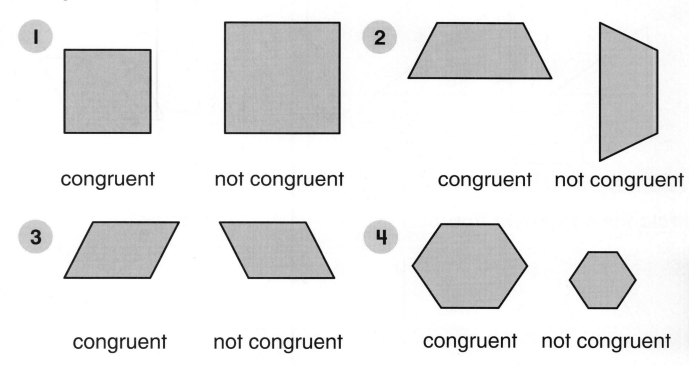

1   congruent   not congruent

2   congruent   not congruent

3   congruent   not congruent

4   congruent   not congruent

Chapter 8

ACTIVITY Revisit figures that have the same shape, then figures that are the same size. Explain to students that figures having both the same shape and the same size are called **congruent**. Tell students that figures can be congruent even if they are shown in different directions. Provide pairs of students with pattern blocks and paper. Have one student draw a figure by tracing the pattern blocks. Then have the other student draw a figure that is congruent to the one the first student drew.

WORKSHEET DIRECTIONS Tell students to look at each pair of shapes in each exercise. Tell them to determine if the shapes are congruent. Have them circle their answer.

Name _____

Skills Practice

Compare. Are these figures congruent? Write "yes" or "no."

1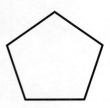

_____

2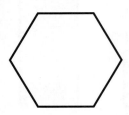

_____

3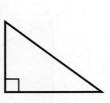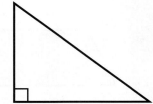

_____

4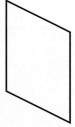

_____

Circle the congruent figures.

5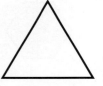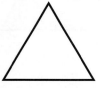

6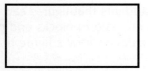

Math Triumphs

Name _____

Problem-Solving Practice

Solve.

1 A square is 3 units wide and 3 units tall. Draw a congruent square.

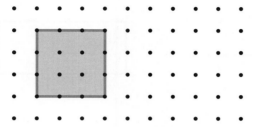

2 Adam drew these two figures. Are the figures congruent? Explain.

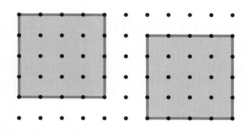

_____

_____

_____

3 Look at the figures. Are the figures congruent? Explain.

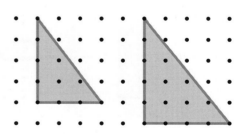

_____

_____

_____

Name _____

Homework Practice

Compare. Are these figures congruent? Write "yes" or "no."

1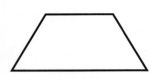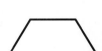

_____

2

_____

Circle the congruent figures.

3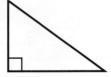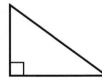

Solve.

4 Elise drew the two rectangles below. Are the rectangles congruent? Explain.

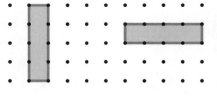

_____

_____

_____

Math Triumphs

Name _____

Vocabulary and English Language Development

symmetry

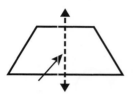

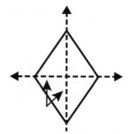

I line of symmetry   **2 lines of symmetry**

Count.

I

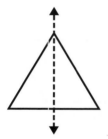

_____ line of symmetry

2

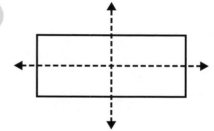

_____ lines of symmetry

3

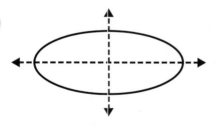

_____ lines of symmetry

4

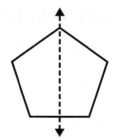

_____ line of symmetry

ACTIVITY Provide students with a sheet of paper. Say: "Let's fold the paper in half and then open it." Point to the two parts and say: "The two parts are congruent." Point out the line that divides both sides. Explain that the line that divides a figure into equal parts is called a **line of symmetry**. Tell students that figures can have more than one line of symmetry.

WORKSHEET DIRECTIONS Have students look at the figures in Exercises 1–4. Ask them to count the line(s) of symmetry for each and write it.

Math Triumphs

Chapter 8

Name _____

Skills Practice

Count the lines of symmetry for each figure.
Draw each line of symmetry.

1

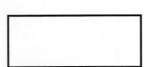

_____ lines of symmetry

2

_____ line of symmetry

3

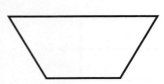

_____ line of symmetry

4

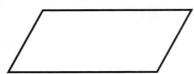

_____ lines of symmetry

Circle each figure that has symmetry.

5

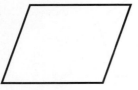

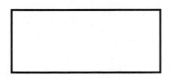

6

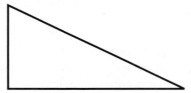

Problem-Solving Practice

Solve.

1 Todd drew a square with a line of symmetry. Which figure did Todd draw? Explain.

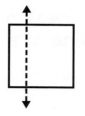 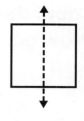

Figure A   Figure B

_____

_____

_____

2 Does the figure show a line of symmetry? Explain.

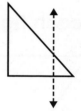

_____

_____

_____

_____

3 Marcos drew a figure that has two lines of symmetry. Which figure did Marcos draw? Explain.

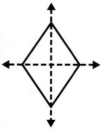 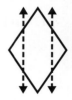

Figure A   Figure B

_____

_____

_____

Chapter 8

Name _____

Homework Practice

Count the lines of symmetry for each figure. Draw each line of symmetry.

1

_____ line of symmetry

2

_____ lines of symmetry

Circle each figure that has symmetry.

3

Solve.

4 Sarah drew a hexagon showing 2 lines of symmetry. Which figure did Sarah draw? Explain.

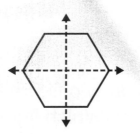

Figure A   Figure B

_____

_____

_____

Foldables Study Organizer

F̲OLDABLES®
Study Organizer

Dinah Zike's Foldables

Help students with the steps below to create their Foldables.

1 Begin with 7 sheets of notebook paper. Staple the sheets of notebook paper together to form a booklet.

2 Cut a tab as shown. On the third page, make the tab longer, and so on.

3 Write the chapter title on the cover. Label each tab with a lesson number.

TAKING NOTES

As students read through the chapter, have them select and write key vocabulary terms on the front tabs of their foldable. Under each tab, draw an example and write the definition of each term.

USING YOUR FOLDABLE

As students review, have them check their understanding by saying the definition of each term they have drawn. Have them lift each tab to check their work.

USING YOUR FOLDABLE

In pairs, have the students take turns asking each to explain the data they have drawn for each term.

Games and Puzzles
Race to the Finish!

GET READY

- Give each group of students a sharpened pencil, a paper clip, and a copy of the **Race to the Finish!** spinner.

- Give each student in the group a set of crayons and a copy of the **Race to the Finish!** bar graph.

DIRECTIONS:

- Students take turns. The first student places the point of the pencil inside the paper clip and positions it on the spinner. The student spins and colors one square of the appropriate color on his or her bar graph.

- If the student lands on *lose a turn*, that turn is over and the next student spins.

- If the student lands on *take two more turns*, that student spins and colors two more squares on the bar graph.

- The first student to reach the end of one bar on the graph wins the race.

VARIATION

Students play 15 rounds on the spinner. At the end of 15 spins, students write the number for each color and add to find the total. The student with the most bars colored in wins.

What You Need

- Race to the Finish! spinner
- Race to the Finish! bar graph (one per student)
- red, yellow, blue, and green crayons
- paper clip
- pencil

Number of Players

2-4

Math Triumphs

Spinner
Race to the Finish!

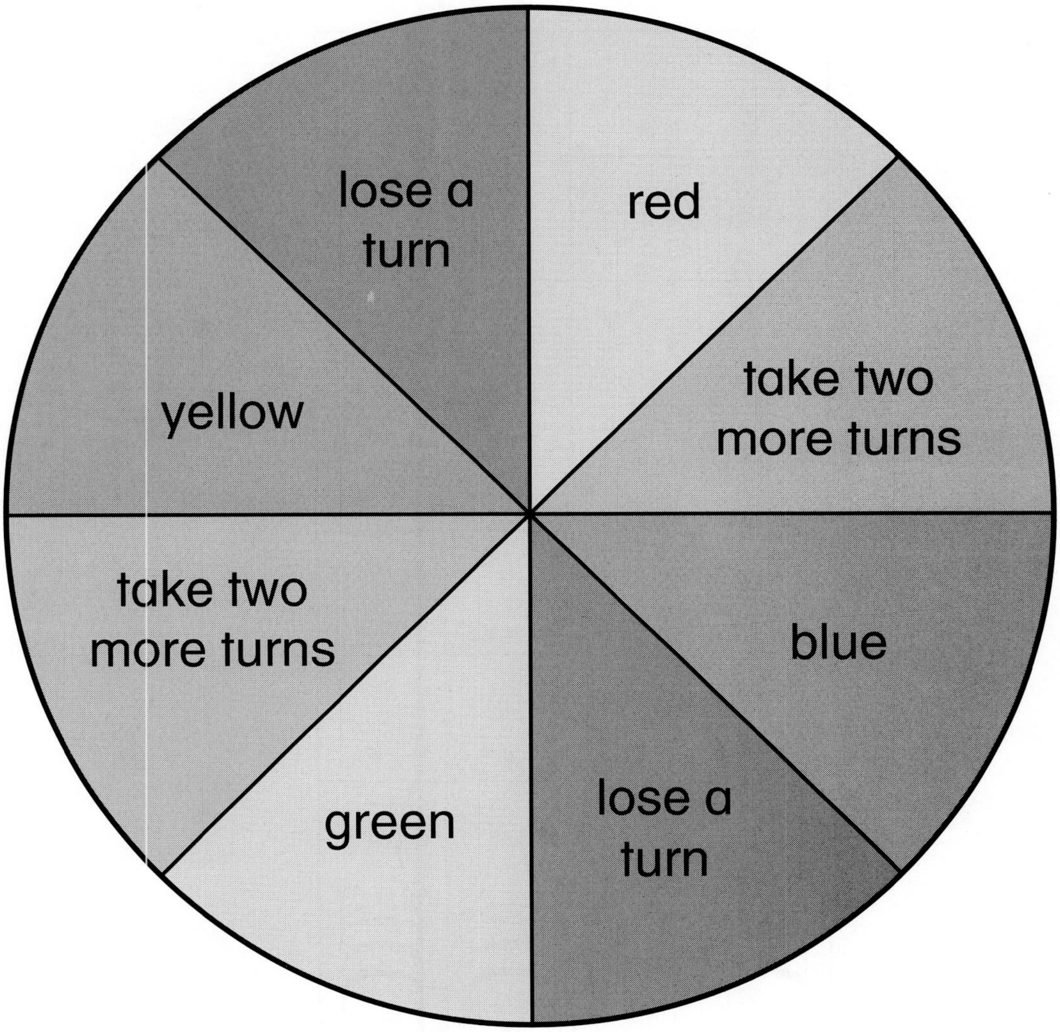

lose a turn

red

yellow

take two more turns

take two more turns

blue

green

lose a turn

Chapter 9

Bar Graph
Race to the Finish!

	1	2	3	4	5	6	7	8
red								
blue								
yellow								
green								

Math Triumphs

Name _____

Vocabulary and English Language Development

Classify and sort. Draw.

Venn diagram

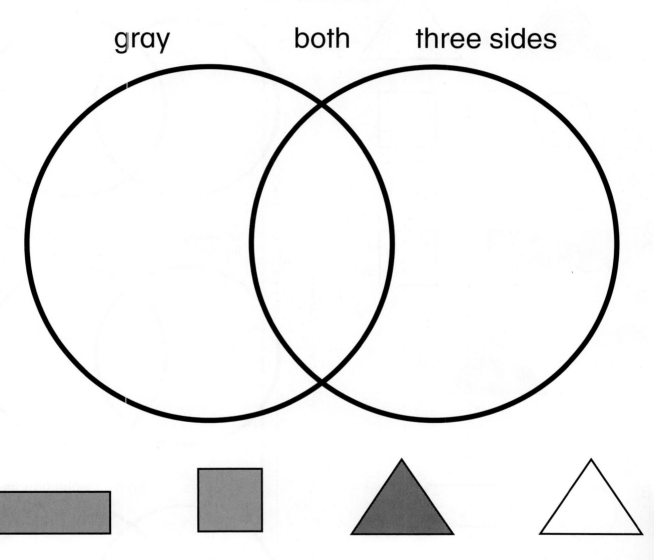

gray   both   three sides

ACTIVITY Draw a large **Venn diagram** on a sheet of poster paper. Provide students with paper cutouts of a red triangle, blue triangle, and red square. Label the Venn diagram: red, both, three sides. Hold up each shape and ask students to name the color and number of sides. Place the shape in the appropriate space on the Venn diagram.

WORKSHEET DIRECTIONS Students draw the correct figure in the appropriate area of the Venn diagram.

Math Triumphs   **Lesson 9-1   A213**

Name _____

Skills Practice

Classify and sort. Draw the figures in the Venn diagram.

1

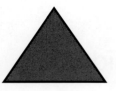 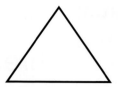

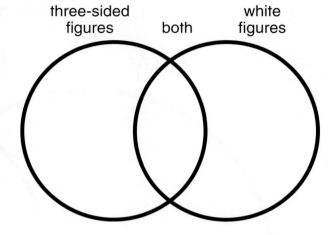

three-sided figures   both   white figures

2

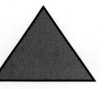

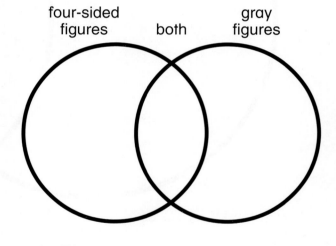

four-sided figures   both   gray figures

3

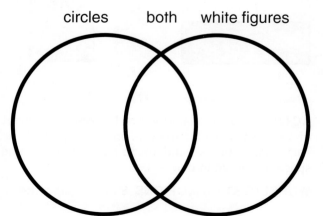

circles   both   white figures

Math Triumphs

Name _____

Problem-Solving Practice

Use the Venn diagram to solve.

1 Derek sorted his sticker collection. How many of his stickers are flowers?

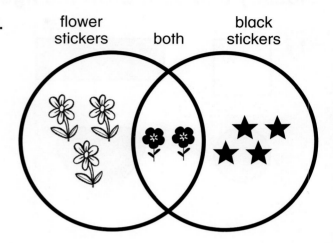

flower stickers   both   black stickers

Count the stickers in the flowers section. _____

Count the stickers in the both section. _____

Derek has _____ flower stickers.

2 Maya sorted her sticker collection. How many of her stickers are hearts?

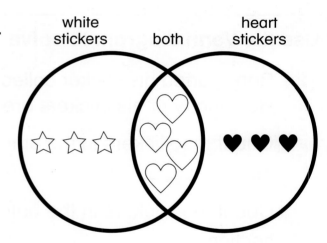

white stickers   both   heart stickers

Count the stickers in the heart section. _____

Count the stickers in the both section. _____

Maya has _____ hearts stickers.

3 What is another figure that would belong in the section with the white stars? Explain.

_____

_____

Chapter 9

Name _____

Homework Practice

Classify and sort. Draw the figures in the Venn diagram.

1.

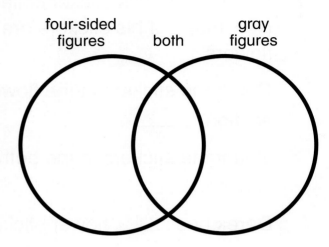

Use the Venn diagram to solve.

2. Benji sorted his sticker collection. How many of his stickers are stars?

   Count the stickers in the star section. _____

   Count the stickers in the both section. _____

   Benji has _____ star stickers.

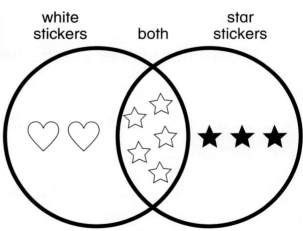

3. What is another figure that would belong in the section with the white hearts? Explain.

   _____

   _____

Math Triumphs

Name _____

Vocabulary and English Language Development

This is a **picture graph**.

Count.

1 How many 🐱? _____

2 How many 🐶? _____

3 How many 🐰? _____

4 How many more 🐱 than 🐰? _____

Copyright © Macmillan/McGraw-Hill, • Glencoe, a division of The McGraw-Hill Companies, Inc.

ACTIVITY Draw a large **pictograph** grid on the board and label it *Favorite Colors*. Label the rows *Red, Blue, Yellow*. Give each student a sticky note and have the student place it on the graph next to his or her favorite color. Count the number in each row with students. Ask students questions such as: "How many students like red the best?" Have them answer in complete sentences.

WORKSHEET DIRECTIONS Discuss the difference between a picture graph and a pictograph. Have students count and answer each question.

Math Triumphs

Chapter 9

Name _____

Skills Practice

Animals In the Pond				
Duck	🦆			
Frog	🐸	🐸	🐸	🐸
Lizard	🦎	🦎		

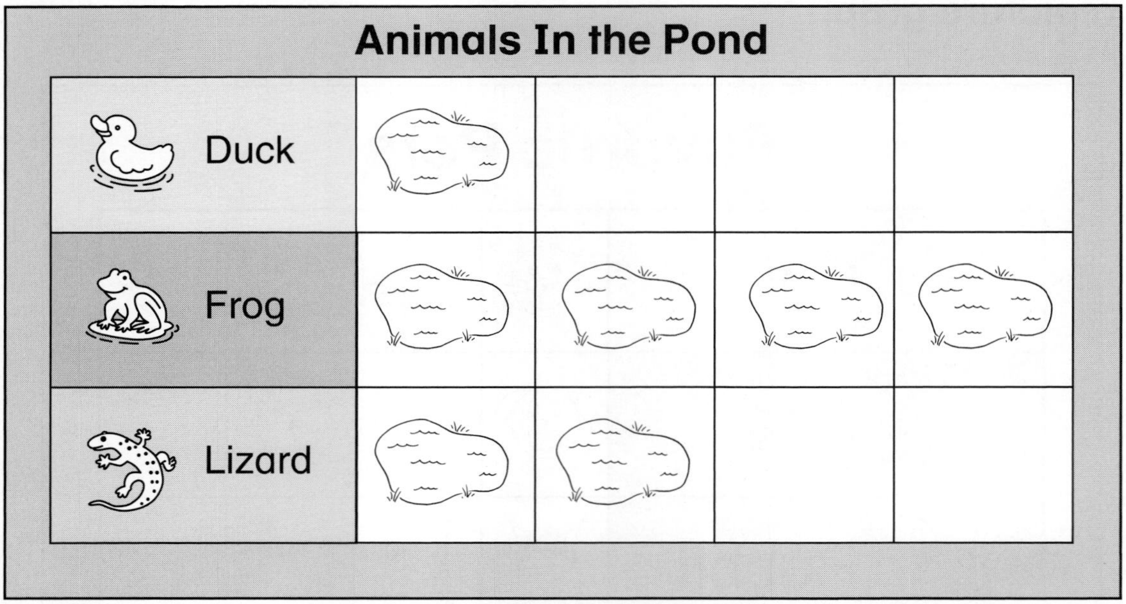

Key:  🌊 = 4 animals

1 How many animals does each 🌊 represent?

_____ animals

2 How many lizards are in the pond?

_____ lizards

3 How many ducks and lizards are in the pond?

_____ ducks and lizards

4 How many more frogs than ducks are in the pond?

_____ more frogs

5 How many animals in all are in the pond?

_____ animals

Math Triumphs

Name _____

Problem-Solving Practice

Solve.

1 Marty made a pictograph with the key: ◯ = 5 homeruns.

What do ◯ ◯ ◯ ◯ represent?

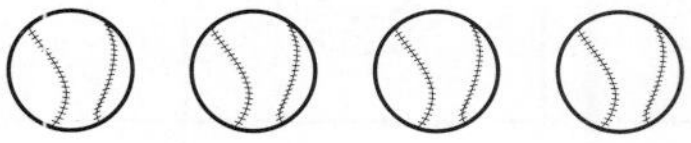

_____ homeruns

2 Suzanne made a pictograph with the key: 🦴 = 3 dogs.

What do 🦴 🦴 🦴 represent?

_____ dogs

3 Raul made a pictograph with the key: 📕 = 2 books read.

What do 📕 📕 📕 📕 📕 represent?

_____ books read

4 Latisha made a pictograph with the key: 🖍 = 10 crayons.

What do 🖍 🖍 🖍 represent?

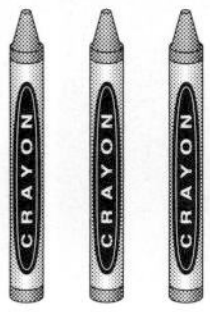

_____ crayons

Chapter 9

Name _____

Homework Practice

Favorite Toys				
🪆 Doll	😊	😊	😊	
🧸 Teddy bear	😊	😊	😊	😊
🪀 Top	😊			

Key: 😊 = 3 people

1 How many people like teddy bears the best?

_____ people

2 How many more people like dolls than tops?

_____ people

Solve.

3 Emily made a pictograph with the key: 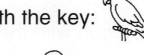 = 5 birds.

What do   represent?

_____ birds

Math Triumphs

Name _____

Vocabulary and English Language Development

This is a table. A table shows data.

Toys at the Store		
Toy	Tally	Total
Airplane	ⵏⵏⵏⵏⵏ ⵏⵏⵏⵏⵏ ‖	12
Car	ⵏⵏⵏⵏⵏ ‖	6
Boat	ⵏⵏⵏⵏⵏ ⵏⵏⵏⵏⵏ	10

Write how many.

1

_____

2

_____

3

_____

Complete.

4 How many and ?

_____ + _____ = _____

5 How many more  than ?

_____ − _____ = _____

ACTIVITY Draw a tally **table** on the board and label it *Students*. Label the rows *Boys* and *Girls*. Have students form groups of boys and girls. Have each student draw a **tally mark** in the table in the appropriate row. Then count the tally marks and write the total numbers of boys and girls in the chart. Ask students: "How many girls?" and "How many more boys than girls?" Have them answer in complete sentences.

WORKSHEET DIRECTIONS Have students count and answer each question.

Math Triumphs

Name _____

Skills Practice

Art Class Supplies		
Supplies	Tally	Total
Paintbrushes	$\cancel{||||}$ $\cancel{||||}$	10
Jars of Paint	$\cancel{||||}$ $\cancel{||||}$ $\cancel{||||}$	15
Easels	$\cancel{||||}$ |||	8

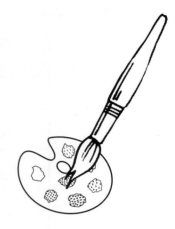

1 How many easels are there in art class?

_____ easels

2 How many paintbrushes are there in art class?

_____ paintbrushes

3 How many more jars of paint are there than easels?

_____ more jars of paint than easels

4 How many jars of paint and paintbrushes are there in all?

_____ in all

5 How many paintbrushes, jars of paint, and easels in all?

_____ in all

Math Triumphs

Name _____

Problem-Solving Practice

Favorite Sport		
Sport	Tally	Number of People
⚽ Soccer	ЖЖ ЖЖ IIII	14
🎾 Baseball	ЖЖ II	7
🏈 Football	ЖЖ ЖЖ I	11
🏒 Hockey	ЖЖ	5

Write a number sentence to solve.

1 How many more people like football than hockey?

_____ − _____ = _____

_____ more people like football than hockey.

2 How many more people like soccer than baseball?

_____ − _____ = _____

_____ more people like soccer than baseball.

3 How many people like baseball and hockey in all?

_____ + _____ = _____

_____ people like baseball and hockey.

4 How many people like soccer and football in all?

_____ + _____ = _____

_____ people like soccer and football.

Math Triumphs

Chapter 9

Name _____

Homework Practice

School Supplies		
Supplies	Tally	Total
✏ Pencils	ЖЖ ЖЖ ЖЖ	15
✂ Scissors	ЖЖ |||	8
📓 Notebooks	ЖЖ		6
🖊 Markers	ЖЖ ЖЖ ||	12

1 How many pencils are there?

_____ pencils

2 How many notebooks are there?

_____ notebooks

Write a number sentence to solve.

3 How many more pencils are there than scissors?

_____ – _____ = _____

There are _____ more pencils than scissors.

4 How many scissors and markers are there in all?

_____ + _____ = _____

There are _____ scissors and markers in all.

Math Triumphs

Name _____

Vocabulary and English Language Development

This is a bar graph.

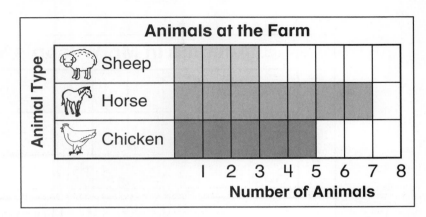

Write how many.

1   _____

2   _____

3   _____

Complete.

4 How many and ?

_____ + _____ = _____

5 How many more than ?

_____ − _____ = _____

ACTIVITY Draw a **bar graph** grid on the board and label it *Our Class's Favorite Pets*. Label the rows *Cats*, *Dogs*, *Birds*. Have students take turns coloring in a bar for their favorite pet. Ask students questions such as: "How many students like cats the best?" Have students answer in complete sentences.

WORKSHEET DIRECTIONS Have students count and answer each question.

Chapter 9

Name _____

Skills Practice

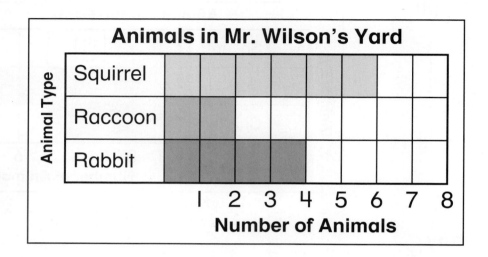

Animals in Mr. Wilson's Yard

Animal Type

Squirrel								
Raccoon								
Rabbit								

1   2   3   4   5   6   7   8
Number of Animals

1 How many raccoons are in Mr. Wilson's yard?

_____ raccoons

2 Which animal was counted four times?

_____

3 How many more squirrels are in Mr. Wilson's yard than rabbits?

_____ more squirrels than rabbits

4 How many animals are in Mr. Wilson's yard in all?

_____ animals in all

5 Robin saw five more chipmunks than rabbits in Mr. Wilson's yard. How many chipmunks did Robin see?

_____ chipmunks

Math Triumphs

Name _____

Problem-Solving Practice

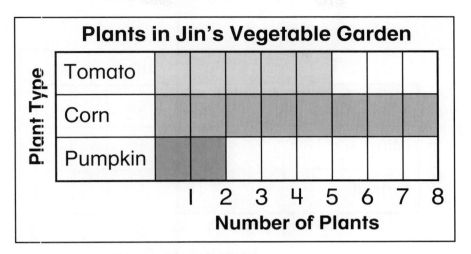

Plants in Jin's Vegetable Garden

Write a number sentence to solve.

I Jin would like to plant twice as many zucchini plants as tomato plants. How many zucchini plants will Jin need?

_____ × _____ = _____

Jin will need _____ zucchini plants.

2 Jin wants to plant five more potato plans than corn plants. How many potato plants will Jin need?

_____ + _____ = _____

Jin will need _____ potato plants.

3 Jin wants to plant 3 times as many strawberry plants as pumpkin plants. How many strawberry plants will Jin need?

_____ × _____ = _____

Jin will need _____ strawberry plants.

Name _____

Homework Practice

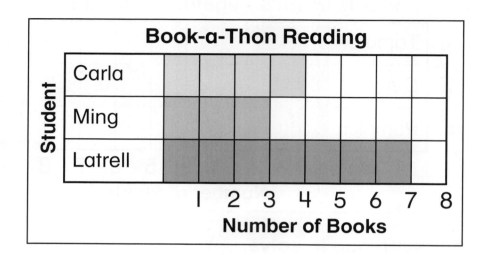

Book-a-Thon Reading

Student								
Carla								
Ming								
Latrell								

1 2 3 4 5 6 7 8
Number of Books

1 How many books did Latrell read?

_____ books

2 How many more books did Latrell read than Ming?

_____ more books than Ming

3 Who read the most books?

_____

Write a number sentence to solve.

4 Jane would like to read twice as many books as Carla.
How many books does Jane need to read?

_____ × _____ = _____

Jane needs to read _____ books.

Math Triumphs

Name _____

Vocabulary and English Language Development

Forest Animals We See		
Type of Animal	Tally	Number of Animals
	|||	3
	|||| |	6
	|||| ||	7

Make a bar graph. Use the data from the table.

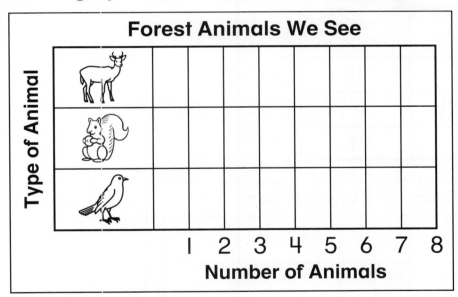

ACTIVITY Draw a **table** on the board and label it *Favorite Flavors*. Include rows for *Vanilla*, *Chocolate*, and *Strawberry*. Have students vote for their favorite and fill in the table. Next, draw a large **bar graph** grid on the board and label it *Favorite Flavors*. Label the rows *Vanilla*, *Chocolate*, and *Strawberry*. Color in the bars as you relate the number of bars to the table. Count aloud with students as you color.

WORKSHEET DIRECTIONS Have students color the bar graph using the data in the table.

Chapter 9

Name _____

Skills Practice

Use the tables to complete each bar graph.

1

Toys Sold at the Fair		
Type of Toy	Tally	Number of Toys
Dolls	ＨＨ |||	8
Boats	||	2
Bears	ＨＨ	5

Toys Sold at the Fair

Type of Toys								
Dolls								
Boats								
Bears								

1 2 3 4 5 6 7 8
Number of Toys

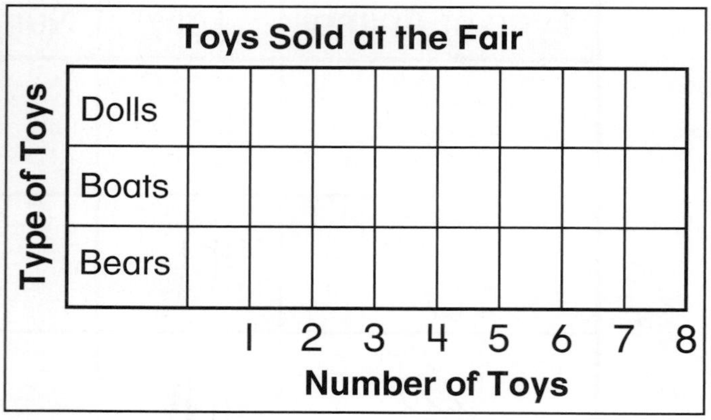

2

Color of Cars We See		
Color of Car	Tally	Number of Cars
Red	||||	4
Blue	ＨＨ ||	7
Black	||||	4

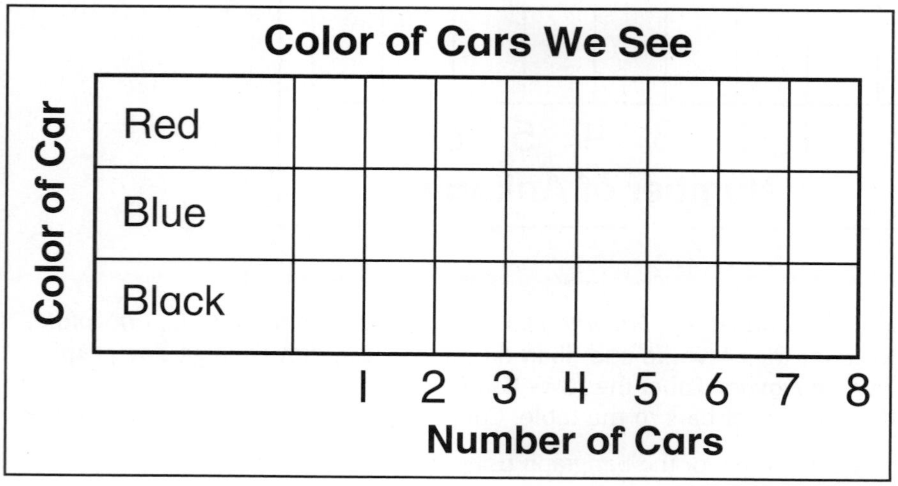

Color of Cars We See

Color of Car								
Red								
Blue								
Black								

1 2 3 4 5 6 7 8
Number of Cars

Math Triumphs

Name _____

Problem-Solving Practice

I Use the table to complete the bar graph.

Favorite Jungle Cats		
Type of Jungle Cat	Tally	Number of People
Lion	IIII	4
Tiger	HHT III	8
Leopard	HHT I	6

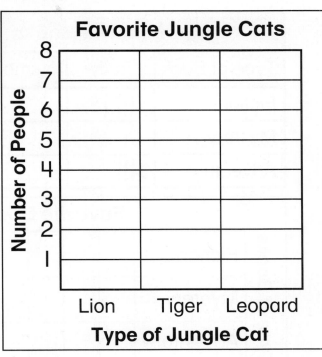

Favorite Jungle Cats

Use the bar graph to solve.

2 How many people like tigers the best? _____

3 How many people like lions the best? _____

4 How many more people like tigers better than lions?

_____ – _____ = _____

_____ more people like tigers better than lions.

5 How many people like leopards the best? _____

6 How many more people like tigers better than leopards?

_____ – _____ = _____

_____ more people like tigers better than leopards.

Name _____

Homework Practice

1 Use the table to complete the bar graph.

Favorite Books		
Type of Book	Tally	Number of Books
Fiction	卌 I	6
Mystery	III	3
Adventure	卌	5

Favorite Books

Type of Books								
Fiction								
Mystery								
Adventure								

1 2 3 4 5 6 7 8
Number of Books

Use the bar graph to solve.

2 How many people like mystery books the best? _____

3 How many people like adventure books the best? _____

4 How many more people like adventure books better than mystery books?

_____ − _____ = _____

_____ more people

Math Triumphs

Name _____

Vocabulary and English Language Development

This is a line plot.

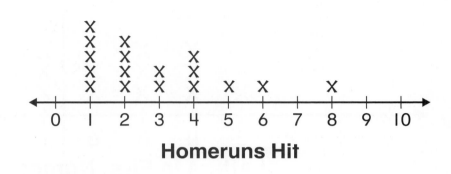

Homeruns Hit

Count the Xs.

1   1 homerun _____   **2**   2 homeruns _____

3   3 homeruns _____   **4**   4 homeruns _____

5   5 homeruns _____   **6**   6 homeruns _____

7   7 homeruns _____   **8**   8 homeruns _____

9   9 homeruns _____   **10**   10 homeruns _____

ACTIVITY Tell students that a **line plot** is another way to show **data**. Draw a line plot on the board. Ask each student to draw an X above the number that shows how many people are in his or her family. Count the number for each. Ask questions about the line plot such as: "How many students have four family members?"

WORKSHEET DIRECTIONS Have students count and write how many homeruns for each number on the line plot.

Name _____

Skills Practice

This line plot shows the number of letters in students' first names.

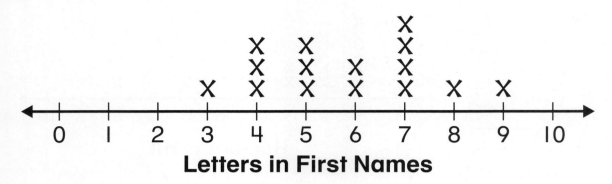

Letters in First Names

Use the line plot to answer each question.

1 How many students have 7 letters in their first name?
_____ students

2 How many letters do 2 students have in their names?
_____ letters

3 How many letters are in the longest name?
_____ letters

4 How many more students have 5 letters in their
names than 3 letters? _____ more students

Math Triumphs

Name _____

Problem-Solving Practice

This line plot shows the number of books each student read.

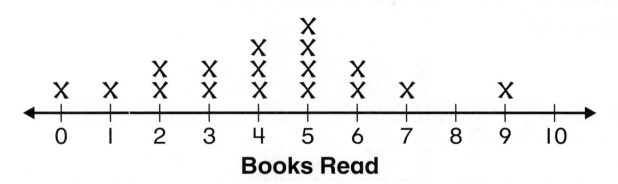

Books Read

Write a number sentence to solve.

1 How many more students read 5 books than 9 books?

_____ − _____ = _____

_____ more students read 5 books than 9 books.

2 How many more students read 4 books than 1 book?

_____ − _____ = _____

_____ more students read 4 books than 1 book.

3 How many students read 1, 2, 3, or 4 books in all?

_____ + _____ + _____ + _____ = _____

_____ students read 1, 2, 3, or 4 books in all.

Chapter 9

Name _____

Homework Practice

This line plot shows the number of points scored during a game.

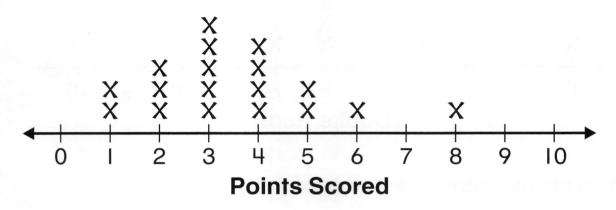

Points Scored

Use the line plot to answer each question.

1 How many students scored 5 points? _____ students

2 How many students scored 3 points? _____ students

Write a number sentence to solve.

3 How many more students scored 3 points than 1 point?

_____ − _____ = _____

_____ more students scored 3 points than 1 point.

4 How many students scored 1, 5, or 8 points?

_____ + _____ + _____ = _____

_____ students scored 1, 5, or 8 points in all.

Math Triumphs

Answer Key (Lesson 1-1)

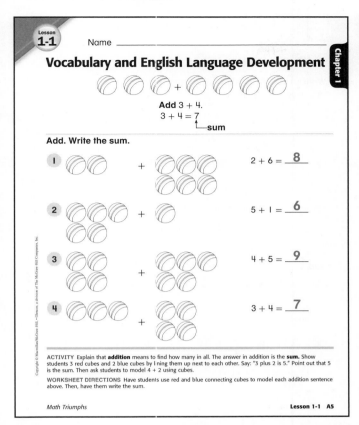

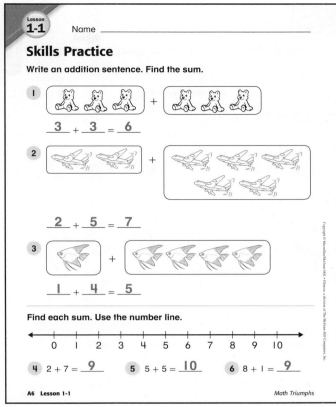

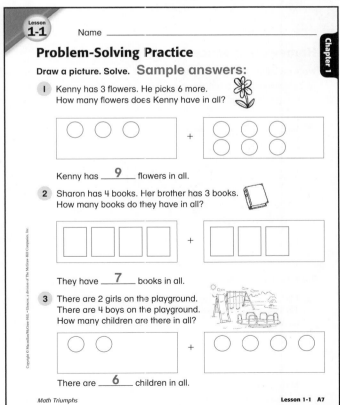

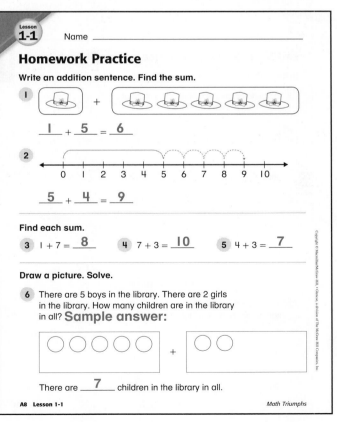

Answer Key (Lesson 1-2)

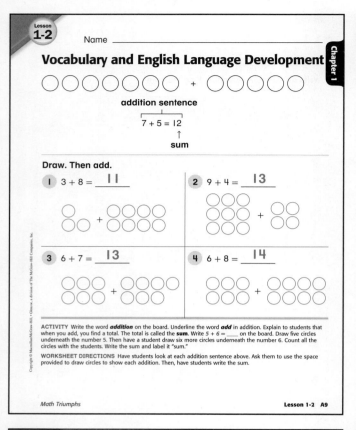

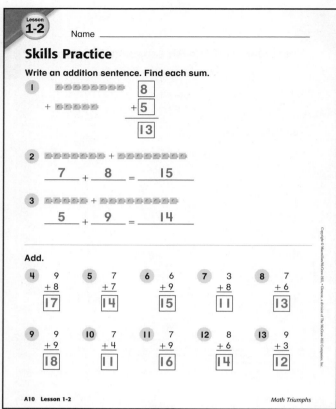

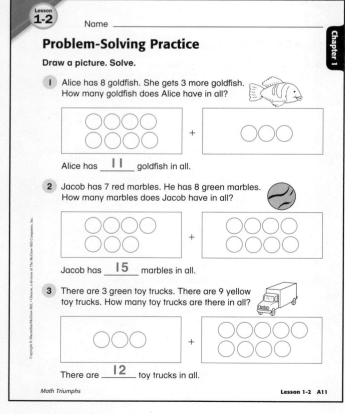

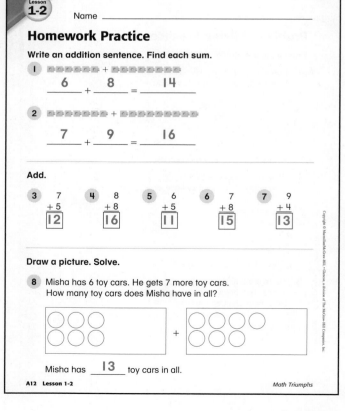

Answer Key (Lesson 1-3)

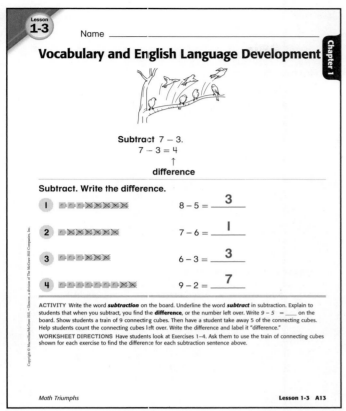

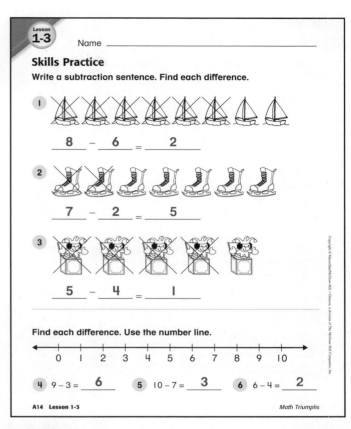

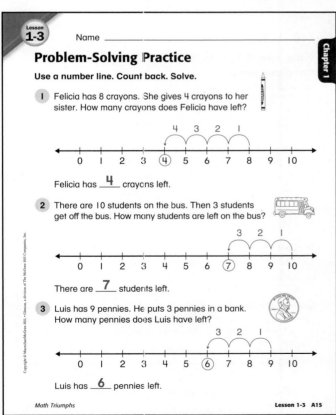

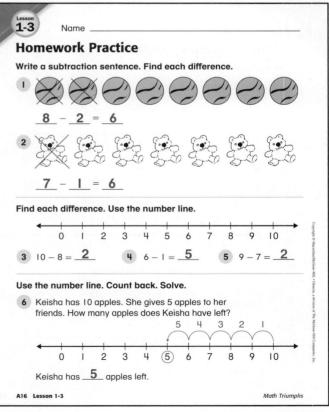

Answer Key (Lesson 1-4)

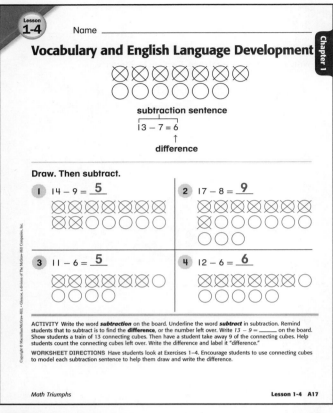

Vocabulary and English Language Development

Chapter 1

⊗⊗⊗⊗⊗⊗⊗
○○○○○○○

subtraction sentence
13 − 7 = 6
↑
difference

Draw. Then subtract.

1 14 − 9 = __5__
⊗⊗⊗⊗⊗
○○○○○

2 17 − 8 = __9__
⊗⊗⊗⊗⊗⊗⊗⊗⊗
○○○○○○○○
○

3 11 − 6 = __5__
⊗⊗⊗⊗⊗⊗
○○○○○

4 12 − 6 = __6__
⊗⊗⊗⊗⊗⊗
○○○○○○

ACTIVITY Write the word **subtraction** on the board. Underline the word **subtract** in subtraction. Remind students that to subtract is to find the **difference**, or the number left over. Write 13 − 9 = _____ on the board. Show students a train of 13 connecting cubes. Then have a student take away 9 of the connecting cubes. Help students count the connecting cubes left over. Write the difference and label it "difference."

WORKSHEET DIRECTIONS Have students look at Exercises 1–4. Encourage students to use connecting cubes to model each subtraction sentence to help them draw and write the difference.

Math Triumphs   **Lesson 1-4 A17**

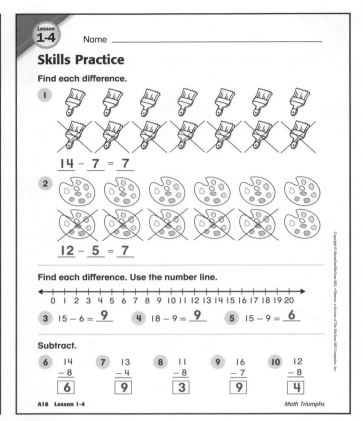

Skills Practice

Find each difference.

1 __14__ − __7__ = __7__

2 __12__ − __5__ = __7__

Find each difference. Use the number line.

0 1 2 3 4 5 6 7 8 9 10 11 12 13 14 15 16 17 18 19 20

3 15 − 6 = __9__   4 18 − 9 = __9__   5 15 − 9 = __6__

Subtract.

6 14
  − 8
  ┌─┐
  │6│
  └─┘

7 13
  − 4
  ┌─┐
  │9│
  └─┘

8 11
  − 8
  ┌─┐
  │3│
  └─┘

9 16
  − 7
  ┌─┐
  │9│
  └─┘

10 12
  − 8
  ┌─┐
  │4│
  └─┘

A18 Lesson 1-4   *Math Triumphs*

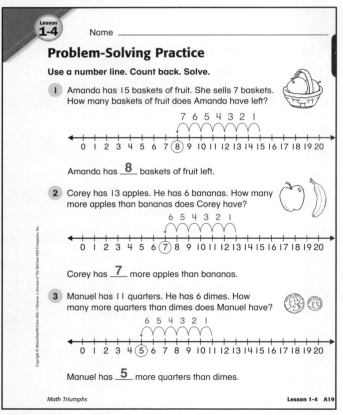

Problem-Solving Practice

Use a number line. Count back. Solve.

1 Amanda has 15 baskets of fruit. She sells 7 baskets. How many baskets of fruit does Amanda have left?

7 6 5 4 3 2 1
0 1 2 3 4 5 6 7 ⑧ 9 10 11 12 13 14 15 16 17 18 19 20

Amanda has __8__ baskets of fruit left.

2 Corey has 13 apples. He has 6 bananas. How many more apples than bananas does Corey have?

6 5 4 3 2 1
0 1 2 3 4 5 6 ⑦ 8 9 10 11 12 13 14 15 16 17 18 19 20

Corey has __7__ more apples than bananas.

3 Manuel has 11 quarters. He has 6 dimes. How many more quarters than dimes does Manuel have?

6 5 4 3 2 1
0 1 2 3 4 ⑤ 6 7 8 9 10 11 12 13 14 15 16 17 18 19 20

Manuel has __5__ more quarters than dimes.

Math Triumphs   **Lesson 1-4 A19**

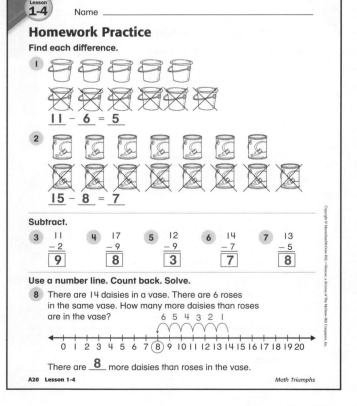

Homework Practice

Find each difference.

1 __11__ − __6__ = __5__

2 __15__ − __8__ = __7__

Subtract.

3 11
  − 2
  ┌─┐
  │9│
  └─┘

4 17
  − 9
  ┌─┐
  │8│
  └─┘

5 12
  − 9
  ┌─┐
  │3│
  └─┘

6 14
  − 7
  ┌─┐
  │7│
  └─┘

7 13
  − 5
  ┌─┐
  │8│
  └─┘

Use a number line. Count back. Solve.

8 There are 14 daisies in a vase. There are 6 roses in the same vase. How many more daisies than roses are in the vase?

6 5 4 3 2 1
0 1 2 3 4 5 6 7 ⑧ 9 10 11 12 13 14 15 16 17 18 19 20

There are __8__ more daisies than roses in the vase.

A20 Lesson 1-4   *Math Triumphs*

Answer Key (Lesson 1-5)

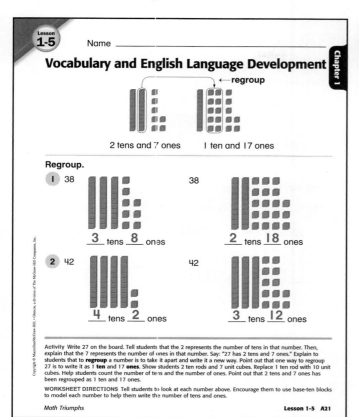

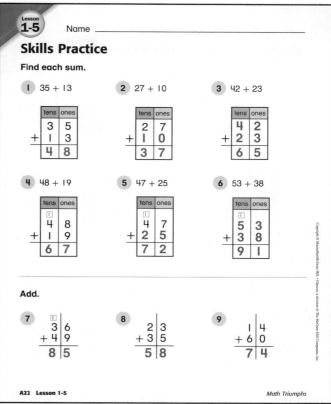

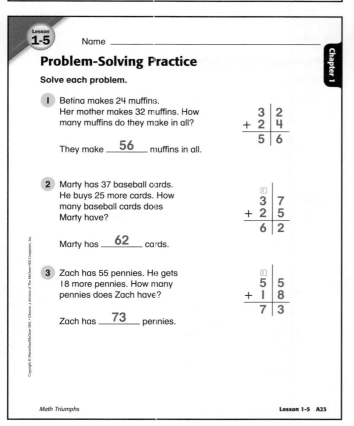

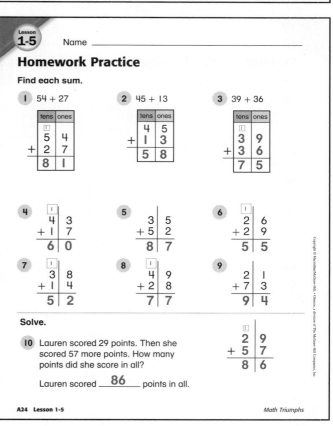

Answer Key (Lesson 1-6)

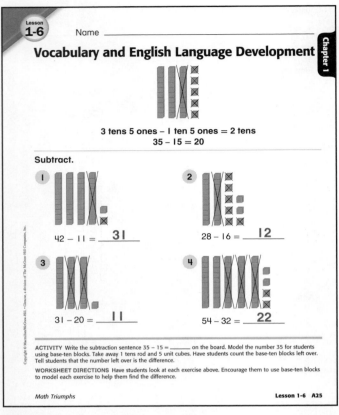

Lesson 1-6

Name _____

Vocabulary and English Language Development

Chapter 1

3 tens 5 ones – 1 ten 5 ones = 2 tens
35 – 15 = 20

Subtract.

1. 42 – 11 = **31**

2. 28 – 16 = **12**

3. 31 – 20 = **11**

4. 54 – 32 = **22**

ACTIVITY Write the subtraction sentence 35 – 15 = _____ on the board. Model the number 35 for students using base-ten blocks. Take away 1 tens rod and 5 unit cubes. Have students count the base-ten blocks left over. Tell students that the number left over is the difference.

WORKSHEET DIRECTIONS Have students look at each exercise above. Encourage them to use base-ten blocks to model each exercise to help them find the difference.

Math Triumphs Lesson 1-6 A25

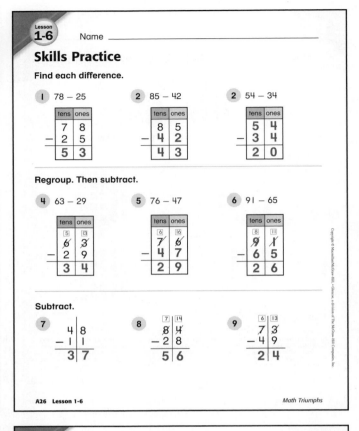

Lesson 1-6

Name _____

Skills Practice

Find each difference.

1. 78 – 25

tens	ones
7	8
– 2	5
5	3

2. 85 – 42

tens	ones
8	5
– 4	2
4	3

2. 54 – 34

tens	ones
5	4
– 3	4
2	0

Regroup. Then subtract.

4. 63 – 29

tens	ones
5	13
6̶	3̶
– 2	9
3	4

5. 76 – 47

tens	ones
6	16
7̶	6̶
– 4	7
2	9

6. 91 – 65

tens	ones
8	11
9̶	1̶
– 6	5
2	6

Subtract.

7.
```
  4 | 8
– 1 | 1
  3 | 7
```

8.
```
  7 |14
  8̶ | 4̶
– 2 | 8
  5 | 6
```

9.
```
  6 |13
  7̶ | 3̶
– 4 | 9
  2 | 4
```

A26 Lesson 1-6 *Math Triumphs*

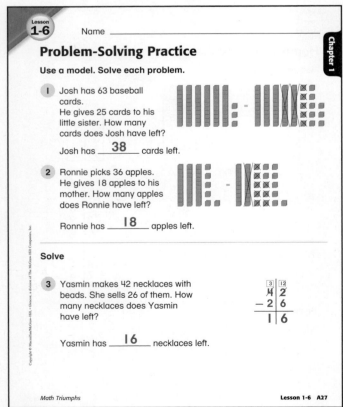

Lesson 1-6

Name _____

Problem-Solving Practice

Chapter 1

Use a model. Solve each problem.

1. Josh has 63 baseball cards. He gives 25 cards to his little sister. How many cards does Josh have left?

Josh has **38** cards left.

2. Ronnie picks 36 apples. He gives 18 apples to his mother. How many apples does Ronnie have left?

Ronnie has **18** apples left.

Solve

3. Yasmin makes 42 necklaces with beads. She sells 26 of them. How many necklaces does Yasmin have left?

```
  3 |12
  4̶ | 2̶
– 2 | 6
  1 | 6
```

Yasmin has **16** necklaces left.

Math Triumphs Lesson 1-6 A27

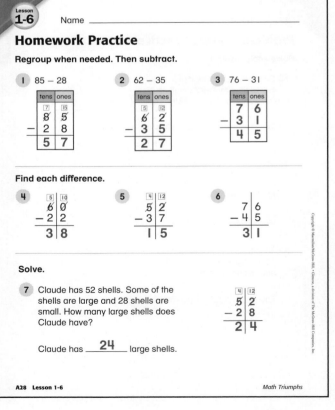

Lesson 1-6

Name _____

Homework Practice

Regroup when needed. Then subtract.

1. 85 – 28

tens	ones
7	15
8̶	5̶
– 2	8
5	7

2. 62 – 35

tens	ones
5	12
6̶	2̶
– 3	5
2	7

3. 76 – 31

tens	ones
7	6
– 3	1
4	5

Find each difference.

4.
```
  5 |10
  6̶ | 0̶
– 2 | 2
  3 | 8
```

5.
```
  4 |12
  5̶ | 2̶
– 3 | 7
  1 | 5
```

6.
```
  7 | 6
– 4 | 5
  3 | 1
```

Solve.

7. Claude has 52 shells. Some of the shells are large and 28 shells are small. How many large shells does Claude have?

```
  4 |12
  5̶ | 2̶
– 2 | 8
  2 | 4
```

Claude has **24** large shells.

A28 Lesson 1-6 *Math Triumphs*

Answer Key (Lesson 2-1)

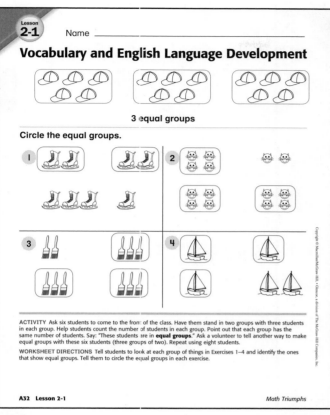

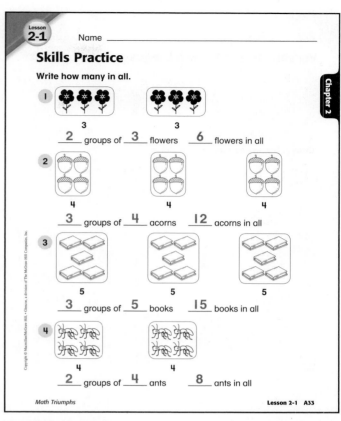

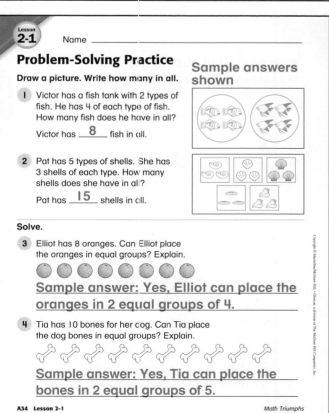

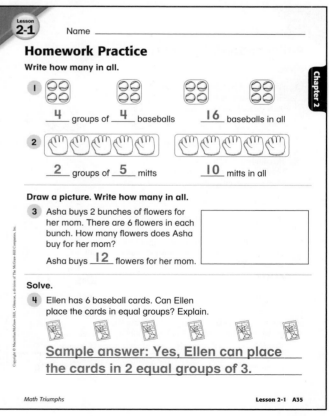

Answer Key (Lesson 2-2)

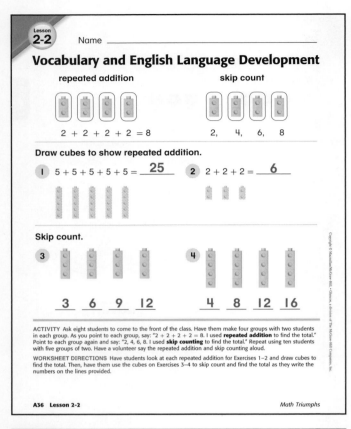

Vocabulary and English Language Development

repeated addition

$2 + 2 + 2 + 2 = 8$

skip count

2,   4,   6,   8

Draw cubes to show repeated addition.

1. $5 + 5 + 5 + 5 + 5 = \underline{25}$
2. $2 + 2 + 2 = \underline{6}$

Skip count.

3.   3   6   9   12

4.   4   8   12   16

ACTIVITY Ask eight students to come to the front of the class. Have them make four groups with two students in each group. As you point to each group, say: "2 + 2 + 2 + 2 = 8. I used **repeated addition** to find the total." Point to each group again and say: "2, 4, 6, 8. I used **skip counting** to find the total." Repeat using ten students with five groups of two. Have a volunteer say the repeated addition and skip counting aloud.

WORKSHEET DIRECTIONS Have students look at each repeated addition for Exercises 1–2 and draw cubes to find the total. Then, have them use the cubes on Exercises 3–4 to skip count and find the total as they write the numbers on the lines provided.

A36   Lesson 2-2   *Math Triumphs*

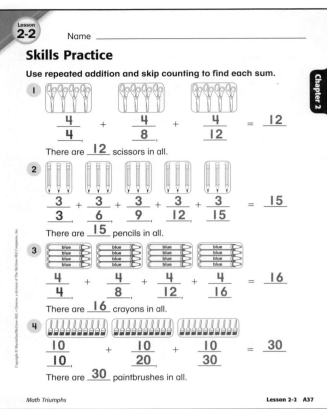

Skills Practice

Use repeated addition and skip counting to find each sum.

1. $\dfrac{4}{4} + \dfrac{4}{8}, + \dfrac{4}{12} = \underline{12}$

   There are $\underline{12}$ scissors in all.

2. $\dfrac{3}{3} + \dfrac{3}{6}, + \dfrac{3}{9}, + \dfrac{3}{12}, + \dfrac{3}{15} = \underline{15}$

   There are $\underline{15}$ pencils in all.

3. $\dfrac{4}{4}, + \dfrac{4}{8}, + \dfrac{4}{12}, + \dfrac{4}{16} = \underline{16}$

   There are $\underline{16}$ crayons in all.

4. $\dfrac{10}{10}, + \dfrac{10}{20}, + \dfrac{10}{30} = \underline{30}$

   There are $\underline{30}$ paintbrushes in all.

Math Triumphs   Lesson 2-2   A37

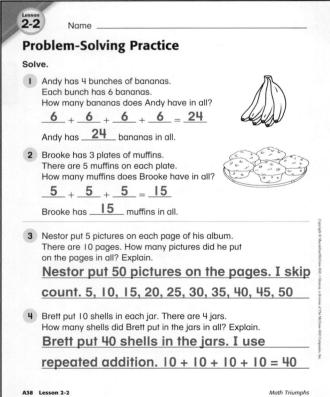

Problem-Solving Practice

Solve.

1. Andy has 4 bunches of bananas. Each bunch has 6 bananas. How many bananas does Andy have in all?

   $\underline{6} + \underline{6} + \underline{6} + \underline{6} = \underline{24}$

   Andy has $\underline{24}$ bananas in all.

2. Brooke has 3 plates of muffins. There are 5 muffins on each plate. How many muffins does Brooke have in all?

   $\underline{5} + \underline{5} + \underline{5} = \underline{15}$

   Brooke has $\underline{15}$ muffins in all.

3. Nestor put 5 pictures on each page of his album. There are 10 pages. How many pictures did he put on the pages in all? Explain.

   Nestor put 50 pictures on the pages. I skip count. 5, 10, 15, 20, 25, 30, 35, 40, 45, 50

4. Brett put 10 shells in each jar. There are 4 jars. How many shells did Brett put in the jars in all? Explain.

   Brett put 40 shells in the jars. I use repeated addition. 10 + 10 + 10 + 10 = 40

A38   Lesson 2-2   *Math Triumphs*

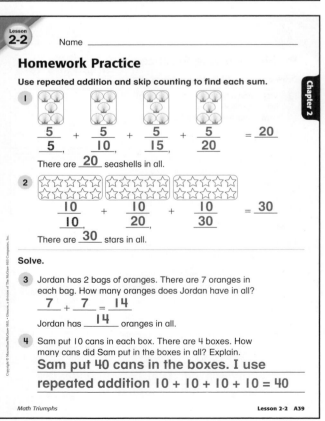

Homework Practice

Use repeated addition and skip counting to find each sum.

1. $\dfrac{5}{5}, + \dfrac{5}{10}, + \dfrac{5}{15}, + \dfrac{5}{20} = \underline{20}$

   There are $\underline{20}$ seashells in all.

2. $\dfrac{10}{10}, + \dfrac{10}{20}, + \dfrac{10}{30} = \underline{30}$

   There are $\underline{30}$ stars in all.

Solve.

3. Jordan has 2 bags of oranges. There are 7 oranges in each bag. How many oranges does Jordan have in all?

   $\underline{7} + \underline{7} = \underline{14}$

   Jordan has $\underline{14}$ oranges in all.

4. Sam put 10 cans in each box. There are 4 boxes. How many cans did Sam put in the boxes in all? Explain.

   Sam put 40 cans in the boxes. I use repeated addition 10 + 10 + 10 + 10 = 40

Math Triumphs   Lesson 2-2   A39

Answer Key (Lesson 2-3)

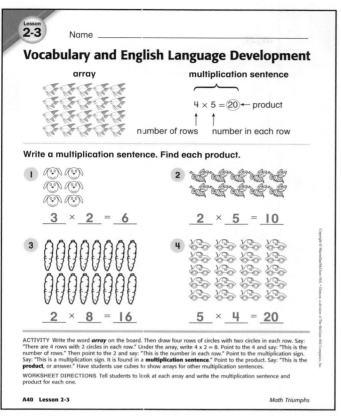

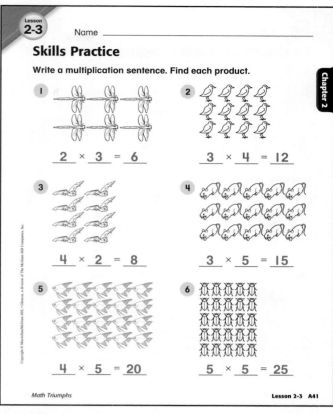

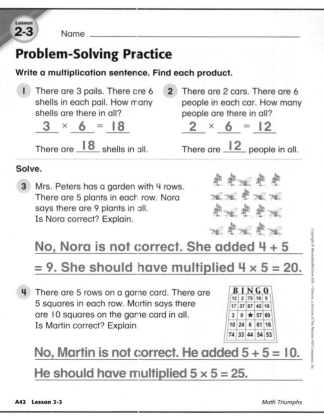

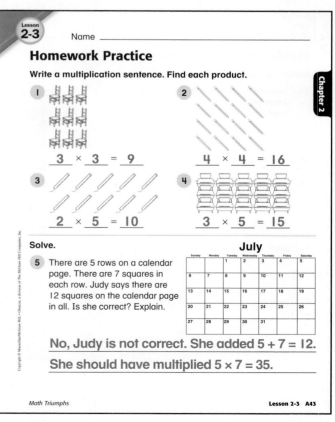

Answer Key (Lesson 2-4)

Lesson 2-4

Name _____

Vocabulary and English Language Development

area model

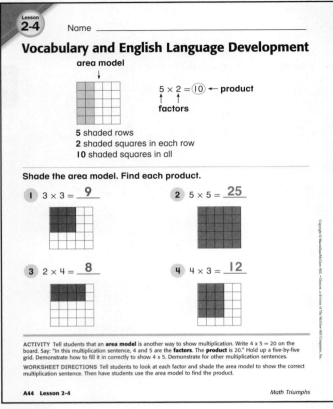

$5 \times 2 = \boxed{10}$ ← product

↑ ↑
factors

5 shaded rows
2 shaded squares in each row
10 shaded squares in all

Shade the area model. Find each product.

1. $3 \times 3 = \underline{9}$

2. $5 \times 5 = \underline{25}$

3. $2 \times 4 = \underline{8}$

4. $4 \times 3 = \underline{12}$

ACTIVITY Tell students that an **area model** is another way to show multiplication. Write 4 x 5 = 20 on the board. Say: "In this multiplication sentence, 4 and 5 are the **factors**. The **product** is 20." Hold up a five-by-five grid. Demonstrate how to fill it in correctly to show 4 x 5. Demonstrate for other multiplication sentences.

WORKSHEET DIRECTIONS Tell students to look at each factor and shade the area model to show the correct multiplication sentence. Then have students use the area model to find the product.

Math Triumphs

Lesson 2-4

Name _____

Skills Practice

Shade the area model. Find each product.

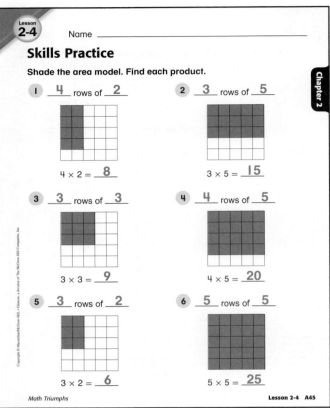

1. __4__ rows of __2__

   $4 \times 2 = \underline{8}$

2. __3__ rows of __5__

   $3 \times 5 = \underline{15}$

3. __3__ rows of __3__

   $3 \times 3 = \underline{9}$

4. __4__ rows of __5__

   $4 \times 5 = \underline{20}$

5. __3__ rows of __2__

   $3 \times 2 = \underline{6}$

6. __5__ rows of __5__

   $5 \times 5 = \underline{25}$

Math Triumphs

Lesson 2-4

Name _____

Problem-Solving Practice

Shade the area model. Find each product.

1. Jose has 4 new CDs. Each new CD has 5 songs. How many new songs does Jose have in all?

   __4__ new CDs × __5__ songs
   on each CD = __20__ new songs

   Jose has __20__ new songs.

2. Juanita has 5 cats. Each cat has 5 kittens. How many kittens does Juanita have in all?

   __5__ cats × __5__ kittens
   from each cat = __25__ kittens

   Juanita has __25__ kittens.

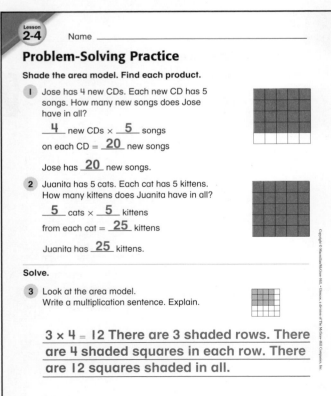

Solve.

3. Look at the area model.
   Write a multiplication sentence. Explain.

   $3 \times 4 = 12$ **There are 3 shaded rows. There are 4 shaded squares in each row. There are 12 squares shaded in all.**

Math Triumphs

Lesson 2-4

Name _____

Homework Practice

Shade the area model. Find the each product.

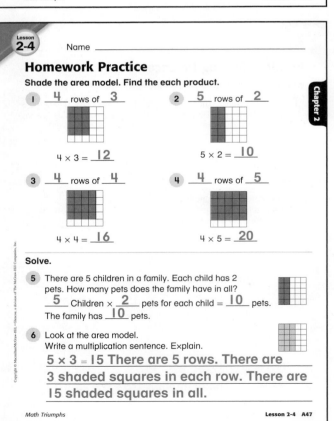

1. __4__ rows of __3__

   $4 \times 3 = \underline{12}$

2. __5__ rows of __2__

   $5 \times 2 = \underline{10}$

3. __4__ rows of __4__

   $4 \times 4 = \underline{16}$

4. __4__ rows of __5__

   $4 \times 5 = \underline{20}$

Solve.

5. There are 5 children in a family. Each child has 2 pets. How many pets does the family have in all?

   __5__ Children × __2__ pets for each child = __10__ pets.
   The family has __10__ pets.

6. Look at the area model.
   Write a multiplication sentence. Explain.

   $5 \times 3 = 15$ **There are 5 rows. There are 3 shaded squares in each row. There are 15 shaded squares in all.**

Math Triumphs

Math Triumphs

Answer Key (Lesson 2-5)

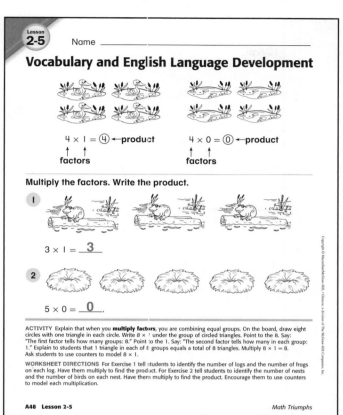

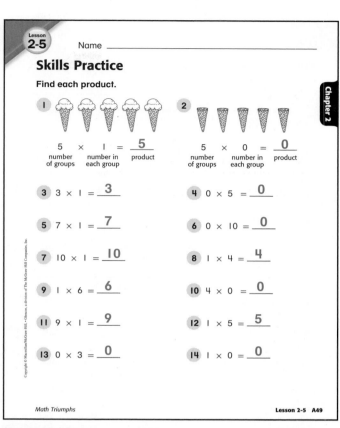

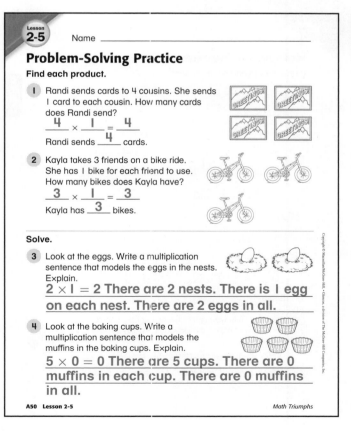

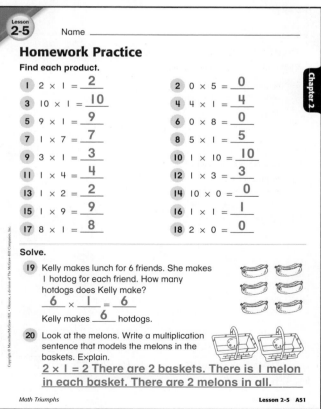

Answer Key (Lesson 2-6)

Lesson 2-6 — Vocabulary and English Language Development

Name _____

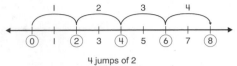

4 jumps of 2
$2 \times 4 = 8$ ←product

Use the number line to skip count. Find each product.

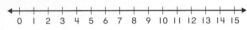

1. $2 \times 6 = 12$ 2, _4_, _6_, _8_, _10_, _12_

2. $2 \times 3 = 6$ 2, _4_, _6_

3. $5 \times 4 = 20$ 5, _10_, _15_, _20_

4. $5 \times 6 = 30$ 5, _10_, _15_, _20_, _25_, _30_

ACTIVITY Display a 0–20 number line. On the board, write 2×5. Say: "Let's use the number line and skip count to find the **product.** Two is a factor. Skip count by 2s." As students skip count, point to each skip on the number line. Then reverse the problem to 5×2. Say: "Five is a factor. Skip count by 5s." Once again, as the students skip count, point to each skip on the number line. Then have students use number lines to find the product for other multiplications where they have to skip count by 2s and by 5s.

WORKSHEET DIRECTIONS Tell students to use the number lines and skip count to find the product.

A52   Lesson 2-6   *Math Triumphs*

Lesson 2-6 — Skills Practice

Name _____

Skip count to find each product.

1. $5 \times 5 = 25$ _5_, _10_, _15_, _20_, _25_

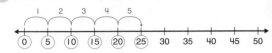

2. $2 \times 7 = 14$ _2_, _4_, _6_, _8_, _10_, _12_, _14_

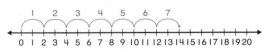

3. $2 \times 8 = 16$
   _2_, _4_, _6_, _8_, _10_, _12_, _14_, _16_

4. $5 \times 8 = 40$
   _5_, _10_, _15_, _20_, _25_, _30_, _35_, _40_

5. $2 \times 9 = 18$
   _2_, _4_, _6_, _8_, _10_, _12_, _14_, _16_, _18_

6. $5 \times 7 = 35$
   _5_, _10_, _15_, _20_, _25_, _30_, _35_

Math Triumphs   **Lesson 2-6   A53**

Lesson 2-6 — Problem-Solving Practice

Name _____

Skip count to find each product.

1. Brenda has 6 pairs of gloves. How many gloves does she have in all?

   2, _4_, _6_, _8_, _10_, _12_

   2 × 6 = _12_

2. Bertha has 8 pairs of boots. How many shoes does she have in all?

   2, _4_, _6_, _8_, _10_, _12_, _14_, _16_

   2 × 8 = _16_

Solve.

3. Tim has 7 jars of buttons. There are 5 buttons in each jar. How many buttons does Tim have in all? Explain.

   Tim has 35 buttons. There are 7 groups of 5 buttons. Skip count by five 7 times to find the product. 5, 10, 15, 20, 25, 30, 35.
   5 × 7 = 35

A54   Lesson 2-6   *Math Triumphs*

Lesson 2-6 — Homework Practice

Name _____

Skip count to find each product.

1. $2 \times 2 = 4$
   _2_, _4_

2. $5 \times 3 = 15$
   _5_, _10_, _15_

3. $5 \times 4 = 20$
   _5_, _10_, _15_, 20

4. $5 \times 2 = 10$
   _5_, _10_

5. $5 \times 5 = 25$
   _5_, _10_, _15_, _20_, _25_

6. $2 \times 7 = 14$
   _2_, _4_, _6_, _8_, _10_, _12_, _14_

7. $5 \times 9 = 45$
   _5_, _10_, _15_, _20_, _25_, _30_, _35_, _40_, _45_

Solve.

8. Jim sees 10 ladybugs. Each ladybug has 5 spots. How many spots do the ladybugs have in all? Explain.

   The ladybugs have 50 spots in all.
   Skip count by five 10 times. 5, 10, 15, 20, 25, 30, 35, 40, 45, 50.

Math Triumphs   **Lesson 2-6   A55**

Answer Key (Lesson 3-1)

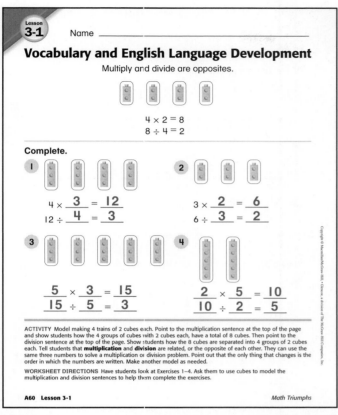

A60 Lesson 3-1

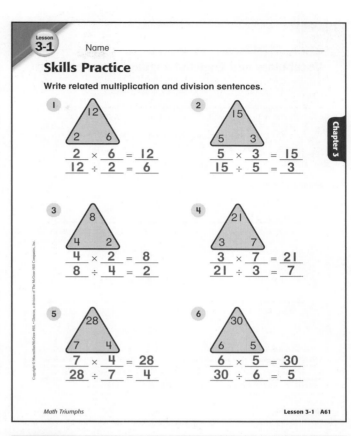

Lesson 3-1 A61

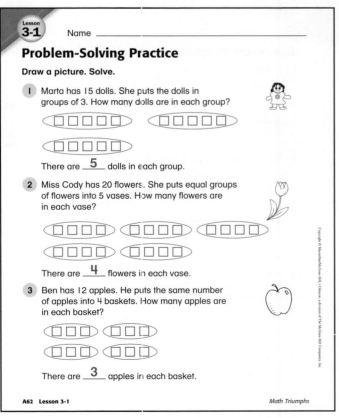

A62 Lesson 3-1

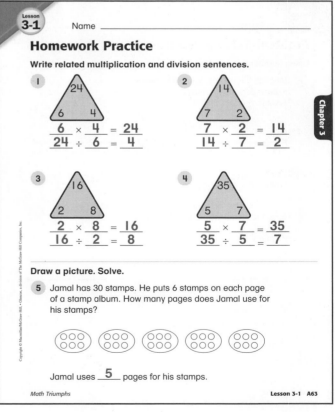

Lesson 3-1 A63

Answer Key (Lesson 3-2)

Vocabulary and English Language Development

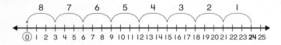

You can subtract to help divide.

$24 - 3 - 3 - 3 - 3 - 3 - 3 - 3 - 3 = 0$

$24 \div 3 = 8$

Subtract to divide.

1.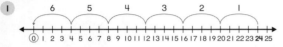

$24 - 4 - 4 - 4 - 4 - 4 - 4 = 0$

$24 \div 4 = \underline{6}$

2.

$24 - 2 - 2 - 2 - 2 - 2 - 2 - 2 - 2 - 2 - 2 - 2 - 2 = 0$

$24 \div 2 = \underline{12}$

ACTIVITY Before beginning, review **skip counting** with students. Show 10 cube trains of 2 and help students skip count aloud to 20. Next, draw a number line on the board and repeat the skip counting. Then, show how to skip count backward by 2s from 20. Skip count aloud as you draw jumps on the number line. Then write the **repeated subtraction**: $20 - 2 - 2 - 2 - 2 - 2 - 2 - 2 - 2 - 2 - 2 = 0$. Count the number of 2s aloud and write the answer (10). Relate this to the division sentence $20 \div 2 = 10$. Repeat for counting by 4s and 5s.
WORKSHEET DIRECTIONS Have students skip count along the number lines and use the number of skips to find the quotient.

Skills Practice

Divide. Use the number line.

1. $16 \div 2 = \underline{8}$
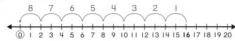

2. $20 \div 5 = \underline{4}$
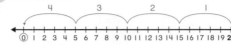

3. $18 \div 3 = \underline{6}$
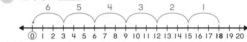

Write a division sentence. Use the number line

4.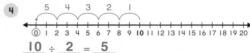

$10 \div 2 = 5$

5.

$24 \div 4 = 6$

Problem-Solving Practice

Use a number line to solve.

1. Sara has 28 pennies. She puts 4 pennies on each page of a coin album. How many pages does she use?

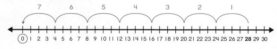

$28 \div 4 = \underline{7}$

Sara uses __7__ pages.

2. Hank has 30 nickels. He puts the nickels into stacks of 5 each. How many stacks of nickels does Hank have?

$30 \div 5 = \underline{6}$

Hank has __6__ stacks of nickels.

Homework Practice

1. Divide. Use the number line.

$20 \div 4 = \underline{5}$

2. Write a division sentence. Use the number line.

$14 \div 2 = 7$

Use a number line to solve.

3. Kim buys 16 treats for her party's goody bags. She puts 4 treats in each goody bag. How many goody bags does Kim make?

$16 \div 4 = \underline{4}$

Kim makes __4__ goody bags.

Answer Key (Lesson 3-3)

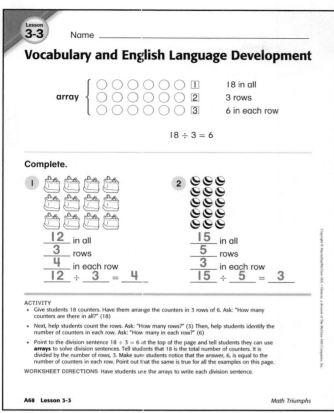

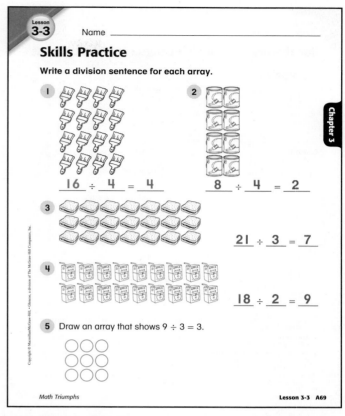

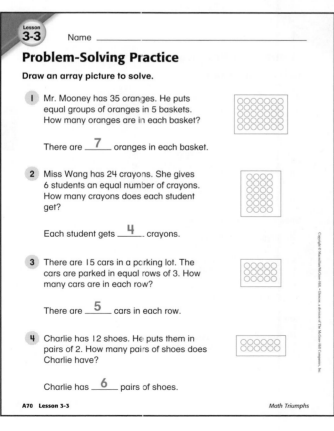

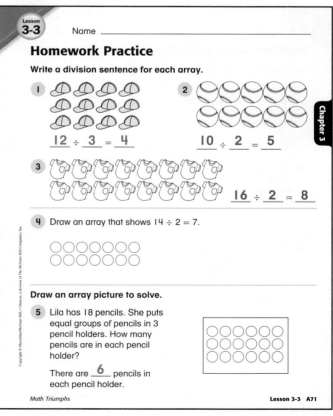

Answer Key (Lesson 3-4)

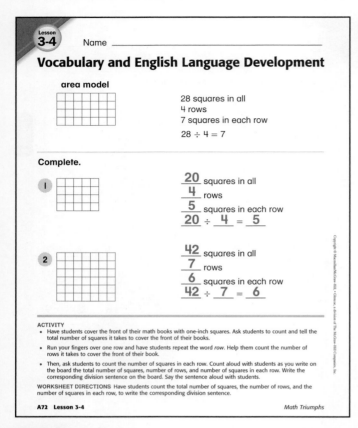

Vocabulary and English Language Development

area model

28 squares in all
4 rows
7 squares in each row
$28 \div 4 = 7$

Complete.

1. 20 squares in all
    4 rows
    5 squares in each row
    $20 \div 4 = 5$

2. 42 squares in all
    7 rows
    6 squares in each row
    $42 \div 7 = 6$

ACTIVITY
- Have students cover the front of their math books with one-inch squares. Ask students to count and tell the total number of squares it takes to cover the front of their books.
- Run your fingers over one row and have students repeat the word *row*. Help them count the number of rows it takes to cover the front of their book.
- Then, ask students to count the number of squares in each row. Count aloud with students as you write on the board the total number of squares, number of rows, and number of squares in each row. Write the corresponding division sentence on the board. Say the sentence aloud with students.

WORKSHEET DIRECTIONS Have students count the total number of squares, the number of rows, and the number of squares in each row, to write the corresponding division sentence.

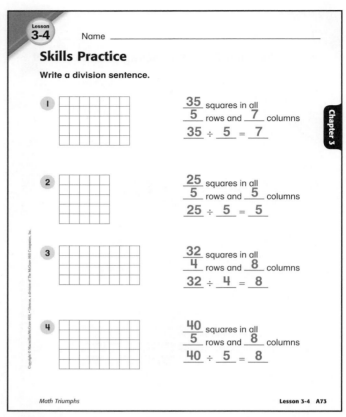

Skills Practice

Write a division sentence.

1. 35 squares in all
    5 rows and 7 columns
    $35 \div 5 = 7$

2. 25 squares in all
    5 rows and 5 columns
    $25 \div 5 = 5$

3. 32 squares in all
    4 rows and 8 columns
    $32 \div 4 = 8$

4. 40 squares in all
    5 rows and 8 columns
    $40 \div 5 = 8$

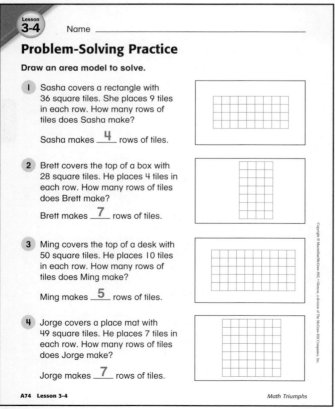

Problem-Solving Practice

Draw an area model to solve.

1. Sasha covers a rectangle with 36 square tiles. She places 9 tiles in each row. How many rows of tiles does Sasha make?

    Sasha makes **4** rows of tiles.

2. Brett covers the top of a box with 28 square tiles. He places 4 tiles in each row. How many rows of tiles does Brett make?

    Brett makes **7** rows of tiles.

3. Ming covers the top of a desk with 50 square tiles. He places 10 tiles in each row. How many rows of tiles does Ming make?

    Ming makes **5** rows of tiles.

4. Jorge covers a place mat with 49 square tiles. He places 7 tiles in each row. How many rows of tiles does Jorge make?

    Jorge makes **7** rows of tiles.

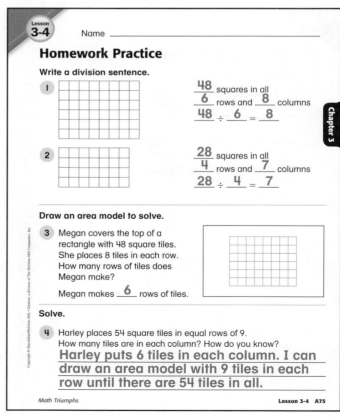

Homework Practice

Write a division sentence.

1. 48 squares in all
    6 rows and 8 columns
    $48 \div 6 = 8$

2. 28 squares in all
    4 rows and 7 columns
    $28 \div 4 = 7$

Draw an area model to solve.

3. Megan covers the top of a rectangle with 48 square tiles. She places 8 tiles in each row. How many rows of tiles does Megan make?

    Megan makes **6** rows of tiles.

Solve.

4. Harley places 54 square tiles in equal rows of 9. How many tiles are in each column? How do you know?

    Harley puts 6 tiles in each column. I can draw an area model with 9 tiles in each row until there are 54 tiles in all.

Answer Key (Lesson 3-5)

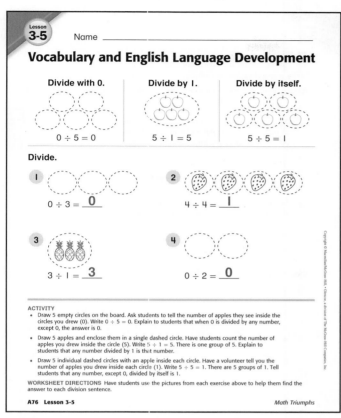

Lesson 3-5 Name _____

Vocabulary and English Language Development

Divide with 0.	Divide by 1.	Divide by itself.

$0 \div 5 = 0$ $5 \div 1 = 5$ $5 \div 5 = 1$

Divide.

1. $0 \div 3 = \underline{0}$

2. $4 \div 4 = \underline{1}$

3. $3 \div 1 = \underline{3}$

4. $0 \div 2 = \underline{0}$

ACTIVITY
- Draw 5 empty circles on the board. Ask students to tell the number of apples they see inside the circles you drew (0). Write $0 \div 5 = 0$. Explain to students that when 0 is divided by any number, except 0, the answer is 0.
- Draw 5 apples and enclose them in a single dashed circle. Have students count the number of apples you drew inside the circle (5). Write $5 \div 1 = 5$. There is one group of 5. Explain to students that any number divided by 1 is that number.
- Draw 5 individual dashed circles with an apple inside each circle. Have a volunteer tell you the number of apples you drew inside each circle (1). Write $5 \div 5 = 1$. There are 5 groups of 1. Tell students that any number, except 0, divided by itself is 1.

WORKSHEET DIRECTIONS Have students use the pictures from each exercise above to help them find the answer to each division sentence.

A76 **Lesson 3-5**   *Math Triumphs*

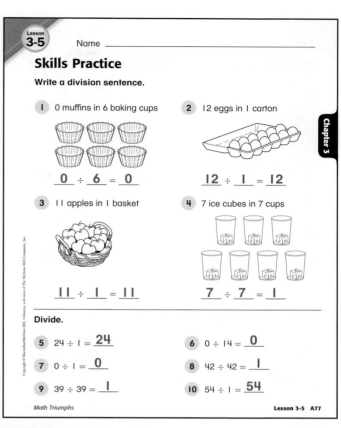

Lesson 3-5 Name _____

Skills Practice

Write a division sentence.

1. 0 muffins in 6 baking cups

   $\underline{0} \div \underline{6} = \underline{0}$

2. 12 eggs in 1 carton

   $\underline{12} \div \underline{1} = \underline{12}$

3. 11 apples in 1 basket

   $\underline{11} \div \underline{1} = \underline{11}$

4. 7 ice cubes in 7 cups

   $\underline{7} \div \underline{7} = \underline{1}$

Divide.

5. $24 \div 1 = \underline{24}$

6. $0 \div 14 = \underline{0}$

7. $0 \div 1 = \underline{0}$

8. $42 \div 42 = \underline{1}$

9. $39 \div 39 = \underline{1}$

10. $54 \div 1 = \underline{54}$

Math Triumphs   **Lesson 3-5 A77**

Chapter 3

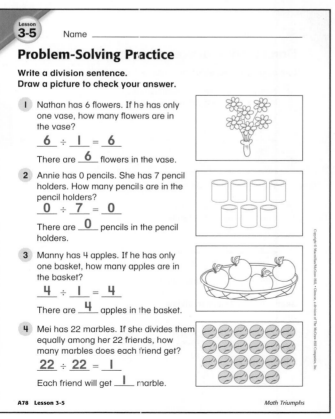

Lesson 3-5 Name _____

Problem-Solving Practice

Write a division sentence.
Draw a picture to check your answer.

1. Nathan has 6 flowers. If he has only one vase, how many flowers are in the vase?

   $\underline{6} \div \underline{1} = \underline{6}$

   There are $\underline{6}$ flowers in the vase.

2. Annie has 0 pencils. She has 7 pencil holders. How many pencils are in the pencil holders?

   $\underline{0} \div \underline{7} = \underline{0}$

   There are $\underline{0}$ pencils in the pencil holders.

3. Manny has 4 apples. If he has only one basket, how many apples are in the basket?

   $\underline{4} \div \underline{1} = \underline{4}$

   There are $\underline{4}$ apples in the basket.

4. Mei has 22 marbles. If she divides them equally among her 22 friends, how many marbles does each friend get?

   $\underline{22} \div \underline{22} = \underline{1}$

   Each friend will get $\underline{1}$ marble.

A78 **Lesson 3-5**   *Math Triumphs*

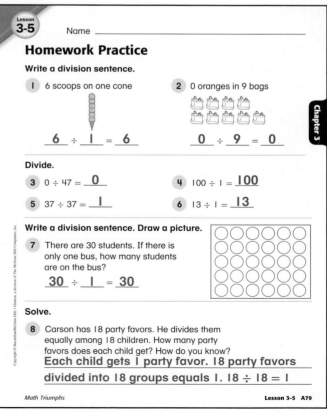

Lesson 3-5 Name _____

Homework Practice

Write a division sentence.

1. 6 scoops on one cone

   $\underline{6} \div \underline{1} = \underline{6}$

2. 0 oranges in 9 bags

   $\underline{0} \div \underline{9} = \underline{0}$

Divide.

3. $0 \div 47 = \underline{0}$

4. $100 \div 1 = \underline{100}$

5. $37 \div 37 = \underline{1}$

6. $13 \div 1 = \underline{13}$

Write a division sentence. Draw a picture.

7. There are 30 students. If there is only one bus, how many students are on the bus?

   $\underline{30} \div \underline{1} = \underline{30}$

Solve.

8. Carson has 18 party favors. He divides them equally among 18 children. How many party favors does each child get? How do you know?

   Each child gets 1 party favor. 18 party favors divided into 18 groups equals 1. $18 \div 18 = 1$

Math Triumphs   **Lesson 3-5 A79**

Chapter 3

Math Triumphs   **Lesson 3-5 A253**

Answer Key (Lesson 3-6)

Lesson 3-6

Name _____

Vocabulary and English Language Development

Skip count backward.

by 2s:

12, 10, 8, 6, 4, 2, 0

by 5s:

25, 20, 15, 10, 5, 0

Skip count. Divide.

1 $16 \div 2 =$ __8__

16, 14, 12, 10, 8, 6, 4, 2, 0

2 $14 \div 2 =$ __7__

14, 12, 10, 8, 6, 4, 2, 0

3 $25 \div 5 =$ __5__

25, 20, 15, 10, 5, 0

4 $20 \div 5 =$ __4__

20, 15, 10, 5, 0

ACTIVITY Display or draw a number line. Starting with the number 12, skip count backward to 0 aloud. Help students count along with you. Write $12 \div 2 = ?$ on the board. Skip count backward again, making a checkmark above each number you count. Next, count the number of checkmarks aloud as students count with you. Write $12 \div 2 = 6$. Tell students that the number of skips is the answer to the **division** sentence. Say the division sentence aloud as students repeat after you. Repeat for $25 \div 5 = 5$.

WORKSHEET DIRECTIONS Have students use the number line to skip count and divide.

A80 Lesson 3-6

Math Triumphs

Lesson 3-6

Name _____

Skills Practice

Write each division sentence.

1 Mr. Potter has 30 tomato plants. He wants to plant a garden with 5 plants in each row. How many rows will Mr. Potter have in his garden?

__30__ $\div$ __5__ $=$ __6__

Mr. Potter will have __6__ rows in his garden.

2 Nicholas divides 16 pencils into 2 equal groups. How many pencils does Nicholas put in each group?

__16__ $\div$ __2__ $=$ __8__

Nicholas puts __8__ pencils in each group.

Skip count backward to divide.

3 $18 \div 2 =$ __9__

18, 16, 14, 12, 10, 8, 6, 4, 2, 0

4 $40 \div 5 =$ __8__

40, 35, 30, 25, 20, 15, 10, 5, 0

Math Triumphs

Lesson 3-6 A81

Chapter 3

Lesson 3-6

Name _____

Problem-Solving Practice

Use a number line. Skip count backward to solve.

1 Elliot puts 25 baseball cards in equal groups of 5. How many groups of baseball cards does Elliot have?

Elliot has __5__ groups of baseball cards.

2 Latisha displays 20 dolls in sets of 2. How many sets of dolls does Latisha have?

Latisha has __10__ sets of dolls.

3 Miss Peters makes 55 muffins. She puts 5 muffins on each plate. How many plates does Miss Peters use?

Miss Peters uses __11__ plates.

A82 Lesson 3-6

Math Triumphs

Lesson 3-6

Name _____

Homework Practice

Use a number line. Skip count backward to solve.

1 Nagi puts 25 flowers in equal bunches of 5. How many flowers are in each bunch?

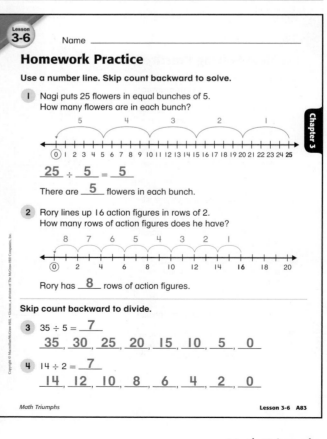

__25__ $\div$ __5__ $=$ __5__

There are __5__ flowers in each bunch.

2 Rory lines up 16 action figures in rows of 2. How many rows of action figures does he have?

Rory has __8__ rows of action figures.

Skip count backward to divide.

3 $35 \div 5 =$ __7__

35, 30, 25, 20, 15, 10, 5, 0

4 $14 \div 2 =$ __7__

14, 12, 10, 8, 6, 4, 2, 0

Math Triumphs

Lesson 3-6 A83

Chapter 3

Math Triumphs

Answer Key (Lesson 4-1)

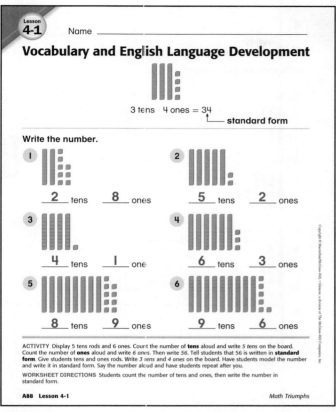

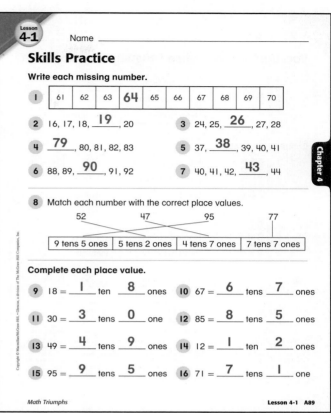

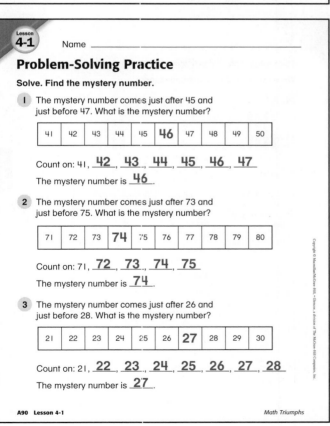

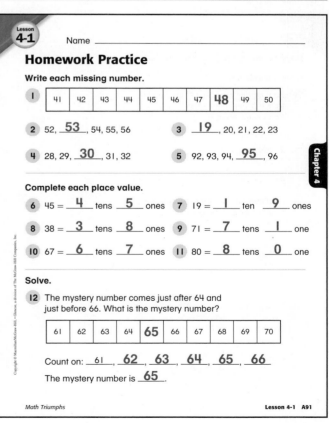

Answer Key (Lesson 4-2)

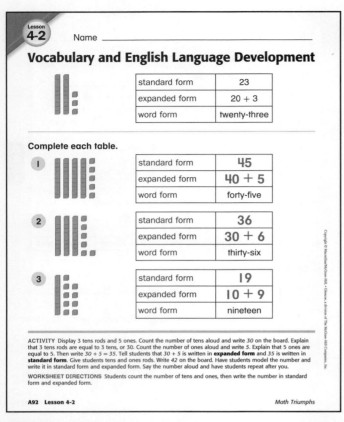

Lesson 4-2

Name

Vocabulary and English Language Development

standard form	23
expanded form	20 + 3
word form	twenty-three

Complete each table.

1.

standard form	45
expanded form	40 + 5
word form	forty-five

2.

standard form	36
expanded form	30 + 6
word form	thirty-six

3.

standard form	19
expanded form	10 + 9
word form	nineteen

ACTIVITY Display 3 tens rods and 5 ones. Count the number of tens aloud and write *30* on the board. Explain that 3 tens rods are equal to 3 tens, or 30. Count the number of ones aloud and write 5. Explain that 5 ones are equal to 5. Then write *30 + 5 = 35*. Tell students that *30 + 5* is written in **expanded form** and *35* is written in **standard form**. Give students tens and ones rods. Write *42* on the board. Have students model the number and write it in standard form and expanded form. Say the number aloud and have students repeat after you.

WORKSHEET DIRECTIONS Students count the number of tens and ones, then write the number in standard form and expanded form.

A92 Lesson 4-2

Math Triumphs

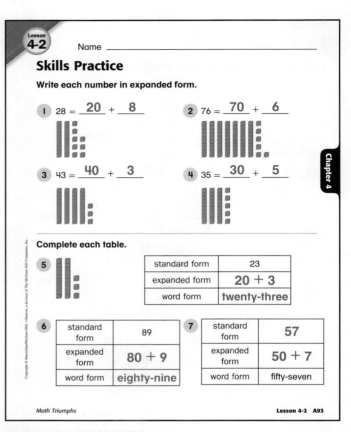

Lesson 4-2

Name

Skills Practice

Write each number in expanded form.

1. 28 = __20__ + __8__

2. 76 = __70__ + __6__

3. 43 = __40__ + __3__

4. 35 = __30__ + __5__

Complete each table.

5.

standard form	23
expanded form	20 + 3
word form	twenty-three

6.

standard form	89
expanded form	80 + 9
word form	eighty-nine

7.

standard form	57
expanded form	50 + 7
word form	fifty-seven

Math Triumphs

Lesson 4-2 A93

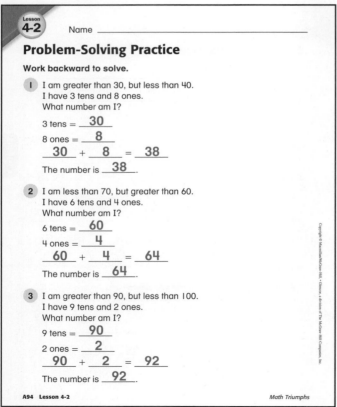

Lesson 4-2

Name

Problem-Solving Practice

Work backward to solve.

1. I am greater than 30, but less than 40.
   I have 3 tens and 8 ones.
   What number am I?

   3 tens = __30__

   8 ones = __8__

   __30__ + __8__ = __38__

   The number is __38__.

2. I am less than 70, but greater than 60.
   I have 6 tens and 4 ones.
   What number am I?

   6 tens = __60__

   4 ones = __4__

   __60__ + __4__ = __64__

   The number is __64__.

3. I am greater than 90, but less than 100.
   I have 9 tens and 2 ones.
   What number am I?

   9 tens = __90__

   2 ones = __2__

   __90__ + __2__ = __92__

   The number is __92__.

A94 Lesson 4-2

Math Triumphs

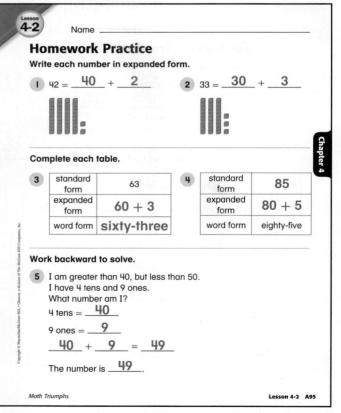

Lesson 4-2

Name

Homework Practice

Write each number in expanded form.

1. 42 = __40__ + __2__

2. 33 = __30__ + __3__

Complete each table.

3.

standard form	63
expanded form	60 + 3
word form	sixty-three

4.

standard form	85
expanded form	80 + 5
word form	eighty-five

Work backward to solve.

5. I am greater than 40, but less than 50.
   I have 4 tens and 9 ones.
   What number am I?

   4 tens = __40__

   9 ones = __9__

   __40__ + __9__ = __49__

   The number is __49__.

Math Triumphs

Lesson 4-2 A95

Answer Key (Lesson 4-3)

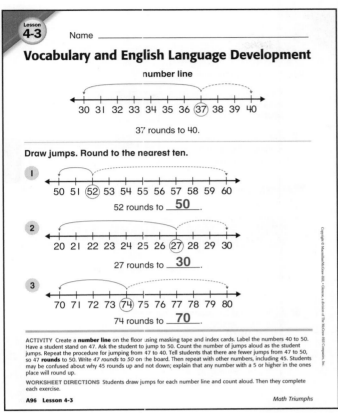

Lesson 4-3

Name _____

Vocabulary and English Language Development

number line

30 31 32 33 34 35 36 (37) 38 39 40

37 rounds to 40.

Draw jumps. Round to the nearest ten.

1 50 51 (52) 53 54 55 56 57 58 59 60
52 rounds to **50**.

2 20 21 22 23 24 25 26 (27) 28 29 30
27 rounds to **30**.

3 70 71 72 73 (74) 75 76 77 78 79 80
74 rounds to **70**.

ACTIVITY Create a **number line** on the floor using masking tape and index cards. Label the numbers 40 to 50. Have a student stand on 47. Ask the student to jump to 50. Count the number of jumps aloud as the student jumps. Repeat the procedure for jumping from 47 to 40. Tell students that there are fewer jumps from 47 to 50, so 47 **rounds** to 50. Write *47 rounds to 50* on the board. Then repeat with other numbers, including 45. Students may be confused about why 45 rounds up and not down; explain that any number with a 5 or higher in the ones place will round up.

WORKSHEET DIRECTIONS Students draw jumps for each number line and count aloud. Then they complete each exercise.

A96 Lesson 4-3

Math Triumphs

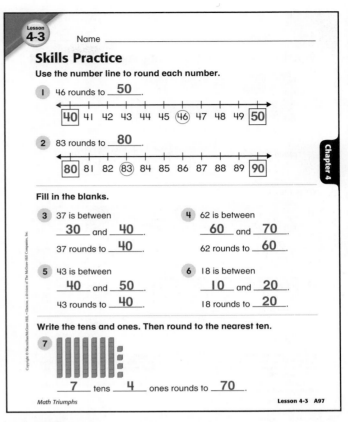

Lesson 4-3

Name _____

Skills Practice

Use the number line to round each number.

1 46 rounds to **50**.

[40] 41 42 43 44 45 (46) 47 48 49 [50]

2 83 rounds to **80**.

[80] 81 82 (83) 84 85 86 87 88 89 [90]

Fill in the blanks.

3 37 is between
30 and **40**.
37 rounds to **40**.

4 62 is between
60 and **70**.
62 rounds to **60**.

5 43 is between
40 and **50**.
43 rounds to **40**.

6 18 is between
10 and **20**.
18 rounds to **20**.

Write the tens and ones. Then round to the nearest ten.

7 **7** tens **4** ones rounds to **70**.

Math Triumphs

Lesson 4-3 A97

Chapter 4

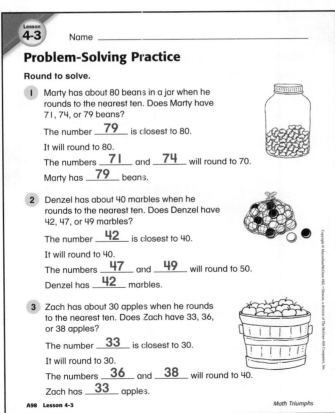

Lesson 4-3

Name _____

Problem-Solving Practice

Round to solve.

1 Marty has about 80 beans in a jar when he rounds to the nearest ten. Does Marty have 71, 74, or 79 beans?

The number **79** is closest to 80.

It will round to 80.

The numbers **71** and **74** will round to 70.

Marty has **79** beans.

2 Denzel has about 40 marbles when he rounds to the nearest ten. Does Denzel have 42, 47, or 49 marbles?

The number **42** is closest to 40.

It will round to 40.

The numbers **47** and **49** will round to 50.

Denzel has **42** marbles.

3 Zach has about 30 apples when he rounds to the nearest ten. Does Zach have 33, 36, or 38 apples?

The number **33** is closest to 30.

It will round to 30.

The numbers **36** and **38** will round to 40.

Zach has **33** apples.

A98 Lesson 4-3

Math Triumphs

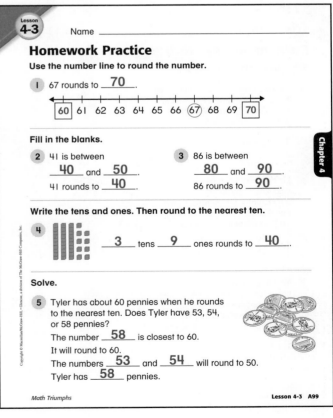

Lesson 4-3

Name _____

Homework Practice

Use the number line to round the number.

1 67 rounds to **70**.

[60] 61 62 63 64 65 66 (67) 68 69 [70]

Fill in the blanks.

2 41 is between
40 and **50**.
41 rounds to **40**.

3 86 is between
80 and **90**.
86 rounds to **90**.

Write the tens and ones. Then round to the nearest ten.

4 **3** tens **9** ones rounds to **40**.

Solve.

5 Tyler has about 60 pennies when he rounds to the nearest ten. Does Tyler have 53, 54, or 58 pennies?
The number **58** is closest to 60.
It will round to 60.
The numbers **53** and **54** will round to 50.
Tyler has **58** pennies.

Math Triumphs

Lesson 4-3 A99

Chapter 4

Math Triumphs

Lesson 4-3 A257

Answer Key (Lesson 4-4)

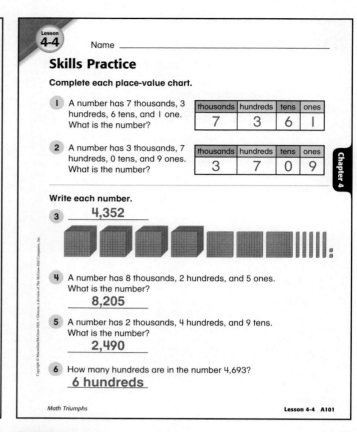

Lesson 4-4

Name _____

Vocabulary and English Language Development

4 thousands   6 hundreds   3 tens 2 ones

place-value chart →

thousands	hundreds	tens	ones
4	6	3	2

Write the number.

1. __2__ thousands __5__ hundreds __8__ tens __3__ ones
   2,583

2.
thousands	hundreds	tens	ones
5	9	2	6

__5__ thousands __9__ hundreds __2__ tens __6__ ones
5,926

ACTIVITY Draw a **place-value chart** on the board and write the number *3,627*. Model the number using place-value blocks, then write 3 *thousands*, 6 *hundreds*, 2 *tens*, and 7 *ones*. Say the numbers aloud and have students repeat after you. Then write *3,627* and say the number aloud. Students should again repeat after you. Repeat, having students model the number *2,849*.

WORKSHEET DIRECTIONS Students can use place-value blocks to model the numbers in each exercise. Work with students as they model the numbers saying each number aloud.

A100 Lesson 4-4   *Math Triumphs*

Lesson 4-4

Name _____

Skills Practice

Complete each place-value chart.

1. A number has 7 thousands, 3 hundreds, 6 tens, and 1 one. What is the number?

thousands	hundreds	tens	ones
7	3	6	1

2. A number has 3 thousands, 7 hundreds, 0 tens, and 9 ones. What is the number?

thousands	hundreds	tens	ones
3	7	0	9

Write each number.

3. __4,352__

4. A number has 8 thousands, 2 hundreds, and 5 ones. What is the number?
   8,205

5. A number has 2 thousands, 4 hundreds, and 9 tens. What is the number?
   2,490

6. How many hundreds are in the number 4,693?
   6 hundreds

Chapter 4

Math Triumphs   Lesson 4-4 A101

Lesson 4-4

Name _____

Problem-Solving Practice

Solve. Use a place-value chart.

1. Jessie's house has a number. The house number has 4 thousands, 8 tens, and 3 ones. What is Jessie's house number?

   The number is __4,083__.

2. Liz punches a number into a calculator. The number has 2 thousands, 9 hundreds, 4 tens, and 5 ones. What number does Liz punch into the calculator?

   The number is __2,945__.

3. Mr. Green drives a car. The car has a license plate with a number. The number has 6 thousands, 4 hundreds, and 8 ones. What is Mr. Green's license plate number?

   The number is __6,408__.

A102 Lesson 4-4   *Math Triumphs*

Lesson 4-4

Name _____

Homework Practice

Complete the place-value chart.

1. A number has 3 thousands, 2 hundreds, 8 tens, and 7 ones. What is the number?

thousands	hundreds	tens	ones
3	2	8	7

Write each number.

2. __1,574__

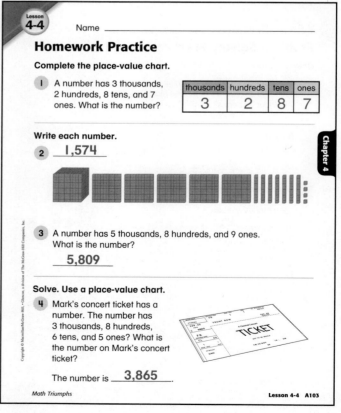

3. A number has 5 thousands, 8 hundreds, and 9 ones. What is the number?
   5,809

Solve. Use a place-value chart.

4. Mark's concert ticket has a number. The number has 3 thousands, 8 hundreds, 6 tens, and 5 ones? What is the number on Mark's concert ticket?

   The number is __3,865__.

Chapter 4

Math Triumphs   Lesson 4-4 A103

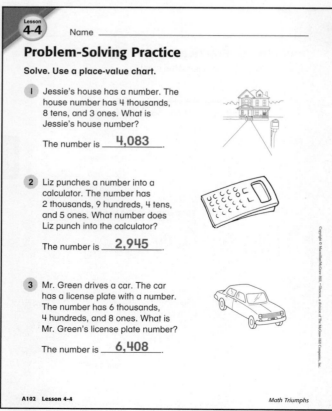

Answer Key (Lesson 5-1)

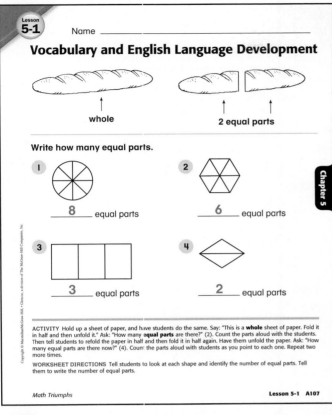

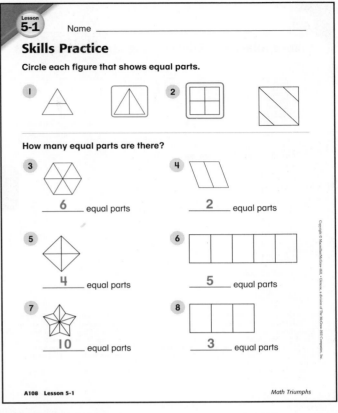

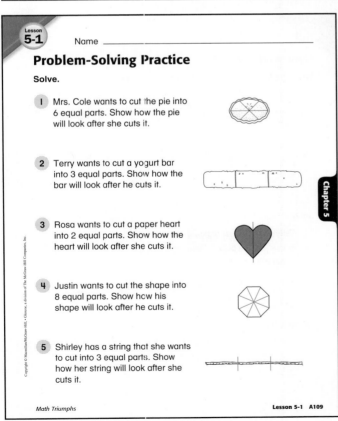

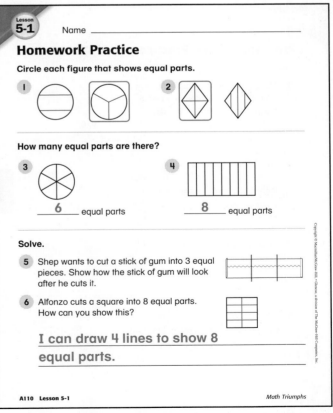

Answer Key (Lesson 5-2)

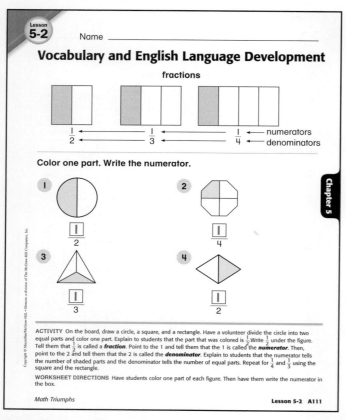

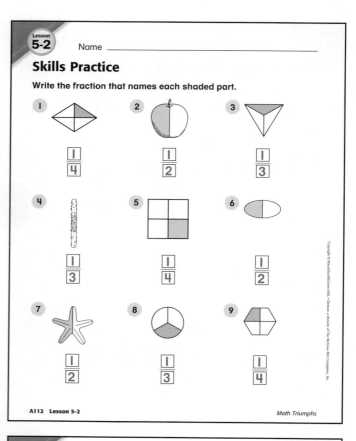

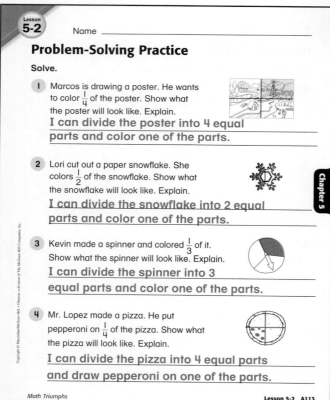

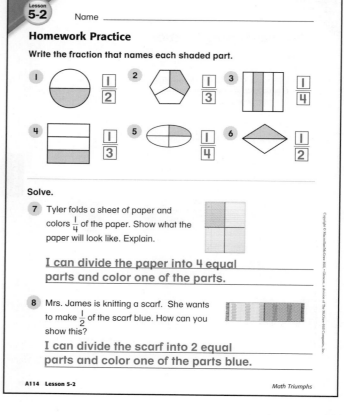

Answer Key (Lesson 5-3)

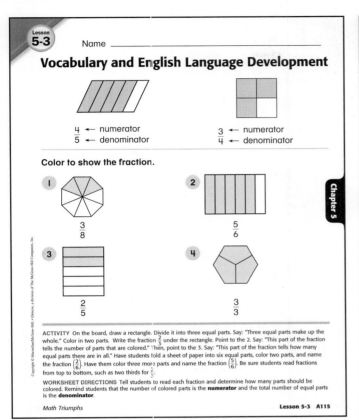

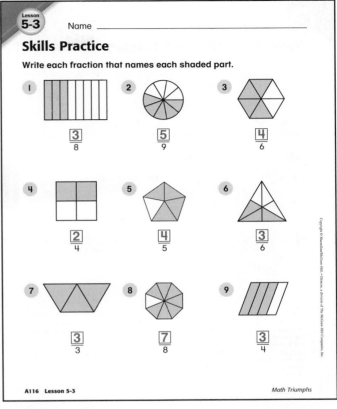

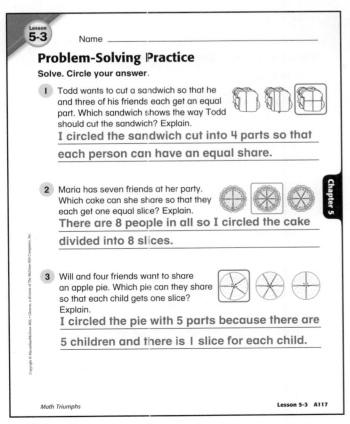

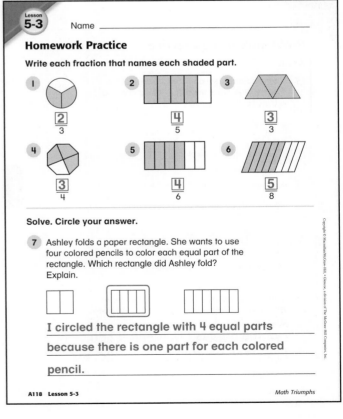

Answer Key (Lesson 5-4)

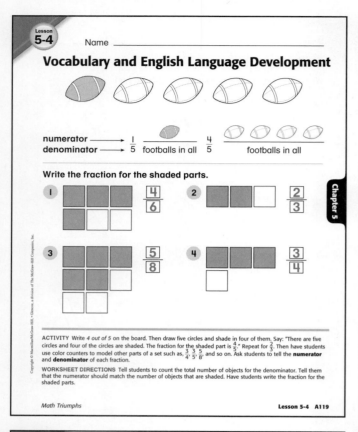

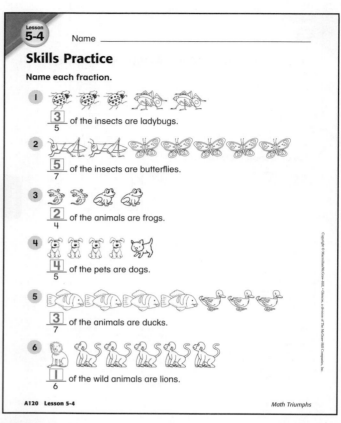

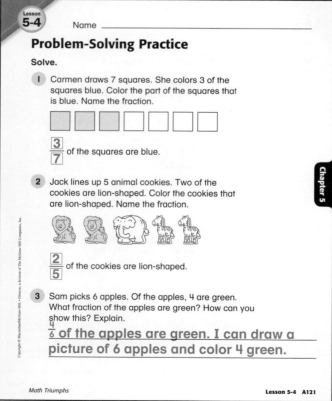

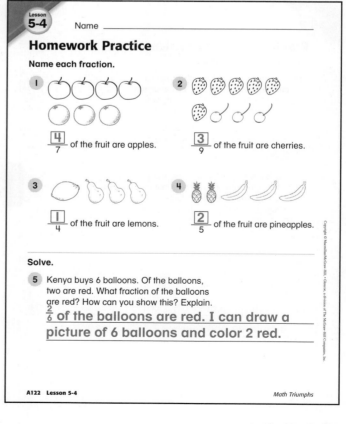

Answer Key (Lesson 5-5)

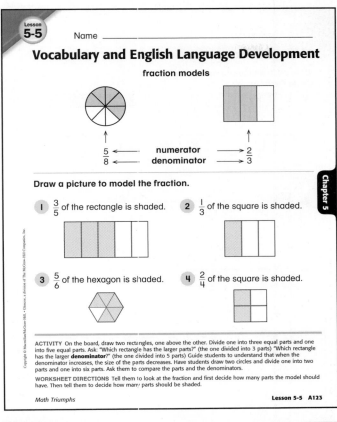

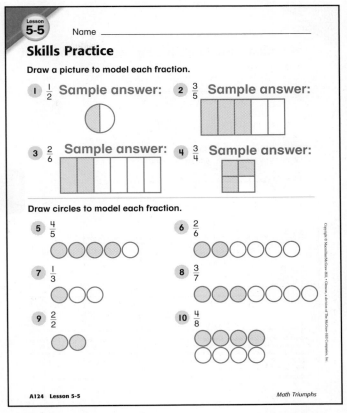

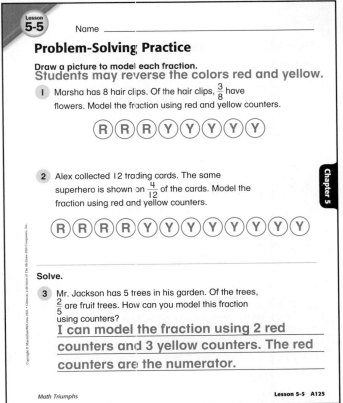

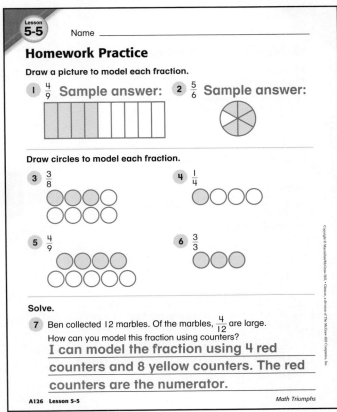

Answer Key (Lesson 5-6)

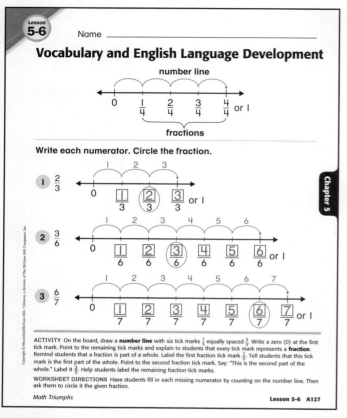

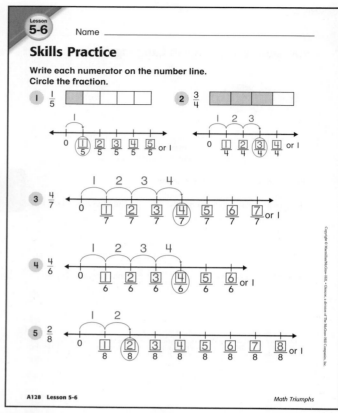

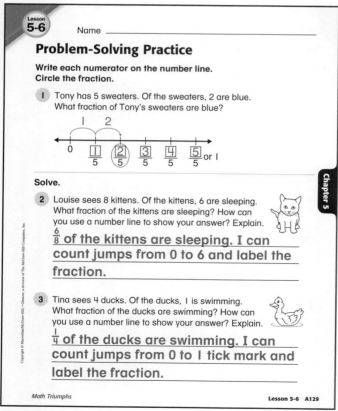

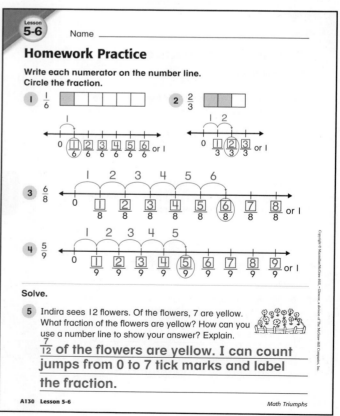

Answer Key (Lesson 6-1)

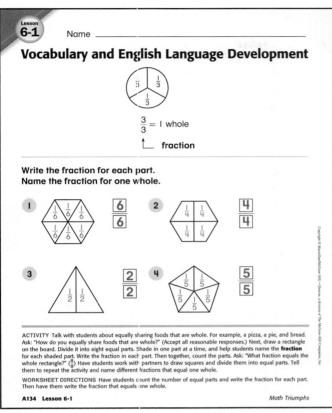

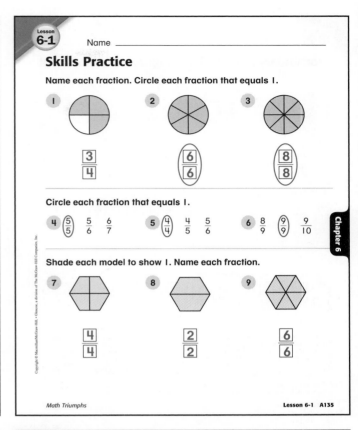

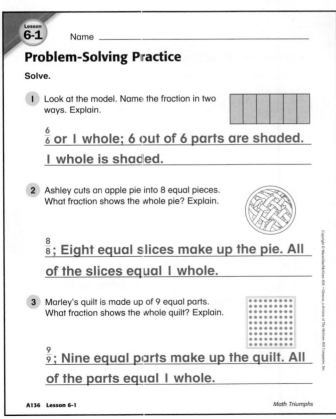

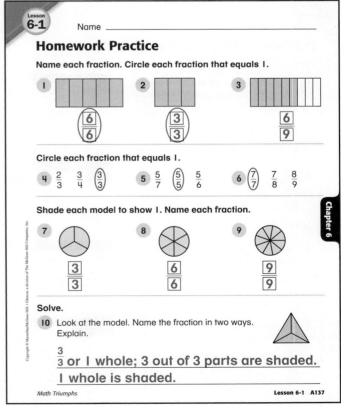

Answer Key (Lesson 6-2)

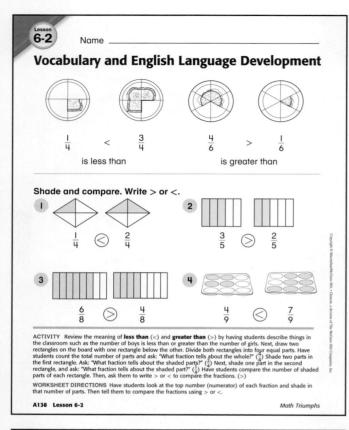

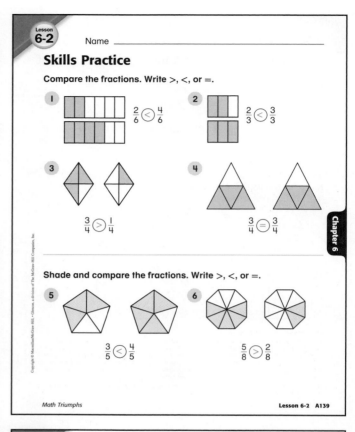

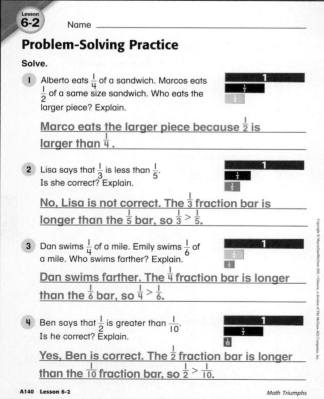

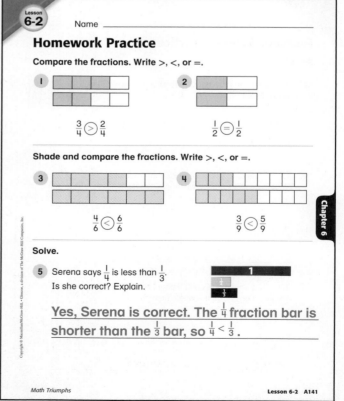

Answer Key (Lesson 6-3)

Name _____

Vocabulary and English Language Development

$\frac{1}{3}$

$\frac{2}{6}$

$\frac{1}{3} = \frac{2}{6}$

equivalent fractions

Write an equivalent fraction.

1   $\frac{1}{2} = \frac{\boxed{5}}{10}$

2   $\frac{4}{4} = \frac{\boxed{8}}{8}$

3   $\frac{2}{6} = \frac{\boxed{4}}{12}$

4   $\frac{3}{7} = \frac{\boxed{6}}{14}$

ACTIVITY Tell students that **equivalent fractions** are fractions that show the same amount. Provide students with fraction strips. Guide them to fold two strips into 4 equal parts and then to fold one strip into 8 equal parts. Say: "Color 3 parts of the 4-part strip." Ask: "What fraction does this show?" ($\frac{3}{4}$) Say: "Color 6 parts of the 8-part strip." Ask: "What fraction does this show?" ($\frac{6}{8}$) Have them place one fraction strip below the other lining up the ends. Ask: "What do you notice about them?" (Both strips and both parts colored are the same length.) Say: "That shows that the fractions are equivalent fractions." On the board, complete more examples as needed.

WORKSHEET DIRECTIONS Tell students to compare the fraction strips and have them write a fraction for the second strip that is equivalent to the first fraction strip.

A142   Lesson 6-3

Math Triumphs

Name _____

Skills Practice

Write an equivalent fraction.

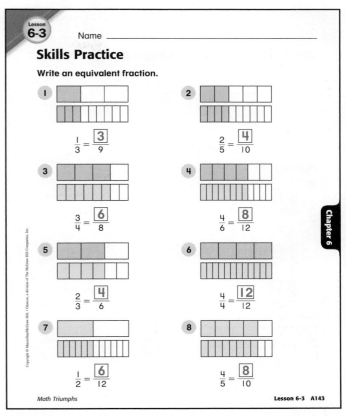

1   $\frac{1}{3} = \frac{\boxed{3}}{9}$

2   $\frac{2}{5} = \frac{\boxed{4}}{10}$

3   $\frac{3}{4} = \frac{\boxed{6}}{8}$

4   $\frac{4}{6} = \frac{\boxed{8}}{12}$

5   $\frac{2}{3} = \frac{\boxed{4}}{6}$

6   $\frac{4}{4} = \frac{\boxed{12}}{12}$

7   $\frac{1}{2} = \frac{\boxed{6}}{12}$

8   $\frac{4}{5} = \frac{\boxed{8}}{10}$

Math Triumphs

Lesson 6-3   A143

Name _____

Problem-Solving Practice

Use the fraction bars to solve.

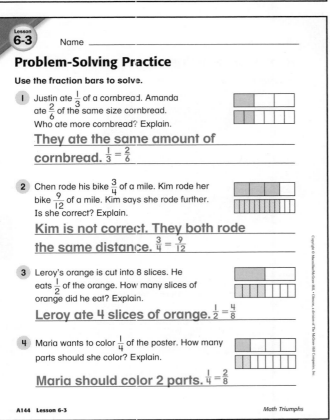

1   Justin ate $\frac{1}{3}$ of a cornbread. Amanda ate $\frac{2}{6}$ of the same size cornbread. Who ate more cornbread? Explain.

They ate the same amount of cornbread. $\frac{1}{3} = \frac{2}{6}$

2   Chen rode his bike $\frac{3}{4}$ of a mile. Kim rode her bike $\frac{9}{12}$ of a mile. Kim says she rode further. Is she correct? Explain.

Kim is not correct. They both rode the same distance. $\frac{3}{4} = \frac{9}{12}$

3   Leroy's orange is cut into 8 slices. He eats $\frac{1}{2}$ of the orange. How many slices of orange did he eat? Explain.

Leroy ate 4 slices of orange. $\frac{1}{2} = \frac{4}{8}$

4   Maria wants to color $\frac{1}{4}$ of the poster. How many parts should she color? Explain.

Maria should color 2 parts. $\frac{1}{4} = \frac{2}{8}$

A144   Lesson 6-3

Math Triumphs

Name _____

Homework Practice

Write an equivalent fraction.

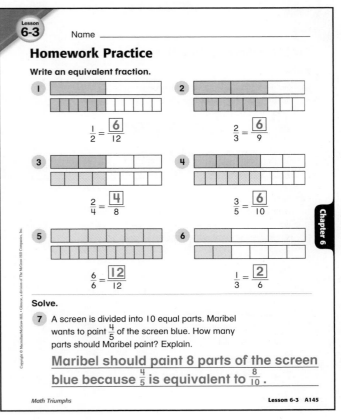

1   $\frac{1}{2} = \frac{\boxed{6}}{12}$

2   $\frac{2}{3} = \frac{\boxed{6}}{9}$

3   $\frac{2}{4} = \frac{\boxed{4}}{8}$

4   $\frac{3}{5} = \frac{\boxed{6}}{10}$

5   $\frac{6}{6} = \frac{\boxed{12}}{12}$

6   $\frac{1}{3} = \frac{\boxed{2}}{6}$

Solve.

7   A screen is divided into 10 equal parts. Maribel wants to paint $\frac{4}{5}$ of the screen blue. How many parts should Maribel paint? Explain.

Maribel should paint 8 parts of the screen blue because $\frac{4}{5}$ is equivalent to $\frac{8}{10}$.

Math Triumphs

Lesson 6-3   A145

Answer Key (Lesson 6-4)

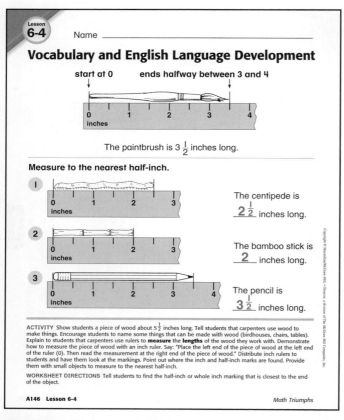

Name _____

Vocabulary and English Language Development

start at 0 — ends halfway between 3 and 4

The paintbrush is 3 $\frac{1}{2}$ inches long.

Measure to the nearest half-inch.

1. The centipede is __2 $\frac{1}{2}$__ inches long.

2. The bamboo stick is __2__ inches long.

3. The pencil is __3 $\frac{1}{2}$__ inches long.

ACTIVITY Show students a piece of wood about 5 $\frac{1}{2}$ inches long. Tell students that carpenters use wood to make things. Encourage students to name some things that can be made with wood (birdhouses, chairs, tables). Explain to students that carpenters use rulers to **measure** the **lengths** of the wood they work with. Demonstrate how to measure the piece of wood with an inch ruler. Say: "Place the left end of the piece of wood at the left end of the ruler (0). Then read the measurement at the right end of the piece of wood." Distribute inch rulers to students and have them look at the markings. Point out where the inch and half-inch marks are found. Provide them with small objects to measure to the nearest half-inch.

WORKSHEET DIRECTIONS Tell students to find the half-inch or whole inch marking that is closest to the end of the object.

A146 Lesson 6-4   *Math Triumphs*

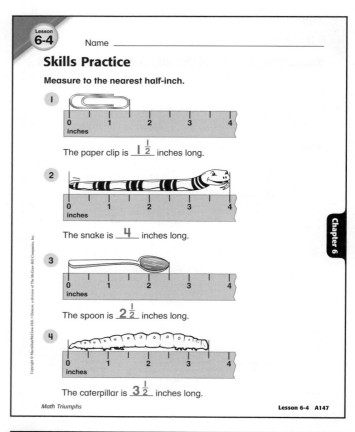

Name _____

Skills Practice

Measure to the nearest half-inch.

1. The paper clip is __1 $\frac{1}{2}$__ inches long.

2. The snake is __4__ inches long.

3. The spoon is __2 $\frac{1}{2}$__ inches long.

4. The caterpillar is __3 $\frac{1}{2}$__ inches long.

Math Triumphs   Lesson 6-4   A147

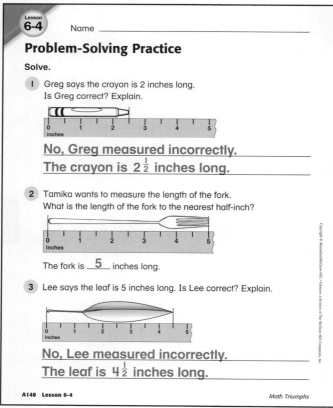

Name _____

Problem-Solving Practice

Solve.

1. Greg says the crayon is 2 inches long. Is Greg correct? Explain.

   __No, Greg measured incorrectly.__
   __The crayon is 2 $\frac{1}{2}$ inches long.__

2. Tamika wants to measure the length of the fork. What is the length of the fork to the nearest half-inch?

   The fork is __5__ inches long.

3. Lee says the leaf is 5 inches long. Is Lee correct? Explain.

   __No, Lee measured incorrectly.__
   __The leaf is 4 $\frac{1}{2}$ inches long.__

A148 Lesson 6-4   *Math Triumphs*

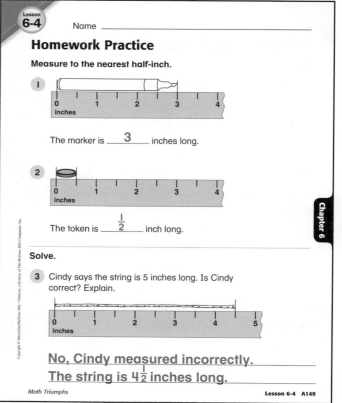

Name _____

Homework Practice

Measure to the nearest half-inch.

1. The marker is __3__ inches long.

2. The token is __$\frac{1}{2}$__ inch long.

Solve.

3. Cindy says the string is 5 inches long. Is Cindy correct? Explain.

   __No, Cindy measured incorrectly.__
   __The string is 4 $\frac{1}{2}$ inches long.__

Math Triumphs   Lesson 6-4   A149

Answer Key (Lesson 6-5)

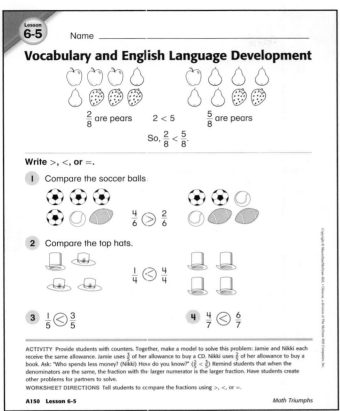

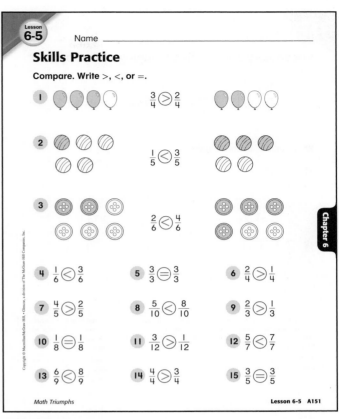

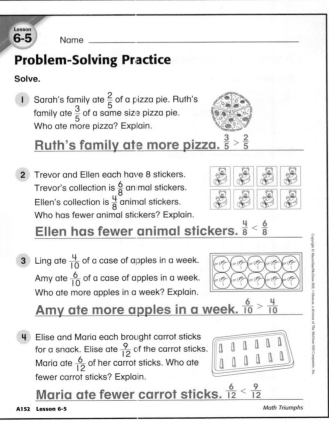

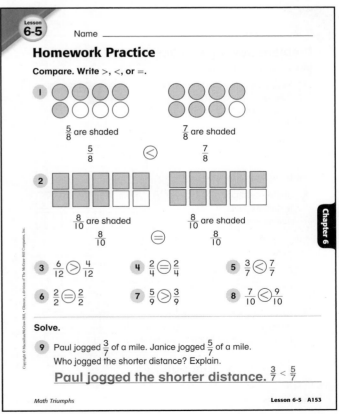

Answer Key (Lesson 6-6)

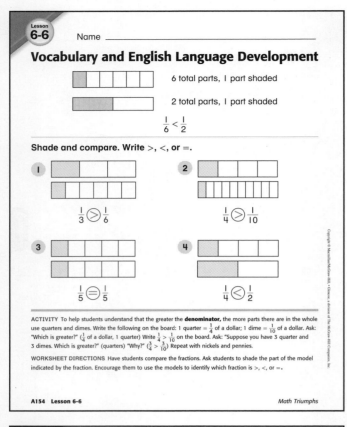

Lesson 6-6

Name _____

Vocabulary and English Language Development

6 total parts, 1 part shaded

2 total parts, 1 part shaded

$\frac{1}{6} < \frac{1}{2}$

Shade and compare. Write >, <, or =.

1. $\frac{1}{3} \bigcirc\!\!> \frac{1}{6}$

2. $\frac{1}{4} \bigcirc\!\!> \frac{1}{10}$

3. $\frac{1}{5} \bigcirc\!\!= \frac{1}{5}$

4. $\frac{1}{4} \bigcirc\!\!< \frac{1}{2}$

ACTIVITY To help students understand that the greater the **denominator,** the more parts there are in the whole use quarters and dimes. Write the following on the board: 1 quarter $= \frac{1}{4}$ of a dollar; 1 dime $= \frac{1}{10}$ of a dollar. Ask: "Which is greater?" ($\frac{1}{4}$ of a dollar, 1 quarter) Write $\frac{1}{4} > \frac{1}{10}$ on the board. Ask: "Suppose you have 3 quarter and 3 dimes. Which is greater?" (quarters) "Why?" ($\frac{3}{4} > \frac{3}{10}$) Repeat with nickels and pennies.

WORKSHEET DIRECTIONS Have students compare the fractions. Ask students to shade the part of the model indicated by the fraction. Encourage them to use the models to identify which fraction is >, <, or =.

A154 Lesson 6-6

Math Triumphs

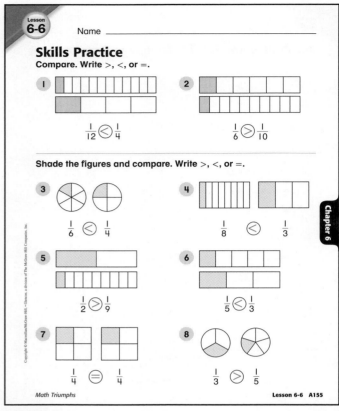

Lesson 6-6

Name _____

Skills Practice

Compare. Write >, <, or =.

1. $\frac{1}{12} \bigcirc\!\!< \frac{1}{4}$

2. $\frac{1}{6} \bigcirc\!\!> \frac{1}{10}$

Shade the figures and compare. Write >, <, or =.

3. $\frac{1}{6} \bigcirc\!\!< \frac{1}{4}$

4. $\frac{1}{8} \bigcirc\!\!< \frac{1}{3}$

5. $\frac{1}{2} \bigcirc\!\!> \frac{1}{9}$

6. $\frac{1}{5} \bigcirc\!\!< \frac{1}{3}$

7. $\frac{1}{4} \bigcirc\!\!= \frac{1}{4}$

8. $\frac{1}{3} \bigcirc\!\!> \frac{1}{5}$

Math Triumphs

Lesson 6-6 A155

Chapter 6

Lesson 6-6

Name _____

Problem-Solving Practice

Use fraction bars to solve.

1. Marcos ate $\frac{1}{2}$ of a cup of cherries. Dana ate $\frac{1}{4}$ of a cup of cherries. Who ate more cherries? How do you know?

   1

   $\frac{1}{2}$

   $\frac{1}{4}$

   Marcos ate more cherries. $\frac{1}{2} > \frac{1}{4}$

Shade the figures to solve.

2. Grettel says that $\frac{1}{6} > \frac{1}{12}$. Is Grettel correct? How do you know?

   Yes, Grettel is correct. The part of the whole divided into 6 parts is greater than the part of the whole divided into 12 parts.

3. John used $\frac{1}{3}$ cup of nuts and $\frac{1}{5}$ cup of raisins to make muffins. Did John use more nuts or raisins? How do you know?

   John used more nuts. $\frac{1}{3} > \frac{1}{5}$

A156 Lesson 6-6

Math Triumphs

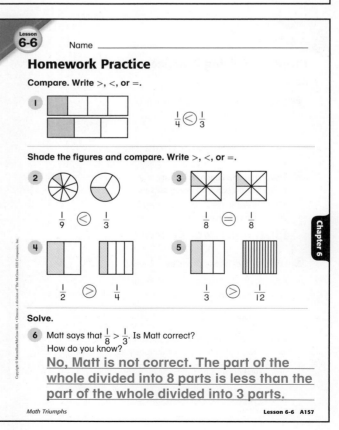

Lesson 6-6

Name _____

Homework Practice

Compare. Write >, <, or =.

1. $\frac{1}{4} \bigcirc\!\!< \frac{1}{3}$

Shade the figures and compare. Write >, <, or =.

2. $\frac{1}{9} \bigcirc\!\!< \frac{1}{3}$

3. $\frac{1}{8} \bigcirc\!\!= \frac{1}{8}$

4. $\frac{1}{2} \bigcirc\!\!> \frac{1}{4}$

5. $\frac{1}{3} \bigcirc\!\!> \frac{1}{12}$

Solve.

6. Matt says that $\frac{1}{8} > \frac{1}{3}$. Is Matt correct? How do you know?

   No, Matt is not correct. The part of the whole divided into 8 parts is less than the part of the whole divided into 3 parts.

Math Triumphs

Lesson 6-6 A157

Chapter 6

Math Triumphs

Answer Key (Lesson 7-1)

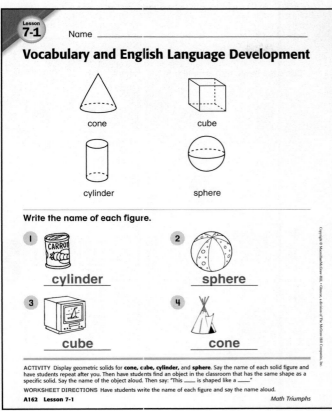

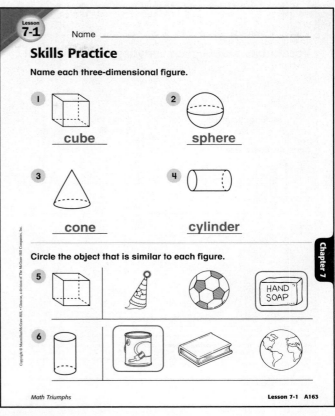

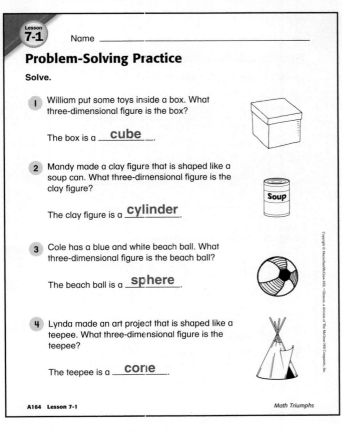

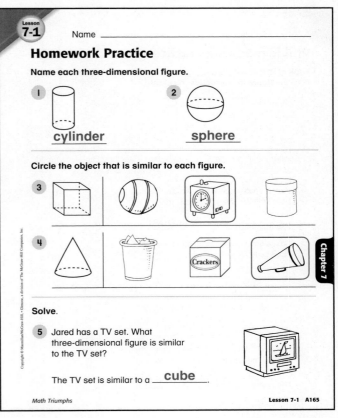

Answer Key (Lesson 7-2)

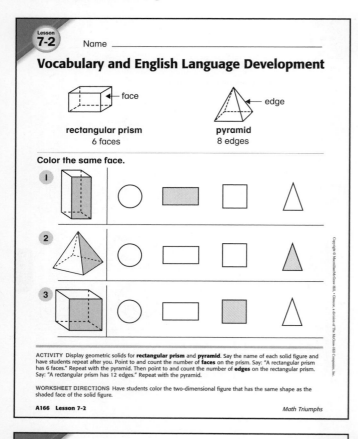

Vocabulary and English Language Development

face

rectangular prism
6 faces

edge

pyramid
8 edges

Color the same face.

ACTIVITY Display geometric solids for **rectangular prism** and **pyramid**. Say the name of each solid figure and have students repeat after you. Point to and count the number of **faces** on the prism. Say: "A rectangular prism has 6 faces." Repeat with the pyramid. Then point to and count the number of **edges** on the rectangular prism. Say: "A rectangular prism has 12 edges." Repeat with the pyramid.

WORKSHEET DIRECTIONS Have students color the two-dimensional figure that has the same shape as the shaded face of the solid figure.

A166   Lesson 7-2   *Math Triumphs*

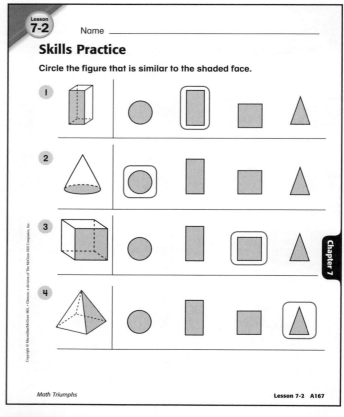

Skills Practice

Circle the figure that is similar to the shaded face.

1

2

3

4

Math Triumphs   Lesson 7-2   A167

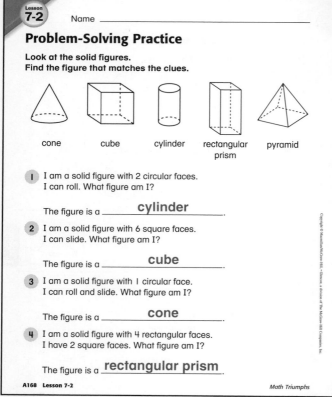

Problem-Solving Practice

Look at the solid figures.
Find the figure that matches the clues.

cone   cube   cylinder   rectangular prism   pyramid

1. I am a solid figure with 2 circular faces. I can roll. What figure am I?

   The figure is a _____ **cylinder** _____.

2. I am a solid figure with 6 square faces. I can slide. What figure am I?

   The figure is a _____ **cube** _____.

3. I am a solid figure with 1 circular face. I can roll and slide. What figure am I?

   The figure is a _____ **cone** _____.

4. I am a solid figure with 4 rectangular faces. I have 2 square faces. What figure am I?

   The figure is a _____ **rectangular prism** _____.

A168   Lesson 7-2   *Math Triumphs*

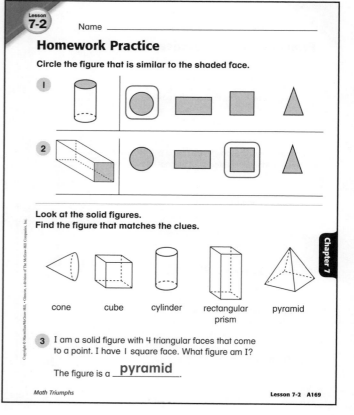

Homework Practice

Circle the figure that is similar to the shaded face.

1

2

Look at the solid figures.
Find the figure that matches the clues.

cone   cube   cylinder   rectangular prism   pyramid

3. I am a solid figure with 4 triangular faces that come to a point. I have 1 square face. What figure am I?

   The figure is a _____ **pyramid** _____.

Math Triumphs   Lesson 7-2   A169

Answer Key (Lesson 7-3)

Lesson 7-3

Name

Vocabulary and English Language Development

○ circle

▭ rectangle

□ square

△ triangle

Color the figure.

1 square

2 triangle

3 circle

4 rectangle

ACTIVITY Provide students with cutouts of a **circle, square, rectangle,** and **triangle.** Help students write the names of the figures on the cutouts. Next, have students place the figures in front of them. Call out the name of a figure. Have students hold up the correct figure. Then have students check the name and say it aloud.
WORKSHEET DIRECTIONS Have students color the correct figure in each row.

Lesson 7-3

Name

Skills Practice

Circle the similar figure.

1

2

3

Name each two-dimensional figure.

4 triangle

5 rectangle

6 circle

7 square

Chapter 7

Lesson 7-3

Name

Problem-Solving Practice

Use the pictures to solve.

1 Dylan wants to draw a triangle. How many sides and angles does he need to draw?

   __3__ sides and __3__ angles

2 Elliot drew two rectangles on top of each other so that they were touching. What new figure did Elliot draw?

   The new figure is a __square__ .

3 Sasha drew this picture. What two-dimensional figures did Sasha use to draw this picture? Explain.

   Sasha used two triangles. One triangle is on top and the other is on the bottom.

4 Amy drew this picture. What two-dimensional figures did Amy use to draw this picture? Explain.

   Amy used a triangle and a rectangle. The rectangle is on top and the triangle is on the bottom.

Lesson 7-3

Name

Homework Practice

Circle the similar figure.

1

2

Name each two-dimensional figure.

3 triangle

4 square

Use the picture to solve.

5 Midori drew this picture. What two-dimensional figures did Midori use to draw this picture? Explain.

   Midori used two triangles. One triangle is next to the other triangle so that they are touching.

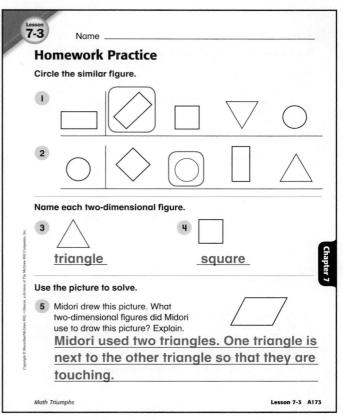

Chapter 7

Answer Key (Lesson 7-4)

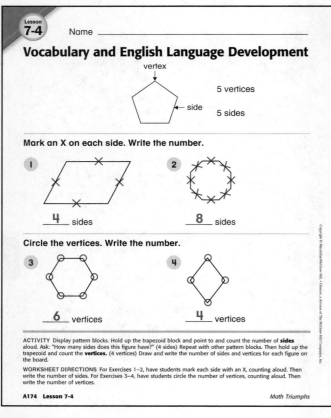

Lesson 7-4

Name _____

Vocabulary and English Language Development

vertex

5 vertices

side

5 sides

Mark an X on each side. Write the number.

1. __4__ sides

2. __8__ sides

Circle the vertices. Write the number.

3. __6__ vertices

4. __4__ vertices

ACTIVITY Display pattern blocks. Hold up the trapezoid block and point to and count the number of **sides** aloud. Ask: "How many sides does this figure have?" (4 sides) Repeat with other pattern blocks. Then hold up the trapezoid and count the **vertices**. (4 vertices) Draw and write the number of sides and vertices for each figure on the board.
WORKSHEET DIRECTIONS For Exercises 1–2, have students mark each side with an X, counting aloud. Then write the number of sides. For Exercises 3–4, have students circle the number of vertices, counting aloud. Then write the number of vertices.

A174 **Lesson 7-4**

Math Triumphs

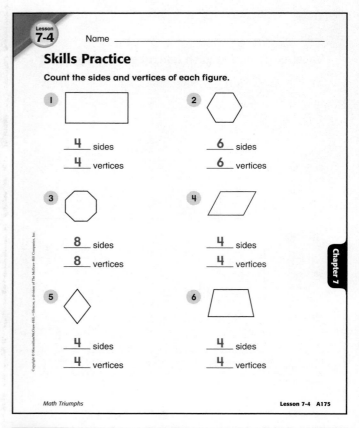

Lesson 7-4

Name _____

Skills Practice

Count the sides and vertices of each figure.

1. __4__ sides
    __4__ vertices

2. __6__ sides
    __6__ vertices

3. __8__ sides
    __8__ vertices

4. __4__ sides
    __4__ vertices

5. __4__ sides
    __4__ vertices

6. __4__ sides
    __4__ vertices

Chapter 7

Math Triumphs

Lesson 7-4 A175

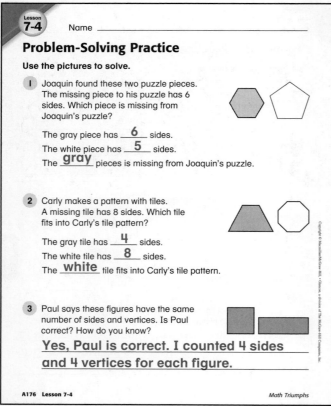

Lesson 7-4

Name _____

Problem-Solving Practice

Use the pictures to solve.

1. Joaquin found these two puzzle pieces. The missing piece to his puzzle has 6 sides. Which piece is missing from Joaquin's puzzle?

    The gray piece has __6__ sides.
    The white piece has __5__ sides.
    The __gray__ pieces is missing from Joaquin's puzzle.

2. Carly makes a pattern with tiles. A missing tile has 8 sides. Which tile fits into Carly's tile pattern?

    The gray tile has __4__ sides.
    The white tile has __8__ sides.
    The __white__ tile fits into Carly's tile pattern.

3. Paul says these figures have the same number of sides and vertices. Is Paul correct? How do you know?

    Yes, Paul is correct. I counted 4 sides and 4 vertices for each figure.

A176 **Lesson 7-4**

Math Triumphs

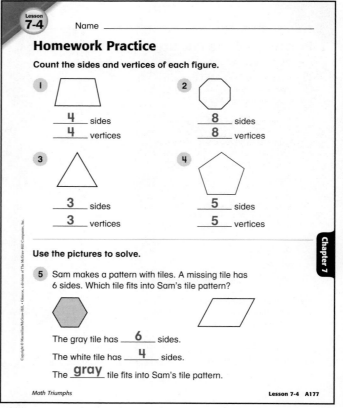

Lesson 7-4

Name _____

Homework Practice

Count the sides and vertices of each figure.

1. __4__ sides
    __4__ vertices

2. __8__ sides
    __8__ vertices

3. __3__ sides
    __3__ vertices

4. __5__ sides
    __5__ vertices

Use the pictures to solve.

5. Sam makes a pattern with tiles. A missing tile has 6 sides. Which tile fits into Sam's tile pattern?

    The gray tile has __6__ sides.
    The white tile has __4__ sides.
    The __gray__ tile fits into Sam's tile pattern.

Math Triumphs

Lesson 7-4 A177

Chapter 7

Answer Key (Lesson 7-5)

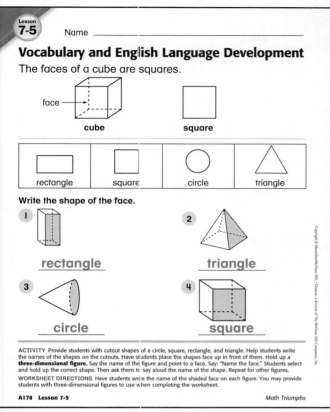

Lesson 7-5

Name _____

Vocabulary and English Language Development

The faces of a cube are squares.

face → cube   square

| rectangle | square | circle | triangle |

Write the shape of the face.

1. rectangle
2. triangle
3. circle
4. square

ACTIVITY Provide students with cutout shapes of a circle, square, rectangle, and triangle. Help students write the names of the shapes on the cutouts. Have students place the shapes face up in front of them. Hold up a **three-dimensional figure.** Say the name of the figure and point to a face. Say: "Name the face." Students select and hold up the correct shape. Then ask them to say aloud the name of the shape. Repeat for other figures.
WORKSHEET DIRECTIONS Have students write the name of the shaded face on each figure. You may provide students with three-dimensional figures to use when completing the worksheet.

A178   Lesson 7-5   *Math Triumphs*

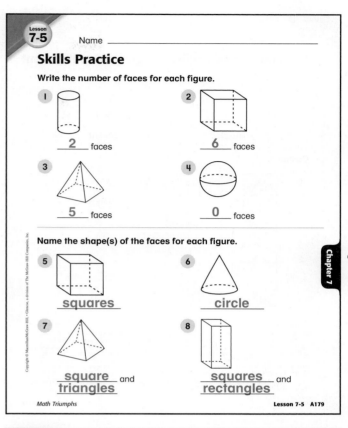

Lesson 7-5

Name _____

Skills Practice

Write the number of faces for each figure.

1. 2 faces
2. 6 faces
3. 5 faces
4. 0 faces

Name the shape(s) of the faces for each figure.

5. squares
6. circle
7. square and triangles
8. squares and rectangles

Math Triumphs   Lesson 7-5 A179

Chapter 7

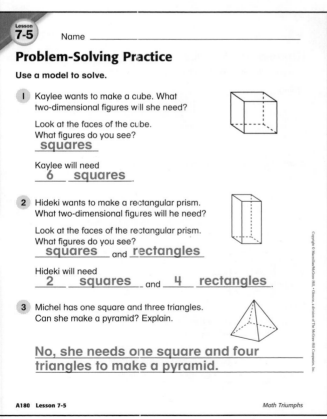

Lesson 7-5

Name _____

Problem-Solving Practice

Use a model to solve.

1. Kaylee wants to make a cube. What two-dimensional figures will she need?

   Look at the faces of the cube. What figures do you see?
   squares

   Kaylee will need
   6 squares.

2. Hideki wants to make a rectangular prism. What two-dimensional figures will he need?

   Look at the faces of the rectangular prism. What figures do you see?
   squares and rectangles

   Hideki will need
   2 squares and 4 rectangles.

3. Michel has one square and three triangles. Can she make a pyramid. Explain.

   No, she needs one square and four triangles to make a pyramid.

A180   Lesson 7-5   *Math Triumphs*

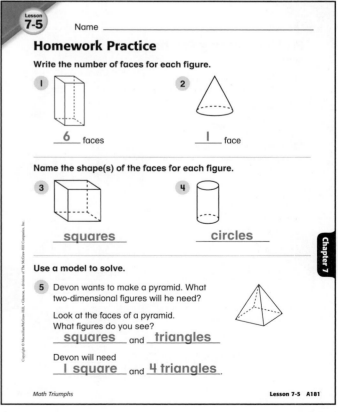

Lesson 7-5

Name _____

Homework Practice

Write the number of faces for each figure.

1. 6 faces
2. 1 face

Name the shape(s) of the faces for each figure.

3. squares
4. circles

Use a model to solve.

5. Devon wants to make a pyramid. What two-dimensional figures will he need?

   Look at the faces of a pyramid. What figures do you see?
   squares and triangles

   Devon will need
   1 square and 4 triangles.

Math Triumphs   Lesson 7-5 A181

Chapter 7

Answer Key (Lesson 8-1)

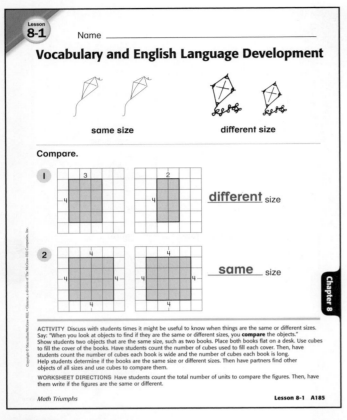

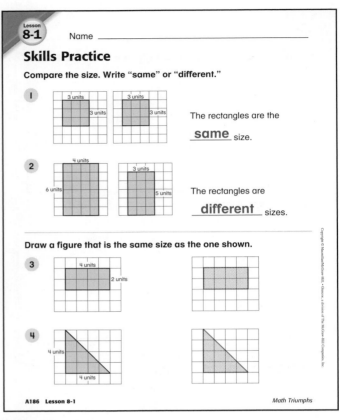

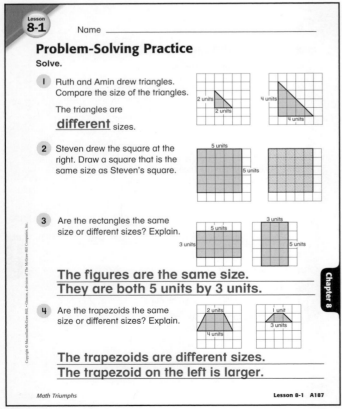

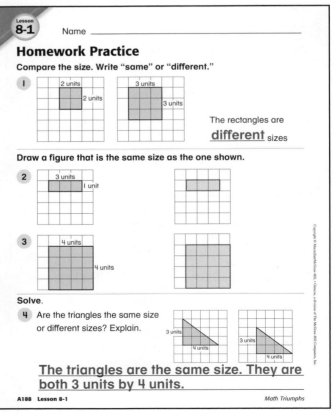

Answer Key (Lesson 8-2)

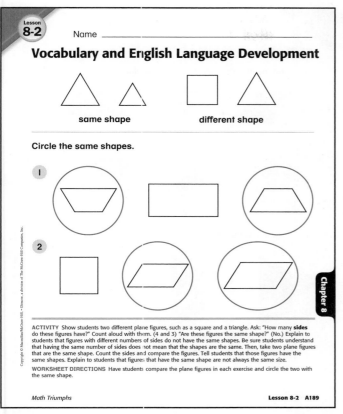

Name _____

Vocabulary and English Language Development

△ △   □ △

same shape   different shape

Circle the same shapes.

1.

2.

ACTIVITY Show students two different plane figures, such as a square and a triangle. Ask: "How many **sides** do these figures have?" Count aloud with them. (4 and 3) "Are these figures the same shape?" (No.) Explain to students that figures with different numbers of sides do not have the same shapes. Be sure students understand that having the same number of sides does not mean that the shapes are the same. Then, take two plane figures that are the same shape. Count the sides and compare the figures. Tell students that those figures have the same shapes. Explain to students that figures that have the same shape are not always the same size.

WORKSHEET DIRECTIONS Have students compare the plane figures in each exercise and circle the two with the same shape.

Math Triumphs   **Lesson 8-2   A189**

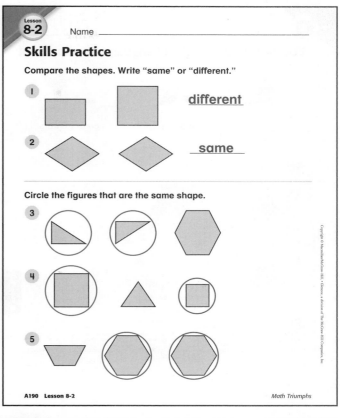

Name _____

Skills Practice

Compare the shapes. Write "same" or "different."

1.   **different**

2.   **same**

Circle the figures that are the same shape.

3.

4.

5.

A190   Lesson 8-2   *Math Triumphs*

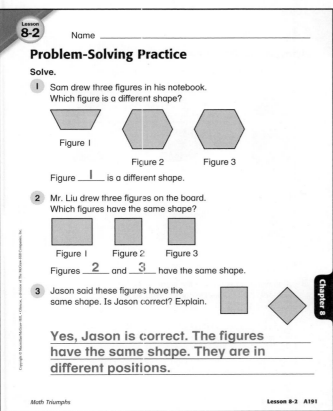

Name _____

Problem-Solving Practice

Solve.

1. Sam drew three figures in his notebook. Which figure is a different shape?

   Figure 1   Figure 2   Figure 3

   Figure __1__ is a different shape.

2. Mr. Liu drew three figures on the board. Which figures have the same shape?

   Figure 1   Figure 2   Figure 3

   Figures __2__ and __3__ have the same shape.

3. Jason said these figures have the same shape. Is Jason correct? Explain.

   Yes, Jason is correct. The figures have the same shape. They are in different positions.

Math Triumphs   **Lesson 8-2   A191**

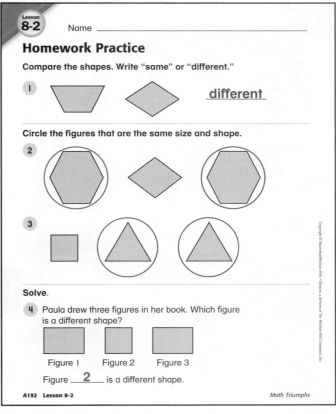

Name _____

Homework Practice

Compare the shapes. Write "same" or "different."

1.   **different**

Circle the figures that are the same size and shape.

2.

3.

Solve.

4. Paula drew three figures in her book. Which figure is a different shape?

   Figure 1   Figure 2   Figure 3

   Figure __2__ is a different shape.

A192   Lesson 8-2   *Math Triumphs*

Answer Key (Lesson 8-3)

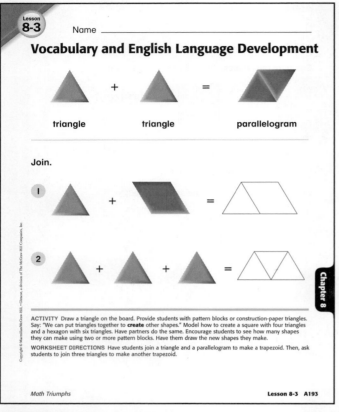

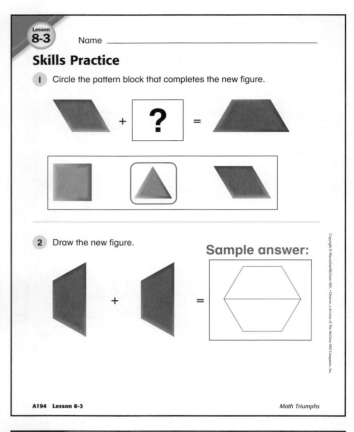

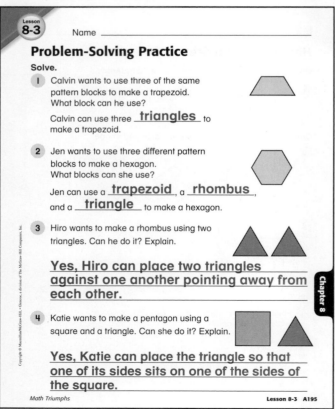

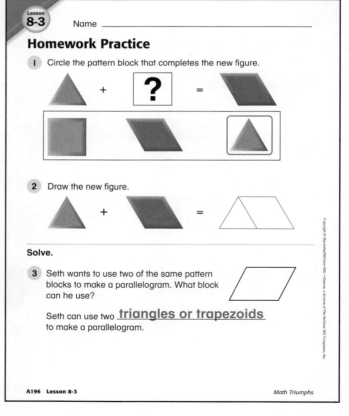

Answer Key (Lesson 8-4)

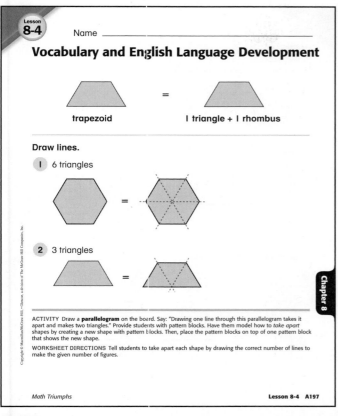

Name _____

Vocabulary and English Language Development

trapezoid = 1 triangle + 1 rhombus

Draw lines.

1 6 triangles

=

2 3 triangles

=

ACTIVITY Draw a **parallelogram** on the board. Say: "Drawing one line through this parallelogram takes it apart and makes two triangles." Provide students with pattern blocks. Have them model how to *take apart* shapes by creating a new shape with pattern blocks. Then, place the pattern blocks on top of one pattern block that shows the new shape.

WORKSHEET DIRECTIONS Tell students to take apart each shape by drawing the correct number of lines to make the given number of figures.

Math Triumphs **Lesson 8-4 A197**

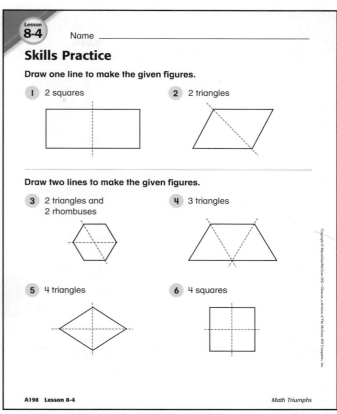

Name _____

Skills Practice

Draw one line to make the given figures.

1 2 squares

2 2 triangles

Draw two lines to make the given figures.

3 2 triangles and 2 rhombuses

4 3 triangles

5 4 triangles

6 4 squares

A198 Lesson 8-4 *Math Triumphs*

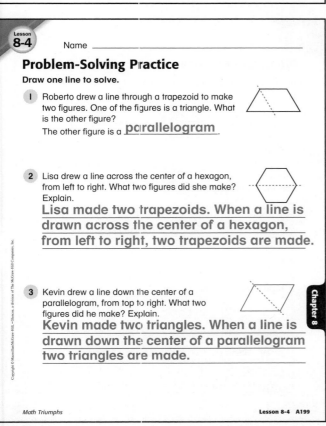

Name _____

Problem-Solving Practice

Draw one line to solve.

1 Roberto drew a line through a trapezoid to make two figures. One of the figures is a triangle. What is the other figure?
The other figure is a __parallelogram__.

2 Lisa drew a line across the center of a hexagon, from left to right. What two figures did she make? Explain.
Lisa made two trapezoids. When a line is drawn across the center of a hexagon, from left to right, two trapezoids are made.

3 Kevin drew a line down the center of a parallelogram, from top to right. What two figures did he make? Explain.
Kevin made two triangles. When a line is drawn down the center of a parallelogram two triangles are made.

Math Triumphs **Lesson 8-4 A199**

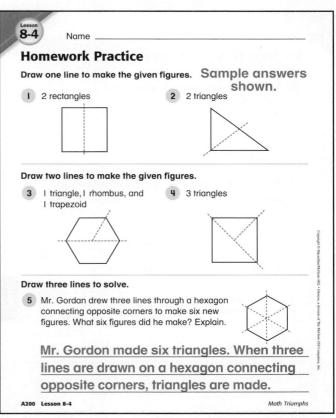

Name _____

Homework Practice

Draw one line to make the given figures. **Sample answers shown.**

1 2 rectangles

2 2 triangles

Draw two lines to make the given figures.

3 1 triangle, 1 rhombus, and 1 trapezoid

4 3 triangles

Draw three lines to solve.

5 Mr. Gordan drew three lines through a hexagon connecting opposite corners to make six new figures. What six figures did he make? Explain.
Mr. Gordon made six triangles. When three lines are drawn on a hexagon connecting opposite corners, triangles are made.

A200 Lesson 8-4 *Math Triumphs*

Answer Key (Lesson 8-5)

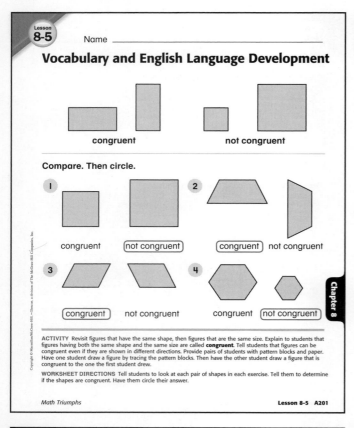

Lesson 8-5

Name _____

Vocabulary and English Language Development

congruent   not congruent

Compare. Then circle.

1. congruent (not congruent)

2. (congruent) not congruent

3. (congruent) not congruent

4. congruent (not congruent)

ACTIVITY Revisit figures that have the same shape, then figures that are the same size. Explain to students that figures having both the same shape and the same size are called **congruent**. Tell students that figures can be congruent even if they are shown in different directions. Provide pairs of students with pattern blocks and paper. Have one student draw a figure by tracing the pattern blocks. Then have the other student draw a figure that is congruent to the one the first student drew.

WORKSHEET DIRECTIONS Tell students to look at each pair of shapes in each exercise. Tell them to determine if the shapes are congruent. Have them circle their answer.

Math Triumphs   **Lesson 8-5   A201**

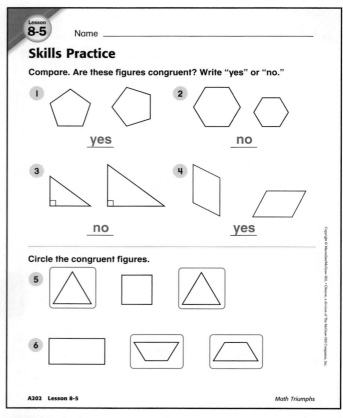

Lesson 8-5

Name _____

Skills Practice

Compare. Are these figures congruent? Write "yes" or "no."

1. yes

2. no

3. no

4. yes

Circle the congruent figures.

5.

6.

A202   Lesson 8-5   *Math Triumphs*

Lesson 8-5

Name _____

Problem-Solving Practice

Solve.

1. A square is 3 units wide and 3 units tall. Draw a congruent square.

2. Adam drew these two figures. Are the figures congruent? Explain.

   Yes, the figures are congruent. The figures are in a different place of the grid but they are the same shape and size.

3. Look at the figures. Are the figures congruent? Explain.

   No, the figures are not congruent. The figures are the same shape but different sizes.

Math Triumphs   **Lesson 8-5   A203**

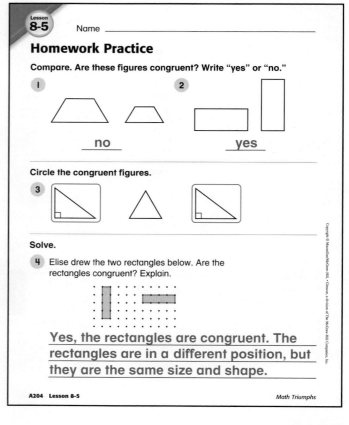

Lesson 8-5

Name _____

Homework Practice

Compare. Are these figures congruent? Write "yes" or "no."

1. no

2. yes

Circle the congruent figures.

3.

Solve.

4. Elise drew the two rectangles below. Are the rectangles congruent? Explain.

   Yes, the rectangles are congruent. The rectangles are in a different position, but they are the same size and shape.

A204   Lesson 8-5   *Math Triumphs*

Answer Key (Lesson 8-6)

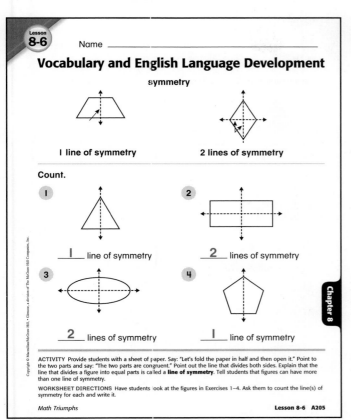

Vocabulary and English Language Development

symmetry

1 line of symmetry   2 lines of symmetry

Count.

1. 1 line of symmetry
2. 2 lines of symmetry
3. 2 lines of symmetry
4. 1 line of symmetry

ACTIVITY Provide students with a sheet of paper. Say: "Let's fold the paper in half and then open it." Point to the two parts and say: "The two parts are congruent." Point out the line that divides both sides. Explain that the line that divides a figure into equal parts is called a **line of symmetry**. Tell students that figures can have more than one line of symmetry.

WORKSHEET DIRECTIONS Have students look at the figures in Exercises 1–4. Ask them to count the line(s) of symmetry for each and write it.

Math Triumphs   Lesson 8-6 A205

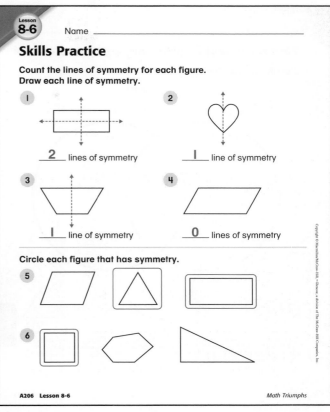

Skills Practice

Count the lines of symmetry for each figure.
Draw each line of symmetry.

1. 2 lines of symmetry
2. 1 line of symmetry
3. 1 line of symmetry
4. 0 lines of symmetry

Circle each figure that has symmetry.

5.

6.

A206 Lesson 8-6   Math Triumphs

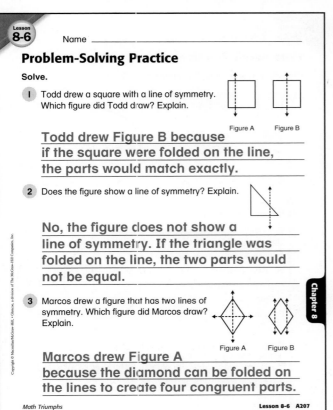

Problem-Solving Practice

Solve.

1. Todd drew a square with a line of symmetry. Which figure did Todd draw? Explain.

   Figure A   Figure B

   Todd drew Figure B because if the square were folded on the line, the parts would match exactly.

2. Does the figure show a line of symmetry? Explain.

   No, the figure does not show a line of symmetry. If the triangle was folded on the line, the two parts would not be equal.

3. Marcos drew a figure that has two lines of symmetry. Which figure did Marcos draw? Explain.

   Figure A   Figure B

   Marcos drew Figure A because the diamond can be folded on the lines to create four congruent parts.

Math Triumphs   Lesson 8-6 A207

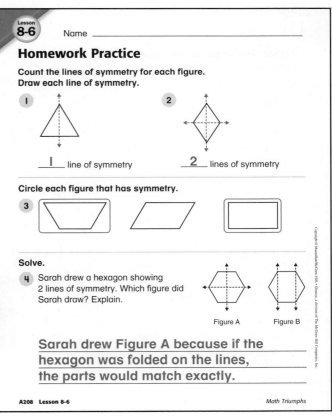

Homework Practice

Count the lines of symmetry for each figure.
Draw each line of symmetry.

1. 1 line of symmetry
2. 2 lines of symmetry

Circle each figure that has symmetry.

3.

Solve.

4. Sarah drew a hexagon showing 2 lines of symmetry. Which figure did Sarah draw? Explain.

   Figure A   Figure B

   Sarah drew Figure A because if the hexagon was folded on the lines, the parts would match exactly.

A208 Lesson 8-6   Math Triumphs

Answer Key (Lesson 9-1)

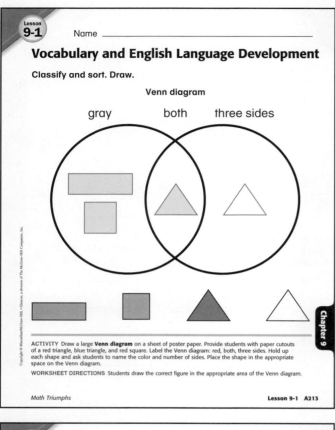

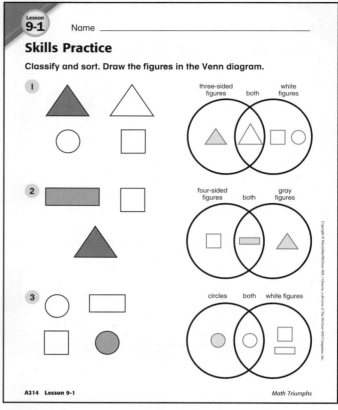

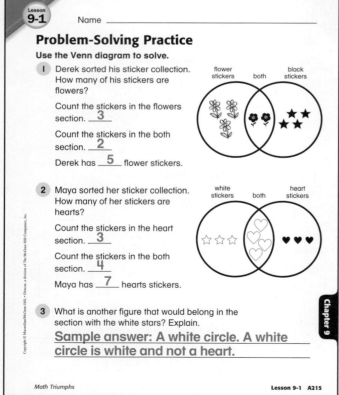

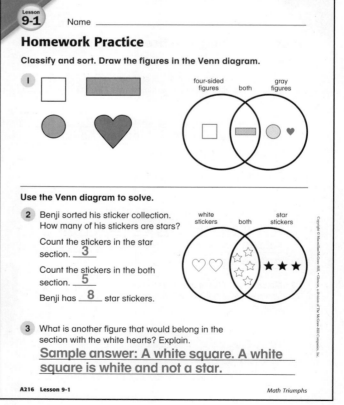

Answer Key (Lesson 9-2)

Name _____

Vocabulary and English Language Development

This is a **picture graph**.

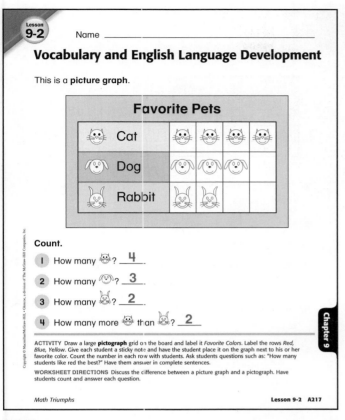

Favorite Pets

Count.

1 How many 🐱? __4__.

2 How many 🐶? __3__.

3 How many 🐰? __2__.

4 How many more 🐱 than 🐰? __2__.

ACTIVITY Draw a large **pictograph** grid on the board and label it *Favorite Colors*. Label the rows *Red, Blue, Yellow*. Give each student a sticky note and have the student place it on the graph next to his or her favorite color. Count the number in each row with students. Ask students questions such as: "How many students like red the best?" Have them answer in complete sentences.

WORKSHEET DIRECTIONS Discuss the difference between a picture graph and a pictograph. Have students count and answer each question.

Name _____

Skills Practice

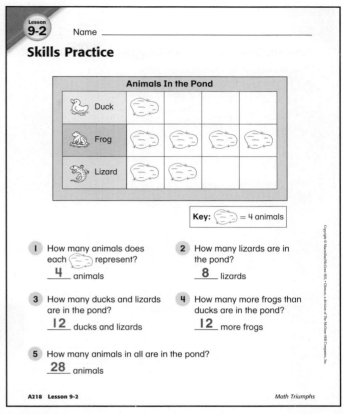

Animals In the Pond

Key: 🐟 = 4 animals

1 How many animals does each 🐟 represent?
__4__ animals

2 How many lizards are in the pond?
__8__ lizards

3 How many ducks and lizards are in the pond?
__12__ ducks and lizards

4 How many more frogs than ducks are in the pond?
__12__ more frogs

5 How many animals in all are in the pond?
__28__ animals

Name _____

Problem-Solving Practice

Solve.

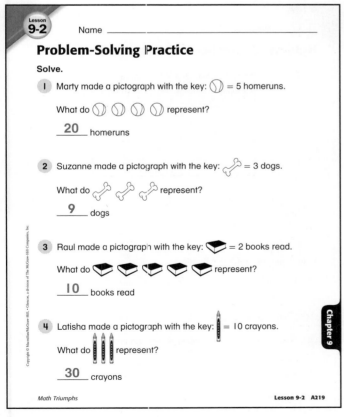

1 Marty made a pictograph with the key: ⚾ = 5 homeruns.

What do ⚾⚾⚾⚾ represent?

__20__ homeruns

2 Suzanne made a pictograph with the key: 🦴 = 3 dogs.

What do 🦴🦴🦴 represent?

__9__ dogs

3 Raul made a pictograph with the key: 📕 = 2 books read.

What do 📕📕📕📕📕 represent?

__10__ books read

4 Latisha made a pictograph with the key: ✏️ = 10 crayons.

What do ✏️✏️✏️ represent?

__30__ crayons

Name _____

Homework Practice

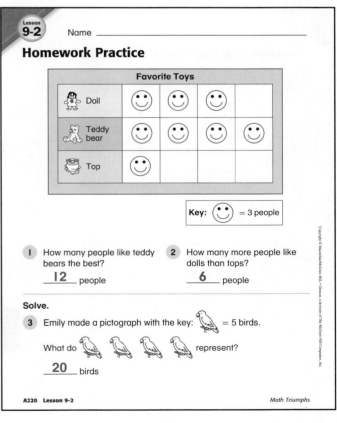

Favorite Toys

Key: 🙂 = 3 people

1 How many people like teddy bears the best?
__12__ people

2 How many more people like dolls than tops?
__6__ people

Solve.

3 Emily made a pictograph with the key: 🦜 = 5 birds.

What do 🦜🦜🦜🦜 represent?

__20__ birds

Answer Key (Lesson 9-3)

Lesson 9-3

Name _____

Vocabulary and English Language Development

This is a table. A table shows data.

Toys at the Store		
Toy	Tally	Total
✈ Airplane	卌 卌 ll	12
🚗 Car	卌 l	6
⛵ Boat	卌 卌	10

Write how many.

 1   2   3

   __6__   __12__   __10__

Complete.

4 How many 🚗 and ⛵ ?

   __6__ + __10__ = __16__

5 How many more ✈ than 🚗 ?

   __12__ – __6__ = __6__

ACTIVITY Draw a tally **table** on the board and label it *Students*. Label the rows *Boys* and *Girls*. Have students form groups of boys and girls. Have each student draw a **tally mark** in the table in the appropriate row. Then count the tally marks and write the total numbers of boys and girls in the chart. Ask students: "How many girls?" and "How many more boys than girls?" Have them answer in complete sentences.
WORKSHEET DIRECTIONS Have students count and answer each question.

Math Triumphs   **Lesson 9-3 A221**

Lesson 9-3

Name _____

Skills Practice

Art Class Supplies		
Supplies	Tally	Total
Paintbrushes	卌 卌	10
Jars of Paint	卌 卌 卌	15
Easels	卌 lll	8

1 How many easels are there in art class?

   __8__ easels

2 How many paintbrushes are there in art class?

   __10__ paintbrushes

3 How many more jars of paint are there than easels?

   __7__ more jars of paint than easels

4 How many jars of paint and paintbrushes are there in all?

   __25__ in all

5 How many paintbrushes, jars of paint, and easels in all?

   __33__ in all

A222 Lesson 9-3   *Math Triumphs*

Lesson 9-3

Name _____

Problem-Solving Practice

Favorite Sport		
Sport	Tally	Number of People
⚽ Soccer	卌 卌 llll	14
⚾ Baseball	卌 ll	7
🏈 Football	卌 卌 l	11
🏒 Hockey	卌	5

Write a number sentence to solve.

1 How many more people like football than hockey?

   __11__ – __5__ = __6__

   __6__ more people like football than hockey.

2 How many more people like soccer than baseball?

   __14__ – __7__ = __7__

   __7__ more people like soccer than baseball.

3 How many people like baseball and hockey in all?

   __7__ + __5__ = __12__

   __12__ people like baseball and hockey.

4 How many people like soccer and football in all?

   __14__ + __11__ = __25__

   __25__ people like soccer and football.

Math Triumphs   **Lesson 9-3 A223**

Lesson 9-3

Name _____

Homework Practice

School Supplies		
Supplies	Tally	Total
✏ Pencils	卌 卌 卌	15
✂ Scissors	卌 lll	8
📓 Notebooks	卌 l	6
🖊 Markers	卌 卌 ll	12

1 How many pencils are there?

   __15__ pencils

2 How many notebooks are there?

   __6__ notebooks

Write a number sentence to solve.

3 How many more pencils are there than scissors?

   __15__ – __8__ = __7__

   There are __7__ more pencils than scissors.

4 How many scissors and markers are there in all?

   __8__ + __12__ = __20__

   There are __20__ scissors and markers in all.

A224 Lesson 9-3   *Math Triumphs*

Answer Key (Lesson 9-4)

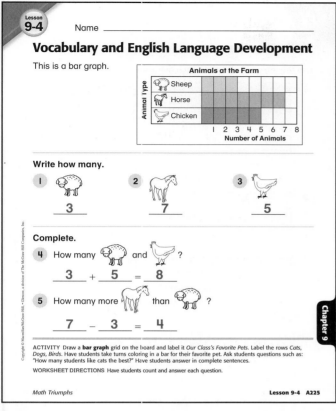

Lesson 9-4

Name _____

Vocabulary and English Language Development

This is a bar graph.

	Animals at the Farm							
Sheep								
Horse								
Chicken								
	1 2 3 4 5 6 7 8							
	Number of Animals							

Write how many.

1. __3__

2. __7__

3. __5__

Complete.

4. How many 🐑 and 🐓 ?

__3__ + __5__ = __8__

5. How many more 🐴 than 🐑 ?

__7__ – __3__ = __4__

ACTIVITY Draw a **bar graph** grid on the board and label it *Our Class's Favorite Pets*. Label the rows *Cats, Dogs, Birds*. Have students take turns coloring in a bar for their favorite pet. Ask students questions such as: "How many students like cats the best?" Have students answer in complete sentences.
WORKSHEET DIRECTIONS Have students count and answer each question.

Math Triumphs　　　　　　　　　　Lesson 9-4　A225

Lesson 9-4

Name _____

Skills Practice

	Animals in Mr. Wilson's Yard							
Squirrel								
Raccoon								
Rabbit								
	1 2 3 4 5 6 7 8							
	Number of Animals							

1. How many raccoons are in Mr. Wilson's yard?
__2__ raccoons

2. Which animal was counted four times?
__rabbit__

3. How many more squirrels are in Mr. Wilson's yard than rabbits?
__2__ more squirrels than rabbits

4. How many animals are in Mr. Wilson's yard in all?
__12__ animals in all

5. Robin saw five more chipmunks than rabbits in Mr. Wilson's yard. How many chipmunks did Robin see?
__9__ chipmunks

A226　Lesson 9-4　　　　　　　　　　*Math Triumphs*

Lesson 9-4

Name _____

Problem-Solving Practice

	Plants in Jin's Vegetable Garden							
Tomato								
Corn								
Pumpkin								
	1 2 3 4 5 6 7 8							
	Number of Plants							

Write a number sentence to solve.

1. Jin would like to plant twice as many zucchini plants as tomato plants. How many zucchini plants will Jin need?
__5__ × __2__ = __10__
Jin will need __10__ zucchini plants.

2. Jin wants to plant five more potato plans than corn plants. How many potato plants will Jin need?
__8__ + __5__ = __13__
Jin will need __13__ potato plants.

3. Jin wants to plant 3 times as many strawberry plants as pumpkin plants. How many strawberry plants will Jin need?
__2__ × __3__ = __6__
Jin will need __6__ strawberry plants.

Math Triumphs　　　　　　　　　　Lesson 9-4　A227

Lesson 9-4

Name _____

Homework Practice

	Book-a-Thon Reading							
Carla								
Ming								
Latrell								
	1 2 3 4 5 6 7 8							
	Number of Books							

1. How many books did Latrell read?
__7__ books

2. How many more books did Latrell read than Ming?
__4__ more books than Ming

3. Who read the most books?
__Latrell__

Write a number sentence to solve.

4. Jane would like to read twice as many books as Carla. How many books does Jane need to read?
__4__ × __2__ = __8__
Jane needs to read __8__ books.

A228　Lesson 9-4　　　　　　　　　　*Math Triumphs*

Answer Key (Lesson 9-5)

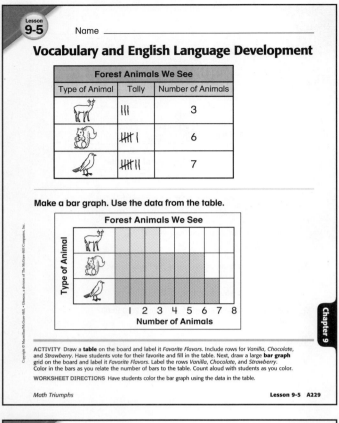

Lesson 9-5

Name _____

Vocabulary and English Language Development

Forest Animals We See

Type of Animal	Tally	Number of Animals
(deer)	IIII	3
(squirrel)	HHT I	6
(bird)	HHT II	7

Make a bar graph. Use the data from the table.

Forest Animals We See

Type of Animal / Number of Animals
1 2 3 4 5 6 7 8

ACTIVITY Draw a **table** on the board and label it *Favorite Flavors*. Include rows for *Vanilla, Chocolate*, and *Strawberry*. Have students vote for their favorite and fill in the table. Next, draw a large **bar graph** grid on the board and label it *Favorite Flavors*. Label the rows *Vanilla, Chocolate*, and *Strawberry*. Color in the bars as you relate the number of bars to the table. Count aloud with students as you color.

WORKSHEET DIRECTIONS Have students color the bar graph using the data in the table.

Math Triumphs   **Lesson 9-5   A229**

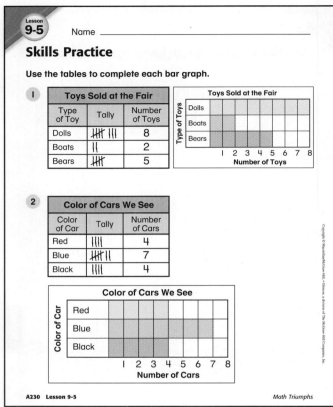

Lesson 9-5

Name _____

Skills Practice

Use the tables to complete each bar graph.

1

Toys Sold at the Fair

Type of Toy	Tally	Number of Toys
Dolls	HHT III	8
Boats	II	2
Bears	HHT	5

Toys Sold at the Fair
Type of Toys: Dolls, Boats, Bears
Number of Toys 1 2 3 4 5 6 7 8

2

Color of Cars We See

Color of Car	Tally	Number of Cars
Red	IIII	4
Blue	HHT II	7
Black	IIII	4

Color of Cars We See
Color of Car: Red, Blue, Black
Number of Cars 1 2 3 4 5 6 7 8

A230   Lesson 9-5   *Math Triumphs*

Lesson 9-5

Name _____

Problem-Solving Practice

1 Use the table to complete the bar graph.

Favorite Jungle Cats

Type of Jungle Cat	Tally	Number of People
Lion	IIII	4
Tiger	HHT III	8
Leopard	HHT I	6

Favorite Jungle Cats
Number of People 8 7 6 5 4 3 2 1
Lion   Tiger   Leopard
Type of Jungle Cat

Use the bar graph to solve.

2 How many people like tigers the best? __8__

3 How many people like lions the best? __4__

4 How many more people like tigers better than lions?
   __8__ – __4__ = __4__
   __4__ more people like tigers better than lions.

5 How many people like leopards the best? __6__

6 How many more people like tigers better than leopards?
   __8__ – __6__ = __2__
   __2__ more people like tigers better than leopards.

Math Triumphs   **Lesson 9-5   A231**

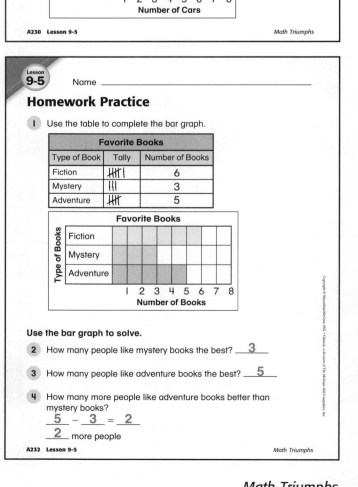

Lesson 9-5

Name _____

Homework Practice

1 Use the table to complete the bar graph.

Favorite Books

Type of Book	Tally	Number of Books
Fiction	HHT I	6
Mystery	III	3
Adventure	HHT	5

Favorite Books
Type of Books: Fiction, Mystery, Adventure
Number of Books 1 2 3 4 5 6 7 8

Use the bar graph to solve.

2 How many people like mystery books the best? __3__

3 How many people like adventure books the best? __5__

4 How many more people like adventure books better than mystery books?
   __5__ – __3__ = __2__
   __2__ more people

A232   Lesson 9-5   *Math Triumphs*

Answer Key (Lesson 9-6)

Lesson 9-6

Name _____

Vocabulary and English Language Development

This is a line plot.

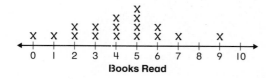

Homeruns Hit

Count the Xs.

1. 1 homerun __5__
2. 2 homeruns __4__
3. 3 homeruns __2__
4. 4 homeruns __3__
5. 5 homeruns __1__
6. 6 homeruns __1__
7. 7 homeruns __0__
8. 8 homeruns __1__
9. 9 homeruns __0__
10. 10 homeruns __0__

ACTIVITY Tell students that a **line plot** is another way to show **data**. Draw a line plot on the board. Ask each student to draw an X above the number that shows how many people are in his or her family. Count the number for each. Ask questions about the line plot such as: "How many students have four family members?"

WORKSHEET DIRECTIONS Have students count and write how many homeruns for each number on the line plot.

Math Triumphs

Lesson 9-6   A233

Chapter 9

Lesson 9-6

Name _____

Skills Practice

This line plot shows the number of letters in students' first names.

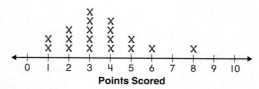

Letters in First Names

Use the line plot to answer each question.

1. How many students have 7 letters in their first name?
   __4__ students

2. How many letters do 2 students have in their names?
   __6__ letters

3. How many letters are in the longest name?
   __9__ letters

4. How many more students have 5 letters in their names than 3 letters? __2__ more students

A234   Lesson 9-6

Math Triumphs

Lesson 9-6

Name _____

Problem-Solving Practice

This line plot shows the number of books each student read.

Books Read

Write a number sentence to solve.

1. How many more students read 5 books than 9 books?
   __4__ – __1__ = __3__
   __3__ more students read 5 books than 9 books.

2. How many more students read 4 books than 1 book?
   __3__ – __1__ = __2__
   __2__ more students read 4 books than 1 book.

3. How many students read 1, 2, 3, or 4 books in all?
   __1__ + __2__ + __2__ + __3__ = __8__
   __8__ students read 1, 2, 3, or 4 books in all.

Math Triumphs

Lesson 9-6   A235

Chapter 9

Lesson 9-6

Name _____

Homework Practice

This line plot shows the number of points scored during a game.

Points Scored

Use the line plot to answer each question.

1. How many students scored 5 points? __2__ students
2. How many students scored 3 points? __5__ students

Write a number sentence to solve.

3. How many more students scored 3 points than 1 point?
   __5__ – __2__ = __3__
   __3__ more students scored 3 points than 1 point.

4. How many students scored 1, 5, or 8 points?
   __2__ + __2__ + __1__ = __5__
   __5__ students scored 1, 5, or 8 points in all.

A236   Lesson 9-6

Math Triumphs

Math Triumphs

Lesson 9-6   A287